METHODS OF CONTOUR INTEGRATION

NORTH-HOLLAND SERIES IN

APPLIED MATHEMATICS AND MECHANICS

EDITORS

H. A. LAUWERIER

Institute of Applied Mathematics

University of Amsterdam

W. T. KOITER

Laboratory of Applied Mechanics

Technical University, Delft

VOLUME 3

NORTH-HOLLAND PUBLISHING COMPANY - AMSTERDAM

METHODS OF CONTOUR INTEGRATION

BY

M. L. RASULOV

Translated by
SCRIPTA TECHNICA LTD.

1967

NORTH-HOLLAND PUBLISHING COMPANY — AMSTERDAM

PUBLISHERS:

NORTH-HOLLAND PUBLISHING CO. - AMSTERDAM

SOLE DISTRIBUTORS FOR U.S.A. AND CANADA:

INTERSCIENCE PUBLISHERS, a division of

JOHN WILEY & SONS, INC. - NEW YORK

Library of Congress Catalog Card Number 67-20014

PRINTED IN THE NETHERLANDS

Preface

This book contains primarily the results of investigations made by the author over several years. The substance of lectures given by him at the Mechanical-Mathematical Departments of the Universities of Lvov and Azerbaydzhan was used in writing the book.

The author has tried to make the book useful to a broad class of readers. In connection with this, the results of Tamarkin are expounded in the first three chapters and used in the subsequent ones. Also, the author has not tried to avoid certain repetitions. For example, in Section 4.2, the solution of the spectral problem for systems of equations is constructed although this had been done for a single equation in Section 3.3.

The book is divided into two parts, the first of which is devoted to a systematic exposition of the computational method of solving boundary and mixed problems (Chapters 3-5) developed by the author.

In Chapter 3, formulae are given for expanding arbitrary vector-valued functions in series from integral residues of solutions of boundary-value problems for systems of ordinary differential equations with discontinuous coefficients. With the aid of these formulae, residue representations of solutions of the corresponding one-dimensional mixed problems for equations with discontinuous coefficients are obtained in Chapter 4. In Chapter 5 it is proved that the scheme of the given residue method is also applicable to the solution of multi-dimensional mixed problems if the corresponding expansion formula is valid. Then, a computational method of separating the variables - a generalisation of the ordinary method of separating variables to the case of non-self-adjoint operators - is given. Here, we also obtain residue representations of the multi-dimensional boundary-value and mixed problems in question. In addition, this method is used to prove the validity of the formula for expanding arbitrary functions in series of residues of solutions of multi-dimensional spectral problems with separable variables.

In the second part (Chapters 6-10), the contour-integral method is given in connection with an investigation of general linear mixed problems.

In Chapters 6 and 7, a study is made of one-dimensional mixed problems for equations with discontinuous coefficients. The existence of solutions of these problems and the representability of the solutions in the form of contour integrals with respect to a complex parameter is proved under regular boundary conditions. The residue method is also used to establish the conditions for the correct formulation of these problems.

Chapter 8 is devoted to a study of a boundary-value problem with a complex parameter for second-order elliptic equations in a three-dimensional region (in general, an infinite region). Here, a proof is given of the existence of a solution to this problem in the unbounded portion of the complex plane, and approximating expressions for this solution are obtained in that portion.

In Chapter 9 these results are used to prove the existence of a solution of the mixed problem for a three-dimensional region (in general, unbounded) and the representability of this solution in the form of a contour integral.

In Chapter 10, the contour-integral method is used to solve three-dimensional mixed problems for equations with discontinuous coefficients.

In contrast with the Laplace-transform method, the contour-integral method is also applicable to equations in which the coefficients are functions of time, and, in the case of mixed problems for parabolic equations, it is easily justified owing to the rapidity of convergence of the contour integrals. Furthermore, in contrast with the residue method, it can be used for problems with continuous spectra.

It is assumed that the reader has had courses in analysis, ordinary differential equations and the elements of the theory of functions of a complex variable (see, for example, [23a]).

Chapters 6 and 7 can be read independently.

The greater portion of the material in the book was reported and discussed at the seminar on differential equations by Academicians S.L. Sobolev and I.N. Vekua at the Moscow State University in 1957-1959.

The author wishes to express his deep gratitude to Academicians Sobolev and Vekua and to Member-Correspondent of the Academy of Sciences of the USSR, A.V. Bitsadze, for their attention to the author's investigations, which aroused in him the desire to write this book.

The author also wishes to thank his listeners, N.M. Mamedov, N.A. Alnev, V.M. Namazov and K. Sh. Hadzhibekov for their help in the composition of the manuscript.

In conclusion, the author expresses his deep gratitude to the editor of the book Prof. I.V. Ivanov for his attention to the manuscript.

Editorial Note

The enormous increase in the amount of research information, published in an ever-growing number of scientific journals, has stimulated the demand for authoritative monographs on well-defined topics. Such monographs have become virtually indispensable to young research workers and students working in a particular field, who are either bewildered by the vast quantity of literature in existence, or are in danger of duplicating research that has already been published, but is not readily accessible. Specialists also may benefit from the availability of competent surveys by fellow experts in their own field.

The North-Holland Series in Applied Mathematics and Mechanics is intended to help meet this demand. The editors believe that a continuing close relationship between applied mathematics and mechanics, having proved so fruitful in the past, will continue to benefit both subjects in the future. The series will include original monographs as well as translations of outstanding works which would otherwise have remained inaccessible to many readers.

Contents

Introduction

The application of the Fourier method to solving mixed problems with separable variables t and x of the type

$$\begin{aligned} & M\left(t, \frac{\partial}{\partial t}\right) u = L\left(x, \frac{\partial}{\partial x}\right) u + f(x, t) \\ & L_\nu(u) = 0 \quad \text{on } \Gamma \\ & \left.\frac{\partial^k u}{\partial t^k}\right|_{t=0} = \Phi_k(x) \quad (k = 0, 1, \ldots, q-1) \end{aligned} \tag{1}$$

involves the expansion of an arbitrary function of a certain class in eigenfunctions of the corresponding boundary-value problem with parameter, of the form

$$\begin{aligned} & L\left(x, \frac{\partial}{\partial x}\right) v - \lambda^m v = h(x) \\ & L_\nu(v) = 0 \quad \text{on } \Gamma \end{aligned} \tag{2}$$

where M is a linear differential expression with respect to the time t, q the highest order of any of the derivatives with respect to t in M, L a linear differential operator with respect to the point x (the point of some n-dimensional region with boundary Γ), m the order of the operator L and λ a complex parameter. The expansion of functions has gradually become the central problem in the spectral theory of linear self-adjoint operators in a Hilbert space.

This theory has been thoroughly worked out. If the operator defined by (2) is self-adjoint, the system of eigenfunctions of this operator is complete and orthogonal; consequently, an arbitrary function of the class in question can be expanded in a series of eigenfunctions of that operator (in the case of a discrete spectrum). A difficulty arises, however, when the operator defined by (2) is not self-adjoint. Here we do not have orthogonality in the usual sense and the question of existence and completeness of a system of eigenfunctions is, in general, still an open question.

Cauchy was the first to apply, without rigorous justification, an integral residue to the solution of mixed problems with separable variables for equations with constant coefficients (see [21a, b and 23a]). The outline of Cauchy's residue method is as follows: suppose that $F_1(\lambda)$ and $F_2(\lambda)$ are polynomials in λ with constant coefficients, such that F_1 is of degree n and F_2 of degree m. Suppose also $f_{k0}(\lambda)$ and $f_{k1}(\lambda)$ (where $k=1, \ldots, n$) are polynomials in λ with constant coefficients but that the degrees of these last two sets of polynomials do not exceed $n-1$. Consider the differential equation

$$F_1\left(\frac{\partial}{\partial x}\right) z + F_2\left(\frac{\partial}{\partial t}\right) z = 0$$

with regular boundary-value conditions of the form

$$f_{k0}\left(\frac{\partial}{\partial x}\right) z\Big|_{x=x_0} + f_{k1}\left(\frac{\partial}{\partial x}\right) z\Big|_{x=x_1} = 0 \qquad (k=1, \ldots, n)$$

and initial conditions of the form (1). We shall call this mixed problem the problem (K). Suppose also that $V(x, \lambda)$ is a solution of the differential equation

$$F_1\left(\frac{d}{dx}\right) V = F_1(\lambda) V$$

that satisfies the boundary conditions

$$f_{k0}\left(\frac{d}{dx}\right) V\Big|_{x=x_0} + f_{k1}\left(\frac{d}{dx}\right) V\Big|_{x=x_1} = -f_{k0}(\lambda)$$
$$(k=1, \ldots, n)$$

Cauchy noted that the formal solution of (K) can be represented in the form of a complete double integral residue

$$z = \mathscr{E}_\lambda \mathscr{E}_s \frac{e^{st} V(x, \lambda)}{F_1(\lambda) + F_2(s)} \int_{x_0}^{x_1} e^{-\lambda(\xi - x_0)} \frac{F_1(\lambda) - F_1(\Phi(\xi))}{\lambda - \Phi(\xi)} d\xi \qquad (3)$$

where $\mathscr{E}_\lambda$ denotes the complete residue with respect to λ and

$$\frac{F_1(\lambda)-F_1(\Phi(\xi))}{\lambda-\Phi(\xi)}$$

should be understood in the sense that after dividing by $\lambda-\Phi$, the expression obtained can be expanded in powers of Φ with subsequent replacement of Φ^k with $\Phi_k(\xi)$. Here, it turns out that

$$\left.\frac{\partial^k z}{\partial t^k}\right|_{t=0}=\Phi_k(x)=\mathscr{E}_\lambda V(x,\lambda)\int_{x_0}^{x_1} e^{-\lambda(\xi-x_0)}\Phi_k(\xi)\,d\xi \tag{4}$$

The validity of (4) was proved by Cauchy without regard to strict rigour by means of the theorem below.

Theorem: Cauchy Suppose that $f(x)$ is a function that satisfies the Dirichlet conditions on the interval $[x_0, x_1]$ and $\psi(\lambda)$, $\varkappa(\lambda)$ and $\pi(\lambda)$ are entire functions of the complex variable λ that satisfy the following conditions:

1. $\pi(\lambda)$ has a finite number of zeros that do not coincide with the zeros of the functions

$$\psi(\lambda), \quad \varkappa(\lambda)$$

2. $\psi(\lambda)+\varkappa(\lambda)=\pi(\lambda)$
3. $\lim\limits_{\mathrm{Re}\,\lambda\to+\infty}\frac{\psi(\lambda)}{\pi(\lambda)}e^{\lambda(x-x_0)}=0$
4. $\lim\limits_{\mathrm{Re}\,\lambda\to+\infty}\frac{\psi(-\lambda)}{\pi(-\lambda)}=1$
5. $\lim\limits_{\mathrm{Re}\,\lambda\to+\infty}\frac{\varkappa(\lambda)}{\pi(\lambda)}=1$
6. $\lim\limits_{\mathrm{Re}\,\lambda\to+\infty}\frac{\varkappa(-\lambda)}{\pi(-\lambda)}e^{\lambda(x_1-x)}=0$

Then, for $x\in(x_0, x_1)$,

$$f(x)=\mathscr{E}_\lambda\frac{\varkappa(\lambda)}{\pi(\lambda)}\int_{x_0}^{x_1} e^{\lambda(x-\xi)}f(\xi)\,d\xi \tag{5}$$

Cauchy proved this theorem by assuming that the function under the residue symbol converges uniformly (with respect to $\arg\lambda\in[0, 2\pi]$) to its limit as $|\lambda|\to\infty$, which is a stringent restriction.

Cauchy obtained (3) by an artificial device, following the

procedure generally used in connection with the method of separating the variables. The chief defect in Cauchy's residue method is that the solution of the mixed problem which he was considering can be represented in the form of a complete residue of a meromorphic function, the choice of which is conditioned primarily, not by the mixed problem itself, but by the method of reasoning, which is suitable only for problems with separable variables for equations with constant coefficients. Other defects in Cauchy's method are as follows:

1. There is no rigorous proof of the formulae.
2. It is not clear how the outline of the method might be applied to equations with variable coefficients and problems with nonseparable variables.
3. The plan of the method does not enable us to obtain a residue representation of a sufficiently smooth solution of the mixed problems in question.

An extensive investigation of the residue method, on the part of the author, has shown that a suitable residue scheme can be obtained only by a favourable choice of the corresponding boundary-value problem with a complex parameter (the spectral problem) since the success of a residue scheme is conditioned basically by the formula for expanding arbitrary functions of a definite class in a series of residues of the corresponding spectral problem.

In this sense, the chief defect in Cauchy's residue method for solving mixed problems is the unsuccessful choice of corresponding spectral problems; the result is, the residue scheme is based on an unsuitable formula for expanding arbitrary functions of the given class in a series of residues of the solution of the chosen spectral problem.

It turned out that, for the solution of certain mixed problems, the boundary conditions for which do not contain time derivatives, a successful formula is that of Poincaré, since it enables us to obtain a residue representation of a sufficiently smooth solution of the corresponding mixed problem. Poincaré noted this formula in connection with the application of an integral residue to the solution of the mixed problem for the heat-flow equation in a three-dimensional domain D [39].

Suppose that a solution of Problem (2) exists, is of the form

$$v(x, \lambda, h) = \int_D G(x, \xi, \lambda) h(\xi) d_\xi D$$

and is a meromorphic function of the parameter λ. The formula for expanding an arbitrary function $h(x)$ in a series of residues of the solution of (2) which was noted by Poincaré for a particular case (for the equation $\Delta\, v - \lambda^2 v = h(x)$, applying to the three-dimensional region D with the usual boundary conditions) is of the form

$$h(x) = -\mathscr{E}_\lambda \lambda^{m-1} \int_D G(x, \xi, \lambda)\, h(\xi)\, d_\xi D \tag{6}$$

where $\mathscr{E}_\lambda$ denotes, as before, the complete residue with respect to λ.

Formula (6) on the one hand expresses the fact that the system of residues of the solution of (2) is complete and on the other makes it possible to calculate the coefficients in the expansion if the Green's function is constructed and its poles are found. Finally, the connection between (6) and the mixed problem (1) is completely clear.

This formula of Poincaré was studied in two interesting articles by the American mathematician Birkhoff, published in 1908 (see [3a, b]). The first of these gives an asymptotic representation of the complete system of independent solutions of the ordinary linear differential equation of order m

$$\frac{d^m y}{dx^m} + P_1(x, \lambda) \frac{d^{m-1} y}{dx^{m-1}} + \ldots + P_m(x, \lambda)\, y = h(x) \tag{7}$$

Here the coefficients depend on the complex parameter λ. For the coefficient of the derivative of order k, the point at infinity of the λ-plane is a pole of order $m - k$, i.e. for sufficiently large λ, we have the expansion

$$P_k(x, \lambda) = \sum_{\nu=0}^{\infty} \lambda^{k-\nu} p_{k\nu}(x)$$

where $p_{k\nu}(x)$ are sufficiently smooth functions on $[a, b]$. The roots of the characteristic equation

$$\begin{aligned} f(\theta) = \theta^m + p_{10}(x)\,\theta^{m-1} + p_{20}(x)\,\theta^{m-2} + \ldots \\ \ldots + p_{m-1,0}(x)\,\theta + p_{m0}(x) = 0 \end{aligned} \tag{8}$$

are assumed to be simple and non-zero for $x \in [a, b]$.

In the second of Birkhoff's articles, the results of the article [3a] are used to prove the validity of Poincaré's formula for a type-(2) problem when L is an ordinary linear differential operator applying to a finite interval $D = [a, b]$, and the L_ν (for $\nu = 1, \ldots, m$) are independent linear forms of derivatives of the desired function at the end-points of the interval $[a, b]$, the coefficients in which are independent of the parameter λ; the boundary condition is assumed regular. It is also shown that, if all the poles of the Green's function are simple, the eigenfunctions of the type-(2) problem in question and the problem adjoint to it constitute complete bi-orthogonal systems on the interval $[a, b]$. In connection with this, we may assume that, in solving the corresponding mixed type-(1) problem, Birkhoff evidently intended to use the Fourier procedure, i.e. to find a solution of the corresponding type-(1) problem in the form of a series expansion

$$u(x, t) = \sum_\nu T_\nu(t)\, v_\nu(x)$$

in the eigenfunctions of the type-(2) problem. Obviously, the coefficients in this series are easily evaluated, owing to the bi-orthogonality of the systems of eigenfunctions.

Thus, Birkhoff did not notice the advantage of (6) for solving the corresponding mixed problem and he proceeded in the traditional manner to use the concept of orthogonality although Poincaré's formula itself is completely unconnected with that concept.

Furthermore, it should be pointed out that, in the case of multiple poles of the Green's function of a type-(2) problem, the question of whether the Fourier-Birkhoff procedure can be applied to the solution of the mixed type-(1) problem has remained open; since to obtain complete systems corresponding to the systems of eigenfunctions of this problem and its adjoint problem, it is necessary to include the associated functions. The systems obtained in this way turn out not to be bi-orthogonal. In this connection, we should note the important article of Academician M.V. Keldysh [20], in which there is a rigorous spectral theory of a non-self-adjoint operator equation of the form

$$y = Ay + \lambda HBy + \ldots + \lambda^{n-1}H^{n-1}B_{n-1}y + \lambda^n H^n y + f$$

applying to the corresponding Hilbert space. Here, A is an arbitrary completely continuous operator, B a bounded operator and H a complete self-adjoint operator, some power of which has a finite absolute norm.

However, in the case of the one-dimensional mixed problem for differential equations, if the Green's function of the corresponding spectral problem has multiple poles, then the application of the Fourier-Birkhoff method can, regardless of its simplicity, lead to an extremely complicated procedure. An article by Zhdanovich [14], emphasises this. In that article, the Fourier-Birkhoff method is used for solving the particular case of a one-dimensional mixed problem, an extremely simple solution of which (by the residue method) was published by the author of this book in 1952 [40b].

In 1924, Geppert published an article [11] in Germany, in which he attempted to justify Cauchy's residue scheme. By assuming the possibility of differentiating and taking the limit under the complete residue sign as $t \to 0$ and using Cauchy's theorem on the expansion of functions in a series of residues with the aid of meromorphic functions and the method in the second of the two articles by Birkhoff (i.e. the method of asymptotic approximation), Geppert showed that the function defined by Cauchy's residue formula satisfies the initial conditions of the mixed problem in question with separable variables for equations with constant coefficients.

The articles mentioned above do not include spectral problems containing a complex parameter in the boundary condition. The possibility of proving the validity of Poincaré's formula for such problems was studied in two fundamental works by Tamarkin, which appeared in 1917 and 1928 [46a, b].

The first two chapters of Tamarkin's book [46a] are devoted to the asymptotic representation of the complete set of independent solutions of a system of first-order linear differential equations (with large values of the parameter), the coefficients in which are independent of the complex parameter λ, and in which, for all the coefficients of the system, the point at infinity of the λ-plane is a pole of some finite order p. The remaining three chapters of the book are devoted to a proof of the validity of Poincaré's formula for an equation of the form (7)* with boundary condition containing parameter λ for the case in which, for $x \in [a, b]$, the roots of the characteristic equation are simple and nonzero and the arguments of these roots and of their differences

* An examination is made of equations of the type (7) when $P_k(x, \lambda)$ is a polynomial in λ of degree not exceeding k.

are independent of x. Here, the coefficients of the boundary conditions are polynomials in λ of degrees not exceeding m.

The 1928 article by Tamarkin [46b] contains certain generalisations of the results of the last three chapters of his book.

The possibility of generalising and improving Tamarkin's results was also discussed in two articles by Wilder [7a, b]. The first of these gives a proof of the validity of Poincaré's formula for a type-(2) ordinary linear differential equation with continuous coefficients and with boundary condition relating the values of the derivative of the unknown function at several points of the basic interval. In this case, in contrast with the type-(2) problem considered by Birkhoff in his investigation of the asymptotic behaviour of the Green's function, Wilder arrives at an exponential polynomial (with asymptotically constant coefficients) in which the number of terms exceeds two. Other asymptotic representations of this polynomial and its zeros are studied by an extremely simple method. This same method was used by Tamarkin in his article [46b] in the investigation of the asymptotic behaviour of the Green's function.

Although Tamarkin proved the validity of Poincaré's formula for a more general case than that of Birkhoff, his articles do not apply this formula to the solution of the corresponding mixed problems.

It is surprising that, for a long time after Cauchy's studies, the question of developing a residue method to apply to mixed problems for equations with variable coefficients remained unsolved. In the meantime, the investigation of this question is of great scientific and practical interest.

In this connection, the author of this book has developed a residue method which can be used to solve broad classes of mixed and boundary-value problems for systems of linear differential equations. The book is devoted to a systematic exposition of two methods devised by the author, i.e. the residue method and the contour-integral method, and also to the application of these methods to the study of certain classes of mixed problems that up to now have not been solved by other methods.

The first part of the book deals with the residue method of solving mixed and boundary-value problems for linear differential equations and the second part with the contour-integral method of solving such mixed problems.

The outline of the residue method for solving mixed

problems is as follows. According to a definite procedure, a correspondence is made between a given mixed problem and some boundary-value problem with a complex parameter (the spectral problem). With the aid of the solution of this spectral problem, a meromorphic function of a complex parameter is defined, the complete residue of which gives a residue representation of the formal solution of the given mixed problem. Then, the formula for the expansion of an arbitrary vector-valued function (of the corresponding dimension) in a series of residues of the solution of the spectral problem is used to show that, if the mixed boundary-value problem in question has a sufficiently smooth solution, it can be represented by the given residue formula. It turns out that the residue representation of the solution of mixed problems with boundary conditions which do not contain time derivatives can be obtained by means of the Poincaré Birkhoff expansion formula for the corresponding spectral problem (see (6)).

The greatest difficulties are encountered in applying the residue method to mixed problems with boundary conditions which do contain time derivatives. We must therefore study the one-dimensional mixed problem of the form

$$\frac{\partial^q u^{(i)}}{\partial t^q} = \sum_{\substack{mk+l\leq p \\ k\leq q-1}} A_{kl}^{(i)}(x) \frac{\partial^{k+l} u^{(i)}}{\partial t^k \partial x^l} + f^{(i)}(x, t), \quad x \in (a_i, b_i) \tag{9}$$

with boundary condition (10) and initial conditions (11)

$$\sum_{i=1}^{n} \sum_{\substack{l\leq p-1 \\ k\leq q}} \left\{ \alpha_{kl}^{(i)} \frac{\partial^{k+l} u^{(i)}}{\partial t^k \partial x^l}\bigg|_{x=a_i} + \beta_{kl}^{(i)} \frac{\partial^{k+l} u^{(i)}}{\partial t^k \partial x^l}\bigg|_{x=b_i} \right\} = 0 \tag{10}$$

$$\frac{\partial^k u^{(i)}}{\partial t^k}\bigg|_{t=0} = \Phi_k^{(i)}(x), \quad x \in (a_i, b_i) \quad (i = 1, \ldots, n) \tag{11}$$

where $A_{kl}^{(i)}(x)$ is an $r \times r$ matrix which is sufficiently smooth in the interval (a_i, b_i), $\alpha_{kl}^{(i)}$, $\beta_{kl}^{(i)}$ are constant $nrp \times r$ matrices, the (a_i, b_i) are disjoint intervals which have common boundary points and are contained in the basic interval $[a_1, b_n]$, and where $p = mq$.

The chief difficulty in study of this problem is that it is impossible to obtain a residue representation of the solution with the aid of the Poincaré-Birkhoff expansion formula.

Consequently, it is necessary to choose a spectral problem and an expansion formula associated with it for expanding an arbitrary vector-valued function in a series of residues of the solution of this problem in such a way that, with the aid of the established expansion formula, it is possible to obtain a residue representation of the solution of (9)-(11).

For Problem (9)-(11), it proved expedient to choose a spectral problem in the following manner:

$$
\begin{gathered}
v_{k+1}^{(i)} - \lambda^m v_k^{(i)} = \Phi_k^{(i)}(x) \qquad (k=0, \ldots, q-2) \\
\sum_{\substack{mk+l\leqslant p \\ k\leqslant q-1}} \lambda^{mk} A_{kl}^{(i)}(x) \frac{d^l v_k^{(i)}}{dx^l} - \lambda^m v_{q-1}^{(i)} = \Phi_{q-1}^{(i)}(x) \\
x \in (a_i,\ b_i)
\end{gathered}
\tag{12}
$$

$$
\sum_{i=1}^{n} \sum_{\substack{l\leqslant p-1 \\ k\leqslant q}} \lambda^{mk} \left\{ \alpha_{kl}^{(i)} \frac{d^l v_k^{(i)}}{dx^l}\bigg|_{x=a_i} + \beta_{kl}^{(i)} \frac{d^l v_k^{(i)}}{dx^l}\bigg|_{x=b_i} \right\} = 0 \tag{13}
$$

Let us denote by $v_k^{(i)}(x,\ \lambda,\ \Phi)$ the solution of Problem (12)-(13) for $x \in (a_i, b_i)$. A proof of the validity of the formula (see Theorem 9)

$$
\Phi_k^{(i)}(x) = \frac{-1}{2\pi\sqrt{-1}} \sum_{\nu} \int_{c_\nu} \lambda^{m-1} v_k^{(i)}(x,\ \lambda,\ \Phi)\, d\lambda \tag{14}
$$

for sufficiently smooth functions $\Phi_k^{(i)}(x)$ on an interval $[a_i,\ b_i]$ under certain conditions is given in Section 3.2. Here, c_ν is a simple closed contour encircling only a single pole λ_ν of the integrand, and the summation with respect to ν is taken over all poles of this function. The convergence of (14) to be understood in the sense of the metric $L_2(a_i,\ b_i)$.

Formula (14) on the one hand expresses the fact of q-square completeness of the system of eigenfunctions and associated functions (in the terminology of Keldysh) and on the other hand makes it possible to compute the coefficients in the expansion. In particular, we obtain from this formula, for $\Phi_k(x) \equiv 0$ (where $k=1, \ldots, q-2$) a formula of type (6) generalising the Poincaré-Birkhoff formula to the case of a system of equations with discontinuous coefficients when the boundary conditions of the problem connect the derivatives of the unknown vector-valued function at points of discontinuity of the coefficients (see Theorem 10).

Formula (14) is proved by reducing Problem (12)-(13) to a spectral problem for a system of first-order equations, the coefficients in which contain negative as well as positive powers of the parameter λ. Therefore, in Section 3.1, we find the solution $y^{(i)}(x, \lambda, f)$ of the system

$$\frac{dy^{(i)}}{dx} - a^{(i)}(x, \lambda)\, y^{(i)} = f^{(i)}(x), \qquad x \in (a_i, b_i) \tag{15}$$

with boundary condition of the form

$$\sum_{i=1}^{n} \{\alpha^{(i)}(\lambda)\, y^{(i)}(a_i, \lambda) + \beta^{(i)}(\lambda)\, y^{(i)}(b_i, \lambda)\} = 0 \tag{16}$$

where $a^{(i)}(x, \lambda)$ is an $r \times r$ matrix admitting the expansion

$$a^{(i)}(x, \lambda) = \lambda a^{(i)}(x) + \sum_{\nu=0}^{Q} \lambda^{-\nu} a_{\nu}^{(i)}(x)$$

where $y^{(i)}$ and $f^{(i)}$ are columns of the appropriate dimensions and $\alpha^{(i)}(\lambda)$, and $\beta^{(i)}(\lambda)$ are $nr \times r$ matrices of polynomials in λ.

It is shown (see Theorem 8, Section 3.1) that, if the functions $a^{(i)}(x)$ and $a_{\nu}^{(i)}(x)$ are sufficiently smooth on the interval $[a_i, b_i]$, if Condition (16) is regular, if the roots of the characteristic equation

$$\det(a^{(i)}(x) - \theta E) = 0$$

are simple and if the arguments of these roots and their differences are independent of x, then, for $f^{(i)}(x) \in L_2$, there exists a sequence of closed expanding contours Γ_ν such that

$$\frac{-1}{2\pi\sqrt{-1}} \lim_{\nu\to\infty} \int_{\Gamma_\nu} y^{(i)}(x, \lambda, f)\, d\lambda = (a^{(i)}(x))^{-1} f^{(i)}(x) \tag{17}$$

In particular, for $n = 1$, if the coefficients in (15) do not contain negative powers of λ and the boundary condition does not depend on the parameter λ, the validity of (17) is shown in the contemporary work of Birkhoff and Langer [4]. In this case, the left-hand side of Equation (17) coincides with the series of residues and we obtain the expansion of the vector-valued function $f^{(i)}(x)$ in a series of eigenfunctions and associated functions of (15) and (16).

Also, in Section 3.1, a proof is given of the theorem (see Theorem 7) on the asymptotic representation of the zeros of the characteristic determinant of Green's matrix for Problem (15)-(16) and on the behaviour of this determinant outside a δ-neighbourhood of the spectrum.

Theorems 7 and 8 are proved by means of asymptotic representations of the fundamental matrix of the corresponding homogeneous system (15) which were obtained by Tamarkin.

Thus the first two chapters of this book are devoted to an exposition of the necessary results in Tamarkin's book [46a] on the asymptotic representation of the fundamental system of particular solutions of linear equations (see Theorems 1-6).

It is shown, with the aid of (14) in Section 4.1, that if the Problem (9)-(11) for sufficiently smooth given conditions has a sufficiently smooth solution $u^{(i)}(x, t)$ then it can be represented by the formula

$$u^{(i)}(x, t) = \frac{-1}{2\pi\sqrt{-1}} \sum_{\nu} \int_{c_\nu} \lambda^{m-1} e^{\lambda^m t}\, d\lambda$$

$$\times \Big\{ \sum_{j=1}^{n} \int_{a_j}^{b_j} G^{(i,j)}(x, \xi, \lambda) \Big(\mathcal{F}_0^{(j)}(\xi, \Phi, \lambda^m)$$

$$+ \int_0^t e^{-\lambda^m \tau} f^{(j)}(\xi, \tau)\, d\tau \Big) d\xi + \Delta^{(i)}(x, \Phi, \lambda^m) \Big\}$$

whereas $G^{(i,j)}(x, \xi, \lambda)$ is Green's matrix of the problem obtained from (13) and (14) by eliminating all the $v_k^{(i)}$, for $k = 1, \ldots, q-1$, and $\Delta^{(i)}(x, \xi, \lambda)$ is the solution of this problem that corresponds to the homogeneous system (see Theorem 11). Numerous applications of these results appear in [40c, d] and details of the results for equations with continuous coefficients (for $n = 1$) are given in [40f].

In Section 3.2 it is shown that, if the boundary conditions of Problem (9)-(11) do not contain time derivatives, the residue representation of a sufficiently smooth solution can be obtained by using an expansion formula of type (6) (see Theorem 12).

Section 4.3 deals with the mixed problem of a system of

the form

$$M_1\left(t, \frac{\partial}{\partial t}\right) u^{(i)} = M_2\left(t, \frac{\partial}{\partial t}\right) L^{(i)}\left(x, \frac{\partial}{\partial x}\right) u^{(i)} + f^{(i)}(x, t)$$
$$x \in (a_i, b_i)$$

with type-(10) boundary condition which does not contain time derivatives and with initial condition (11), where

$$L^{(i)}\left(x, \frac{\partial}{\partial x}\right)$$

is a square matrix of differential operators of order p with coefficients which are continuous on $[a_i, b_i]$ and the

$$M_k\left(t, \frac{\partial}{\partial t}\right)$$

are linear differential operators with continuous coefficients on the finite interval $[0, T]$.

It is proved that a sufficiently smooth solution of the last problem can be represented by the residue formula

$$u^{(i)}(x, t) = \frac{-1}{2\pi\sqrt{-1}} \sum_{\nu} \int_{c_\nu} d\mu \sum_{j=1}^{n} \int_{a_j}^{b_j} G^{(i, j)}(x, \xi, \mu) y^{(j)}(t, \xi, \mu) \, d\xi$$

where $G^{(i, j)}(x, \xi, \mu)$ (for $\mu = \lambda^p$) is the Green's matrix of the corresponding spectral problem and $y^{(i)}(t, \xi, \mu)$ is the solution of the Cauchy problem

$$M_1\left(t, \frac{\partial}{\partial t}\right) y^{(i)} - \mu M_2\left(t, \frac{\partial}{\partial t}\right) y^{(i)} = f^{(i)}(\xi, t)$$
$$\left.\frac{d^k y^{(i)}}{dt^k}\right|_{t=0} = \Phi_k^{(i)}(\xi) \tag{18}$$

Here it is assumed that $y^{(i)}(t, \xi, \mu)$ has no singularity which is a pole of the Green's matrix $G^{(i, j)}$ (see Theorems 13 and 14 of Chapter 4).

In Chapter 5, a residue method is given for separating the variables in multi-dimensional mixed and boundary problems. This is a generalisation of the ordinary method for separation of variables to the case of non-orthogonal eigenfunctions. Also given are residue representations of sufficiently smooth solutions of these problems (see Theorems 15-19).

All the results of Chapters 3, 4 and 5 are in the author's

doctoral dissertation [40n]. His works [40l, m) are devoted to a residue method of solving multi-dimensional boundary and mixed problems and its application to certain problems in subterranean hydromechanics.

For one-dimensional mixed problems, it is shown in [40a, b] that the function defined by a given residue representation is the solution of the mixed boundary-value problem in question if the order of the poles of the corresponding spectral problem does not become infinite. In this book the author has tried, while investigating mixed problems, to free himself from this restriction, imposed on the spectrum of the corresponding spectral problem. He has therefore proposed another method of solving mixed problems, which he has called the contour-integral method [40g, h, i, j, k, o].

In Chapter 6 the contour-integral method is given for solving one-dimensional mixed problems for equations with discontinuous coefficients. The boundary conditions of these problems in general contain derivatives with respect to time. The solutions of these problems are given in the form of contour integrals, with respect to a complex parameter, of functions which can be expressed in terms of solutions of the corresponding boundary-value problems with the same complex parameters. Section 1.1 deals with the mixed problem for second-order equations with discontinuous coefficients which contain only first-order time derivatives

$$\frac{\partial v^{(i)}}{\partial t} = c_{02}^{(i)}(x)\frac{\partial^2 v^{(i)}}{\partial x^2} + c_{01}^{(i)}(x)\frac{\partial v^{(i)}}{\partial x} + c_{00}^{(i)}(x)v^{(i)} + f^{(i)}(x,t)$$

$$\sum_{i=1}^{n}\sum_{l=0}^{1}\sum_{k=0}^{1}\left\{\alpha_{slk}^{(i)}\frac{\partial^{k+l}v^{(i)}}{\partial t^k\,\partial x^l}\bigg|_{x=a_i} + \beta_{slk}^{(i)}\frac{\partial^{k+l}v^{(i)}}{\partial t^k\,\partial x^l}\bigg|_{x=b_i}\right\} = \gamma_s \tag{19}$$

$$v^i(x,0) = \Phi^{(i)}(x) \quad (x \in [a_i, b_i];\ i = 1, 2, \ldots, n;\ s = 1, 2, \ldots, 2n)$$

where the $\alpha_{slk}^{(i)}$, $\beta_{slk}^{(i)}$ and γ_s are constants.

Section 6.2 contains an approximate asymptotic representation of the solution of the spectral problem

$$c_{02}^{(i)}(x)\frac{d^2y^{(i)}}{dx^2} + c_{01}^{(i)}(x)\frac{dy^{(i)}}{dx} + (c_{00}^{(i)}(x) - \lambda^2)y^{(i)} = \Phi^{(i)}(x)$$

$$\sum_{i=1}^{n}\sum_{l=0}^{1}\sum_{k=0}^{1}\left\{\alpha_{slk}^{(i)}\lambda^k\frac{d^l y^{(i)}}{dx^l}\bigg|_{x=a_i} + \beta_{slk}^{(i)}\lambda^k\frac{d^l y^{(i)}}{dx^l}\bigg|_{x=b_i}\right\} = \gamma_s \tag{20}$$

$$(s = 1, 2, \ldots, 2n)$$

outside a δ-neighbourhood of the spectrum (see Theorems 21-23) with regularity conditions assumed for the boundary conditions and some smoothness assumed for the coefficients in the equations of the problem (20) on the interval $[a_i, b_i]$ (for $i = 1, \ldots, n$). Here, the arguments of the θ-roots $\varphi_k^{(i)}(x)$ of the equation $c_{02}^{(i)}\theta^2 - 1 = 0$ do not depend on x.

In Section 6.3 it is shown with the aid of the asymptotic representation obtained in Section 6.2 for the solution of the spectral problem outside a δ-neighbourhood of the spectrum that, under certain smoothness requirements imposed on the given conditions of Problem (19) and regularity of the boundary conditions of Problem (20),*

$$-\frac{\pi}{2} < \arg c_{02}^{(i)}(x) < \frac{\pi}{2}$$

the mixed problem (19) has a solution $v^{(i)}(x, t)$, that, together with its derivatives occurring in (19) is continuous for $x \in [a_i, b_i]$ and $t \in [0, T]$ and which can be represented in the form of an integral over an infinite open contour M (see Theorems 24 and 25)

$$\begin{aligned} v^{(i)}(x, t) = \frac{1}{\pi\sqrt{-1}} \int_M \Bigg\{ & e^{\lambda^2 t} \frac{\Delta^{(i)}(x, \lambda)}{\lambda\Delta(\lambda)} \\ & + \lambda \sum_{j=1}^{n} \int_{a_j}^{b_j} G^{(i, j)}(x, \xi, \lambda) \Big(e^{\lambda^2 t}\Phi^{(j)}(\xi) \\ & + \int_0^t e^{\lambda^2(t-\tau)} f^{(j)}(\xi, \tau)\, d\tau \Big) (c_{02}^{(j)}(\xi))^{-1}\, d\xi \Bigg\}\, d\lambda \end{aligned} \tag{21}$$

where M is a contour lying outside a δ-neighbourhood of the spectrum on which $\operatorname{Re} \lambda^2 \to -\infty$ and

$$\frac{\Delta^{(i)}(x, \lambda)}{\Delta(\lambda)} + \sum_{j=1}^{n} \int_{a_j}^{b_j} G^{(i, j)}(x, \xi, \lambda)\, \Phi^{(j)}(\xi)\, d\xi$$

is a solution of the spectral problem (20).

In Section 6.4 a proof is given for the formula for expanding the function $\Phi^{(i)}x$ in a series of residues of the solution of the spectral problem (20) with homogeneous boundary

* This condition is equivalent to parabolicity of the equations of Problems (19). Here it is assumed that $\arg c_{02}^{(i)}(x)$ does not depend on x.

conditions in the sense of pointwise convergence (see Theorem 26).

In the same section, it is shown that the mixed problem under the condition is well formulated.

$$-\frac{\pi}{2} < \arg c_{02}^{(i)}(x) < \frac{\pi}{2}$$

Finally, it is shown in Section 6.4 that, if

$$\frac{\pi}{2} < \arg c_{02}^{(i)}(x) < \frac{3\pi}{2}$$

then (19) cannot have a solution no matter how smooth the given conditions are (see Theorem 29).

In Section 6.5 we shall study the following mixed problem for equations with discontinuous coefficients and with a second-order time derivative

$$\frac{\partial^2 v^{(i)}}{\partial t^2} - \sum_{\substack{k+l\leqslant 2\\ k\leqslant 1}} c_{kl}^{(i)}(x)\frac{\partial^{k+l} v^{(i)}}{\partial t^k \partial x^l} = f^{(i)}(x,\ t)$$

$$(x\in[a_i,\ b_i];\qquad i=1,\ \dots,\ n)$$

$$\sum_{i=1}^{n}\sum_{l=0}^{1}\sum_{k=0}^{2}\left\{\alpha_{skl}^{(i)}\frac{\partial^{k+l}v^{(i)}}{\partial t^k\partial x^l}\bigg|_{x=a_i} + \beta_{skl}^{(i)}\frac{\partial^{k+l}v^{(i)}}{\partial t^k\partial x^l}\bigg|_{x=b_i}\right\}=0 \tag{22}$$

$$(s=1,\ \dots,\ 2n)$$

$$v^{(i)}(x,\ 0)=\Phi_0^{(i)}(x),\quad \frac{\partial v^{(i)}}{\partial t}\bigg|_{t=0}=\Phi_1^{(i)}(x)$$

$$(x\in[a_i,\ b_i];\qquad i=1,\ \dots,\ n)$$

We shall derive a more precise asymptotic representation of the solution of the corresponding spectral problem outside a δ-neighbourhood of the spectrum (see Theorem 30). Hence we show that, under certain smoothness requirements on the given conditions and regularity of the boundary conditions of the corresponding spectral problem, if the arguments of θ-roots of the characteristic equations

$$c_{02}^{(i)}(x)\,\theta^2 + c_{11}^{(i)}(x)\,\theta - 1 = 0 \qquad (x\in[a_i,\ b_i];\qquad i=1,\ \dots,\ n) \tag{23}$$

are independent of x and are real, then (22) has a unique

solution given by

$$v^{(i)}(x,t)=\frac{-1}{2\pi\sqrt{-1}}\lim_{\nu\to\infty}\int_{\Gamma_\nu} e^{\lambda t}\,d\lambda$$

$$\times\sum_{j=1}^{n}\int_{a_j}^{b_j} G^{(i,j)}(x,\xi,\lambda)\Big(\mathscr{F}_0^{(j)}(\xi,\Phi,\lambda) \tag{24}$$

$$+\int_0^t e^{-\lambda\tau}f^{(j)}(\xi,\tau)\,d\tau\Big)\,(c_{02}^{(j)}(\xi))^{-1}d\xi$$

Furthermore this solution depends continuously on the given functions $f^{(i)}(x,t)$ and $\Phi^{(i)}(x)$ where the Γ_ν form a sequence of closed contours which are located outside a δ-neighbourhood of the spectrum of the corresponding spectral problem and which encircle all the poles of the solution of the spectral problem as ν increases, $G^{(i,j)}(x,\xi,\lambda)$ is the Green's function of the corresponding spectral problem and

$$\mathscr{F}_0^{(i)}(\xi,\Phi,\lambda)=\sum_{k=0}^{1}\lambda^{(1-k)}\Phi_k^{(i)}(\xi)$$

$$-\sum_{l=0}^{1}c_{1l}^{(i)}(\xi)\frac{d^l}{d\xi^l}\Phi_0^{(i)}(\xi)$$

(see Theorem 31).

It turns out that for the mixed problem (22) to have a solution, under the conditions mentioned above, it is necessary that the θ-roots of the characteristic equations (23) be real independently of the smoothness of the given conditions (see Theorem 32).

Chapter 7 is devoted to the application of the contour-integral method to the solution of one-dimensional mixed problems (containing a time derivative in the boundary conditions) for linear equations with discontinuous coefficients of order $p>2$.

In Section 7.1 we give a suitable asymptotic representation for the solution of the spectral problem

$$\sum_{\substack{mk+l\leqslant p\\ 0\leqslant k\leqslant q-1}} \lambda^{mk} A_{kl}^{(i)}(x)\frac{d^l y^{(i)}}{dx^l} - \lambda^{mq} y^{(i)} = \mathcal{F}_0^{(i)}(x, \Phi, \lambda^m)$$

$$\sum_{i=1}^{n} \sum_{\substack{k\leqslant q\\ l\leqslant mq-1}}^{l} \lambda^{mk}\left\{ \alpha_{skl}^{(i)} \frac{d^l y^{(i)}}{dx^l}\bigg|_{x=a_i} + \beta_{skl}^{(i)} \frac{d^l y^{(i)}}{dx^l}\bigg|_{x=b_i}\right\} = \gamma_s \tag{25}$$

outside a δ-neighbourhood of the spectrum, where m is a natural number (see Theorems 33 and 34).

In Section 7.2 we shall consider the mixed problem for equations of order $p>2$ with discontinuous coefficients and with only a first-order time derivative

$$\frac{\partial u^{(i)}}{\partial t} = \sum_{l=0}^{p} A_{0l}^{(i)}(x)\frac{\partial^l u^{(i)}}{\partial x^l} + f^{(i)}(x, t)$$

$$\sum_{i=1}^{n} \sum_{\substack{k\leqslant 1\\ l\leqslant p-1}} \left\{\alpha_{skl}^{(i)} \frac{\partial^{k+l} u^{(i)}}{\partial t^k \partial x^l}\bigg|_{x=a_i} + \beta_{skl}^{(i)} \frac{\partial^{k+l} u^{(i)}}{\partial t^k \partial x^l}\bigg|_{x=b_i}\right\} = 0 \tag{26}$$

$$u^{(i)}(x, 0) = \Phi^{(i)}(x) \quad (x \in [a_i, b_i];\ \ i = 1, 2, \ldots, n)$$

Suppose that the given conditions of the problem are smooth and that the boundary condition of the corresponding spectral problem (which is obtained from (25) for $m=p$) is regular. Suppose also that, under the mapping

$$\lambda^m = z \tag{27}$$

all the rays d_k (for $k=1, 2, \ldots, 2\mu \leqslant 2p$) in the complex λ-plane that are defined by the equations $\operatorname{Re}\lambda\varphi_j^{(i)}=0$, where the $\varphi_j^{(i)}(x)$ are the θ-roots* of the characteristic equations

$$A_{0p}^{(i)}(x)\,\theta^p - 1 = 0 \tag{28}$$

are mapped into rays lying in the left half-plane (and not

*It is assumed that the arguments of these roots do not depend on x.

coinciding with the imaginary half-axis). Under these conditions (26) has a unique solution given by

$$u^{(i)}(x, t)=\frac{-1}{2\pi\sqrt{-1}}\sum_{k=1}^{2\mu}\int_{s_k}\lambda^{p-1}d\lambda$$

$$\times\sum_{j=1}^{n}\int_{a_j}^{b_j}G^{(i,j)}(x, \xi, \lambda)\Big(e^{\lambda^p t}\Phi^{(j)}(\xi) \tag{29}$$

$$+\int_0^t e^{\lambda^p(t-\tau)}f^{(j)}(\xi, \tau)\,d\tau\Big)(A_{0p}^{(j)}(\xi))^{-1}d\xi$$

This solution depends continuously on the given $\Phi^{(i)}(x)$ and $f^{(i)}(x, t)$, where the s_k are open contours lying outside a δ-neighbourhood of the spectrum and Re $\lambda^p\to-\infty$ on these contours (see Theorems 35 and 36).

Finally, it is shown that if (27) maps one of the rays d_j of the complex λ-plane into a ray lying in the right half of the z-plane (not coinciding with the imaginary half-axis), Problem (19) will, with regular boundary conditions, have no solution regardless of the degree of smoothness of the given conditions (see Theorem 37).

Chapters 8 and 9 are devoted to an application of the contour-integral method to finding a solution $u(x, t)$ of the equation

$$c(x)M\left(t, \frac{\partial}{\partial t}\right)u=L\left(x, \frac{\partial}{\partial x}\right)u+f(x, t) \tag{30}$$

as applied to a three-dimensional domain D with boundary Γ under the boundary condition

$$\lim_{x\to y}B\left(y, \frac{d}{dn_y}, M\right)u(x, t)$$

$$=\psi(y)\exp\left(-\int_0^t b_0^{-1}(\tau)b_1(\tau)\,d\tau\right), \quad y\in\Gamma \tag{31}$$

and the initial condition

$$u(x, 0)=\Phi(x), \qquad x\in D \tag{32}$$

where

$$M=b_0(t)\frac{\partial}{\partial t}+b_1(t)$$

$$L\left(x,\frac{\partial}{\partial x}\right)=\sum_{i=1}^{3}\left(\frac{\partial^2}{\partial x_i^2}+a_i(x)\frac{\partial}{\partial x_i}\right)+a(x)$$

$$B\left(y,\frac{d}{dn_y},M\right)=\alpha_1(y)\frac{d}{dn_y}+\alpha_2(y)M\left(\frac{d}{dn_y}+\alpha_3(y)\right)+\alpha_4(y)$$

and n_y is the direction of the inner normal to Γ at the point y. It is assumed that either D is a domain bounded by a closed Lyapunov surface Γ (in the case of the internal problem) or that D is a portion of the three-dimensional space of points x lying outside a surface Γ (in the case of the external problem).

For the mixed problem in question, the corresponding spectral problem is formulated

$$\begin{gathered}L\left(x,\frac{\partial}{\partial x}\right)v-\lambda^2 c(x)v=F(x)\\ \lim_{x\to y}B\left(y,\frac{d}{dn_y},\lambda^2\right)v(x,\lambda)=\psi(y),\qquad y\in\Gamma\end{gathered}\tag{33}$$

It is easy to see that the operators both of the equation and of the boundary condition of the spectral problem are obtained, respectively, from the operators of the equation and of the boundary condition of the mixed problem which is formally replacing M with λ^m, where m is the ratio of the order of the highest derivative with respect to x to the order of the highest derivative with respect to t (in the present case, $m=2$).

The corresponding Cauchy problem with a parameter is formulated in the form

$$\begin{gathered}M\left(t,\frac{\partial}{\partial t}\right)y-\lambda^2 y=f(\xi,t)\\ y(0)=\Phi(\xi)c(\xi)\end{gathered}\tag{34}$$

Let $R>0$ be a sufficiently large number and let $\delta>0$ be a sufficiently small number. The following assertions are proved.

1. In the region R_δ of values of λ that satisfy the inequalities

$$|\lambda|\geqslant R,\ \cos\arg\lambda\geqslant\delta$$

the spectral problem (33) has a solution in the form of an analytic function which decreases exponentially of the order $\lambda \in R_\delta$ (see Lemma 2 of the Section 8.3 and Lemma 3 of Section 8.4).

2. When the given conditions are smooth, the solution of the mixed problem (30)-(32) can be represented in the form of the contour integral

$$u(x, t) = \frac{1}{2\pi\sqrt{-1}} \int_S \left\{ \frac{y_1(t, \lambda)\, v_1(x, \lambda)}{\lambda} \right.$$

$$\left. + \lambda \int_D G(x, \xi, \lambda)\, y(t, \xi, \lambda)\, d_\xi D \right\} d\lambda$$

where S is an infinite contour that is situated in the region R_δ and whose branches approach asymptotically the rays cos-arg $\lambda = \delta$, where $y_1(t, \lambda)$ is a solution of the homogeneous equation corresponding to the equation of Problem (34) which satisfies the condition $y(0, \lambda) = 1$, $v_1(x, \lambda)$ is a solution of Problem (33) for the homogeneous equation, $G(x, \xi, \lambda)$ is the Green's function of (33) and $y(t, \xi, \lambda)$ is the solution of (34) (see Theorem 38 of Section 9.1 and Theorem 39 of Section (9.2).

These results for a finite domain D are published in [40g, h, i].

In Chapter 10 analogous results are obtained by the same method for an equation with discontinuous coefficients when similar boundary conditions [4] are given at the inner boundaries determined by the discontinuities (see Lemma 1 of Section 10.2, Lemma 2 of Section 10.3 and Theorems 40 and 41 of Section 10.4).

Part One

THE RESIDUE METHOD

CHAPTER 1

Dini's theorem generalised

1.1 LAGRANGE'S FORMULA AND SYSTEMS OF INTEGRAL EQUATIONS

Consider the system of first-order linear differential equations

$$L_i\left(x, \frac{d}{dx}\right) y \equiv \frac{dy_i}{dx} - \sum_{j=1}^{n} a_{ij}(x)\, y_j = f_i(x) \qquad (1.1.1)$$
$$(i = 1, 2, \ldots, n)$$

the coefficients in which are summable functions of the variable x in some finite interval (a, b). Let $u_i(x)$ and $v_i(x)$ (for $i = 1, 2, \ldots, n$) be absolutely continuous functions on the interval $[a, b]$. Let us denote by x_0 an arbitrary fixed value in the interval $[a, b]$.

As we know from the theory of functions of a real variable, an absolutely continuous function $u_i(x)$ on an interval $[a, b]$ has almost everywhere a finite derivative, which is a Lebesgue-summable function. Consequently, by virtue of the restrictions imposed on the coefficients in the system (1.1.1) and the familiar properties of the Lebesgue integral, the functions

$$v_i(x)\, L_i\left(x, \frac{d}{dx}\right) u(x)$$

are summable on an arbitrary subinterval $[x_0, x]$ of the interval $[a, b]$. Therefore, integrating by parts, we obtain

$$\int_{x_0}^{x}\sum_{i=1}^{n} v_i(\xi)\, L_i\left(\xi, \frac{d}{d\xi}\right) u(\xi)\, d\xi$$

$$= \int_{x_0}^{x}\sum_{i=1}^{n} v_i(\xi)\left(\frac{du_i(\xi)}{d\xi} - \sum_{j=1}^{n} a_{ij}(\xi)\, u_j(\xi)\right) d\xi$$

$$= \sum_{i=1}^{n}\int_{x_0}^{x} v_i(\xi)\,\frac{du_i(\xi)}{d\xi}\, d\xi - \int_{x_0}^{x}\sum_{i=1}^{n}\sum_{j=1}^{n} a_{ij}(\xi)\, v_i(\xi)\, u_j(\xi)\, d\xi$$

$$= \sum_{i=1}^{n} u_i(\xi)\, v_i(\xi)\Big|_{x_0}^{x} - \int_{x_0}^{x}\sum_{i=1}^{n} u_i(\xi)\,\frac{dv_i(\xi)}{d\xi}\, d\xi - \int_{x_0}^{x}\sum_{i=1}^{n}\sum_{j=1}^{n} a_{ij}(\xi)\, v_i(\xi)\, u_j(\xi)\, d\xi \tag{1.1.2}$$

$$= \sum_{i=1}^{n} u_i(x)\, v_i(x) - \sum_{i=1}^{n} u_i(x_0)\, v_i(x_0) - \int_{x_0}^{x}\sum_{i=1}^{n} u_i(\xi)\left(\frac{dv_i(\xi)}{d\xi} + \sum_{j=1}^{n} a_{ji}(\xi)\, v_j(\xi)\right) d\xi$$

Equation (1.1.2) can be written in the form

$$\sum_{i=1}^{n} u_i(x)\, v_i(x) = c + \int_{x_0}^{x}\sum_{i=1}^{n}\left\{v_i(\xi)\, L_i\left(\xi, \frac{d}{d\xi}\right) u(\xi) + u_i(\xi)\, M_i\left(\xi, \frac{d}{d\xi}\right) v(\xi)\right\} d\xi \tag{1.1.3}$$

where

$$\sum_{i=1}^{n} u_i(x_0)\, v_i(x_0) = c$$

$$M_i\left(\xi, \frac{d}{d\xi}\right) v(\xi) \equiv \frac{dv_i}{d\xi} + \sum_{j=1}^{n} a_{ji}(\xi)\, v_j(\xi) \tag{1.1.4}$$

The operator $M_i\left(\xi, \frac{d}{d\xi}\right)$ is said to be adjoint in the sense of Lagrange to the operator $L_i\left(\xi, \frac{d}{d\xi}\right)$.

Consider an arbitrary matrix

$$Z(\xi) = (z_{ij}(\xi))_{i,\,j=1}^{n}$$

of functions $z_{ij}(\xi)$ which are absolutely continuous on the interval $[a, b]$ such that the determinant

$$\Delta(x) = \begin{vmatrix} z_{11}(x) & \dots & z_{1n}(x) \\ \cdot & \cdot \, \cdot \, \cdot & \cdot \\ z_{n1}(x) & \dots & z_{nn}(x) \end{vmatrix}$$

does not vanish in the interval $[a, b]$.

Let $y_1(x), \ldots, y_n(x)$ be some solution of System (1.1.1) and x_j (for $j = 1, 2, \ldots, n$) be fixed points in the interval $[a, b]$. Putting

$$x_0 = x_j, \quad u_i(x) = y_i(x), \quad v_i(x) = z_{ji}(x)$$

in (1.1.3), we obtain

$$\begin{aligned} \sum_{i=1}^{n} y_i(x) z_{ji}(x) = \int_{x_j}^{x} \sum_{i=1}^{n} z_{ji}(\xi) f_i(\xi)\, d\xi \\ + \int_{x_j}^{x} \sum_{i=1}^{n} y_i(\xi) M_i\left(\xi, \frac{d}{d\xi}\right) z_j(\xi)\, d\xi + c_j \end{aligned} \tag{1.1.5}$$

where

$$M_i\left(\xi, \frac{d}{d\xi}\right) z_j(\xi) = \frac{dz_{ji}(\xi)}{d\xi} + \sum_{k=1}^{n} a_{ki}(\xi) z_{jk}(\xi) \tag{1.1.6}$$

$$\sum_{i=1}^{n} y_i(x_j) z_{ji}(x_j) = c_j \qquad (j = 1, 2, \ldots, n) \tag{1.1.7}$$

We now solve System (1.1.5) for the functions $y_i(x)$, assuming that the right-hand sides of the equations are known. Clearly, to do this, it will be sufficient to multiply the equations (1.1.5) by the cofactor $\Delta_{jk}(x)$ of the element $z_{jk}(x)$ in the determinant $\Delta(x)$ and sum over j.

We then obtain

$$\sum_{i=1}^{n} y_i(x) \sum_{j=1}^{n} z_{ji}(x)\,\Delta_{jk}(x) = \sum_{j=1}^{n} \Delta_{jk}(x) \int_{x_j}^{x} \sum_{i=1}^{n} z_{ji}(\xi) f_i(\xi)\,d\xi$$

$$+ \sum_{j=1}^{n} \Delta_{jk}(x) \int_{x_j}^{x} \sum_{i=1}^{n} y_i(\xi) M_i\left(\xi, \frac{d}{d\xi}\right) z_j(\xi)\,d\xi + \sum_{j=1}^{n} c_j \Delta_{jk}(x)$$

In accordance with a familiar property of determinants, we have

$$\sum_{j=1}^{n} z_{ji}(x)\,\Delta_{jk}(x) = \begin{cases} \Delta(x) & \text{for} \quad i = k \\ 0 & \text{for} \quad i \neq k \end{cases}$$

Therefore, from the preceding equation, we obtain

$$\begin{aligned} y_k(x) = {} & \sum_{j=1}^{n} \frac{\Delta_{jk}(x)}{\Delta(x)} \int_{x_j}^{x} \sum_{i=1}^{n} z_{ji}(\xi) f_i(\xi)\,d\xi \\ & + \sum_{j=1}^{n} \frac{\Delta_{jk}(x)}{\Delta(x)} \int_{x_j}^{x} \sum_{i=1}^{n} y_i(\xi) M_i\left(\xi, \frac{d}{d\xi}\right) z_j(\xi)\,d\xi + \sum_{j=1}^{n} c_j \frac{\Delta_{jk}(x)}{\Delta(x)} \end{aligned} \tag{1.1.8}$$

Thus, from the derivation of (1.1.8), we have the following theorem.

Theorem 1 Every solution of System (1.1.1) satisfying (1.1.7) for arbitrary constants c_j, satisfies the integral equations (1.1.8) also. Every solution $y_1(x), \ldots, y_n(x)$ of the system of integral equations (1.1.8) is almost everywhere on $[a, b]$ a solution of System (1.1.1) which satisfies Condition (1.1.7).

Proof We shall prove the second assertion of the theorem first. We multiply both sides of (1.1.8) by $z_{sk}(x)$ and sum over k. According to a familiar property of determinants we obtain

$$\begin{aligned} \sum_{k=1}^{n} y_k(x)\, z_{sk}(x) = {} & \sum_{k=1}^{n} \sum_{j=1}^{n} \frac{z_{sk}(x)\,\Delta_{jk}(x)}{\Delta(x)} \left\{ \int_{x_j}^{x} \sum_{i=1}^{n} z_{ji}(\xi) f_i(\xi)\,d\xi \right. \\ & \left. + \int_{x_j}^{x} \sum_{i=1}^{n} y_i(\xi) M_i\left(\xi, \frac{d}{d\xi}\right) z_j(\xi)\,d\xi + c_j \right\} = \end{aligned} \tag{1.1.9}$$

$$= \int_{x_s}^{x} \sum_{i=1}^{n} z_{si}(\xi) f_i(\xi)\, d\xi + \int_{x_s}^{x} \sum_{i=1}^{n} y_i(\xi) M_i\left(\xi, \frac{d}{d\xi}\right) z_s(\xi)\, d\xi + c_s \tag{1.1.9 (cont.)}$$

From this equation with $x = x_s$, we obtain

$$\sum_{k=1}^{n} y_k(x_s) z_{sk}(x_s) = c_s$$

which proves the second assertion of the theorem.

To prove the first assertion, we note that the integral equations (1.1.8) imply that every solution $y_1(x), \ldots, y_n(x)$ of this system is an absolutely continuous function on the interval $[a, b]$. Therefore, by putting $x_0 = x_j$, $u_i = y_i(x)$ and $v_i(x) = z_{ji}(x)$ in Lagrange's formula (1.1.3), we obtain

$$\sum_{i=1}^{n} y_i(x) z_{ji}(x) = \int_{x_j}^{x} \sum_{i=1}^{n} z_{ji}(\xi) L_i\left(\xi, \frac{d}{d\xi}\right) y(\xi)\, d\xi + \int_{x_j}^{x} \sum_{i=1}^{n} y_i(\xi) M_i\left(\xi, \frac{d}{d\xi}\right) z_j(\xi)\, d\xi + c_j \tag{1.1.5a}$$

Equating the right-hand sides of (1.1.5a) and (1.1.5), we find that

$$\int_{x_j}^{x} \sum_{i=1}^{n} z_{ji}(\xi) L_i\left(\xi, \frac{d}{d\xi}\right) y(\xi)\, d\xi = \int_{x_j}^{x} \sum_{i=1}^{n} z_{ji}(\xi) f_i(\xi)\, d\xi \tag{1.1.10}$$

Differentiating equations (1.1.10) with respect to x, we have*

$$\sum_{i=1}^{n} z_{ji}(x) L_i\left(x, \frac{d}{dx}\right) y(x) = \sum_{i=1}^{n} z_{ji}(x) f_i(x) \tag{1.1.11}$$

Multiplying both sides of (1.1.11) by $\Delta_{jk}(x)$ and summing

* If the integrands in (1.1.10) are continuous on $[a, b]$ we see, by differentiating this equation, that (1.1.11) is satisfied everywhere on $[a, b]$.

over j, we obtain

$$\sum_{j=1}^{n}\sum_{i=1}^{n}\Delta_{jk}(x)\,z_{ji}(x)\,L_i\left(x, \frac{d}{dx}\right)y(x) = \sum_{j=1}^{n}\sum_{i=1}^{n}\Delta_{jk}(x)\,z_{ji}(x)\,f_i(x)$$

or

$$\sum_{i=1}^{n}L_i\left(x, \frac{d}{dx}\right)y(x)\sum_{j=1}^{n}\Delta_{jk}(x)\,z_{ji}(x) = \sum_{i=1}^{n}f_i(x)\sum_{j=1}^{n}\Delta_{jk}(x)\,z_{ji}(x)$$

From the last equation, it follows that

$$\Delta(x)\,L_k\left(x, \frac{d}{dx}\right)y = \Delta(x)\,f_k(x)$$

Dividing by $\Delta(x) \neq 0$ we obtain the equation

$$L_k\left(x, \frac{d}{dx}\right)y = f_k(x)$$

which is satisfied almost everywhere on $[a, b]$.

Remark If the coefficients of the system are continuous functions on $[a, b]$ and if the $y_i(x)\,z_{ji}(x)$ are continuously differentiable on $[a, b]$, it follows from the footnote to (1.1.11) that $y_k(x)$ is a solution of System (1.1.1) everywhere on $[a, b]$.

1.2 GENERALISED EXISTENCE THEOREM

We will now consider the problem of finding a solution of the system of differential equations (1.1.1) that satisfies Condition (1.1.7) for given sets of absolutely continuous functions $z_{ji}(x)$ (for $i, j = 1, \ldots, n$) (with non-zero determinant) and constants c_j (for $j = 1, \ldots, n$).

As shown in Section 1.1 (see Theorem 1), this problem is equivalent to solving the system of integral equations (1.1.8).

Consequently, to prove the existence of a solution of the problem, we may confine ourselves to proving the existence of a solution of Equation (1.1.8)

Let us introduce the notations

$$F_k(x) = \sum_{j=1}^{n} \frac{\Delta_{jk}(x)}{\Delta(x)} \left\{ \int_{x_j}^{x} \sum_{i=1}^{n} z_{ji}(\xi) f_i(\xi)\, d\xi + c_j \right\} \qquad (1.2.1)$$

$$q_{ki}^{(j)}(x, \xi) = \frac{\Delta_{jk}(x)}{\Delta(x)} M_i\left(\xi, \frac{d}{d\xi}\right) z_j(\xi)$$

$$= \frac{\Delta_{jk}(x)}{\Delta(x)} \left\{ \frac{dz_{ji}(\xi)}{d\xi} + \sum_{s=1}^{n} a_{si}(\xi) z_{js}(\xi) \right\} \qquad (1.2.2)$$

With these notations, (1.1.8) may be written in the form

$$y_k(x) = F_k(x) + \sum_{j=1}^{n} \sum_{i=1}^{n} \int_{x_j}^{x} q_{ki}^{(j)}(x, \xi) y_i(\xi)\, d\xi \qquad (1.2.3)$$

$$(k = 1, 2, \ldots, n),$$

Here, because of the restrictions imposed on the coefficients of System (1.1.1) and on the functions $z_{ji}(x)$ (for i, $j = 1, \ldots, n$), the functions $F_k(x)$ are absolutely continuous on the interval $[a, b]$ and the kernels $q_{ki}^{(j)}(x, \xi)$ are summable with respect to ξ on that interval and they are absolutely continuous with respect to x at almost every value of $\xi \in [a, b]$.

We will construct a sequence of functions $u_k^{(m)}(x)$ (where $(m = 0, 1, 2, \ldots)$ according to the following formulae

$$u_k^{(0)}(x) = F_k(x)$$

$$u_k^{(m)}(x) = \sum_{j=1}^{n} \sum_{i=1}^{n} \int_{x_j}^{x} q_{ki}^{(j)}(x, \xi) u_i^{(m-1)}(\xi)\, d\xi \qquad (1.2.4)$$

$$(m = 1, 2, \ldots)$$

Obviously, all the functions $u_k^{(m)}(x)$ are absolutely continuous on $[a, b]$.

Let $y_k(x)$ denote the functions representing the sums of the series

$$\sum_{m=0}^{\infty} u_k^{(m)}(x) \qquad (k = 1, 2, \ldots, n) \qquad (1.2.5)$$

Then, we can easily prove Theorem 2 below.

Theorem 2: Dini's theorem generalised Suppose that the coefficients $a_{ik}(x)$ and $f_i(x)$ in System (1.1.1) are Lebesgue-summable functions on the interval $[a, b]$. Let $Z(x)$ be a matrix of absolutely continuous functions $z_{ji}(x)$ (for $i, j = 1, \ldots, n$) with determinant $\Delta(x)$ non-zero on $[a, b]$. Let $c_1, c_2, \ldots, c_n$ be n constants. Let $F_k(x)$ and $q_{ki}^{(j)}(x, \xi)$ be functions defined by (1.2.1) and (1.2.2). Then the sum $y_k(x)$ of the infinite series (1.2.5) satisfies System (1.1.1) and Conditions (1.1.7) almost everywhere on the interval $[a, b]$ if

1. the series (1.2.5) converge almost everywhere on the interval $[a, b]$ and
2. the series $\sum_{m=0}^{\infty} u_i^{(m)}(\xi)\, q_{ki}^{(j)}(x, \xi)$ can be integrated term by term in the interval $[a, b]$.

Proof We need only show that the functions

$$y_k(x) = \sum_{m=0}^{\infty} u_k^{(m)}(x) \tag{1.2.6}$$

satisfy the integral equations (1.2.3). This can be directly verified if we substitute $y_k(x)$ into the right-hand sides of (1.2.3) and recall Conditions 1 and 2 of the theorem. Specifically, by virtue of these conditions and of (1.2.4), we have

$$\begin{aligned}
&\sum_{j=1}^{n} \sum_{i=1}^{n} \int_{x_j}^{x} q_{ki}^{(j)}(x, \xi)\, y_i(\xi)\, d\xi \\
&\equiv \sum_{j=1}^{n} \sum_{i=1}^{n} \int_{x_j}^{x} q_{ki}^{(j)}(x, \xi) \sum_{m=0}^{\infty} u_i^{(m)}(\xi)\, d\xi \\
&\equiv \sum_{j=1}^{n} \sum_{i=1}^{n} \int_{x_j}^{x} \sum_{m=0}^{\infty} q_{ki}^{(j)}(x, \xi)\, u_i^{(m)}(\xi)\, d\xi \\
&\equiv \sum_{j=1}^{n} \sum_{i=1}^{n} \sum_{m=0}^{\infty} \int_{x_j}^{x} q_{ki}^{(j)}(x, \xi)\, u_i^{(m)}(\xi)\, d\xi \\
&\equiv \sum_{m=0}^{\infty} \sum_{j=1}^{n} \sum_{i=1}^{n} \int_{x_j}^{x} q_{ki}^{(j)}(x, \xi)\, u_i^{(m)}(\xi)\, d\xi \\
&\equiv \sum_{m=0}^{\infty} u_k^{(m+1)}(x) \equiv \sum_{m=1}^{\infty} u_k^{(m)}(x) \\
&\equiv \sum_{m=0}^{\infty} u_k^{(m)}(x) - u_k^{(0)}(x) \equiv y_k(x) - F_k(x)
\end{aligned}$$

which completes the proof.

1.3 EXISTENCE THEOREMS

In this section, we shall prove the existence almost everywhere on $[a, b]$ of a solution of System (1.1.1) that satisfies Condition (1.1.7) for arbitrary constants c_j (for $j=1, \ldots, n$) when all the $x_j=x_0$ for $j=1, 2, \ldots, n$. It follows from Theorem 1 that, to do this, it will be sufficient to show that the series (1.2.5) converge absolutely and uniformly on the interval $[a, b]$ and, consequently, that their sums $y_k(x)$ are absolutely continuous functions on that interval.

As was noted above, the $F_k(x) \equiv u_k^{(0)}(x)$ are absolutely continuous functions on the interval $[a, b]$. Therefore, there exist constants P and N such that*

$$|F_k(x)| \leqslant P$$
$$\left|\frac{\Delta_{jk}(x)}{\Delta(x)}\right| \leqslant N \qquad (1.3.1)$$
$$(k=1, 2, \ldots, n)$$

Since the coefficients $a_{ij}(x)$ are summable on the interval $[a, b]$, it follows from the known properties of summable functions that

$$\omega(x)=\sum_{j=1}^{n} \sum_{i=1}^{n}\left|\frac{dz_{ji}(x)}{dx}+\sum_{k=1}^{n} a_{ki}(x) z_{jk}(x)\right| \qquad (1.3.2)$$

is a Lebesgue-summable function on $[a, b]$.

Define

$$\int_a^b \omega(x)\, dx=M \qquad (1.3.3)$$

In view of (1.2.1), (1.2.2), (1.3.1) and (1.3.2), we obtain from (1.2.4)

$$\begin{aligned} |u_k^{(1)}(x)| &\leqslant \sum_{j=1}^{n} \sum_{i=1}^{n} \int_{x_0}^{x} |q_{ki}^{(j)}(x, \xi)\, u_i^{(0)}(\xi)|\, d\xi \\ &= \sum_{j=1}^{n} \sum_{i=1}^{n} \int_{x_0}^{x}\left|\frac{\Delta_{jk}(x)}{\Delta(x)}\right|\left|\frac{dz_{ji}}{d\xi}+\sum_{s=1}^{n} a_{si}(\xi)\, z_{js}(\xi)\right| |F_i(\xi)|\, d\xi \end{aligned} \qquad (1.3.4)$$

*According to the hypotheses, the $z_{ji}(x)$ are absolutely continuous and there exists a constant $P_0>0$ such that $|\Delta(x)|>P_0$. It follows that the $F_k(x)$ are absolutely continuous and bounded on $[a, b]$

$$\leqslant PN\int_{x_0}^{x}\sum_{j=1}^{n}\sum_{i=1}^{n}\left|\frac{dz_{ji}(\xi)}{d\xi}+\sum_{s=1}^{n}a_{si}(\xi)\,z_{js}(\xi)\right|d\xi=PN\int_{x_0}^{x}\omega(\xi)\,d\xi \qquad (1.3.4)\ \text{(cont.)}$$

Similarly, we obtain from (1.2.4)

$$|u_k^{(2)}(x)|\leqslant\sum_{j=1}^{n}\sum_{i=1}^{n}\int_{x_0}^{x}|q_{ki}^{(j)}(\xi)\,u_i^{(1)}(\xi)|\,d\xi$$

$$=\sum_{j=1}^{n}\sum_{i=1}^{n}\int_{x_0}^{x}\left|\frac{\Delta_{jk}(x)}{\Delta(x)}\right|\left|\frac{dz_{ji}(\xi)}{d\xi}+\sum_{s=1}^{n}a_{si}(\xi)\,z_{js}(\xi)\right||u_i^{(1)}(\xi)|\,d\xi$$

$$\leqslant\int_{x_0}^{x}\sum_{j=1}^{n}\sum_{i=1}^{n}N\left|\frac{dz_{ji}(\xi)}{d\xi}+\sum_{s=1}^{n}a_{si}(\xi)\,z_{js}(\xi)\right|PN\,d\xi\int_{x_0}^{\xi}\omega(\xi_1)\,d\xi_1 \qquad (1.3.5)$$

$$=PN^2\int_{x_0}^{x}d\xi\int_{x_0}^{\xi}\omega(\xi_1)\,d\xi_1\sum_{j=1}^{n}\sum_{i=1}^{n}\left|\frac{dz_{ji}(\xi)}{d\xi}+\sum_{s=1}^{n}a_{si}(\xi)\,z_{js}(\xi)\right|$$

$$=PN^2\int_{x_0}^{x}d\xi\,\omega(\xi)\int_{x_0}^{\xi}\omega(\xi_1)\,d\xi_1$$

It is easy to show by induction that

$$|u_k^{(m)}(x)|\leqslant PN^m\int_{x_0}^{x}\omega(\xi)\,d\xi\int_{x_0}^{\xi}\omega(\xi_1)\,d\xi_1\ldots\int_{x_0}^{\xi_{m-2}}\omega(\xi_{m-1})\,d\xi_{m-1} \qquad (1.3.6)$$

for every natural number m.

This inequality can be obtained from (1.2.4) by virtue of (1.2.1), (1.2.2) and (1.3.1) - (1.3.3).

For a simplification of (1.3.6), we note that

$$\int_{x_0}^{\xi_{m-3}}\omega(\xi_{m-2})\,d\xi_{m-2}\int_{x_0}^{\xi_{m-2}}\omega(\xi_{m-1})\,d\xi_{m-1}$$

$$=\int_{x_0}^{\xi_{m-3}}\left(\int_{x_0}^{\xi_{m-2}}\omega(\xi_{m-1})\,d\xi_{m-1}\right)d\left(\int_{x_0}^{\xi_{m-2}}\omega(\xi_{m-1})\,d\xi_{m-1}\right)$$

$$=\int_{x_0}^{\xi_{m-3}}\frac{1}{2!}\,d\left(\int_{x_0}^{\xi_{m-2}}\omega(\xi_{m-1})\,d\xi_{m-1}\right)^2$$

$$=\frac{1}{2!}\left(\int_{x_0}^{\xi_{m-2}}\omega(\xi_{m-1})\,d\xi_{m-1}\right)^2\Bigg|_{x_0}^{\xi_{m-3}}=\frac{1}{2!}\left(\int_{x_0}^{\xi_{m-3}}\omega(\xi_{m-1})\,d\xi_{m-1}\right)^2$$

Similarly,

$$\int_{x_0}^{\xi_{m-4}} \omega(\xi_{m-3})\, d\xi_{m-3} \int_{x_0}^{\xi_{m-3}} \omega(\xi_{m-2})\, d\xi_{m-2} \int_{x_0}^{\xi_{m-2}} \omega(\xi_{m-1})\, d\xi_{m-1}$$

$$= \frac{1}{2\cdot 3} \int_{x_0}^{\xi_{m-4}} d\left(\int_{x_0}^{\xi_{m-3}} \omega(\xi_{m-1})\, d\xi_{m-1} \right)^3$$

$$= \frac{1}{2\cdot 3} \left(\int_{x_0}^{\xi_{m-4}} \omega(\xi_{m-1})\, d\xi_{m-1} \right)^3 = \frac{1}{2\cdot 3} \left(\int_{x_0}^{\xi_{m-4}} \omega(\xi_{m-3})\, d\xi_{m-3} \right)^3$$

Thus, by successive integration, we obtain

$$\int_{x_0}^{x} \omega(\xi)\, d\xi \int_{x_0}^{\xi} \omega(\xi_1)\, d\xi_1 \ldots \int_{x_0}^{\xi_{m-2}} \omega(\xi_{m-1})\, d\xi_{m-1} = \frac{1}{m!} \left(\int_{x_0}^{x} \omega(\xi)\, d\xi \right)^m \tag{1.3.7}$$

In accordance with (1.3.7), the inequality (1.3.6) can be written

$$|u_k^{(m)}(x)| \leqslant PN^m \frac{1}{m!} \left(\int_{x_0}^{x} \omega(\xi)\, d\xi \right)^m \leqslant \frac{P\,(NM)^m}{m!} \tag{1.3.8}$$

$$(m = 0,\ 1,\ 2,\ \ldots)$$

Inequality (1.3.8) implies the absolute and uniform convergence of the series (1.2.5).

Let us now show that the series

$$\sum_{m=0}^{\infty} u_i^{(m)}(\xi)\, q_{ki}^{(j)}(x, \xi) \tag{1.3.9}$$

can be integrated term by term.

We denote by $S_{kir}^{(j)}(x, \xi)$ the sum of the first $r+1$ terms of the series (1.3.9)

$$S_{kir}^{(j)}(x, \xi) = \sum_{m=0}^{r} q_{ki}^{(j)}(x, \xi)\, u_i^{(m)}(\xi)$$

Bearing in mind (1.2.2) and (1.3.2) and the inequalities (1.3.1) and (1.3.8), we obtain, for all x and ξ in $[a, b]$ and all natural numbers r.

$$| S_{kir}^{(j)}(x, \xi) | \leqslant \sum_{m=0}^{r} | q_{ki}^{(j)}(x, \xi) | \, | u_i^{(m)}(\xi) |$$

$$= \sum_{m=0}^{r} \left| \frac{\Delta_{jk}(x)}{\Delta(x)} \right| \left| \frac{dz_{ji}(\xi)}{d\xi} + \sum_{s=1}^{n} a_{si}(\xi) z_{js}(\xi) \right| \left| u_i^{(m)}(\xi) \right|$$

$$\leqslant \sum_{m=0}^{r} N \frac{P(NM)^m}{m!} \left| \frac{dz_{ji}(\xi)}{d\xi} + \sum_{s=1}^{n} a_{si}(\xi) z_{js}(\xi) \right| \tag{1.3.10}$$

$$\leqslant \sum_{m=0}^{r} NP \frac{(NM)^m}{m!} \sum_{j=1}^{n} \sum_{i=1}^{n} \left| \frac{dz_{ji}(\xi)}{d\xi} + \sum_{s=1}^{n} a_{si}(\xi) z_{js}(\xi) \right|$$

$$= NP\omega(\xi) \sum_{m=0}^{r} \frac{(NM)^m}{m!} \leqslant NP\omega(\xi) \sum_{m=0}^{\infty} \frac{(NM)^m}{m!}$$

$$= NPe^{NM}\omega(\xi)$$

Because of the inequality (1.3.10) and the convergence of the series (1.3.9) almost everywhere on $[a, b]$, Lebesgue's theorem on taking the limit under the integral sign is applicable to the sequence $S_{kir}^{(j)}(x, \xi)$ (for $r = 1, 2, \ldots$), so that we have

$$\lim_{r\to\infty} \int_{x_0}^{x} S_{kir}^{(j)}(x, \xi)\, d\xi = \lim_{r\to\infty} \int_{x_0}^{x} \sum_{m=0}^{r} q_{ki}^{(j)}(x, \xi) u_i^{(m)}(\xi)\, d\xi$$

$$= \lim_{r\to\infty} \sum_{m=0}^{r} \int_{x_0}^{x} q_{ki}^{(j)}(x, \xi) u_i^{(m)}(\xi)\, d\xi = \sum_{m=0}^{\infty} \int_{x_0}^{x} q_{ki}^{(j)}(x, \xi) u_i^{(m)}(\xi)\, d\xi$$

$$= \int_{x_0}^{x} \lim_{r\to\infty} S_{kir}^{(j)}(x, \xi)\, d\xi = \int_{x_0}^{x} \sum_{m=0}^{\infty} q_{ki}^{(j)}(x, \xi) u_i^{(m)}(\xi)\, d\xi$$

The last equation indicates that the second condition of Theorem 2 is also satisfied. Therefore, in accordance with Theorem 2, the sums of the series (1.2.5) satisfy the system of integral equations (1.2.3).

Then, by virtue of Theorem 1, the $y_k(x)$ satisfy (1.1.7) and, almost everywhere on $[a, b]$, the equations of System (1.1.1).

Thus, we have proved Theorem 3 below.

Theorem 3 Suppose that the coefficients $a_{ik}(x)$ and $f_i(x)$ of System (1.1.1) are Lebesgue-summable functions on the interval $[a, b]$. Let $Z(x)$ be a matrix of absolutely continuous functions $z_{ji}(x)$ with non-zero determinant on the interval $[a, b]$, let c_j (for $j=1, \ldots, n$) be constants, and let x_0 be any point in the interval $[a, b]$. Then, there exist functions $y_1(x), \ldots, y_n(x)$, which are absolutely continuous on $[a, b]$, satisfy System (1.1.1) almost everywhere on $[a, b]$, and satisfy the conditions

$$\sum_{i=1}^{n} y_i(x_0) z_{ji}(x_0) = c_j \qquad (1.3.11)$$

If stronger restrictions are imposed on the functions $a_{ik}(x)$ and $f_i(x)$, we have the stronger Theorem 4 below.

Theorem 4 If the functions $a_{ik}(x)$, and $f_i(x)$ are continuous on the interval $[a, b]$ and if $Z(x)$ is the matrix of continuously (once) differentiable functions with non-zero determinant on that interval, then there exist functions $y_1(x), \ldots, y_n(x)$ which satisfy Equations (1.1.1) almost everywhere on (a, b) and which satisfy Conditions (1.3.11) for arbitrary given constants c_j for $j=1, \ldots, n$.

Proof To prove this theorem, it will, by virtue of the footnote to (1.1.11), be sufficient to show that, for the functions $y_k(x)$ defined by (1.2.6), the functions $L_i\left(x, \frac{d}{dx}\right) y(x)$ are continuous functions on the interval (a, b).

Because of the continuous differentiability of the functions $z_{ji}(x)$ the kernels $q_{ki}^{(j)}(x, \xi)$ are continuous with respect to x and ξ on (a, b). Therefore, the functions $u_k^{(m)}(x)$, are also continuous on the interval (a, b) and

$$\frac{du_k^{(m)}(x)}{dx} = \sum_{j=1}^{n} \sum_{i=1}^{n} q_{ki}^{(j)}(x, x) u_i^{(m-1)}(x) + \sum_{j=1}^{n} \sum_{i=1}^{n} \int_{x_0}^{x} \frac{dq_{ki}^{(j)}(x, \xi)}{dx} u_i^{(m-1)}(\xi)\, d\xi$$

where the last identity is obtained by differentiating the identity (1.2.4). Substituting $q_{ki}^{(j)}(x, x)$ as defined by (1.2.2) and $\frac{dq_{ki}^{(j)}(x, \xi)}{dx}$ into the last identity, we obtain

$$\frac{du_k^{(m)}(x)}{dx} = \sum_{j=1}^{n} \sum_{i=1}^{n} \frac{\Delta_{jk}(x)}{\Delta(x)} M_i\left(x, \frac{d}{dx}\right) z_j(x)\, u_i^{(m-1)}(x)$$

$$+ \sum_{j=1}^{n} \sum_{i=1}^{n} \int_{x_0}^{x} \frac{d}{dx}\left(\frac{\Delta_{jk}(x)}{\Delta(x)}\right) \left\{\frac{dz_{ji}(\xi)}{d\xi}\right. \tag{1.3.12}$$

$$\left. + \sum_{s=1}^{n} a_{si}(\xi)\, z_{js}(\xi)\right\} u_i^{(m-1)}(\xi)\, d\xi$$

By virtue of the restrictions imposed on the functions $z_{ji}(x)$, there exists a constant Q such that

$$\left| \frac{d}{dx} \frac{\Delta_{ji}(x)}{\Delta(x)} \right| \leqslant Q \tag{1.3.13}$$

Using the generalisation (1.3.2) and the inequalities (1.3.1), (1.3.8) and (1.3.13), we obtain from (1.3.12)

$$\left|\frac{du_k^{(m)}(x)}{dx}\right| \leqslant \frac{P(NM)^{m-1}}{(m-1)!} \left\{ N\omega(x) + \int_{x_0}^{x} Q\omega(\xi)\, d\xi \right\}$$

$$\leqslant \frac{P(NM)^{m-1}}{(m-1)!} \left[N\omega(x) + Q\int_a^b \omega(t)\, dt \right] \tag{1.3.14}$$

$$\leqslant L \frac{(NM)^{m-1}}{(m-1)!}$$

The inequalities (1.3.8) and (1.3.14) show that the series

$$\sum_{m=0}^{\infty} u_k^{(m)}(x), \quad \sum_{m=0}^{\infty} \frac{du_k^{(m)}(x)}{dx}$$

converge uniformly. It then follows, because of the continuity of the functions $u_k^{(m)}(x)$ and $\frac{du_k^{(m)}(x)}{dx}$, that the functions

$$y_k(x) = \sum_{m=0}^{\infty} u_k^{(m)}(x), \quad \frac{dy_k(x)}{dx} = \sum_{m=0}^{\infty} \frac{du_k^{(m)}(x)}{dx}$$

are continuous. This in turn implies continuity of the functions $L_i\left(x, \frac{d}{dx}\right) y(x)$, and hence the proof is completed.

CHAPTER 2

Asymptotic representations of solutions of linear differential equations with a complex parameter

2.1 FORMAL SOLUTIONS OF FIRST-ORDER SYSTEMS

Consider the system of differential equations

$$L_i\left(x, \frac{d}{dx}\right) y \equiv \frac{dy_i}{dx} - \sum_{j=1}^{n} a_{ij}(x, \lambda)\, y_j = 0 \qquad (i = 1, \ldots, n) \tag{2.1.1}$$

the coefficients in which are single-valued functions of a complex parameter λ which are analytic in a neighbourhood of the point $\lambda = \infty$, i.e. for

$$|\lambda| \geqslant R \tag{2.1.2}$$

where R is a sufficiently large positive number, and which have a pole of order p at the point $\lambda = \infty$. It follows that the functions $a_{ij}(x, \lambda)$ have expansions of the following form in a region Ω of values of λ which satisfy Condition (2.1.2)

$$a_{ij}(x, \lambda) = \sum_{\nu=0}^{\infty} \lambda^{p-\nu} a_{ij}^{(p-\nu)}(x) \tag{2.1.3}$$

where the coefficients in these expansions are real or complex functions of a real variable x in some finite interval (a, b).

We also assume that the functions $a_{ij}^{(p-\nu)}(x)$ (for $i, j = 1, \dots, n$ and $\nu = 0, 1, \dots$) are uniformly bounded and continuous in the interval (a, b).

If we denote by $a(x, \lambda)$ and $a^{(p-\nu)}(x)$ the matrices of the functions $a_{ij}(x, \lambda)$ and $a_{ij}^{(p-\nu)}(x)$ respectively, (for $i, j = 1, \dots, n$), then (2.1.1) and (2.1.3) can obviously be written in the matric form

$$L\left(x, \frac{d}{dx}\right) y(x) \equiv \frac{dy}{dx} - a(x, \lambda) y = 0 \tag{2.1.1a}$$

$$a(x, \lambda) = \sum_{\nu=0}^{\infty} \lambda^{p-\nu} a^{(p-\nu)}(x) \tag{2.1.3a}$$

where y is the column composed of the functions $y_1, y_2, \dots, y_n$.

Let us construct series in decreasing powers of λ which formally satisfy Equations (2.1.1), i.e. series (in decreasing powers of λ) which satisfy (2.1.1) provided they can be differentiated term by term.

We call the equation

$$\det(a^{(p)}(x) - \theta e) \equiv \begin{vmatrix} a_{11}^{(p)}(x) - \theta & a_{12}^{(p)}(x) & a_{13}^{(p)}(x) & \dots & a_{1n}^{(p)}(x) \\ a_{21}^{(p)}(x) & a_{22}^{(p)}(x) - \theta & a_{23}^{(p)}(x) & \dots & a_{2n}^{(p)}(x) \\ \dots & \dots & \dots & \dots & \dots \\ a_{n1}^{(p)}(x) & \dots & \dots & \dots & a_{nn}^{(p)}(x) - \theta \end{vmatrix} = 0 \tag{2.1.4}$$

the characteristic equation of System (2.1.1), and denote by e the unit matrix of corresponding order.

To simplify our calculations, we assume that all the θ-roots of the characteristic equation (2.1.4) for all values of $x \in (a, b)$ are distinct and denote them by

$$\theta_1^{(p)}(x), \ \theta_2^{(p)}(x), \ \dots, \ \theta_n^{(p)}(x)$$

Then, for every $x \in (a, b)$ there exists a matrix $m(x)$ such that the matrix $m^{-1}(x) a^{(p)}(x) m(x)$ is a diagonal matrix

$$m^{-1}(x)\,a^{(p)}(x)\,m(x)=\begin{pmatrix}\theta_1^{(p)}(x) & 0 & 0 & 0\\ 0 & \theta_2^{(p)}(x) & 0 & 0\\ \cdots & \cdots & \cdots & \cdots\\ 0 & \cdots & 0 & \theta_n^{(p)}(x)\end{pmatrix}\qquad(2.1.5)$$

Now, to simplify System (2.1.1a), we introduce a new unknown vector-valued function by putting

$$y=m(x)Z\qquad(2.1.6)$$

If we substitute (2.1.6) into (2.1.1a), we have

$$\frac{dm(x)}{dx}Z+m(x)\frac{dZ}{dx}=a(x,\lambda)\,m(x)\,Z(x)$$

Multiplying this equation on the left by $m^{-1}(x)$, we obtain the differential equation

$$\frac{dZ}{dx}=\left(m^{-1}(x)\,a(x,\lambda)\,m(x)-m^{-1}(x)\frac{dm(x)}{dx}\right)Z\equiv b(x,\lambda)\,Z\qquad(2.1.7)$$

where

$$b(x,\lambda)=\sum_{\nu=0}^{\infty}\lambda^{p-\nu}b^{(p-\nu)}(x)\qquad(2.1.8)$$

$$\begin{aligned}b^{(0)}(x)&=m^{-1}(x)\,a^{(0)}(x)\,m(x)-m^{-1}(x)\frac{dm(x)}{dx}\\ b^{(\nu)}(x)&=m^{-1}(x)\,a^{(\nu)}(x)\,m(x)\end{aligned}\qquad(2.1.9)$$

$$(\nu=p,\ p-1,\ \ldots,1,\ -1,\ -2,\ldots)$$

We note that, for System (2.1.7), the matrix $b^{(p)}(x)$ is a diagonal matrix

$$b^{(p)}(x)=m^{-1}a^{(p)}m=\begin{pmatrix}\theta_1^{(p)} & 0 & 0\ldots 0\\ 0 & \theta_2^{(p)} & 0\ldots 0\\ \cdots & \cdots & \cdots\\ 0 & \cdots & \theta_n^{(p)}\end{pmatrix}\qquad(2.1.10)$$

Let us now construct formal solutions of System (2.1.7). First, we write (2.1.7) in expanded form

$$\frac{dz_i}{dx}-\sum_{j=1}^{n}b_{ij}(x,\lambda)\,z_j=0\quad(i=1,\ldots,n)\qquad(2.1.7\text{a})$$

We denote by $z_{1s},\ z_{2s},\ \ldots,z_{ns}$ a solution of the fundamental system of particular solutions of (2.1.7a) that corresponds to the root $\theta_s^{(p)}$ of the characteristic equation (2.1.4).

We seek functions z_{is} of the form

$$z_{is}=\exp\left(\int_a^x (\lambda^p\theta_s^{(p)}(\xi)+\lambda^{p-1}\theta_s^{(p-1)}(\xi)+\dots+\lambda\theta_s^{(1)}(\xi))\,d\xi\right)\sum_{k=0}^{\infty}\lambda^{-k}g_{is}^{(k)}(x) \tag{2.1.11}$$

where the functions $\theta_s^{(p-1)}(x), \dots, \theta_s^{(1)}(x)$, $g_{is}^{(k)}(x)$ are still to be determined.

If we substitute the $b_{ij}(x, \lambda)$ and z_{is} into (2.1.7a) and assume the validity of termwise differentiation of the series (2.1.11), we obtain from (2.1.8) and (2.1.11)

$$\begin{aligned}\Big\{&(\lambda^p\theta_s^{(p)}(x)+\lambda^{p-1}\theta_s^{(p-1)}(x)+\dots+\lambda\theta_s^{(1)}(x))\\ &\times\sum_{k=0}^{\infty}\lambda^{-k}g_{is}^{(k)}(x)+\sum_{k=0}^{\infty}\lambda^{-k}\frac{dg_{is}^{(k)}(x)}{dx}\\ &-\sum_{j=1}^{n}\sum_{\nu=0}^{\infty}\sum_{k=0}^{\infty}\lambda^{p-\nu-k}b_{ij}^{(p-\nu)}(x)\,g_{js}^{(k)}(x)\Big\}\\ &\times\exp\left(\int_a^x(\lambda^p\theta_s^{(p)}(\xi)+\lambda^{p-1}\theta_s^{(p-1)}(\xi)+\dots+\lambda\theta_s^{(1)}(\xi))\,d\xi\right)\equiv 0\end{aligned} \tag{2.1.12}$$

If we put the coefficients of the different powers of λ equal to zero in (2.1.12), this gives us an infinite set of groups of equations. The $(m+1)$ th group of equations is obtained by putting the coefficient of λ^{p-m} (for $m=0, 1, 2, \dots$) equal to zero:

$$\begin{aligned}&1)\quad \theta_s^{(p)}g_{is}^{(0)}-\sum_{j=1}^{n}b_{ij}^{(p)}g_{js}^{(0)}=0\\ &2)\quad \theta_s^{(p)}g_{is}^{(1)}+\theta_s^{(p-1)}g_{is}^{(0)}-\sum_{j=1}^{n}(b_{ij}^{(p-1)}g_{js}^{(0)}+b_{ij}^{(p)}g_{js}^{(1)})=0\end{aligned} \tag{2.1.13}$$

$$3)\quad \theta_s^{(p)} g_{is}^{(2)} + \theta_s^{(p-1)} g_{is}^{(1)} + \theta_s^{(p-2)} g_{is}^{(0)} - \sum_{j=1}^{n} (b_{ij}^{(p-2)} g_{js}^{(0)} + b_{ij}^{(p-1)} g_{js}^{(1)} + b_{ij}^{(p)} g_{js}^{(2)}) = 0$$

. . . .

$$p)\quad \theta_s^{(p)} g_{is}^{(p-1)} + \theta_s^{(p-1)} g_{is}^{(p-2)} + \ldots + \theta_s^{(1)} g_{is}^{(0)} - \sum_{j=1}^{n} (b_{ij}^{(p)} g_{js}^{(p-1)} + b_{ij}^{(p-1)} g_{js}^{(p-2)} + \ldots + b_{ij}^{(2)} g_{js}^{(1)} + b_{ij}^{(1)} g_{js}^{(0)}) = 0$$

$$p+1)\quad \theta_s^{(p)} g_{is}^{(p)} + \theta_s^{(p-1)} g_{is}^{(p-1)} + \ldots + \theta_s^{(1)} g_{is}^{(1)} + \frac{dg_{is}^{(0)}}{dx} - \sum_{j=1}^{n} (b_{ij}^{(p)} g_{js}^{(p)} + b_{ij}^{(p-1)} g_{js}^{(p-1)} + \ldots + b_{ij}^{(1)} g_{js}^{(1)} + b_{ij}^{(0)} g_{js}^{(0)}) = 0 \qquad \begin{matrix}(2.1.13)\\ (\text{cont.})\end{matrix}$$

. . . .

$$p+\nu+1)\quad \theta_s^{(p)} g_{is}^{(p+\nu)} + \theta_s^{(p-1)} g_{is}^{(p+\nu-1)} + \ldots + \theta_s^{(1)} g_{is}^{(\nu+1)} + \frac{dg_{is}^{(\nu)}}{dx} - \sum_{j=1}^{n} (b_{ij}^{(p)} g_{js}^{(p+\nu)} + b_{ij}^{(p-1)} g_{js}^{(p+\nu-1)} + \ldots + b_{ij}^{(0)} g_{js}^{(\nu)} + b_{ij}^{(-1)} g_{js}^{(\nu-1)} + \ldots + b_{ij}^{(-\nu)} g_{js}^{(0)}) = 0$$

$$(i = 1,\ 2,\ \ldots,\ n)$$

Remembering that $b^{(p)}(x)$ is a diagonal matrix, we can simplify (2.1.13). Then, the equations of the first group take the form

$$1)\quad (\theta_s^{(p)}(x) - \theta_i^{(p)}(x))\, g_{is}^{(0)} = 0 \quad (i = 1, 2, \ldots, n) \qquad (2.1.14)$$

From these equations, we see that

$$g_{is}^{(0)} = 0 \ \text{ for } \ i \neq s \qquad (2.1.15)$$

The function $g_{ss}^{(0)}$ is non-zero and cannot be determined with the aid of the first group of equations (2.1.13).

The equations of the second group are of the form

$$(\theta_s^{(p)} - \theta_i^{(p)})\, g_{is}^{(1)} + \theta_s^{(p-1)} g_{is}^{(0)} - \sum_{j=1}^{n} b_{ij}^{(p-1)} g_{js}^{(0)} = 0$$

Hence we obtain on the basis of (2.1.15)

$$2)\quad (\theta_s^{(p)}-\theta_i^{(p)})\, g_{is}^{(1)}+\theta_s^{(p-1)}g_{is}^{(0)}-b_{is}^{(p-1)}g_{ss}^{(0)}=0$$

Putting $i=s$ in this equation, we obtain in turn

$$(\theta_s^{(p-1)}-b_{ss}^{(p-1)})\, g_{ss}^{(0)}=0$$

Since $g_{ss}^{(0)}\neq 0$, the last equation gives

$$\theta_s^{(p-1)}=b_{ss}^{(p-1)} \tag{2.1.16}$$

Furthermore, for $i\neq s$, since $\theta_s^{(p)}-\theta_i^{(p)}\neq 0$, we obtain from the equations of the second group

$$g_{is}^{(1)}=\frac{b_{is}^{(p-1)}}{\theta_s^{(p)}-\theta_i^{(p)}}\, g_{ss}^{(0)}\equiv P_{i0}^{(1)}g_{ss}^{(0)}\quad \text{for}\quad i\neq s \tag{2.1.17}$$

The function $g_{ss}^{(1)}$ cannot be determined with the aid of the equations of the second group.

The equations of the third group are of the form

$$(\theta_s^{(p)}-\theta_i^{(p)})\, g_{is}^{(2)}+\theta_s^{(p-1)}g_{is}^{(1)}+\theta_s^{(p-2)}g_{is}^{(0)} - \sum_{j=1}^{n}(b_{ij}^{(p-1)}g_{js}^{(1)}+b_{ij}^{(p-2)}g_{js}^{(0)})=0$$

Bearing in mind (2.1.15) and (2.1.16), we can write these equations as

$$3)\quad (\theta_s^{(p)}-\theta_i^{(p)})\, g_{is}^{(2)}+b_{ss}^{(p-1)}g_{is}^{(1)}+\theta_s^{(p-2)}g_{is}^{(0)} -b_{is}^{(p-2)}g_{ss}^{(0)}-\sum_{j=1}^{n}b_{ij}^{(p-1)}g_{js}^{(1)}=0$$

In accordance with (2.1.17), for $i=s$, we obtain from this equation

$$b_{ss}^{(p-1)}g_{ss}^{(1)}+(\theta_s^{(p-2)}-b_{ss}^{(p-2)})\, g_{ss}^{(0)}-b_{ss}^{(p-1)}\, g_{ss}^{(1)} - \sum_{\substack{j=1\\ j\neq s}}^{n} b_{sj}^{(p-1)}\frac{b_{js}^{(p-1)}}{\theta_s^{(p)}-\theta_j^{(p)}}\, g_{ss}^{(0)}=0$$

or

$$\theta_s^{(p-2)}=b_{ss}^{(p-2)}+\sum_{\substack{j=1\\ j\neq s}}^{n} b_{sj}^{(p-1)}\frac{b_{js}^{(p-1)}}{\theta_s^{(p)}-\theta_j^{(p)}} \tag{2.1.18}$$

Thus, for $i=s$, the equations of the third group make it possible to determine the unknown function $\theta_s^{(p-2)}$. For $i\neq s$, we obtain from these equations, using (2.1.17),

$$g_{is}^{(2)}=\Big\{-b_{ss}^{(p-1)}\frac{b_{is}^{(p-1)}}{\theta_s^{(p)}-\theta_i^{(p)}}g_{ss}^{(0)}+b_{is}^{(p-2)}g_{ss}^{(0)}+b_{is}^{(p-1)}g_{ss}^{(1)}$$

$$+\sum_{\substack{j=1\\ j\neq s}}^{n}b_{ij}^{(p-1)}\frac{b_{js}^{(p-1)}}{\theta_s^{(p)}-\theta_j^{(p)}}g_{ss}^{(0)}\Big\}(\theta_s^{(p)}-\theta_i^{(p)})^{-1}\quad (i\neq s). \tag{2.1.19}$$

Thus, for $i\neq s$, the unknown functions $g_{is}^{(2)}$ can be expressed in the form of linear functions of $g_{ss}^{(0)}$ and $g_{ss}^{(1)}$ and, for $i=s$, the unknown function $\theta_s^{(p-2)}$ can be determined. Here, it should be noted that the unknown function $\theta_s^{(p-2)}$ does not depend on the functions $g_{ss}^{(0)}$ and $g_{ss}^{(1)}$.

By induction, we can prove the following assertions:

1. The equations of the $(\nu+1)$th group of (2.1.13) determine the functions $g_{is}^{(\nu)}$ for $i\neq s$ in the form of linear functions of $g_{ss}^{(0)}, g_{ss}^{(1)}, \ldots, g_{ss}^{(\nu-1)}$, the coefficients of which contain the functions $\theta_s^{(k)}(x)$ and the operator $D=\frac{d}{dx}$ (if $\nu\geqslant p$).
2. If we substitute into the sth equations of all the groups the expressions found for $g_{is}^{(\nu)}$ (where $i\neq s$), these equations determine the remaining unknown functions

$$\theta_s^{(p-1)},\ \theta_s^{(p-2)},\ \ldots,\ \theta_s^{(1)},\ g_{ss}^{(\nu)}\quad (\nu=0,\ 1,\ 2,\ \ldots)$$

   Here, the sth equations of the second, third, ..., pth, $(p+1)$th, $(p+2)$th, ..., $(p+\nu+1)$th, ... groups respectively determine $\theta_s^{(p-1)}$, $\theta_s^{(p-2)}$, ..., $\theta_s^{(1)}$, $g_{ss}^{(0)}$, $g_{ss}^{(1)}$, ..., $g_{ss}^{(\nu)}$, ...
3. The functions determined in this way

$$\theta_s^{(p-1)},\ \theta_s^{(p-2)},\ \ldots,\ \theta_s^{(1)}$$

   are completely independent of the functions

$$g_{ss}^{(0)},\ g_{ss}^{(1)},\ \ldots,\ g_{ss}^{(\nu)},\ \ldots$$

   which in turn are determined from the first-order linear differential equations. Therefore, they contain arbitrary constants.

The first assertion is proved simply. The $(\nu+1)$th group of Equations (2.1.13) for $i \neq s$ makes it possible to express functions $g_{is}^{(\nu)}$ linearly in terms of functions $g_{is}^{(\nu-1)}, \ldots, g_{is}^{(0)}$.

Suppose that the first assertion holds for $\nu-1$ (it is proved for $\nu-1=1,\ 2$) and that, for $i \neq s$,

$$g_{is}^{(q)} = \sum_{k=0}^{q-1} P_{ik}^{(q)} g_{ss}^{(k)} \qquad (q=1,\ 2,\ \ldots,\ \nu-1) \tag{2.1.20}$$

where the $P_{ik}^{(q)}$ do not depend on the functions $g_{ss}^{(h)}$. If we substitute this result into the expression $g_{is}^{(\nu)}$ which is obtained from the equations of the $(\nu+1)$th group of (2.1.13), we express the $g_{is}^{(\nu)}$ linearly in terms of $g_{ss}^{(0)}, \ldots, g_{ss}^{(\nu-1)}$, i.e. (2.1.20) holds for all $\nu=1,\ 2,\ \ldots$, where the coefficients $P_{ik}^{(q)}$ are completely independent of the functions $g_{is}^{(h)}$.

To prove 2 and 3, we first show that the coefficients $P_{ik}^{(q)}$ possess the following property :

$$P_{ik}^{(q)} = P_{ik-1}^{(q-1)} = P_{ik-2}^{(q-2)} = \ldots = P_{i0}^{(q-k)} \tag{2.1.21}$$
$$(k=0,\ 1,\ \ldots,\ q-1, \quad i=1,\ \ldots,\ n)$$

We can see that this is true for $q=2,\ k=1$ by equating the coefficients $P_{i1}^{(2)}$ and $P_{i0}^{(1)}$ in (2.1.19) and (2.1.17). We now suppose that (2.1.21) is valid for $q-1$ and prove its validity for q. From the equations of the $(q+1)$th group of System (2.1.13), we have, for $i \neq s$,

$$g_{is}^{(q)} = \frac{1}{\theta_s^{(p)} - \theta_i^{(p)}} \sum_{j=1}^{n} \{\gamma_{ij}^{(p-1)} g_{js}^{(q-1)} + \gamma_{ij}^{(p-2)} g_{js}^{(q-2)} + \ldots + \gamma_{ij}^{(p-q)} g_{js}^{(0)}\} \tag{2.1.22}$$

where

$$\begin{aligned} &\gamma_{ij}^{(\nu)} = b_{ij}^{(\nu)} \quad \text{for} \quad i \neq j \\ &\qquad\qquad (\nu = p,\ p-1, \ldots,\ 0, -1,\ -2,\ \ldots) \\ &\left.\begin{aligned} &\gamma_{ii}^{(\nu)} = b_{ii}^{(\nu)} - \theta_s^{(\nu)} \quad \text{for} \quad \nu \geqslant 1, \\ &\gamma_{ii}^{(\nu)} = b_{ii}^{(\nu)} \quad \text{for} \quad \nu \leqslant -1, \\ &\gamma_{ii}^{(0)} = b_{ii}^{(0)} - \frac{d}{dx} \end{aligned}\right\} \text{for} \quad j = i \end{aligned} \tag{2.1.23}$$

Substituting $g_{js}^{(q-1)}, g_{js}^{(q-2)}, \ldots, g_{js}^{(1)}$ from (2.1.20) into (2.1.22) (which is permissible because of the hypothesis)

$$g_{is}^{(q)}=\frac{1}{\theta_s^{(p)}-\theta_i^{(p)}}\sum_{\substack{j=1\\ j\neq s}}^{n}\Big\{\gamma_{ij}^{(p-1)}\sum_{h=0}^{q-2}P_{jk}^{(q-1)}g_{ss}^{(h)}$$

$$+\gamma_{ij}^{(p-2)}\sum_{h=0}^{q-3}P_{jk}^{(q-2)}g_{ss}^{(h)}+\ldots+\gamma_{ij}^{(p-q+2)}\sum_{h=0}^{1}P_{jk}^{(2)}g_{ss}^{(h)}$$

$$+\gamma_{ij}^{(p-q+1)}P_{j0}^{(1)}g_{ss}^{(0)}\Big\}+\frac{1}{\theta_s^{(p)}-\theta_i^{(p)}}\{\gamma_{is}^{(p-1)}g_{ss}^{(q-1)}$$

$$+\gamma_{is}^{(p-2)}g_{ss}^{(q-2)}+\ldots+\gamma_{is}^{(p-q)}g_{ss}^{(0)}\}$$

Grouping together the terms with $g_{ss}^{(0)}, g_{ss}^{(1)}, \ldots, g_{ss}^{(q-1)}$, we obtain, for $i\neq s$,

$$g_{is}^{(q)}=\frac{1}{\theta_s^{(p)}-\theta_i^{(p)}}\Big\{\gamma_{is}^{(p-q)}+\sum_{\substack{j=1\\ j\neq s}}^{n}(\gamma_{ij}^{(p-q+1)}P_{j0}^{(i)}$$

$$+\gamma_{ij}^{(p-q+2)}P_{j0}^{(2)}+\ldots+\gamma_{ij}^{(p-2)}P_{j0}^{(q-2)}+\gamma_{ij}^{(p-1)}P_{j0}^{(q-1)})\Big\}g_{ss}^{(0)}$$

$$+\frac{1}{\theta_s^{(p)}-\theta_i^{(p)}}\Big\{\gamma_{is}^{(p-q+1)}+\sum_{\substack{j=1\\ j\neq s}}^{n}(\gamma_{ij}^{(p-q+2)}P_{j1}^{(2)}+$$

$$+\gamma_{ij}^{(p-q+3)}P_{j1}^{(3)}+\ldots+\gamma_{ij}^{(p-2)}P_{j1}^{(q-2)}+\gamma_{ij}^{(p-1)}P_{j1}^{(q-1)})\Big\}g_{ss}^{(1)}$$

$$+\frac{1}{\theta_s^{(p)}-\theta_i^{(p)}}\Big\{\gamma_{is}^{(p-q+2)}+\sum_{\substack{j=1\\ j\neq s}}^{n}(\gamma_{ij}^{(p-q+3)}P_{j2}^{(3)}$$

$$+\gamma_{ij}^{(p-q+4)}P_{j2}^{(4)}+\ldots+\gamma_{ij}^{(p-2)}P_{j2}^{(q-2)}+\gamma_{ij}^{(p-1)}P_{j2}^{(q-1)})\Big\}g_{ss}^{(2)} \qquad (2.1.24)$$

$$+\frac{1}{\theta_s^{(p)}-\theta_i^{(p)}}\Big\{\gamma_{is}^{(p-q+3)}+\sum_{\substack{j=1\\ j\neq s}}^{n}(\gamma_{ij}^{(p-q+4)}P_{j3}^{(4)}$$

$$+\gamma_{ij}^{(p-q+5)}P_{j3}^{(5)}+\ldots+\gamma_{ij}^{(p-2)}P_{j3}^{(q-2)}+\gamma_{ij}^{(p-1)}P_{j3}^{(q-1)})\Big\}g_{ss}^{(3)}$$

. . . .

$$+\frac{1}{\theta_s^{(p)}-\theta_i^{(p)}}\Big\{\gamma_{is}^{(p-3)}+\sum_{\substack{j=1\\ j\neq s}}^{n}(\gamma_{ij}^{(p-2)}P_{jq-3}^{(q-2)}+\gamma_{ij}^{(p-1)}P_{jq-3}^{(q-1)})\Big\}g_{ss}^{(q-3)}$$

$$+\frac{1}{\theta_s^{(p)}-\theta_i^{(p)}}\Big\{\gamma_{is}^{(p-2)}+\sum_{\substack{j=1\\ j\neq s}}^{n}\gamma_{ij}^{(p-1)}P_{jq-2}^{(q-1)}\Big\}g_{ss}^{(q-2)}+\Big\{\frac{\gamma_{is}^{(p-1)}}{\theta_s^{(p)}-\theta_i^{(p)}}\Big\}g_{ss}^{(q-1)}$$

From (2.1.24), we obtain, for all $m \leqslant q-2$ the following expression for the coefficient $P_{im}^{(q)}$ of $g_{ss}^{(m)}$

$$P_{im}^{(q)} = \frac{1}{\theta_s^{(p)} - \theta_i^{(p)}} \Big\{ \gamma_{is}^{(p-q+m)} + \sum_{\substack{j=1 \\ j \neq s}}^{n} (\gamma_{ij}^{(p-q+m+1)} P_{jm}^{(m+1)} \tag{2.1.25}$$

$$+ \gamma_{ij}^{(p-q+m+2)} P_{jm}^{(m+2)} + \ldots + \gamma_{ij}^{(p-2)} P_{jm}^{(q-2)} + \gamma_{ij}^{(p-1)} P_{jm}^{(q-1)}) \Big\}$$

For $m = q-1$

$$P_{iq-1}^{(q)} = \frac{\gamma_{is}^{(p-1)}}{\theta_s^{(p)} - \theta_i^{(p)}}$$

According to our hypothesis, (2.1.21) holds for all $\nu < q$. Therefore, using (2.1.21), we obtain from (2.1.25)

$$P_{im}^{(q)} = \frac{1}{\theta_s^{(p)} - \theta_i^{(p)}} \Big\{ \gamma_{is}^{(p-q+m)} + \sum_{\substack{j=1 \\ j \neq s}}^{n} (\gamma_{ij}^{(p-q+m+1)} P_{jm-1}^{(m)} \tag{2.1.26}$$

$$+ \gamma_{ij}^{(p-q+m+2)} P_{jm-1}^{(m+1)} + \ldots + \gamma_{ij}^{(p-2)} P_{jm-1}^{(q-3)} + \gamma_{ij}^{(p-1)} P_{jm-1}^{(q-2)}) \Big\}$$

It is clear that the right-hand side of (2.1.26) coincides with the expression obtained from (2.1.25) by replacing q with $q-1$ and m with $m-1$, i.e. $P_{im-1}^{(q-1)} = P_{im}^{(q)}$.

This completes the proof of Relations (2.1.21).

It is now easy to prove assertions 2 and 3. First of all, we note that the result of substituting the expressions

$$g_{is}^{(k)} \quad (k = 1,\ 2,\ \ldots,\ \nu - 1;\ i \neq s;\ i = 1,\ \ldots,\ n)$$

into the right-hand side of the sth equation of the $(\nu+1)$th group of System (2.1.13) is a linear combination of $g_{ss}^{(0)}, g_{ss}^{(1)}, \ldots, g_{ss}^{(\nu-1)}$, the coefficients of which, in general, contain also the differential operator $\frac{d}{dx}$ (if $\nu \geqslant p$). Specifically, from the equations of the $(\nu+1)$th group of System (2.1.13), we obtain for $i = s$

$$\sum_{j=1}^{n} \{ \gamma_{sj}^{(p)} g_{js}^{(\nu)} + \gamma_{sj}^{(p-1)} g_{js}^{(\nu-1)} + \ldots + \gamma_{sj}^{(p-\nu+1)} g_{js}^{(1)} + \gamma_{sj}^{(p-\nu)} g_{js}^{(0)} \} = 0$$

If we set apart the terms corresponding to the index $j = s$, we obtain

$$\gamma_{ss}^{(p)}g_{ss}^{(\nu)}+\gamma_{ss}^{(p-1)}g_{ss}^{(\nu-1)}+\ldots+\gamma_{ss}^{(p-\nu+1)}g_{ss}^{(1)}+\gamma_{ss}^{(p-\nu)}g_{ss}^{(0)}$$
$$+\sum_{\substack{j=1\\ j\neq s}}^{n}\{\gamma_{sj}^{(p)}g_{js}^{(\nu)}+\gamma_{sj}^{(p-1)}g_{js}^{(\nu-1)}+\ldots+\gamma_{sj}^{(p-\nu+1)}g_{js}^{(1)}\}=0$$

Since $\gamma_{ss}^{(p)}=b_{ss}^{(p)}-\theta_{s}^{(p)}=0$, we have, from the last equation,

$$\gamma_{ss}^{(p-1)}g_{ss}^{(\nu-1)}+\gamma_{ss}^{(p-2)}g_{ss}^{(\nu-2)}+\ldots+\gamma_{ss}^{(p-\nu+1)}g_{ss}^{(1)}+\gamma_{ss}^{(p-\nu)}g_{ss}^{(0)}$$
$$+\sum_{\substack{j=1\\ j\neq s}}^{n}\{\gamma_{sj}^{(p)}g_{js}^{(\nu)}+\gamma_{sj}^{(p-1)}g_{js}^{(\nu-1)}+\ldots+\gamma_{sj}^{(p-\nu+1)}g_{js}^{(1)}\}=0$$

Substituting the expressions $g_{js}^{(\nu)},\ldots,g_{js}^{(1)}$ (for $j\neq s$) given by (2.1.20), we reduce this last equation to the form

$$\gamma_{ss}^{(p-1)}g_{ss}^{(\nu-1)}+\gamma_{ss}^{(p-2)}g_{ss}^{(\nu-2)}+\ldots+\gamma_{ss}^{(p-\nu+1)}g_{ss}^{(1)}+\gamma_{ss}^{(p-\nu)}g_{ss}^{(0)}$$
$$+\sum_{\substack{j=1\\ j\neq s}}^{n}\Big\{\gamma_{sj}^{(p)}\sum_{k=0}^{\nu-1}P_{jk}^{(\nu)}g_{ss}^{(k)}+\gamma_{sj}^{(p-1)}\sum_{k=0}^{\nu-2}P_{jk}^{(\nu-1)}g_{ss}^{(k)}+$$
$$\ldots+\gamma_{sj}^{(p-\nu+2)}\sum_{k=0}^{1}P_{jk}^{(2)}g_{ss}^{(k)}+\gamma_{sj}^{(p-\nu+1)}P_{j0}^{(1)}g_{ss}^{(0)}\Big\}=0$$

Grouping together terms containing the functions $g_{ss}^{(\nu-1)},g_{ss}^{(\nu-2)},\ldots,g_{ss}^{(0)}$, we see that

$$\sum_{k=0}^{\nu-1}Q_{k}^{(\nu)}g_{ss}^{(k)}=0 \tag{2.1.27}$$

where the coefficient $Q_m^{(\nu)}$ of $g_{ss}^{(m)}$ is determined by the formula

$$Q_m^{(\nu)}=\gamma_{ss}^{(p-\nu+m)}+\sum_{\substack{j=1\\ j\neq s}}^{n}(\gamma_{sj}^{(p)}P_{jm}^{(\nu)}+\gamma_{sj}^{(p-1)}P_{jm}^{(\nu-1)}+ \ldots+\gamma_{sj}^{(p-\nu+m+1)}P_{jm}^{(m+1)}) \tag{2.1.28}$$

which is obtained from the preceding equation.

By virtue of the properties (2.1.21), we have

$$P_{jm}^{(\nu)}=P_{jm-1}^{(\nu-1)},\quad P_{jm}^{(\nu-1)}=P_{jm-1}^{(\nu-2)},\ \ldots,\ P_{jm}^{(m+1)}=P_{jm-1}^{(m)}$$

Substituting these values into (2.1.28), we obtain for $Q_m^{(\nu)}$, in accordance with (2.1.28), an expression coinciding with the expression for $Q_{m-1}^{(\nu-1)}$. Thus, by using the properties (2.1.21) of the coefficients $P_{jm}^{(\nu)}$, we have shown that, for the coefficients $Q_m^{(\nu)}$ of $g_{ss}^{(m)}$ in (2.1.27),

$$Q_k^{(\nu)} = Q_{k-1}^{(\nu-1)} = Q_{k-2}^{(\nu-2)} = \ldots = Q_0^{(\nu-k)} \qquad (k = 0, 1, \ldots, \nu-1) \tag{2.1.29}$$

We now prove assertions 2 and 3 by induction. First we assume that $\nu < p$ and suppose that the functions

$$\theta_s^{(p-1)}, \ \theta_s^{(p-2)}, \ \ldots, \ \theta_s^{(p-\nu+1)}$$

are already determined from the equations preceding the $(\nu+1)$th group of equations in (2.1.13) and that they are independent of

$$g_{ss}^{(0)}, \ g_{ss}^{(1)}, \ \ldots$$

We show that, under this condition, the function $\theta_s^{(p-\nu)}$ is determined from the sth equation of the $(\nu+1)$th group of Equations (2.1.13) and that it is also independent of

$$g_{ss}^{(0)}, \ g_{ss}^{(1)}, \ \ldots$$

As can be seen from Equations (2.1.13), the functions $\theta_s^{(p-\nu)}$ do not appear at all in the equations of the groups preceding the $(\nu+1)$th group and they appear in the sth equation of the $(\nu+1)$th group with coefficients $g_{ss}^{(0)}$. On the basis of what was stated above, this equation is of the form (2.1.27).

Suppose that the functions

$$\theta_s^{(p-1)} \ \theta_s^{(p-2)}, \ \ldots, \ \theta_s^{(p-\nu+1)}$$

are so chosen that all the preceding equations of the form (2.1.27), for $\nu-1$, $\nu-2$, ... are reduced to identities, i.e.

$$Q_s^{(\mu)} \equiv 0 \quad \text{for} \quad 0 \leqslant s < \mu < \nu$$

Therefore, it follows from Relations (2.1.29) that

$$Q_s^{(\nu)} \equiv 0 \quad \text{for} \quad s = 1, 2, 3, \ldots, \nu-1$$

Then, Relation (2.1.27) is reduced to the equation

$$Q_0^{(\nu)} g_{ss}^{(0)} = 0$$

Dividing by $g_{ss}^{(0)}$,

$$Q_0^{(\nu)} = 0$$

Here, $Q_0^{(\nu)}$ necessarily contains $\theta_s^{(p-\nu)}$ with coefficient equal to unity. Thus, we have

$$\theta_s^{(p-\nu)} - A_{p-\nu} = 0$$

where $A_{p-\nu}$ depends only on $\theta_s^{(p-1)}, \ldots, \theta_s^{(p-\nu+1)}$ and is independent of $g_{ss}^{(0)}, g_{ss}^{(1)}, \ldots$. This proves assertions 2 and 3 for $\nu < p$.

Now we consider values $\nu \geqslant p$. We note that the sth equation of the $(p+1)$th group of Equations (2.1.13) contains $\frac{dg_{is}^{(0)}}{dx}$ and that, in this equation, the coefficients of $g_{ss}^{(1)}, g_{ss}^{(2)}, \ldots$ vanish identically. Consequently, this sth equation of the $(p+1)$th group is reduced to the form

$$-A_0 g_{ss}^{(0)} + \frac{dg_{ss}^{(0)}}{dx} = 0$$

From this equation, $g_{ss}^{(0)}$ is determined up to a constant factor

$$g_{ss}^{(0)} = c_0 e^{\int_a^x A_0(\xi)\, d\xi}$$

In the sth equation of the $(p+2)$th group, the coefficient of $g_{ss}^{(1)}$ must coincide with the coefficient of $g_{ss}^{(0)}$ in the sth equation of the $(p+1)$th group. The coefficients of $g_{ss}^{(2)}, g_{ss}^{(3)}, \ldots$ vanish identically. Therefore, the sth equation of the $(p+2)$th group is of the form

$$\frac{dg_{ss}^{(1)}}{dx} = A_0 g_{ss}^{(1)} + B_1$$

where B_1 depends on $g_{ss}^{(0)}$. Thus, $g_{ss}^{(1)}$ also contains an arbitrary constant.

Similar conclusions hold for the functions $g_{ss}^{(2)}, g_{ss}^{(3)}$, etc. This completes the proof of assertions 2 and 3.

Thus, we have proved the existence of the series (2.1.11) which formally satisfy Equations (2.1.7a), i.e. these series satisfy the equations of System (2.1.7a) if termwise differentiation is permissible. In the above, our conclusions are applied to only one column (the sth) of the matrix $Z(x, \lambda)$, which was a matrix of formal particular solutions of the fundamental system. If we assign to s the values $1, 2, \ldots, n$, we obtain from (2.1.11) all formal solutions of the fundamental system.

Furthermore, if, in (2.1.6), we turn from the elements $z_{is}(x, \lambda)$ of the matrix $Z(x, \lambda)$ to the elements $y_{is}(x, \lambda)$ of the matrix $Y(x, \lambda)$, we see that there exist formal series of the form

$$y_{is}(x, \lambda) = \exp\left(\int_a^x (\lambda^p \theta_s^{(p)}(\xi) + \lambda^{p-1}\theta_s^{(p-1)}(\xi) + \ldots \right. \qquad (2.1.30)$$
$$\left. \ldots + \lambda\theta_s^{(1)}(\xi))\, d\xi\right) \sum_{k=0}^{\infty} \lambda^{-k} y_{is}^{(k)}(x)$$

representing n distinct formal solutions of System (2.1.1) which are obtained for $s = 1, \ldots, n$, where

$$Y^{(k)}(x) = m(x)\, g^{(k)}(x), \quad g^{(k)}(x) = \begin{pmatrix} g_{11}^{(k)}(x) & \ldots & g_{1n}^{(k)}(x) \\ \cdot & \cdots & \cdot \\ g_{n1}^{(k)}(x) & \ldots & g_{nn}^{(k)}(x) \end{pmatrix} \qquad (2.1.31)$$

In general, these series diverge. However, they may be used for obtaining an asymptotic representation of the fundamental system of particular solutions of (2.1.1).

We now specify the conditions under which the algorithm we have been describing can actually be used.

Following the line of reasoning taken in the proof of Lemma 1, we see that for unrestricted continuation of this algorithm to be possible, we must assume the existence of derivatives of all orders of the elements of the matrices

$$a^{(p)}(x),\ a^{(p-1)}(x),\ \ldots,\ a^{(0)}(x),\ a^{(-1)}(x),\ \ldots,\ a^{(-\nu)}(x),\ \ldots$$

However, to obtain asymptotic representations of the particular solutions of the fundamental system for the differential equations (2.1.1), the requirement of unrestricted continuation of the above-described algorithm is completely superfluous. It will be sufficient to confine ourselves to deciding the first how many terms must be kept in the formal series (2.1.30) for the result of substitution in the differential operation

$$L_i(y) \equiv \frac{dy_i}{dx} - \sum_{k=1}^{n} a_{ik}(x, \lambda)\, y_k \qquad (i = 1, \ldots, n)$$

of the finite sums thus obtained in place of y_i to be of the form

$$\exp\left(\int_a^x \omega_s(\xi, \lambda)\, d\xi\right) \frac{\psi_{is}(x, \lambda)}{\lambda^m} \qquad (i, s = 1, \ldots, n)$$

where

$$\omega_s(x, \lambda) = \lambda^p \theta_s^{(p)}(x) + \lambda^{p-1}\theta_s^{(p-1)} + \ldots + \lambda\theta_s^{(1)}(x) \quad (2.1.32)$$

where the $\psi_{is}(x, \lambda)$ are series in decreasing powers of λ (beginning with the zero th), and where $m \geqslant 1$ is a natural number. In connection with this, we have to determine the conditions which the coefficients of the system of differential equations (2.1.1) must satisfy.

The answer to this question is provided by Lemma 1 below.

Lemma 1 Suppose that

$$\begin{aligned} &g_{ss}^{(\nu)} \quad (\nu = 0, 1, \ldots, m-1) \\ &g_{is}^{(\nu)} \quad (i \neq s;\ i = 1, \ldots, n;\ \nu = m, m+1, \ldots, m+p-1) \end{aligned} \quad (2.1.33)$$

are functions determined from the first $p+m$ groups of equations of System (2.1.13) and that the functions $g_{ss}^{(\nu)}$ (where $\nu = m, \ldots, m+p-1$) are, in general, arbitrary continuous functions. Suppose also that $Y^{(k)}(x)$ is the matrix of the functions $y_{is}^{(k)}(x)$ related to the matrix $g^{(k)}(x)$ of the functions $g_{is}^{(k)}(x)$ by (2.1.31).

Then, the result of substituting into the differential equation for y_i,

$$L_i\left(x, \frac{d}{dx}\right) y \equiv \frac{dy_i}{dx} - \sum_{j=1}^{n} a_{ij}(x, \lambda)\, y_j \quad (2.1.34)$$

a sum of the form

$$u_{is}(x, \lambda) = \exp\left(\int_a^x \omega_s(\xi, \lambda)\, d\xi\right) \sum_{k=0}^{p+m-1} \lambda^{-k} y_{is}^{(k)}(x) \quad (2.1.35)$$

is of the form

$$L_i\left(x, \frac{d}{dx}\right) u_s = \frac{du_{is}(x, \lambda)}{dx} - \sum_{j=1}^{n} a_{ij}(x, \lambda)\, u_{js}(x, \lambda) = e^{\int\limits_a^x \omega_s(\xi, \lambda)\, d\xi} \frac{\psi_{is}(x, \lambda)}{\lambda^m} \qquad (2.1.36)$$

where the $\psi_{is}(x, \lambda)$ are series in decreasing powers of λ beginning with the zero th) and m is a natural number.

Suppose also that

$$m = kp + r + 1 \qquad (0 \leqslant r \leqslant p - 1)$$

Then, the functions $y_{is}^{(h)}(x)$ associated with the functions (2.1.33) defined from the first $p+m$ groups of equations of System (2.1.13) in accordance with (2.1.31) have continuous derivatives of the first q orders, where q is a natural number, if the elements of the matrices*

$$\begin{array}{c} \dfrac{d^{k+1}a^{(p)}(x)}{dx^{k+1}}, \ \ldots, \ \dfrac{d^{k+1}a^{(p-r)}(x)}{dx^{k+1}} \\ \dfrac{d^{k}a^{(p-r-1)}(x)}{dx^{k}}, \ \ldots, \ \dfrac{d^{k}a^{(-r)}(x)}{dx^{k}} \\ \cdots\cdots\cdots\cdots\cdots \\ a^{(-m+p)}(x), \ \ldots, \ a^{(-m+1)}(x) \end{array} \qquad (2.1.37)$$

have them.

To prove this lemma, we first work with the simplified system (2.1.7a). Therefore, instead of the formal series (2.1.30), let us consider the series (2.1.11) and, instead of the differential operators (2.1.34), we shall consider the operators

$$L_i'\left(x, \frac{d}{dx}\right) Z \equiv \frac{dz_i}{dx} - \sum_{j=1}^{n} b_{ij}(x, \lambda)\, z_j \qquad (2.1.38)$$

Then, we shift to the system of the differential equations (2.1.1). Here it is clear that, for this transformation to be possible and for System (2.1.7a) to be meaningful in the

* Beginning with the second row, we obviously have p matrices in each row.

interval (a, b), it will be sufficient to assume that the elements of the matrix $m(x)$ have continuous derivatives of the first q orders or, remembering that these last can be expressed in terms of the elements of the matrix $a^{(p)}(x)$, to assume that the elements $a^{(p)}(x)$ have continuous derivatives of the first q orders.

Consider the partial sums of the series (2.1.11) of form

$$v_{is}(x, \lambda) = \exp\left(\int_a^x \omega_s(\xi, \lambda)\, d\xi\right) \sum_{k=0}^{p+m-1} \lambda^{-k} g_{is}^{(k)}(x) \quad (2.1.39)$$

$$(i = 1, \ldots, n)$$

Recalling that the $(\nu+1)$th group of equations of System (2.1.13) is obtained by putting the coefficient of $\lambda^{p-\nu}$ equal to zero in (2.1.12), we see by substituting (2.1.11) into (2.1.7) that the result of substituting (2.1.39) into (2.1.38) will be of the form*

$$L_i'\left(x, \frac{d}{dx}\right) v_s(x, \lambda) \equiv \frac{dv_{is}(x, \lambda)}{dx} - \sum_{j=1}^{n} b_{ij}(x, \lambda)\, v_{js}(x, \lambda)$$
$$= \exp\left(\int_a^x \omega_s(\xi, \lambda)\, d\xi\right) \frac{\psi_{is}'(x, \lambda)}{\lambda^m} \quad (2.1.40)$$

if the functions (2.1.33) are determined from the first $p+m$ groups of equations of System (2.1.13). The coefficients

$$g_{ss}^{(\nu)}, \quad \nu = m, m+1, \ldots, m+p-1$$

remain, in general, arbitrary.

In order to see this, note that the left-hand side of the $(\nu+1)$th group of System (2.1.13) (for $\nu = 0, 1, \ldots, p+m-1$) is the coefficient of $\lambda^{p-\nu}$, which is equal to zero if the functions (2.1.33) satisfy the equations of the $(\nu+1)$th group of (2.1.13), since, in accordance with assertions 1-3, the equations of the first $p+m$ groups of (2.1.13) make it possible for us to determine the functions

$$g_{ss}^{(\nu)} \quad (\nu = 0, \ldots, m-1)$$

* We can easily arrange to have, see (2.1.12),

$$\psi_{is}'(x, \lambda) = \sum_{j=1}^{n} \sum_{\nu+k \geqslant p+m} b_{ij}^{(p-\nu)}(x)\, g_{js}^{(k)}(x)\, \lambda^{p-\nu-k}$$
$$= \sum_{q=m}^{\infty} \lambda^{-q} \Big(\sum_{j=1}^{n} \sum_{\nu+k=p+q} b_{ij}^{(k-q)} g_{js}^{(p-\nu+q)} \Big)$$

and the functions $g_{is}^{(\nu)}$ for $i \neq s$ and $\nu = m, m+1, \ldots, m+p-1$.

Clearly, from the substitution (2.1.6), we have

$$U(x, \lambda) = m(x) V(x, \lambda)$$

where U and V are matrices composed respectively of the elements $u_{is}(x, \lambda)$ and $v_{is}(x, s)$. Then,

$$\frac{dU}{dx} - a(x, \lambda) U = m(x) \frac{dV}{dx} + \frac{dm(x)}{dx} V - a(x, \lambda) m(x) V$$

from which it follows that

$$\begin{aligned} m^{-1}(x) \left(\frac{dU}{dx} - a(x, \lambda) U \right) &= \frac{dV}{dx} + \left(m^{-1}(x) \frac{dm(x)}{dx} - m^{-1} a(x, \lambda) m \right) V \\ &= \frac{dV}{dx} - \left(m^{-1}(x) a(x, \lambda) m(x) - m^{-1}(x) \frac{dm(x)}{dx} \right) V \\ &= \frac{dV}{dx} - b(x, \lambda) V \end{aligned} \qquad (2.1.41)$$

The right-hand side of the last identity is a matrix whose elements are, according to (2.1.40), equal to

$$\begin{aligned} L_i'\left(x, \frac{d}{dx} \right) v_s &= \frac{dv_{is}(x, \lambda)}{dx} - \sum_{j=1}^{n} b_{ij}(x, \lambda) v_{js}(x, \lambda) \\ &= \exp\left(\int_a^x \omega_s(\xi, \lambda)\, d\xi \right) \frac{\psi_{is}'(x, \lambda)}{\lambda^m} \end{aligned}$$

Substituting this into (2.1.41), we obtain

$$m^{-1}(x) \left(\frac{dU}{dx} - a(x, \lambda) U \right) = \begin{pmatrix} \frac{\psi_{11}'(x, \lambda)}{\lambda^m} X_1 & \ldots & \frac{\psi_{1s}'(x, \lambda)}{\lambda^m} X_s & \ldots & \frac{\psi_{1n}'(x, \lambda)}{\lambda^m} X_n \\ \cdots & \cdots & \cdots & \cdots & \cdots \\ \frac{\psi_{n1}'(x, \lambda)}{\lambda^m} X_1 & \ldots & \frac{\psi_{ns}'(x, \lambda)}{\lambda^m} X_s & \ldots & \frac{\psi_{nn}'(x, \lambda)}{\lambda^m} X_n \end{pmatrix}$$

where $X_i = \exp\left(\int_a^x \omega_i(\xi, \lambda)\, d\xi \right)$, for $i = 1, \ldots, n$.

Multiplying both sides of this identity by the matrix $m(x)$, we get the identity

$$\frac{dU}{dx} - a(x, \lambda) U \equiv m(x)$$

$$\times \begin{pmatrix} \frac{\psi'_{11}(x, \lambda)}{\lambda^m} X_1 \dots \frac{\psi'_{1s}(x, \lambda)}{\lambda^m} X_s \dots \frac{\psi'_{1n}(x, \lambda)}{\lambda^m} X_n \\ \dots\dots\dots\dots\dots\dots \\ \frac{\psi'_{n1}(x, \lambda)}{\lambda^m} X_1 \dots \frac{\psi'_{ns}(x, \lambda)}{\lambda^m} X_s \dots \frac{\psi'_{nn}(x, \lambda)}{\lambda^m} X_n \end{pmatrix} \tag{2.1.42}$$

where $X_i = \exp\left(\int_a^x \omega_i(\xi, \lambda)\, d\xi\right)$, for $i = 1, 2, \dots, n$.

Equating the elements (i, s) on both sides of (2.1.42), we have

$$L_i\left(x, \frac{d}{dx}\right) u_s(x, \lambda) = \frac{du_{is}(x, \lambda)}{dx} - \sum_{j=1}^{n} a_{ij}(x, \lambda) u_{js}(x, \lambda)$$

$$= m_{i1}(x) \frac{\psi'_{1s}(x, \lambda)}{\lambda^m} \exp\left(\int_a^x \omega_s(\xi, \lambda)\, d\xi\right)$$

$$+ m_{i2}(x) \frac{\psi'_{2s}(x, \lambda)}{\lambda^m} \exp\left(\int_a^x \omega_s(\xi, \lambda)\, d\xi\right)$$

$$\dots\dots\dots\dots\dots\dots$$

$$+ m_{in}(x) \frac{\psi'_{ns}(x, \lambda)}{\lambda^m} \exp\left(\int_a^x \omega_s(\xi, \lambda)\, d\xi\right)$$

$$= \frac{m_{i1}(x)\psi'_{1s}(x, \lambda) + m_{i2}(x)\psi'_{2s}(x, \lambda) + \dots + m_{in}(x)\psi'_{ns}(x, \lambda)}{\lambda^m}$$

$$\times \exp\left(\int_a^x \omega_s(\xi, \lambda)\, d\xi\right)$$

Thus, if we define

$$\psi_{is}(x, \lambda) = \sum_{j=1}^{n} m_{ij}(x) \psi'_{js}(x, \lambda)$$

we arrive at (2.1.36), which completes the first part of Lemma 1.

Let us now prove the second part of Lemma 1. From (2.1.31) it is clear that $y_{is}^{(k)}(x)$ have continuous derivatives of the first q orders if the elements of the matrix $m(x)$ and $g_{is}^{(k)}(x)$ have them. The matrix $m(x)$ can be so chosen that its elements will have the same differentiability properties as $a^{(p)}(x)$. Thus, continuous differentiability of the elements of matrix $m(x)$ is ensured by the hypothesis of the lemma.

The functions $g_{is}^{(k)}(x)$ have continuous derivatives of the first q orders if the elements of the matrices

$$\begin{gathered}\frac{d^{k+1}b^{(p)}(x)}{dx^{k+1}}, \ \ldots, \ \frac{d^{k+1}b^{(p-r)}(x)}{dx^{k+1}} \\ \frac{d^{k}b^{(p-r-1)}(x)}{dx^{k}}, \ \ldots, \ \frac{d^{k}b^{(-r)}(x)}{dx^{k}} \\ \cdots\cdots\cdots\cdots\cdots \\ b^{(-m+p)}(x), \ \ldots, \ b^{(-m+1)}(x)\end{gathered} \qquad (2.1.43)$$

have them.

We shall prove this assertion by induction. First we note that $g_{is}^{(\nu-1)}$ for $i \neq s$ and $2 \leqslant \nu \leqslant p$ may be expressed from the νth group of equations of System (2.1.13) in terms of the functions $g_{is}^{(\nu-2)}, g_{is}^{(\nu-3)}, \ldots, g_{is}^{(0)}$ by means of the formula

$$\begin{aligned} g_{is}^{(\nu-1)} = \frac{1}{\theta_s^{(p)}-\theta_i^{(p)}} \Bigg\{ & \sum_{\substack{j=1 \\ j\neq i}}^{n} b_{ij}^{(p)} g_{js}^{(\nu-1)} \\ & + \sum_{j=1}^{n} \left(b_{ij}^{(p-1)} g_{js}^{(\nu-2)} + \ldots + b_{ij}^{(p-\nu+1)} g_{js}^{(0)}\right) \\ & - \theta_s^{(p-1)} g_{is}^{(\nu-2)} - \ldots - \theta_s^{(p-\nu+1)} g_{is}^{(0)} \Bigg\} \quad (2 \leqslant \nu \leqslant p) \end{aligned} \qquad (2.1.44)$$

Similarly, from the $(p+\nu)$th group of equations of the system (2.1.13) we have for $i \neq s$ and $\nu \geqslant 1$

$$\begin{aligned} g_{is}^{(p+\nu-1)} = \frac{1}{\theta_s^{(p)}-\theta_i^{(p)}} \Bigg\{ & \sum_{\substack{j=1 \\ j\neq i}}^{n} b_{ij}^{(p)} g_{js}^{(p+\nu-1)} + \sum_{j=1}^{n} \left(b_{ij}^{(p-1)} g_{js}^{(p+\nu-2)}\right. \\ & + b_{ij}^{(p-2)} g_{js}^{(p+\nu-3)} + \ldots + b_{ij}^{(0)} g_{js}^{(\nu-1)} \\ & \left. + b_{ij}^{(-1)} g_{js}^{(\nu-2)} + \ldots + b_{ij}^{(-\nu+1)} g_{js}^{(0)}\right) - \theta_s^{(p-1)} g_{is}^{(p+\nu-2)} \\ & - \theta_s^{(p-2)} g_{is}^{(p+\nu-3)} - \ldots - \theta_s^{(1)} g_{is}^{(\nu)} - \frac{dg_{is}^{(\nu-1)}}{dx} \Bigg\} \end{aligned} \qquad (2.1.45)$$

We also note that the right-hand sides of (2.1.44) and (2.1.45) can be represented, respectively, in the form of the linear combinations

$$g_{is}^{(\nu-1)}=\sum_{k=0}^{\nu-2} P_{ik}^{(\nu-1)} g_{ss}^{(k)}, \quad 2 \leqslant \nu \leqslant p \tag{2.1.44a}$$

$$g_{is}^{(p+\nu-1)}=\sum_{k=0}^{p+\nu-2} P_{ik}^{(\nu+p-1)} g_{ss}^{(k)}, \quad \nu \geqslant 1 \tag{2.1.45a}$$

the coefficients in which depend, respectively, on the functions

$$b_{ij}^{(p)}, \ldots, b_{ij}^{(p-\nu+1)} \tag{2.1.46}$$

$$b_{ij}^{(p)}, \ldots, b_{ij}^{(0)}, b_{ij}^{(-1)}, \ldots, b_{ij}^{(-\nu+1)}(x) \tag{2.1.47}$$

It was shown above that all the functions $g_{ss}^{(\nu-1)}$ (for $\nu=1, 2, \ldots$) can be determined from differential equations of the form

$$\frac{dg_{ss}^{(\nu-1)}}{dx}-A g_{ss}^{(\nu-1)}+B=0 \tag{2.1.47a}$$

the coefficients in which depend on the functions (2.1.47). Consequently, on the basis of (2.1.44a), for the functions $g_{is}^{(\nu-1)}$, where $1 \leqslant \nu \leqslant p$ and $i \neq s$, to have continuous derivatives of the first q orders, it is sufficient to require that the functions (2.1.46) have them and that all the remaining functions (2.1.47), i.e. the functions

$$b_{ij}^{(p-\nu)}, \ldots, b_{ij}^{(0)}, \ldots, b_{ij}^{(-\nu+1)}$$

be $q-1$ times continuously differentiable.

It is clear from (2.1.45) that for the functions $g_{ij}^{(p+r)}$, where $0 \leqslant r \leqslant p-1$ and $i \neq j$, to have continuous derivatives of the first q orders, it is sufficient to require that the functions

$$b_{ij}^{(p)}, b_{ij}^{(p-1)}, \ldots, b_{ij}^{(0)}, b_{ij}^{(-1)}, \ldots, b_{ij}^{(-r)} \tag{2.1.48}$$

$$\frac{dg_{ij}^{(r)}}{dx} \tag{2.1.49}$$

$$g_{ss}^{(p+r-1)}, \ldots, g_{ss}^{(0)} \tag{2.1.50}$$

have them. As was shown above, for the functions (2.1.49) to be q times continuously differentiable, it is sufficient that the functions

$$\frac{d^{q+1}b_{ij}^{(p)}}{dx^{q+1}}, \ldots, \frac{d^{q+1}b_{ij}^{(p-r)}}{dx^{q+1}} \tag{2.1.51}$$

be continuous.

Since the functions (2.1.50) satisfy the differential equation (2.1.47a), their q times continuous differentiability is ensured by the q times continuous differentiability of the functions (2.1.48).

Thus, $g_{ij}^{(p+r)}$ are continuously differentiable in the interval $[a, b]$ if the derivatives

$$\begin{gathered} \frac{d^{q+1}b_{ij}^{(p)}}{dx^{q+1}}, \ldots, \frac{d^{q+1}b_{ij}^{(p-r)}}{dx^{q+1}} \\ \frac{d^{q}b_{ij}^{(p-r-1)}}{dx^{q}}, \ldots, \frac{d^{q}b_{ij}^{(-r)}}{dx^{q}} \end{gathered} \tag{2.1.52}$$

are continuous on $[a, b]$.

Put $m = kp + r + 1$. Let us show that $g_{is}^{(p+m-1)}(x)$ have continuous derivatives of the first q orders if

$$\begin{gathered} \frac{d^{k+1}b_{ij}^{(p)}}{dx^{k+1}}, \ldots, \frac{d^{k+1}b_{ij}^{(p-r)}}{dx^{k+1}} \\ \frac{d^{k}b_{ij}^{(p-r-1)}}{dx^{k}}, \ldots, \frac{d^{k}b_{ij}^{(-r)}}{dx^{k}} \\ \cdots\cdots\cdots\cdots \\ b_{ij}^{(-m+p)}, \ldots, b_{ij}^{(-m+1)} \end{gathered} \tag{2.1.53}$$

have them. We have already shown this for $k = 0$. Since $m = 1 + r$ in (2.1.52), we have

$$b_{ij}^{(p-r-1)} = b_{ij}^{(-m+p)}, \quad b^{(-r)} = b^{(-m+1)}$$

Let us now suppose that our assertion is valid for

$$m = (k-1)\,p + r + 1$$

and show that it is then valid for $m = kp + r + 1$. Thus, we shall demonstrate that $g_{is}^{(p+(k-1)p+r)}$ have continuous derivatives of the first q orders if

$$
\begin{array}{ccc}
\dfrac{d^k b_{ij}^{(p)}}{dx^k}, & \ldots, & \dfrac{d^k b_{ij}^{(p-r)}}{dx^k} \\[2ex]
\dfrac{d^{k-1} b_{ij}^{(p-r-1)}}{dx^{k-1}}, & \ldots, & \dfrac{d^{k-1} b_{ij}^{(-r)}}{dx^{k-1}} \\[2ex]
\cdots & \cdots & \cdots \\[2ex]
b_{ij}^{(-(k-1)p-r-1+p)}, & \ldots, & b_{ij}^{(-(k-1)p-r)}
\end{array}
\tag{2.1.54}
$$

have them. If we put $\nu = kp + r + 1$ in (2.1.45), we see that, for the functions $g_{is}^{(p+kp+r)}$ to have continuous derivatives of the first q orders, it is sufficient to assume that the functions

$$b_{ij}^{(p)}, \ldots, b_{ij}^{(0)}, \; b_{ij}^{(-1)}, \ldots, b_{ij}^{(-kp-r)} \tag{2.1.55}$$

$$g_{ss}^{(p+kp+r-1)}, \; g_{ss}^{(p+kp+r-2)}, \ldots, g_{ss}^{(0)} \tag{2.1.56}$$

$$\frac{dg_{is}^{(kp+r)}}{dx} \tag{2.1.57}$$

have them.

We note that the functions (2.1.56) are determined from the differential equations, the coefficients in which depend only on the functions

$$b_{ij}^{(p)}, \; b_{ij}^{(p-1)}, \ldots, b_{ij}^{(0)}, \; b_{ij}^{(-1)}, \ldots, b_{ij}^{-((k+1)p+r-1)} \tag{2.1.58}$$

Consequently, the functions (2.1.56) will have continuous derivatives of the first q orders if the functions (2.1.58) have them.

According to our assumption, the functions (2.1.57) will be q times continuously differentiable if the functions (2.1.54) are $q + 1$ times continuously differentiable.

Thus, if

$$\frac{d^{k+1}b_{ij}^{(p)}}{dx^{k+1}}, \quad \ldots, \quad \frac{d^{k+1}b_{ij}^{(p-r)}}{dx^{k+1}}$$

$$\frac{d^{k}b_{ij}^{(p-r-1)}}{dx^{k}}, \quad \ldots, \quad \frac{d^{k}b_{ij}^{(-r)}}{dx^{k}}$$

$$\cdots\cdots\cdots\cdots\cdots$$

$$\frac{db_{ij}^{(-(k-2)p-r-1)}}{dx}, \ldots, \frac{db_{ij}^{(-(k-1)p-r)}}{dx}$$

$$b_{ij}^{(-m+p)}, \ldots, b^{(-m+1)}$$

$$(m = kp + r + 1)$$

are q times continuously differentiable, so are $g_{ij}^{(p+kp+r)}$.

The matrix $m(x)$ can be so chosen that its elements will possess the same differentiability properties as do the elements of the matrix $a^{(p)}(x)$. Therefore, in accordance with (2.1.9), the functions (2.1.43) have continuous derivatives of the first q orders in the interval (a, b), if the functions (2.1.37) have them.

Furthermore, in accordance with (2.1.31), $y_{is}^{(k)}(x)$ have continuous derivatives of the first q orders in the interval (a, b) if $g_{is}^{(k)}(x)$ have them. This completes the proof of Lemma 1.

Remark In particular, if $p = 1$, we can draw the following conclusion from Lemma 1. For the functions $y_{is}^{(0)}(x)$, $y_{is}^{(1)}(x)$, .., $y_{is}^{(m)}(x)$, with $i \neq s$, and the functions $y_{ss}^{(0)}(x)$, $y_{ss}^{(1)}(x)$, ..., $y_{ss}^{(m-1)}(x)$ to have continuous derivatives of the first q orders, it is sufficient that the functions

$$\frac{d^m a_{ij}^{(1)}}{dx^m}, \quad \frac{d^{m-1} a_{ij}^{(0)}}{dx^{m-1}}, \quad \frac{d^{k-1} a_{ij}^{(-1)}}{dx^{k-1}}, \ldots, a_{ij}^{(-m+1)}(x) \quad (i, j = 1, \ldots, n)$$

have them.

If $g_{is}^{(0)}(x), \ldots, g_{is}^{(m)}(x)$, for $i \neq s$, and $g_{ss}^{(0)}(x)\, g_{ss}^{(1)}(x), \ldots, g_{ss}^{(m-1)}(x)$ are determined from the first $m+1$ groups of equations of System (2.1.13), we obtain from the substitution of the functions

$$u_{is}(x, \lambda) = e^{\lambda \int_a^x \theta_s^{(1)}(\xi)d\xi} \sum_{k=0}^{m} \lambda^{-k} y_{is}^{k}(x) \qquad (2.1.59)$$

into the differential operations (2.1.34)

$$L_i\left(x, \frac{d}{dx}\right) U_s \equiv \frac{du_{is}(x, \lambda)}{dx} - \sum_{j=1}^{n} a_{ij}(x, \lambda) u_{js}(x, \lambda)$$
$$= e^{\lambda \int_a^x \theta_s^{(1)}(\xi) d\xi} \frac{\psi_{is}(x, \lambda)}{\lambda^m}$$

where $\psi_{is}(x, \lambda)$ is a series in non-positive powers of λ (beginning, in general, with the power zero).

2.2 ASYMPTOTIC REPRESENTATIONS OF SOLUTIONS OF A SYSTEM OF FIRST-ORDER EQUATIONS

In this section, we shall use the partial sums (2.1.35) of the formal series (2.1.30) that appear in the formulation of Lemma 1 to obtain asymptotic representations of the fundamental system of particular solutions of (2.1.1). We shall prove the following basic theorem.

Theorem 5 Suppose that a system of differential equations

$$\frac{dy_i}{dx} - \sum_{j=1}^{n} a_{ij}(x, \lambda) y_j = 0 \qquad (i = 1, \ldots, n) \tag{2.2.1}$$

is given in which the coefficients can be expanded in the form

$$a_{ij}(x, \lambda) = \sum_{\nu=0}^{\infty} \lambda^{p-\nu} a_{ij}^{(p-\nu)}(x) \tag{2.2.2}$$

for $\lambda \in \Omega$, where Ω is the region of complex values of λ which satisfy the inequality $|\lambda| \geqslant R$ and R is a sufficiently large positive number.

Suppose that the following conditions are satisfied.

1. The functions

$$a_{ij}^{(\nu)}(x) \quad (i, j = 1, \ldots, n; \quad \nu = p, p-1, \ldots, 0, -1, -2, \ldots)$$

are continuous and uniformly bounded on the interval $[a, b]$.

2. All the θ-roots of the characteristic equation

$$\begin{vmatrix} a_{11}^{(p)}(x) - \theta & a_{12}^{(p)}(x) & \ldots & a_{1n}^{(p)}(x) \\ a_{21}^{p}(x) & a_{22}^{(p)}(x) - \theta & \ldots & a_{2n}^{(p)}(x) \\ \cdots & \cdots & \cdots & \cdots \\ a_{n1}^{(p)}(x) & a_{n2}^{(p)}(x) & \ldots & a_{nn}^{(p)}(x) - \theta \end{vmatrix} = 0 \tag{2.2.3}$$

of System (2.2.1) are distinct for all $x \in [a, b]$.

3. For an arbitrary natural number

$$m = kp + r + 1 \quad (0 \leqslant r \leqslant p-1)$$

the elements of the matrices

$$\begin{array}{ccc} \frac{d^{k+1}a^{(p)}}{dx^{k+1}}, & \ldots, & \frac{d^{k+1}a^{(p-r)}}{dx^{k+1}} \\ \frac{d^{k}a^{(p-r-1)}}{dx^{k}}, & \ldots, & \frac{d^{k}a^{(-r)}}{dx^{k}} \\ \cdots & \cdots & \cdots \\ a^{(-m+p)}(x), & \ldots, & a^{(-m+1)}(x) \end{array}$$

have continuous derivatives of the first q orders where $q \geqslant 1$ is an arbitrary natural number.

4. There exists an unbounded subset Ω_1 of the region Ω in which the inequalities

$$\operatorname{Re}\omega_1(x, \lambda) \leqslant \operatorname{Re}\omega_2(x, \lambda) \leqslant \ldots \leqslant \operatorname{Re}\omega_n(x, \lambda) \qquad (2.2.4)$$

are satisfied for all $x \in [a, b]$ and suitable numbering of the functions

$$\omega_s(x, \lambda) = \lambda^p \theta_s^{(p)}(x) + \lambda^{p-1}\theta_s^{(p-1)}(x) + \ldots + \lambda\theta_s^{(1)}(x)$$

(where $\theta_s^{(p)}(x)$ is the root of the characteristic equation).

Under these conditions, there exists a matrix of the formal series

$$\exp\left(\int_a^x \omega(\xi, \lambda)\, d\xi\right) \sum_{\nu=0}^{\infty} y_{is}^{(\nu)}(x)\lambda^{-\nu}$$

the columns in which formally satisfy (2.2.1); the coefficients $\omega_s(x, \lambda)$ and $y_{is}^{(\nu)}(x)$ are obtained by putting the coefficients of the different powers of λ individually equal to zero after substituting these series into (2.2.1) and dividing by the factor

$$\exp\int_a^x \omega_s(\xi, \lambda)\, d\xi$$

Although these series generally diverge, they can be used

for an asymptotic representation of some fundamental system of particular solutions of (2.2.1). For given m, the system of particular solutions is of the form

$$y_{is}(x,\lambda)=\exp\left(\int_a^x \omega_s(\xi,\lambda)\,d\xi\right)\left\{\sum_{\nu=0}^{m-1}\lambda^{-\nu}y_{is}^{(\nu)}(x)+\frac{E_{is}(x,\lambda)}{\lambda^m}\right\} \quad (2.2.5)$$

where the $E_{is}(x,\lambda)$ are continuous functions with respect to x on the interval $[a,b]$ and are bounded for $\lambda\in\Omega_1$. The functions $y_{is}^{(\nu)}(x)$ have continuous derivatives of the first $q-1$ orders on $[a,b]$.

We shall call the representation (2.2.5) the asymptotic representation of the solutions $y_{is}(x,\lambda)$ (for $i=1,\ldots,n$ and $s=1,\ldots,n$) for the values of $\lambda\in\Omega_1$.

Proof First of all, let us show that the determinant of the matrix U of the functions

$$u_{is}(x,\lambda)=\exp\left(\int_a^x \omega_s(\xi,\lambda)\,d\xi\right)\sum_{\nu=0}^{p+m-1} y_{is}^{(\nu)}(x)\lambda^{-\nu} \quad (2.2.6)$$

does not vanish for $x\in[a,b]$. In fact,

$$\det U=\begin{vmatrix} u_{11}(x,\lambda) & \ldots & u_{1n}(x,\lambda)\\ \cdot & \cdot & \cdot\\ u_{n1}(x,\lambda) & \ldots & u_{nn}(x,\lambda)\end{vmatrix}$$

$$=\exp\left(\sum_{s=1}^n\int_a^x\omega_s(\xi,\lambda)d\xi\right)\begin{vmatrix}\sum_{\nu=0}^{p+m-1}y_{11}^{(\nu)}(x)\lambda^{-\nu} & \ldots & \sum_{\nu=0}^{p+m-1}y_{1n}^{(\nu)}(x)\lambda^{-\nu}\\ \cdot & \cdot & \cdot\\ \sum_{\nu=0}^{p+m-1}y_{n1}^{(\nu)}(x)\lambda^{-\nu} & \ldots & \sum_{\nu=0}^{p+m-1}y_{nn}^{(\nu)}(x)\lambda^{-\nu}\end{vmatrix}$$

$$=\exp\left(\sum_{s=1}^n\int_a^x\omega_s(\xi,\lambda)\,d\xi\right)\left\{\det Y^{(0)}(x)+\frac{E(x,\lambda)}{\lambda}\right\} \quad (2.2.7)$$

where $E(x,\lambda)$ is a bounded function for $\lambda\in\Omega$ and

$$Y^{(0)}=\begin{pmatrix} y_{11}^{(0)}(x) & \ldots & y_{1n}^{(0)}(x)\\ \cdot & \cdot & \cdot\\ y_{n1}^{(0)}(x) & \ldots & y_{nn}^{(0)}(x)\end{pmatrix}$$

From (2.1.31), we have

$$\det Y^{(0)}(x) = \det m(x) \det g^{(0)}(x)$$

$$= \det m(x) \begin{vmatrix} g_{11}^{(0)}(x) & 0 & \dots & 0 \\ 0 & g_{22}^{(0)}(x) & \dots & 0 \\ \dots & \dots & \dots & \dots \\ 0 & 0 & \dots & g_{nn}^{(0)}(x) \end{vmatrix} \tag{2.2.8}$$

$$= \det m(x)\, g_{11}^{(0)}(x)\, g_{22}^{(0)}(x) \dots g_{nn}^{(0)}(x)$$

On the basis of (2.2.8), from (2.2.7) we have, for $\lambda \in \Omega$,

$$|\det U| \geqslant \left| \exp \sum_{s=1}^{n} \int_{a}^{x} \omega_s(\xi, \lambda)\, d\xi \right| Q \tag{2.2.9}$$

where Q is a positive constant, independent of x and λ.

Thus, it follows from (2.2.9) that, for $x \in [a, b]$ and $\lambda \in \Omega$, the matrix U has an inverse whose elements are q times continuously differentiable on $[a, b]$.

According to Theorem 1, every summable solution of System (2.2.1) which satisfies an equation of type (1.1.7) satisfies a system of integral equations of the form (1.1.8).

For System (2.2.1), we choose for the matrix Z of absolutely continuous functions z_{ji} the inverse of the matrix U of the functions (2.2.6)

$$ZU = e \quad \text{or} \quad Z = U^{-1} \tag{2.2.10}$$

where e is the unit matrix.

According to Theorem 1, every solution $y_{is}(x, \lambda)$ of (2.2.1) which satisfies the condition

$$\sum_{k=1}^{n} y_{kj}(x_j)\, z_{jk}(x_j) = c_j \tag{2.2.11}$$

for the arbitrary constants c_j and arbitrary fixed points $x_j \in [a, b]$ satisfies the system of integral equations

$$y_{ks}(x, \lambda) = F_k(x, \lambda) + \sum_{j=1}^{n} \sum_{i=1}^{n} \int_{x_j}^{x} q_{ki}^{(j)}(x, \xi, \lambda)\, y_{is}(\xi, \lambda)\, d\xi \tag{2.2.12}$$

where

$$F_k(x, \lambda) = \sum_{j=1}^{n} \frac{\Delta_{jk}(x, \lambda)}{\Delta(x, \lambda)} c_j \tag{2.2.13}$$

$$q_{ki}^{(j)}(x, \xi, \lambda) = \frac{\Delta_{jk}(x, \lambda)}{\Delta(x, \lambda)} \left\{ \frac{dz_{ji}(\xi, \lambda)}{d\xi} + \sum_{r=1}^{n} a_{ri}(\xi, \lambda) z_{jr}(\xi, \lambda) \right\} \tag{2.2.14}$$

Here, just as in Chapter 1, $\Delta(x, \lambda)$ denotes the determinant of the matrix Z and $\Delta_{jk}(x, \lambda)$ denotes the cofactor of the element z_{jk} in it.

From our choice of the matrix Z, in accordance with (2.2.10), it is clear that

$$\frac{\Delta_{jk}(x, \lambda)}{\Delta(x, \lambda)} = u_{kj}(x, \lambda) \tag{2.2.15}$$

Under Conditions (2.2.11), we put

$$c_j = \begin{cases} 1 & \text{for} \quad j = s \\ 0 & \text{for} \quad j \neq s \end{cases}$$

Then, from (2.2.13), we obtain

$$F_k(x, \lambda) = \frac{\Delta_{sk}(x, \lambda)}{\Delta(x, \lambda)} = u_{ks}(x, \lambda) \tag{2.2.16}$$

Let us now show that, with our choice of c_j in the expression $q_{ki}^{(j)}(x, \xi, \lambda)$, the factor depending on ξ is of the form

$$\frac{dz_{ji}(\xi, \lambda)}{d\xi} + \sum_{r=1}^{n} a_{ri}(\xi, \lambda) z_{jr}(\xi, \lambda) = \frac{e^{-\int_a^{\xi} \omega_j(\alpha, \lambda)\, d\alpha}}{\lambda^m} \Phi_{ij}(\xi, \lambda) \tag{2.2.17}$$

where $\Phi_{ij}(\xi, \lambda)$ is a continuous function with respect to ξ on interval $[a, b]$ and is bounded for $\lambda \in \Omega$ (where $|\lambda| \geqslant R$ and R is a sufficiently large number).

Differentiating (2.2.10), we obtain

$$Z \frac{dU}{dx} = -\frac{dZ}{dx} U$$

so that

$$\frac{dZ}{dx} = -Z\frac{dU}{dx}U^{-1}$$

Consequently,

$$\frac{dZ}{dx} + Za(x, \lambda) = -Z\frac{dU}{dx}U^{-1} + Za(x, \lambda)UU^{-1}$$
$$\equiv -Z\left(\frac{dU}{dx} - a(x, \lambda)U\right)U^{-1} \equiv -U^{-1}\left(\frac{dU}{dx} - a(x, \lambda)U\right)U^{-1} \tag{2.2.18}$$

Let $(U^{-1})_{jr}$ denote the element of the matrix U^{-1} in the jth row and rth column and $(\det U)_{ik}$ the cofactor of the element $u_{ik}(x, \lambda)$ in the determinant of the matrix U. Then we have

$$(U^{-1})_{jr} = \frac{(\det U)_{rj}}{\det U}$$

Furthermore,

$$\begin{aligned}
&\left\{U^{-1}\left(\frac{dU}{dx} - a(x, \lambda)U\right)U^{-1}\right\}_{ji} \\
&= \sum_{r=1}^{n} (U^{-1})_{jr}\left\{\left(\frac{dU}{dx} - a(x, \lambda)U\right)U^{-1}\right\}_{ri} \\
&= \sum_{r=1}^{n} (U^{-1})_{jr}\sum_{s=1}^{n}\left(\frac{du_{rs}(x, \lambda)}{dx}\right. \\
&\qquad \left. - \sum_{q=1}^{n} a_{rq}(x, \lambda)u_{qs}(x, \lambda)\right)(U^{-1})_{si} \\
&= \sum_{r=1}^{n} \frac{(\det U)_{rj}}{\det U}\sum_{s=1}^{n}\left(\frac{du_{rs}(x, \lambda)}{dx}\right. \\
&\qquad \left. - \sum_{q=1}^{n} a_{rq}(x, \lambda)u_{qs}(x, \lambda)\right)\frac{(\det U)_{is}}{\det U}
\end{aligned} \tag{2.2.19}$$

It is clear that

$$\frac{(\det U)_{rj}}{\det U} = \exp\left(-\int_{a}^{x} \omega_j(\alpha, \lambda)\,d\alpha\right)E_{rj}(x, \lambda)$$

where $E_{rj}(x, \lambda)$ is a continuous function with respect to x on $[a, b]$ for $\lambda \in \Omega$. Consequently, bearing (2.1.36) and (2.2.19) in mind, we obtain

$$-\left\{U^{-1}\left(\frac{dU}{dx}-a(x,\lambda)U\right)U^{-1}\right\}_{ji}$$

$$=-\sum_{r=1}^{n}E_{rj}(x,\lambda)\exp\left(-\int_{a}^{x}\omega_j(\alpha,\lambda)\,d\alpha\right)$$

$$\times\sum_{s=1}^{n}\exp\left(\int_{a}^{x}\omega_s(\alpha,\lambda)\,d\alpha\right)$$

$$\times\frac{\psi_{rs}}{\lambda^m}\exp\left(-\int_{a}^{x}\omega_s(\alpha,\lambda)\,d\alpha\right)E_{is}(x,\lambda)$$

$$=\exp\left(-\int_{a}^{x}\omega_j(\alpha,\lambda)\,d\alpha\right)\frac{\Phi_{ij}(x,\lambda)}{\lambda^m}$$

On the basis of the last identity, we obtain (2.2.17) from (2.2.18), which completes the proof of our assertion about the validity of (2.2.17).

Furthermore, keeping (2.2.15), (2.1.35) and (2.2.17) in mind, we obtain from (2.2.14)

$$q_{ki}^{(j)}(x,\xi,\lambda)=\exp\left(\int_{a}^{x}\omega_j(\alpha,\lambda)\,d\alpha\right)$$

$$\times\sum_{\nu=0}^{p+m-1}\lambda^{-\nu}y_{kj}^{(\nu)}(x)\frac{\Phi_{ij}(\xi,\lambda)}{\lambda^m}\exp\left(-\int_{a}^{\xi}\omega_j(\alpha,\lambda)\,d\alpha\right) \qquad (2.2.20)$$

$$=\exp\left(\int_{\xi}^{x}\omega_j(\alpha,\lambda)\,d\alpha\right)\frac{\mathscr{E}_{kji}(x,\xi,\lambda)}{\lambda^m}$$

where the $\mathscr{E}_{kji}(x,\xi,\lambda)$ are functions which are continuous with respect to x and ξ on the interval $[a, b]$ and which are bounded for $\lambda\in\Omega$.

Now, to obtain an asymptotic representation of the solutions $y_{ks}(x,\lambda)$ of System (2.2.1), we use the system of integral equations (2.2.12) which the solutions $y_{ks}(x,\lambda)$ satisfy, just as we did in Chapter 1.

To do this, we first use (1.2.4) to construct and find bounds for the approximations $u_k^{(m)}(x,\lambda)$.

From (1.2.4), we obtain

$$u_k^{(0)}(x,\lambda)=F_k(x,\lambda)$$
$$u_k^{(\nu)}(x,\lambda)=\sum_{j=1}^{n}\sum_{i=1}^{n}\int_{x_j}^{x}q_{ki}^{(j)}(x,\xi,\lambda)\,u_i^{(\nu-1)}(\xi,\lambda)\,d\xi \quad (\nu=1,2,\ldots) \qquad (2.2.21)$$

Bearing in mind (2.2.16) and using the representations (2.1.35) and (2.2.20), we obtain from (2.2.21)

$$|u_k^{(1)}(x,\lambda)| = \Big| \sum_{j=1}^{n}\sum_{i=1}^{n}\int_{x_j}^{x} \exp\Big(\int_{\xi}^{x}\omega_j(\alpha,\lambda)\,d\alpha\Big)\frac{\mathscr{E}_{kji}(x,\xi,\lambda)}{\lambda^m} \times \exp\Big(\int_{a}^{\xi}\omega_s(\alpha,\lambda)\,d\alpha\Big)\sum_{\nu=0}^{m+p-1}\lambda^{-\nu}y_{is}^{(\nu)}(\xi)\,d\xi\Big|$$

$$\leqslant \Big|\sum_{j=1}^{s}\sum_{i=1}^{n}\int_{x_j}^{x}\exp\Big(\int_{a}^{\xi}\omega_s(\alpha,\lambda)\,d\alpha+\int_{\xi}^{x}\omega_j(\alpha,\lambda)\,d\alpha\Big) \times \frac{\mathscr{E}_{kji}(x,\xi,\lambda)\sum_{\nu=0}^{m+p-1}\lambda^{-\nu}y_{is}^{(\nu)}(\xi)}{\lambda^m}\,d\xi\Big|$$

$$+\Big|\sum_{j=s+1}^{n}\sum_{i=1}^{n}\int_{x_j}^{x}\exp\Big(\int_{a}^{\xi}\omega_s(\alpha,\lambda)\,d\alpha + \int_{\xi}^{x}\omega_j(\alpha,\lambda)\,d\alpha\Big)\frac{\mathscr{E}_{kji}(x,\xi,\lambda)\sum_{\nu=0}^{m+p-1}\lambda^{-\nu}y_{is}^{(\nu)}(\xi)}{\lambda^m}\,d\xi\Big| \tag{2.2.22}$$

where s is the second index of the solution $y_{is}(x,\lambda)$ of System (2.2.1).

Since the functions $\mathscr{E}_{kji}(x,\xi,\lambda)$ are bounded for $\lambda\in\Omega$, there exists a positive constant C such that

$$\Big|\mathscr{E}_{kji}(x,\xi,\lambda)\sum_{\nu=0}^{m+p-1}\lambda^{-\nu}y_{is}^{(\nu)}(\xi)\Big| < C \tag{2.2.23}$$

Furthermore, if we put

$$x_1 = x_2 = \ldots = x_s = a, \qquad x_{s+1} = x_{s+2} = \ldots = x_n = b$$

and keep (2.2.23) in mind, we obtain from (2.2.22)

$$|u_k^{(1)}(x,\lambda)| \leqslant \frac{nC}{|\lambda|^m}\Big\{\sum_{j=1}^{s}\int_{a}^{x}\Big|\exp\Big(\int_{a}^{\xi}\omega_s(\alpha,\lambda)\,d\alpha+\int_{\xi}^{x}\omega_j(\alpha,\lambda)\,d\alpha\Big)\Big|\,d\xi + \sum_{j=s+1}^{n}\int_{x}^{b}\Big|\exp\Big(\int_{a}^{\xi}\omega_s(\alpha,\lambda)\,d\alpha-\int_{x}^{\xi}\omega_j(\alpha,\lambda)\,d\alpha\Big)\Big|\,d\xi\Big\} = \tag{2.2.24}$$

$$= \frac{nC}{|\lambda|^m}\left\{\sum_{j=1}^{s}\int_a^x \exp\left(\operatorname{Re}\left(\int_a^{\xi}\omega_s(\alpha,\lambda)\,d\alpha + \int_{\xi}^{x}\omega_j(\alpha,\lambda)\,d\alpha\right)\right)d\xi\right. \qquad (2.2.24)\ (\text{cont.})$$
$$\left. + \sum_{j=s+1}^{n}\int_x^b \exp\left(\operatorname{Re}\left(\int_a^{\xi}\omega_s(\alpha,\lambda)\,d\alpha - \int_x^{\xi}\omega_j(\alpha,\lambda)\,d\alpha\right)\right)d\xi\right\}$$

On the basis of the condition of the theorem, the inequalities (2.2.4) are satisfied for all $\lambda \in \Omega_1$. Consequently, in the right-hand side of (2.2.24), we have, for all terms in the first sum,

$$\operatorname{Re}\omega_j(x,\lambda) \leqslant \operatorname{Re}\omega_s(x,\lambda), \quad j \leqslant s \qquad (2.2.25)$$

Similarly, for all terms in the second sum, we have

$$\operatorname{Re}\omega_s(x,\lambda) \leqslant \operatorname{Re}\omega_j(x,\lambda), \quad s < j \qquad (2.2.26)$$

By virtue of (2.2.25) and (2.2.26), we obtain from (2.2.24)

$$|u_k^{(1)}(x,\lambda)|$$
$$\leqslant \frac{nC}{|\lambda|^m}\left\{s\int_a^x \exp\left[\operatorname{Re}\left(\int_a^{\xi}\omega_s(\alpha,\lambda)\,d\alpha + \int_{\xi}^{x}\omega_s(\alpha,\lambda)\,d\alpha\right)\right]d\xi\right.$$
$$\left. + (n-s)\int_x^b \exp\left[\operatorname{Re}\left(\int_a^{\xi}\omega_s(\alpha,\lambda)\,d\alpha - \int_x^{\xi}\omega_s(\alpha,\lambda)\,d\alpha\right)\right]d\xi\right\}$$
$$= \frac{nC}{|\lambda|^m}\left\{s\int_a^x \exp\left[\operatorname{Re}\int_a^x \omega_s(\alpha,\lambda)\,d\alpha\right]d\xi\right. \qquad (2.2.27)$$
$$\left. + (n-s)\int_x^b \exp\left[\operatorname{Re}\int_a^x \omega_s(\alpha,\lambda)\,d\alpha\right]d\xi\right\}$$
$$\leqslant \frac{n^2C(b-a)}{|\lambda|^m}\exp\left[\operatorname{Re}\int_a^x \omega_s(\alpha,\lambda)\,d\alpha\right]$$

If we continue deriving such inequalities, one after the other, we obtain from (2.2.21)

$$|u_k^{(\nu)}(x,\lambda)| \leqslant \left(\frac{n^2C(b-a)}{|\lambda|^m}\right)^{\nu}\left|\exp\int_a^x \omega_s(\alpha,\lambda)\,d\alpha\right| \qquad (2.2.28)$$

The validity of (2.2.28) has been proved for $\nu = 1$. To show that it is valid for an arbitrary natural number ν, let us assume that it is valid for $\nu-1$ and show that it is then valid for ν. From (2.2.21), we have

$$|u_k^{(\nu)}(x,\lambda)|\leqslant\Bigg|\sum_{j=1}^{s}\sum_{i=1}^{n}\int_a^x \exp\Big(\int_\xi^x \omega_j(\alpha,\lambda)\,d\alpha\Big)\times\frac{\mathscr{E}_{kji}(x,\xi,\lambda)}{\lambda^m}u_i^{(\nu-1)}(\xi,\lambda)\,d\xi$$

$$+\sum_{j=s+1}^{n}\sum_{i=1}^{n}\int_b^x \exp\Big(\int_\xi^x \omega_j(\alpha,\lambda)\,d\alpha\Big)\frac{\mathscr{E}_{kji}(x,\xi,\lambda)}{\lambda^m}\times u_i^{(\nu-1)}(\xi,\lambda)\,d\xi\Bigg|\leqslant\frac{nC}{|\lambda|^m}\Big(\frac{n^2C(b-a)}{|\lambda|^m}\Big)^{\nu-1}$$

$$\times\Big\{\sum_{j=1}^{s}\int_a^x\Big|\exp\Big(\int_a^\xi \omega_s(\alpha,\lambda)\,d\alpha+\int_\xi^x \omega_j(\alpha,\lambda)\,d\alpha\Big)\Big|\,d\xi$$

$$+\sum_{j=s+1}^{n}\int_x^b\Big|\exp\Big(\int_a^\xi \omega_s(\alpha,\lambda)\,d\alpha-\int_x^\xi \omega_j(\alpha,\lambda)\,d\alpha\Big)\Big|\,d\xi\Big\}$$

From this, we obtain by using (2.2.25) and (2.2.26)

$$|u_k^{(\nu)}(x,\lambda)|$$

$$\leqslant\frac{nC}{|\lambda|^m}\Big(\frac{n^2C(b-a)}{|\lambda|^m}\Big)^{\nu-1}\Big\{s\int_a^x \exp\Big(\operatorname{Re}\int_a^x \omega_s(\alpha,\lambda)\,d\alpha\Big)\,d\xi$$

$$+(n-s)\int_x^b \exp\Big(\operatorname{Re}\int_a^x \omega_s(\alpha,\lambda)\,d\alpha\Big)\,d\xi\Big\}$$

$$\leqslant\Big(\frac{n^2C(b-a)}{|\lambda|^m}\Big)^{\nu}\exp\Big(\operatorname{Re}\int_a^x \omega_s(\alpha,\lambda)\,d\alpha\Big)$$

Differentiating (2.2.21), we obtain

$$\frac{du_k^{(\nu)}(x,\lambda)}{dx}=\sum_{i,\,j=1}^{n} q_{ki}^{(j)}(x,x)\,u_i^{(\nu-1)}(x,\lambda)+\sum_{i,\,j=1}^{n}\int_{x_j}^{x}\frac{dq_{ki}^{(j)}(x,\xi,\lambda)}{dx}u_i^{(\nu-1)}(\xi,\lambda)\,d\xi \tag{2.2.29}$$

As is clear from (2.2.21), (2.2.16) and (2.2.14), the functions

$$u_k^{(0)}(x,\lambda),\quad q_{ki}^{(j)}(x,\xi,\lambda)\ \text{and}\ \frac{dq_{ki}^{(j)}(x,\xi,\lambda)}{dx}$$

are continuous with respect to x and ξ on the interval $[a, b]$ for $\lambda\in\Omega$. Therefore, there exists a constant C_1 such that

$$|u_k^{(0)}(x, \lambda)|\leqslant C_1, \quad |q_{ki}^{(j)}(x, x, \lambda)|\leqslant C_1$$

$$\left|\frac{dq_{ki}^{(j)}(x, \xi, \lambda)}{dx}\right|\leqslant C_1\left|\exp\left(\int_{\xi}^{x}\omega_j(\alpha, \lambda)\,d\alpha\right)\right| \quad \text{for} \quad x\in[a, b] \tag{2.2.30}$$

Consequently, on the basis of (2.2.28), we obtain from (2.2.29) the inequality

$$\left|\frac{du_k^{(\nu)}(x, \lambda)}{dx}\right|\leqslant C_2\left(\frac{n^2C\,(b-a)}{|\lambda|^m}\right)^{\nu-1}\left|\exp\left(\int_{a}^{x}\omega_s(\alpha, \lambda)\,d\alpha\right)\right| \tag{2.2.31}$$

where C_2 is a positive constant. This inequality, which is valid for every natural number ν, is obtained in just the same way as for $u_k^{(\nu)}(x, \lambda)$.

Furthermore, with the aid of (2.2.21) and (2.2.29), we can easily show by induction that the functions

$$u_k^{(\nu)}(x, \lambda), \quad \frac{du_k^{(\nu)}(x, \lambda)}{dx} \quad (k=1, \ldots, n;\ \nu=0, 1, 2, \ldots) \tag{2.2.32}$$

are continuous on the interval $[a, b]$.

On the other hand, by virtue of (2.2.28) and (2.2.31), the series

$$\sum_{\nu=0}^{\infty}u_k^{(\nu)}(x, \lambda), \quad \sum_{\nu=0}^{\infty}\frac{du_k^{(\nu)}(x, \lambda)}{dx} \tag{2.2.33}$$

converge absolutely and uniformly on the interval $[a, b]$ and in every finite portion of the region Ω_1 in which the inequalities (2.2.4) are satisfied.

Then, in accordance with a familiar test of Weierstrass, the sums of the series (2.2.33) are continuous functions on the interval $[a, b]$ for $\lambda\in\Omega_1$. If $y_{ks}(x, \lambda)$ is the sum of the first of the series (2.2.23), then,

$$\frac{dy_{ks}(x, \lambda)}{dx}=\sum_{\nu=0}^{n}\frac{du_k^{(\nu)}(x, \lambda)}{dx}$$

Thus, we have the conditions under which Theorems 1 and 2 are applicable. According to Theorem 2, the functions $y_{ks}(x, \lambda)$ satisfy the integral equations (2.2.12). Therefore, in accordance with Theorem 1 and the remark following it, the functions $y_{ks}(x, \lambda)$ are solutions of System (2.2.1) everywhere on $[a, b]$ which satisfy the conditions

$$\sum_{k=1}^{n} y_{ks}(a, \lambda) z_{sk}(a, \lambda) = 1$$

$$\sum_{k=1}^{n} y_{kj}(a, \lambda) z_{jk}(a, \lambda) = 0 \quad \text{for} \quad j = 1, \ldots, s-1$$

$$\sum_{k=1}^{n} y_{kj}(b, \lambda) z_{jk}(b, \lambda) = 0 \quad \text{for} \quad j = s+1, \ldots, n$$

Having found bounds for all terms except the first, we may represent the sum of the first of the series (2.2.33) in a simpler form. On the basis of (2.2.28), we obtain

$$\begin{aligned} \left|\sum_{\nu=1}^{\infty} u_k^{(\nu)}(x, \lambda)\right| &\leqslant \sum_{\nu=1}^{\infty} |u_k^{(\nu)}(x, \lambda)| \\ &\leqslant \sum_{\nu=1}^{\infty} \left(\frac{n^2C(b-a)}{|\lambda|^m}\right)^{\nu} \left| e^{\int_a^x \omega_s(\alpha, \lambda)\, d\alpha} \right| \\ &= \left| e^{\int_a^x \omega_s(\xi, \lambda)\, d\xi} \right| \frac{n^2C(b-a)/|\lambda|^m}{1 - \dfrac{n^2C(b-a)}{|\lambda|^m}} \\ &= \left| e^{\int_a^x \omega_s(\xi, \lambda)\, d\xi} \right| \frac{n^2C(b-a)}{|\lambda|^m} \, \frac{|\lambda|^m}{|\lambda|^m - n^2C(b-a)} \end{aligned} \tag{2.2.34}$$

Using the inequality (2.2.34), we have the following representation

$$\sum_{\nu=1}^{\infty} u_k^{(\nu)}(x, \lambda) = \exp\left(\int_a^x \omega_s(\xi, \lambda)\, d\xi\right) \frac{E_1(x, \lambda)}{\lambda^m} \tag{2.2.35}$$

where $E_1(x, \lambda)$ is a continuous function with respect to x on the interval $[a, b]$ and is bounded for $\lambda \in \Omega_1$.

Finally, on the basis of (2.2.16), (2.2.21) and (2.2.6), we

obtain the following asymptotic representation

$$
\begin{aligned}
y_{ks}(x, \lambda) &= \sum_{\nu=0}^{\infty} u_k^{(\nu)}(x, \lambda) \\
&= u_k^{(0)}(x, \lambda) + \sum_{\nu=1}^{\infty} u_k^{(\nu)}(x, \lambda) \\
&= u_{ks}(x, \lambda) + \sum_{\nu=1}^{\infty} u_k^{(\nu)}(x, \lambda) \\
&= \exp\left(\int_a^x \omega_s(\xi, \lambda)\, d\xi\right) \left\{ \sum_{\nu=0}^{m-1} \lambda^{-\nu} y_{ks}^{(\nu)}(x) + \frac{E(x, \lambda)}{\lambda^m} \right\}
\end{aligned}
$$

where $E(x, \lambda)$ is a continuous function with respect to x on the interval $[a, b]$ which is bounded for $\lambda \in \Omega_1$.

To complete the proof of the theorem, we need to show that the solutions $y_{ks}(x, \lambda)$ obtained for $s = 1, 2, \ldots, n$ are independent.

Let us denote by $Y(x, \lambda)$ the matrix of the functions $y_{ks}(x, \lambda)$. Clearly, the s th column of this matrix is one of the solutions of System **(2.2.1)**. The independence of the solutions of **(2.2.1)** which we have constructed is equivalent to independence of the columns of the matrix $Y(x, \lambda)$. To prove this, we need only show that the determinant of this matrix does not vanish for $x \in [a, b]$ and $\lambda \in \Omega_1$. We have

$$
\det Y(x, \lambda) = \exp\left(\sum_{s=1}^{n} \int_a^x \omega_s(\xi, \lambda)\, d\xi \right) \left\{ \det Y^{(0)}(x) + \frac{E_2(x, \lambda)}{\lambda} \right\} \tag{2.2.36}
$$

where $E_2(x, \lambda)$ is a continuous function with respect to x on the interval $[a, b]$ which is bounded for $\lambda \in \Omega_1$. From **(2.1.31)**, we have

$$
\begin{aligned}
\det Y^{(0)}(x) &= \det m(x) \det g^{(0)}(x) \\
&= \det m(x)\, g_{11}^{(0)}(x)\, g_{22}^{(0)}(x) \ldots g_{nn}^{(0)}(x) \neq 0
\end{aligned}
$$

Consequently, we conclude from **(2.2.36)** that $\det Y(x, \lambda) \neq 0$ for $x \in [a, b]$ and $\lambda \in \Omega_1$, which completes the proof.

2.3. ASYMPTOTIC REPRESENTATIONS OF SOLUTIONS OF A SINGLE EQUATION OF HIGHER ORDER

In this section, we shall consider the case of a single linear differential equation of order n

$$\frac{d^n y}{dx^n} + P_1(x, \mu)\frac{d^{n-1}y}{dx^{n-1}} + P_2(x, \mu)\frac{d^{n-2}y}{dx^{n-2}} + \ldots + P_n(x, \mu)y = 0$$

The coefficients in this equation are analytic functions of a complex parameter μ in a neighbourhood of the point $\mu = \infty$ and are assumed to have poles at this point.

Let us denote by $\varkappa_i$ the order of the pole for the coefficient $P_i(x, \mu)$. Then, in a region Ω (for $|\mu| \geqslant R$, where R is a sufficiently large number), the coefficients $P_i(x, \mu)$ have expansions of the form

$$P_i(x, \mu) = \sum_{\nu=0}^{\infty} \mu^{\varkappa_i - \nu} P_{i\nu}(x)$$

Here, not one of the functions $P_{i_0}(x)$ vanishes identically in the interval $[a, b]$.

Out of the numbers

$$\frac{\varkappa_1}{1}, \frac{\varkappa_2}{2}, \ldots, \frac{\varkappa_n}{n}$$

let us choose the largest (which, obviously, must be positive since otherwise the point $\mu = \infty$ would not be the pole of any of the coefficients of the given equation), reduce it to its simplest form and denote by σ the denominator of that fraction. It is clear that the substitution

$$\lambda = (\mu)^{\frac{1}{\sigma}}$$

in the given equation leads to an equation of the form

$$\frac{d^n y}{dx^n} + \lambda^p P_1(x, \lambda)\frac{d^{n-1}y}{dx^{n-1}} + \lambda^{2p} P_2(x, \lambda)\frac{d^{n-2}y}{dx^{n-2}} + \ldots + \lambda^{np} P_n(x, \lambda)\, y = 0 \qquad (2.3.1)$$

where $p \geqslant 1$ is an integer, the coefficients $P_i(x, \lambda)$ are of the form

$$P_i(x, \lambda) = \sum_{\nu=0}^{\infty} \lambda^{-\nu} P_{i\nu}(x) \qquad (i = 1, \ldots, n) \qquad (2.3.2)$$

and at least one of the functions

$$P_{i0}(x) \qquad (i = 1, 2, \ldots, n)$$

is not identically zero on the interval $[a, b]$.

Thus, in what follows we shall assume without loss of generality that the equation in question is of the form (2.3.1). For convenience in writing, we shall denote the unknown function y by y_1.

Substituting

$$\lambda^{-ip} \frac{d^i y_1}{dx^i} = y_{i+1} \qquad (i = 0, 1, \ldots, n-1) \tag{2.3.3}$$

for the unknown function y_1 and its derivatives, we can reduce the differential equation (2.3.1) to a system of first-order equations of the type selected in the preceding section but of a very special form.

Specifically, the substitution (2.3.3) yields

$$\frac{dy_i}{dx} = \lambda^p y_{i+1} \qquad (i = 0, 1, \ldots, n-1)$$

Combining these relations with the first-order equation obtained from (2.3.1) by means of the substitution (2.3.3), we arrive at the following system:

$$\begin{aligned}
&\frac{dy_1}{dx} - \lambda^p y_2 = 0 \\
&\frac{dy_2}{dx} - \lambda^p y_3 = 0 \\
&\cdots\cdots\cdots\cdots\cdots \\
&\frac{dy_{n-1}}{dx} - \lambda^p y_n = 0 \\
&\frac{dy_n}{dx} + \lambda^p P_1(x, \lambda)\, y_n \\
&+ \lambda^p P_2(x, \lambda)\, y_{n-1} + \ldots + \lambda^p P_n(x, \lambda)\, y_1 = 0
\end{aligned} \tag{2.3.4}$$

In the notations of the preceding section, we have, in (2.3.4),

$$\begin{aligned}
&a_{1j}(x, \lambda) = 0 \text{ for } j = 1, 3, \ldots, n; && a_{12}(x, \lambda) = \lambda^p \\
&a_{2j}(x, \lambda) = 0 \text{ for } j = 1, 2, 4, \ldots, n; && a_{23}(x, \lambda) = \lambda^p \\
&a_{3j}(x, \lambda) = 0 \text{ for } j = 1, 2, 3, 5, 6, \ldots, n; && a_{34}(x, \lambda) = \lambda^p \\
&\cdots\cdots\cdots\cdots\cdots\cdots\cdots\cdots \\
&a_{n-1j}(x, \lambda) = 0 \text{ for } j = 1, \ldots, n-1; && a_{n-1n}(x, \lambda) = \lambda^p
\end{aligned}$$

$$\begin{aligned}
&a_{n1}(x, \lambda) = -\lambda^p P_n(x, \lambda), \quad a_{n2}(x, \lambda) = -\lambda^p P_{n-1}(x, \lambda) \\
&\cdots\cdots\cdots\cdots\cdots, \quad a_{nn}(x, \lambda) = -\lambda^p P_1(x, \lambda)
\end{aligned}$$

It is easy to see from (2.3.4) that if the columns of the matrix

$$Y(x,\lambda)=\begin{pmatrix} y_{11}(x,\lambda) & y_{12}(x,\lambda) & \dots & y_{1n}(x,\lambda) \\ y_{21}(x,\lambda) & y_{22}(x,\lambda) & \dots & y_{2n}(x,\lambda) \\ \cdot & \cdot & \cdot & \cdot \\ y_{n1}(x,\lambda) & y_{n2}(x,\lambda) & \dots & y_{nn}(x,\lambda) \end{pmatrix}$$

constitute a fundamental system of particular solutions of System (2.3.4), then the functions

$$y_{11}(x,\lambda),\ y_{12}(x,\lambda),\ \dots,\ y_{1n}(x,\lambda) \tag{2.3.5}$$

constitute a fundamental system of particular solutions of (2.3.1). Specifically, from the first $(n-1)$ equations of (2.3.4), we have

$$\begin{aligned} & y_{2k}(x,\lambda)=\lambda^{-p}\frac{dy_{1k}}{dx},\quad y_{3k}(x,\lambda)=\lambda^{-2p}\frac{d^2y_{1k}}{dx^2} \\ & y_{4k}(x,\lambda)=\lambda^{-3p}\frac{d^3y_{1k}}{dx^3},\ \dots \\ & \qquad \dots,\ y_{nk}(x,\lambda)=\lambda^{-(n-1)p}\frac{d^{n-1}y_{1k}}{dx^{n-1}} \end{aligned} \tag{2.3.6}$$

Substituting these values into the last equation of System (2.3.4) and multiplying the relation obtained by $\lambda^{(n-1)p}$, we obtain the identity

$$\begin{aligned} & \frac{d^n y_{1k}}{dx^n}+\lambda^p P_1(x,\lambda)\frac{d^{n-1}y_{1k}}{dx^{n-1}} \\ & \qquad +\lambda^{2p}P_2(x,\lambda)\frac{d^{n-2}y_{1k}}{dx^{n-2}}+\dots+\lambda^{np}P_n(x,\lambda)\,y_{1k}\equiv 0 \end{aligned}$$

for all $k=1, 2, \dots, n$. This means that all the functions (2.3.5) satisfy (2.3.1).

Let us now show that the functions (2.3.5) are linearly independent. By hypothesis, $Y(x,\lambda)$ is the matrix of a fundamental system of particular solutions of (2.3.4). Consequently,

$$\det Y(x,\lambda)\neq 0 \quad \text{for} \quad x\in[a,b] \tag{2.3.7}$$

In accordance with (2.3.6), in the determinants of the matrix $Y(x,\lambda)$, the elements of all rows beginning with the second can be expressed in terms of the derivatives of the elements of the first row. We obtain

$$\det Y(x,\lambda) = \begin{vmatrix} y_{11}(x,\lambda) & y_{12}(x,\lambda) \ldots & y_{1n}(x,\lambda) \\ \lambda^{-p}\frac{dy_{11}(x,\lambda)}{dx} & \lambda^{-p}\frac{dy_{12}(x,\lambda)}{dx} \ldots & \lambda^{-p}\frac{dy_{1n}(x,\lambda)}{dx} \\ \cdots & \cdots & \cdots \\ \lambda^{-(n-1)p}\frac{d^{n-1}y_{11}(x,\lambda)}{dx^{n-1}} & \lambda^{-(n-1)p}\frac{d^{n-1}y_{12}(x,\lambda)}{dx^{n-1}} \ldots & \lambda^{-(n-1)p}\frac{d^{n-1}y_{1n}(x,\lambda)}{dx^{n-1}} \end{vmatrix}$$

$$= \lambda^{-(1+2+\ldots+n-1)p} \times \begin{vmatrix} y_{11}(x,\lambda) & y_{12}(x,\lambda) \ldots & y_{1n}(x,\lambda) \\ \frac{dy_{11}(x,\lambda)}{dx} & \frac{dy_{12}(x,\lambda)}{dx} \ldots & \frac{dy_{1n}(x,\lambda)}{dx} \\ \cdots & \cdots & \cdots \\ \frac{d^{n-1}y_{11}(x,\lambda)}{dx^{n-1}} & \frac{d^{n-1}y_{12}(x,\lambda)}{dx^{n-1}} \ldots & \frac{d^{n-1}y_{1n}(x,\lambda)}{dx^{n-1}} \end{vmatrix} \neq 0$$

It follows from this relation that the Wronskian determinant of the solutions (2.3.5) of (2.3.1) are non-zero, i.e. that (2.3.5) is a fundamental system of particular solutions of (2.3.1).

Thus, the theorem on the asymptotic representation of a fundamental system of particular solutions of (2.3.1) can be obtained as a consequence of Theorem 5 by applying it to System (2.3.4). To do this, we note first of all that, in the notations of the preceding section for (2.3.4),

$$a(x,\lambda) = \lambda^{p}\begin{pmatrix} 0 & 1 & 0 & 0\ldots 0 & 0 \\ 0 & 0 & 1 & 0\ldots 0 & 0 \\ \cdots & \cdots & \cdots & \cdots & \cdots \\ 0 & 0 & 0 & 0\ldots 0 & 1 \\ -P_n(x,\lambda) & -P_{n-1}(x,\lambda) & -P_{n-2}(x,\lambda) & \ldots & -P_1(x,\lambda) \end{pmatrix}$$

$$a^{(p)}(x) = \begin{pmatrix} 0 & 1 & 0 & 0 & \ldots & 0 & 0 \\ 0 & 0 & 1 & 0 & \ldots & 0 & 0 \\ \cdots & \cdots & \cdots & \cdots & \cdots & \cdots & \cdots \\ -P_{n,0}(x) & -P_{n-1,0}(x) & \ldots & \ldots & \ldots & -P_{2,0}(x) & -P_{1,0}(x) \end{pmatrix}$$

(continued overleaf)

$$a^{(p-\nu)}(x) = \begin{pmatrix} 0 & 0 & 0 & \dots & 0 & 0 \\ \cdot & \cdot & \cdot & \cdot & \cdot & \cdot \\ 0 & 0 & 0 & \dots & 0 & 0 \\ -P_{n\nu}(x) & -P_{n-1,\nu}(x) & -P_{n-2,\nu}(x) & \dots & -P_{2\nu}(x) & -P_{1\nu}(x) \end{pmatrix}$$

where $\nu = 1, 2, \dots$. The characteristic equation for System (2.3.4) is of the form

$$\begin{vmatrix} -\theta & 1 & 0 & 0 & 0 & \dots & 0 & 0 & 0 \\ 0 & -\theta & 1 & 0 & 0 & \dots & 0 & 0 & 0 \\ 0 & 0 & -\theta & 1 & 0 & \dots & 0 & 0 & 0 \\ \cdot & \cdot & \cdot & \cdot & \cdot & \cdot & \cdot & \cdot & \cdot \\ 0 & 0 & & & \dots & & 0 & -\theta & 1 \\ -P_{n,0}(x) & -P_{n-1,0}(x) & & & \dots & & -P_{3,0}(x) & -P_{2,0}(x) & -P_{10}(x)-\theta \end{vmatrix} = 0 \qquad (2.3.8)$$

If we multiply the second column of this determinant by θ, the third by θ^2, the fourth by θ^3, ..., the next to the last by θ^{n-2}, and the last by θ^{n-1} and then add the results to the first column, the determinant becomes

$$\begin{vmatrix} 0 & 1 & 0 & \dots & 0 & 0 \\ 0 & -\theta & 1 & \dots & 0 & 0 \\ \cdot & \cdot & \cdot & & & \\ \cdot & \cdot & \cdot & & & \\ 0 & 0 & 0 & \dots & -\theta & 1 \\ -P_{n0}-P_{n-1,0}\theta-\dots-P_{1,0}\theta^{n-1}-\theta^n & -P_{n-1,0} & -P_{n-2,0} & \dots & -P_{2,0} & -P_{1,0}-\theta \end{vmatrix} = 0$$

Expanding this determinant in terms of elements of the first column, we obtain the equation

$$\theta^n + P_{1,0}(x)\theta^{n-1} + P_{2,0}(x)\theta^{n-2} + \dots + P_{n-1,0}(x)\theta + P_{n,0}(x) = 0 \qquad (2.3.9)$$

which is equivalent to the characteristic equation of (2.3.4). We shall call (2.3.9) the characteristic equation for (2.3.1). Clearly from the expressions for matrices $a^{(p)}(x)$ and $a^{(p-\nu)}(x)$ for System (2.3.4) that the question of differentiability of the elements of matrices (2.1.37) for (2.3.4) is equivalent to the question of differentiability of the functions

$$\begin{aligned} &\frac{d^{k+1}P_{i0}(x)}{dx^{k+1}}, \dots, \frac{d^{k+1}P_{i,r}(x)}{dx^{k+1}} \\ &\frac{d^kP_{i,r+1}(x)}{dx^k}, \dots, \frac{d^kP_{i\,p+r}(x)}{dx^k} \qquad (i = 1, \dots, n) \\ &\dots\dots\dots\dots\dots\dots \\ &P_{im}(x), \dots, P_{i,m+p-1}(x) \end{aligned}$$

Under the hypotheses of Theorem 5, System (2.3.4) has a fundamental system of particular solutions $y_{is}(x, \lambda)$ (where $i, s=1, \ldots, n$) that have an asymptotic representation of the form (2.2.5) in the region $\Omega_1 \subset \Omega$. Here, for (2.3.4), the functions $y_{is}(x, \lambda)$ can, according to (2.3.6), be represented in the form

$$y_{is}(x, \lambda) = \lambda^{-(i-1)p} \frac{d^{i-1} y_{1s}}{dx^{i-1}} \tag{2.3.10}$$

With the aid of the reasoning followed above, by applying Theorem 5 to (2.3.4), we obtain Theorem 6 for (2.3.1).

Suppose that we are given a differential equation (2.3.1) in which the coefficients have expansions of the form

$$P_i(x, \lambda) = \sum_{\nu=0}^{\infty} \lambda^{-\nu} P_{i\nu}(x) \quad (i=1, 2, \ldots, n)$$

in the region Ω of complex values of λ which satisfy the inequality

$$|\lambda| \geqslant R$$

where R is a sufficiently large positive constant. Suppose also that at least one of the functions $P_{i0}(x)$ does not vanish identically on the interval $[a, b]$.

Let m be an arbitrary natural number $\geqslant 1$, where

$$m = kp + r + 1 \quad (0 \leqslant r \leqslant p-1)$$

and the coefficients of the equation in question (2.3.1) possess the following properties

1. The functions $P_{i\nu}(x)$ (for $i=1, \ldots, n$; $\nu=0, 1, \ldots$) are continuous and uniformly bounded on the interval $[a, b]$.
2. The θ-roots $\varphi_k^{(p)}$ (for $k=1, \ldots, n$) of the characteristic equation

$$\theta^n + P_{10}(x)\,\theta^{n-1} + P_{20}(x)\theta^{n-2} + \ldots + P_{n-1,0}(x)\,\theta + P_{n0}(x) = 0$$

are distinct for all values of $x \in [a, b]$.

3. On the interval $[a, b]$, the functions

$$\begin{gathered} \frac{d^{k+1} P_{i0}(x)}{dx^{k+1}}, \ldots, \frac{d^{k+1} P_{ir}(x)}{dx^{k+1}} \\ \frac{d^k P_{i,r+1}(x)}{dx^k}, \ldots, \frac{d^k P_{i,r+p}(x)}{dx^k} \\ \cdots\cdots\cdots\cdots\cdots \\ P_{im}(x), \ldots, P_{i,m+p-1}(x) \quad (i=1, 2, \ldots, n) \end{gathered} \tag{2.3.11}$$

have continuous derivatives of the first q orders, where $q \geqslant 1$ is a natural number.

4. There exists an unbounded portion Ω_1 of the region Ω in which the inequalities

$$\operatorname{Re}\omega_1(x, \lambda) \leqslant \operatorname{Re}\omega_2(x, \lambda) \leqslant \ldots \leqslant \operatorname{Re}\omega_n(x, \lambda) \qquad (2.3.12)$$

hold for all $x \in [a, b]$ with suitable numbering of the $\omega_s(x, \lambda)$.

Theorem 6 Under Conditions 1-4, there exist n formal series of the form

$$\exp\left(\int_a^x \omega_s(\xi, \lambda)\, d\xi\right) \sum_{\nu=0}^{\infty} \lambda^{-\nu} y_{1s}^{(\nu)}(x)$$

which formally satisfy (2.3.1). The coefficients

$$y_{1s}^{(\nu)}(x) \qquad (s = 1, 2, \ldots, n; \quad \nu = 0, 1, \ldots)$$

and the functions

$$\omega_s(x, \lambda) = \lambda^p \varphi_s^{(p)}(x) + \ldots + \lambda \varphi_s^{(1)}(x) \qquad (s = 1, \ldots, n)$$

are obtained by substituting these series for y in (2.3.1) if we divide through by

$$\exp\left(\int_a^x \omega_s(\xi, \lambda)\, d\xi\right)$$

and set the coefficients of the different powers of λ individually equal to zero.

These series, which in general diverge, can be used for an asymptotic representation of some fundamental system of particular solutions of the differential equation (2.3.1). This system of particular solutions and their derivatives of the first $n-1$ orders have asymptotic representations of the following form for $\lambda \in \Omega_1$.

$$\frac{d^{k-1} y_{1s}(x, \lambda)}{dx^{k-1}}$$

$$= \lambda^{(k-1)p} \exp\left(\int_a^x \omega_s(\xi, \lambda)\, d\xi\right) \left\{\sum_{\nu=0}^{m-1} \lambda^{-\nu} y_{1s}^{(\nu)}(x) + \frac{E_{ks}(x, \lambda)}{\lambda^m}\right\} \qquad (2.3.13)$$

$$(s = 1, \ldots, n; \quad k = 1, \ldots, n)$$

Here, $E_{ks}(x, \lambda)$ are continuous functions with respect to x on the interval $[a, b]$ which are bounded for $\lambda \in \Omega_1$ and the $y_{ks}^{(\nu)}(x)$ have continuous derivatives of the first $q-1$ orders on $[a, b]$. The coefficients $y_{ks}^{(\nu)}(x)$ can be obtained by differentiating the expressions

$$\exp\left(\int_a^x \omega_s(\xi, \lambda)\, d\xi\right) \sum_{\nu=0}^{m-1} \lambda^{-\nu} y_{1s}^{(\nu)}(x)$$

and expanding the result in decreasing powers of λ.

It should be pointed out that the last assertion of Theorem 6 does not follow from Theorem 5. It is proved by means of the corollary to (2.3.10) from the first $(n-1)$ equations of System (2.3.4). Specifically, to prove this assertion, we need only substitute into (2.3.10) the asymptotic representations of the functions $y_{is}(x, \lambda)$ and $y_{1s}(x, \lambda)$ from (2.2.5), carry out the differentiation and equate coefficients of like powers of λ.

CHAPTER 3

Expansion of vector-valued functions

3.1 BOUNDARY-VALUE PROBLEMS FOR A SYSTEM OF FIRST-ORDER EQUATIONS WITH PIECEWISE-SMOOTH COEFFICIENTS

From now on, we shall refer to the boundary-value problems which depend on a complex parameter as spectral problems.

The most important result of this section will be the derivation of the expansion formula (see Theorem 8) associated with a spectral problem for a system of first-order linear differential equations. Here, this problem is solved for a case different from those already studied in the literature. The novelty of the result consists in the following.

1. Here, the expansion problem is solved for equations with discontinuous coefficients under boundary conditions connecting the values of the unknown vector-valued function not only with the end-points of a basic interval but also at other points of that interval - at points of discontinuity of the coefficients of the equations of the system in question.
2. The coefficients of the equations contain, in general, both positive and negative integral powers of the complex parameter, i.e. not only the point at infinity but also the origin of the complex plane is a pole for the coefficients.

In particular, if the coefficients of the equations do not contain negative powers of the complex parameter, the expansion formula of the first section yields a formula for expanding an arbitrary vector-valued function in a series of eigenfunctions and associated functions of the given spectral problem, i.e. in a series of residues of the solution of that problem. Consider the problem of finding the solutions of the system of equations

$$\frac{dy_k^{(i)}}{dx} - \sum_{j=1}^{r} a_{kj}^{(i)}(x, \lambda)\, y_j^{(i)} = f_k^{(i)}(x) \quad \text{for } x \in (a_i, b_i) \tag{3.1.1}$$
$$(i = 1, 2, \ldots, n; \quad k = 1, 2, \ldots, r)$$

with the boundary conditions

$$\sum_{i=1}^{n} M_k^{(i)}(y) \equiv \sum_{i=1}^{n} \sum_{j=1}^{r} \{\alpha_{kj}^{(i)}(\lambda)\, y_j^{(i)}(a_i, \lambda) + \beta_{kj}^{(i)}(\lambda)\, y_j^{(i)}(b_i, \lambda)\} = 0 \tag{3.1.2}$$
$$(k = 1, 2, \ldots, nr)$$

where

$$a_{kj}^{(i)}(x, \lambda) = \lambda a_{kj}^{(i)}(x) + \sum_{\nu=0}^{Q} \lambda^{-\nu} a_{kj\nu}^{(i)}(x) \tag{3.1.3}$$

$$M_k^{(i)} y = \sum_{j=1}^{r} \{\alpha_{kj}^{(i)}(\lambda)\, y_j^{(i)}(a_i, \lambda) + \beta_{kj}^{(i)}(\lambda)\, y_j^{(i)}(b_i, \lambda)\} \tag{3.1.4}$$

Here, Q is a natural number, $\alpha_{kj}^{(i)}(\lambda)$ and $\beta_{kj}^{(i)}(\lambda)$ are polynomials in λ and the intervals (a_i, b_i) are non-intersecting open intervals contained in a finite interval of the form $[a_1, b_n]$.

Let us impose the following restrictions on the coefficients of (3.1.1) and the boundary conditions (3.1.2).

1. On the interval $[a_i, b_i]$, $a_{kj\nu}^{(i)}(x)$ are continuous, $a_{kj0}^{(i)}(x)$ have continuous first derivatives, and $a_{kj}^{(i)}(x)$ have continuous first and second derivatives.
2. For $x \in [a_i, b_i]$, the roots $\theta_1^{(i)}(x), \ldots, \theta_r^{(i)}(x)$ of the characteristic equations

$$\begin{vmatrix} a_{11}^{(i)}(x) - \theta & a_{12}^{(i)}(x) & \ldots & a_{1r}^{(i)}(x) \\ a_{21}^{(i)}(x) & a_{22}^{(i)}(x) - \theta & \ldots & a_{2r}^{(i)}(x) \\ \cdots & \cdots & \cdots & \cdots \\ a_{r1}^{(i)}(x) & a_{r2}^{(i)}(x) & \ldots & a_{rr}^{(i)}(x) - \theta \end{vmatrix} = 0 \tag{3.1.5}$$

are distinct and non-zero and their arguments and the arguments of their differences are independent of x.

3. For $\lambda \in \Omega(R)$, the rank of the matrix

$$A(\lambda)=\begin{pmatrix} \alpha_{11}^{(1)}\cdots\alpha_{1r}^{(1)} & \cdots & \alpha_{11}^{(n)} & \cdots & \alpha_{1r}^{(n)} & \beta_{11}^{(1)}\cdots\beta_{1r}^{(1)} & \cdots & \beta_{11}^{(n)} & \cdots & \beta_{1r}^{(n)} \\ \cdot & \cdot & \cdot & \cdot & \cdot & \cdot & \cdot & \cdot & \cdot & \cdot \\ \alpha_{nr,1}^{(1)}\cdots\alpha_{nr,r}^{(1)} & \cdots & \alpha_{nr,1}^{(n)} & \cdots & \alpha_{nr,r}^{(n)} & \beta_{nr,1}^{(1)}\cdots\beta_{nr,r}^{(1)} & \cdots & \beta_{nr,1}^{(n)} & \cdots & \beta_{nr,r}^{(n)} \end{pmatrix}$$

is equal to nr. (As before, $\Omega(R)$ denotes the region $|\lambda| \geqslant R$.)

Let us obtain a convenient representation of the solution $y^{(i)}(x, \lambda, f)$ for $x \in (a_i, b_i)$ of Problem (3.1.1)-(3.1.2) but without yet worrying about its existence. Consider the homogeneous system

$$\frac{dy_k^{(i)}}{dx} - \sum_{j=1}^{n} a_{kj}^{(i)}(x, \lambda)\, y_j^{(i)} = 0, \quad x \in (a_i, b_i) \tag{3.1.1a}$$

corresponding to System (3.1.1). For the coefficients of this system, the infinite point of the λ-plane is a first-order pole, i.e. $p=1$ (in the notations of the preceding chapter). If we take $m=1$ (again using the notations of the preceding chapter) it is clear that Conditions 1 and 3 of Theorem 5 reduce, for $q=1$, to Condition 1 of this section since

$$m = 1 = kp + r + 1 = 1\cdot 0 + 0 + 1, \quad \text{i.e.} \quad r = 0, \quad k = 0.$$

Then, in the case in question, the table of matrices shown in Condition 3 of Theorem 5 consists of

$$\frac{da^{(i)}(x)}{dx}, \quad a_0^{(i)}(x) \tag{3.1.6}$$

where $a^{(i)}(x)$ and $a_0^{(i)}(x)$ denote, respectively, matrices made up of the functions $a_{kj}^{(i)}(x)$ and $a_{kj0}^{(i)}(x)$.

Thus, in the present case, the requirements are continuous differentiability of the elements of the matrices (3.1.6) and continuity of the remaining functions $a_{kj\nu}^{(i)}(x)$ on the interval $[a_i, b_i]$. This leads us to Condition 1 of this section.

Condition 2 is stronger than the corresponding Condition 2 of Theorem 5. With regard to Condition 4 of Theorem 5, its satisfaction is ensured by Conditions 1 and 2 of this section. To see this, note that, since $p=1$ in the present case, we have

$$\omega_s^{(i)}(x, \lambda) = \lambda \theta_s^{(i)}(x), \quad x \in [a_i, b_i]$$

Consider the set of values of λ which satisfy the equation

$$\operatorname{Re} \lambda \theta_k^{(i)}(x) = \operatorname{Re} \lambda \theta_s^{(i)}(x), \quad k \neq s \tag{3.1.7}$$

Obviously,

$$\begin{aligned}
&\operatorname{Re} \lambda \theta_k^{(i)}(x) - \operatorname{Re} \lambda \theta_s^{(i)}(x) \\
&\quad = \operatorname{Re} \lambda \, (\theta_k^{(i)}(x) - \theta_s^{(i)}(x)) = \operatorname{Re} |\lambda| \, |\theta_k^{(i)}(x) \\
&\qquad - \theta_s^{(i)}(x)| \exp\left(\sqrt{-1}\,(\arg\lambda + \arg(\theta_k^{(i)} - \theta_s^{(i)}))\right)
\end{aligned}$$

Thus, (3.1.7) reduces to

$$|\lambda| \, |\theta_k^{(i)}(x) - \theta_s^{(i)}(x)| \cos\{\arg\lambda + \psi_{k,s}\} = 0 \tag{3.1.8}$$

where

$$\psi_{k,s} = \arg(\theta_k^{(i)} - \theta_s^{(i)})$$

On the basis of Condition 2, we have $|\theta_k^{(i)}(x) - \theta_s^{(i)}(x)| \neq 0$ for $x \in [a_i, b_i]$ when $k \neq s$; also ψ_{ks} is independent of x and hence of the index . Therefore, for $\lambda \neq 0$, (3.1.8) is satisfied if and only if

$$\arg\lambda + \psi_{ks} = \pm\frac{\pi}{2}$$

i.e. if and only if

$$\arg\lambda = \pm\frac{\pi}{2} - \psi_{ks} \tag{3.1.9}$$

Thus, the set of values of λ which satisfy (3.1.7) form a straight line which is divided into two rays by the coordinate

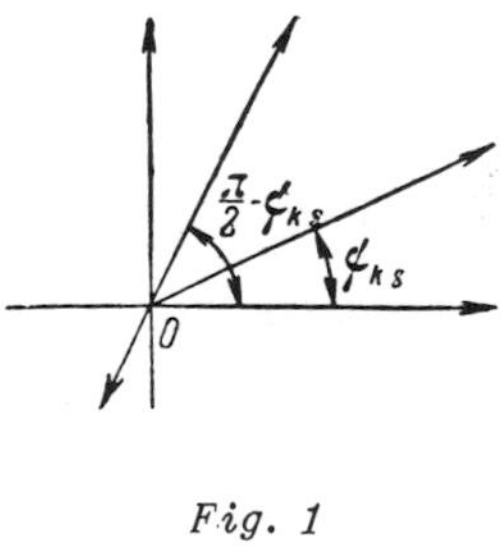

Fig. 1

origin of the λ-plane (see Fig. 1). The arguments of these rays are given by (3.1.9). If we let k and s vary from 1 to r, we obtain a finite number of such rays on which the difference

$$\operatorname{Re}\lambda\theta_k^{(i)}(x)-\operatorname{Re}\lambda\theta_s^{(i)}(x) \tag{3.1.10}$$

can vanish. At the remaining points of the λ-plane, we have

$$\operatorname{Re}\lambda\theta_k^{(i)}(x)-\operatorname{Re}\lambda\theta_s^{(i)}(x)\neq 0, \quad x\in[a_i,\ b_i]$$

because, according to Condition 2, the sign of difference (3.1.10) is independent of x and, therefore, for $x\in[a_i,\ b_i]$, (3.1.7) determines the same straight line for fixed k and s.

Thus, the λ-plane is divided into a finite number of sectors (Σ_j) by rays on each of which the difference (3.1.10) can vanish for certain k and s (where $k\neq s$) and is of a single sign since (3.1.10) can vanish only on boundaries of the sectors (Σ_j).

Let us consider one of the sectors (Σ_j) with fixed index j. Let λ denote an interior point of this sector. Obviously, each of the quantities

$$\operatorname{Re}\lambda\theta_1^{(i)},\quad \operatorname{Re}\lambda\theta_2^{(i)},\ \ldots,\ \operatorname{Re}\lambda\theta_r^{(i)} \tag{3.1.11}$$

has a definite sign except possibly for one of them which may vanish. This is true because, if any pair of these quantities vanished, we would have for this pair

$$\operatorname{Re}\lambda\theta_k^{(i)}=\operatorname{Re}\lambda\theta_s^{(i)}$$

However, this equation can hold only at boundary points of the sectors (Σ_j), which contradicts the fact that λ is an interior point of the sectors (Σ_j).

We arrange (3.1.11) in increasing order

$$\operatorname{Re}\lambda\theta_{k_1}^{(i)}\leqslant\operatorname{Re}\lambda\theta_{k_2}^{(i)}\leqslant\ldots\leqslant\operatorname{Re}\lambda\theta_{k_r}^{(i)} \tag{3.1.12}$$

(According to Condition 2, if these inequalities are satisfied for any $x\in[a_i,\ b_i]$, they are satisfied for all $x\in[a_i,\ b_i]$.) As required by Condition 2, the arguments of the differences $\theta_k^{(i)}-\theta_s^{(i)}$ are independent of x. Consequently, if, for some $x \in [a_i, b_i]$ we have

$$\operatorname{Re} \lambda\theta_k^{(i)} - \operatorname{Re} \lambda\theta_s^{(i)}$$

$$= |\lambda| \, |\theta_k^{(i)}(x) - \theta_s^{(i)}(x)| \cos\{\arg\lambda + \arg(\theta_k^{(i)}(x) - \theta_s^{(i)}(x))\}$$

$$= |\lambda| \, |\theta_k^{(i)}(x) - \theta_s^{(i)}(x)| \{\operatorname{cosarg}\lambda \operatorname{cosarg}(\theta_k^{(i)} - \theta_s^{(i)})$$

$$- \operatorname{sinarg}\lambda \operatorname{sinarg}(\theta_k^{(i)} - \theta_s^{(i)})\} < 0$$

then, this inequality holds for all $x \in [a_i, b_i]$.

Let us denote by $\varphi_1^{(i)}(x), \varphi_2^{(i)}(x), \ldots, \varphi_r^{(i)}(x)$ the roots $\theta_{k_1}^{(i)}(x)$, $\theta_{k_2}^{(i)}(x), \ldots, \theta_{k_r}^{(i)}(x)$ of the characteristic equation (3.1.5) respectively. Then (3.1.12) shows that, in the sector (Σ_j), the inequalities

$$\operatorname{Re} \lambda\varphi_1^{(i)}(x) \leqslant \operatorname{Re} \lambda\varphi_2^{(i)}(x) \leqslant \ldots \leqslant \operatorname{Re} \lambda\varphi_r^{(i)}(x) \qquad (3.1.13)$$

hold for all $x \in [a_i, b_i]$ when the roots of the characteristic equation (3.1.5) are suitably numbered. Also, for each of the sectors (Σ_j), there exists a numbering of the roots $\varphi_k^{(i)}(x)$ such that the inequalities (3.1.13) are satisfied.

Thus, when Conditions 1 and 2 are satisfied for System (3.1.1), all the conditions of Theorem 5 are satisfied. Consequently, corresponding to System (3.1.1a) there exists a fundamental system of particular solutions $y_{ks}^{(i)}(x, \lambda)$ with asymptotic representations of the form

$$y_{ks}^{(i)}(x, \lambda) = e^{\lambda \int_{a_i}^{x} \varphi_s^{(i)}(\xi)\, d\xi} \left\{ y_{ks0}^{(i)}(x) + \frac{E_{ks}^{(i)}(x, \lambda)}{\lambda} \right\} \qquad (3.1.14)$$

in the sector (Σ_j) for $|\lambda| \geqslant R$, where $y_{ks0}^{(i)}(x)$ is a continuously differentiable function on the interval $[a_i, b_i]$ and $E_{ks}^{(i)}(x, \lambda)$ is continuous with respect to x on this interval and is bounded in the sector (Σ_j) for $|\lambda| \geqslant R$.

If we replace Condition 1 with the stronger condition, then we can obtain a more precise asymptotic representation for $y_{ks}^{(i)}(x, \lambda)$. Specifically, let us assume that the following stronger condition is satisfied.

1a. On the interval $[a_i, b_i]$, the functions

$$\frac{d^2 a_{kj}^{(i)}(x)}{dx^2}, \quad \frac{d a_{kj0}^{(i)}(x)}{dx}, \quad a_{k,\,j-1}^{(i)}(x)$$

are once continuously differentiable. Then, when Condition 2 is satisfied, (3.1.1a) has a fundamental system of particular solutions $y_{hs}^{(i)}(x, \lambda)$ which has the asymptotic representation

$$y_{hs}^{(i)}(x, \lambda) = e^{\lambda \int_{a_i}^{x} \varphi_s^{(i)}(\xi)\, d\xi} \left\{ y_{hs0}^{(i)}(x) + \frac{y_{hs1}^{(i)}(x)}{\lambda} + \frac{E_{hs}^{(i)}(x, \lambda)}{\lambda^2} \right\} \quad (3.1.15)$$

in the sector (Σ_j) (for $|\lambda| \geqslant R$), where the function $y_{hs0}^{(i)}(x)$ is twice and the function $y_{hs1}^{(i)}(x)$ is once continuously differentiable on the interval $[a_i, b_i]$, and the function $E_{hs}^{(i)}(x, \lambda)$ is continuous with respect to x on that interval and bounded in the sector (Σ_j) for $|\lambda| \geqslant R$.

It should be pointed out that the existence of a fundamental system of particular solutions of System (3.1.1a) easily follows on the basis of continuity of the coefficients $a_{kj}^{(i)}(x, \lambda)$ on $[a_i, b_i]$ from an existence theorem taught in any university course on ordinary differential equations.

The general solution of System (3.1.1a) as considered on the interval $[a_i, b_i]$ is of the form

$$y_k^{(i)}(x, \lambda) = \sum_{s=1}^{r} c_s^{(i)} y_{ks}^{(i)}(x, \lambda) \quad (3.1.16)$$

where the $c_s^{(i)}$ are arbitrary constants.

To construct the general solution (3.1.1), we use the method of variation of parameters, i.e. we shall find the general solution of the non-homogeneous system (3.1.1) in the form (3.1.16), treating the $c_j^{(i)}$ as functions depending on x.

Then, we obtain from (3.1.16)

$$\frac{dy_k^{(i)}(x, \lambda)}{dx} = \sum_{s=1}^{r} \left(\frac{dc_s^{(i)}}{dx} y_{ks}^{(i)}(x, \lambda) + c_s^{(i)} \frac{dy_{ks}^{(i)}(x, \lambda)}{dx} \right)$$

Substituting the last two expressions into System (3.1.1)

and requiring that (3.1.16) be a solution of this non-homogeneous system, we have

$$\sum_{s=1}^{r} y_{ks}^{(i)}(x, \lambda) \frac{dc_s^{(i)}(x)}{dx} + \sum_{s=1}^{r} c_s^{(i)}(x) \left\{ \frac{dy_{ks}^{(i)}(x, \lambda)}{dx} - \sum_{j=1}^{r} a_{kj}^{(i)}(x, \lambda)\, y_{js}^{(i)}(x, \lambda) \right\} = f_k^{(i)}(x)$$

Bearing in mind the identity

$$\frac{dy_{ks}^{(i)}(x, \lambda)}{dx} - \sum_{j=1}^{r} a_{kj}^{(i)}(x, \lambda)\, y_{js}^{(i)}(x, \lambda) \equiv 0$$

we obtain the following system of algebraic equations for determining the functions $\frac{dc_s^{(i)}(x)}{dx}$

$$\sum y_{ks}^{(i)}(x, \lambda) \frac{dc_s^{(i)}(x, \lambda)}{dx} = f_k^{(i)}(x) \qquad (k = 1, \ldots, r)$$

Solving this system for $\frac{dc_s^{(i)}(x)}{dx}$, we get

$$\frac{dc_s^{(i)}(x)}{dx} = \frac{1}{W^{(i)}(x, \lambda)} \times \begin{vmatrix} y_{11}^{(i)}(x, \lambda) \ldots y_{1s-1}^{(i)}(x, \lambda) & f_1^{(i)}(x) & y_{1s+1}^{(i)}(x, \lambda) \ldots y_{1r}^{(i)}(x, \lambda) \\ \ldots\ldots\ldots & \ldots & \ldots\ldots\ldots \\ y_{r1}^{(i)}(x, \lambda) \ldots y_{rs-1}^{(i)}(x, \lambda) & f_r^{(i)}(x) & y_{rs+1}^{(i)}(x, \lambda) \ldots y_{rr}^{(i)}(x, \lambda) \end{vmatrix}$$

where $W^{(i)}(x, \lambda)$ is the Wronskian determinant of the solutions $y_{ks}^{(i)}(x, \lambda)$:

$$W^{(i)}(x, \lambda) = \begin{vmatrix} y_{11}^{(i)}(x, \lambda) & y_{12}^{(i)}(x, \lambda) & \ldots & y_{1r}^{(i)}(x, \lambda) \\ \ldots & \ldots & \ldots & \ldots \\ y_{r1}^{(i)}(x, \lambda) & y_{r2}^{(i)}(x, \lambda) & \ldots & y_{rr}^{(i)}(x, \lambda) \end{vmatrix}$$

If we expand the determinant in the numerator of the expression for $\frac{dc_s^{(i)}(x)}{dx}$ in terms of elements of the sth column, we obtain

$$\frac{dc_s^{(i)}(x)}{dx} = \sum_{j=1}^{r} \frac{W_{js}^{(i)}(x, \lambda)}{W^{(i)}(x, \lambda)} f_j^{(i)}(x)$$

Integrating this identity from a_i to $x \in (a_i, b_i)$, we have

$$c_s^{(i)}(x) = c_s^{(i)}(a_i) + \int_{a_i}^{x} \sum_{j=1}^{r} \frac{W_{js}^{(i)}(\xi, \lambda)}{W^{(i)}(\xi, \lambda)} f_j^{(i)}(\xi)\, d\xi$$

where $W_{js}^{(i)}(\xi, \lambda)$ is the cofactor of the element $y_{js}^{(i)}(\xi)$ in the determinant $W^{(i)}(\xi, \lambda)$.

Substituting the expression $c_s^{(i)}(x)$ into (3.1.16), we obtain the following representation for the general solution of the non-homogeneous system (3.1.1)

$$y_k^{(i)}(x, \lambda) = \sum_{j=1}^{r} c_j^{(i)}(a_i)\, y_{kj}^{(i)}(x, \lambda) + \int_{a_i}^{x} \sum_{j=1}^{r} \sum_{s=1}^{r} \frac{W_{js}^{(i)}(\xi, \lambda)}{W^{(i)}(\xi, \lambda)} y_{ks}^{(i)}(x, \lambda) f_j^{(i)}(\xi)\, d\xi \tag{3.1.17}$$

Similarly, if we take $x = b_i$ for the lower limit of integration, we have

$$y_k^{(i)}(x, \lambda) = \sum_{j=1}^{r} c_j^{(i)}(b_i)\, y_{kj}^{(i)}(x, \lambda) + \int_{b_i}^{x} \sum_{j=1}^{r} \sum_{s=1}^{r} \frac{W_{js}^{(i)}(\xi, \lambda)}{W^{(i)}(\xi, \lambda)} y_{ks}^{(i)}(x, \lambda) f_j^{(i)}(\xi)\, d\xi \tag{3.1.18}$$

Adding (3.1.17) and (3.1.18) and dividing the result by 2, we obtain a suitable representation of the general solution of System (3.1.1) for $x \in (a_i, b_i)$.

$$y_k^{(i)}(x, \lambda) = \sum_{j=1}^{r} \left\{ c_j^{(i)} y_{kj}^{(i)}(x, \lambda) + \int_{a_i}^{b_i} g_{kj}^{(i)}(x, \xi, \lambda) f_j^{(i)}(\xi)\, d\xi \right\} \tag{3.1.19}$$

where $c_j^{(i)}$ are arbitrary constants (obviously, $2c_j^{(i)}=c_j^{(i)}(a_i)+c_j^{(i)}(b_i)$). For the functions $g_{kj}^{(i)}(x, \xi, \lambda)$,

$$g_{kj}^{(i)}(x, \xi, \lambda)=\begin{cases} +\frac{1}{2}\sum_{s=1}^{r} y_{ks}^{(i)}(x, \lambda)\, z_{js}^{(i)}(\xi, \lambda) & \text{for } a_i \leqslant \xi \leqslant x \leqslant b_i \\ -\frac{1}{2}\sum_{s=1}^{r} y_{ks}^{(i)}(x, \lambda)\, z_{js}^{(i)}(\xi, \lambda) & \text{for } a_i \leqslant x \leqslant \xi \leqslant b_i \end{cases} \tag{3.1.20}$$

$$z_{js}^{(i)}(\xi, \lambda)=\frac{W_{js}^{(i)}(\xi, \lambda)}{W^{(i)}(\xi, \lambda)} \tag{3.1.21}$$

Now, to find the solution $y^{(i)}(x, \lambda, f)$ of Problem (3.1.1)-(3.1.2), it would be sufficient to substitute the general solution (3.1.19) into the boundary conditions (3.1.2) and the determinant $c_j^{(i)}$ of the equations obtained. Hence we have the following system of equations

$$\sum_{i=1}^{n}\sum_{j=1}^{r} u_{kj}^{(i)}(\lambda)\, c_j^{(i)} = -\sum_{i=1}^{n}\sum_{j=1}^{r}\int_{a_i}^{b_i} g_{kj}^{(i)}(\xi, \lambda)\, f_j^{(i)}(\xi)\, d\xi \qquad (k=1, 2, \ldots, nr) \tag{3.1.22}$$

where

$$u_{kj}^{(i)}(\lambda)=\sum_{l=0}^{r}\{\alpha_{kl}^{(i)}(\lambda)\, y_{lj}^{(i)}(a_i, \lambda)+\beta_{kl}^{(i)}(\lambda)\, y_{lj}^{(i)}(b_i, \lambda)\} \tag{3.1.23}$$

$$g_{kj}^{(i)}(\xi, \lambda)=\sum_{l=1}^{r}\{\alpha_{kl}^{(i)}(\lambda)\, g_{lj}^{(i)}(a_i, \xi, \lambda) + \beta_{kl}^{(i)}(\lambda)\, g_{lj}^{(i)}(b_i, \xi, \lambda)\} \tag{3.1.24}$$

Obviously, System (3.1.22) has a unique solution for all λ for which the determinant of that system is non-zero.

If we solve (3.1.22) for $c_j^{(i)}$, we obtain

$$c_j^{(i)}=\frac{1}{\Delta(\lambda)}\left|U^{(1)} \ldots U^{(i-1)} U_j^{(i)} U^{(i+1)} \ldots U^{(n)}\right|$$

where

$$U^{(k)} = \begin{pmatrix} u_{11}^{(k)} & \dots & u_{1r}^{(k)} \\ \dots & \dots & \dots \\ u_{nr,1}^{(k)} & \dots & u_{nr,r}^{(k)} \end{pmatrix}$$

$$U_j^{(i)} = \begin{pmatrix} u_{11}^{(i)} & \dots & u_{1,j-1}^{(i)} & A_1 & u_{1,j+1}^{(i)} & \dots & u_{1r}^{(i)} \\ \dots & \dots & \dots & \dots & \dots & \dots & \dots \\ u_{nr,1}^{(i)} & \dots & u_{nr,j-1}^{(i)} & A_{nr} & u_{nr,j+1}^{(i)} & \dots & u_{nr,r}^{(i)} \end{pmatrix}$$

where, in turn,

$$A_k = -\sum_{p=1}^{n} \sum_{q=1}^{r} \int_{a_p}^{b_p} g_{kq}^{(p)}(\xi, \lambda) f_q^{(p)}(\xi)\, d\xi$$

and

$$\Delta(\lambda) = \begin{vmatrix} u_{11}^{(1)}(\lambda) & \dots & u_{1r}^{(1)}(\lambda) & \dots & u_{11}^{(n)}(\lambda) & \dots & u_{1r}^{(n)}(\lambda) \\ \dots & \dots & \dots & \dots & \dots & \dots & \dots \\ u_{nr,1}^{(1)}(\lambda) & \dots & u_{nr,r}^{(1)}(\lambda) & \dots & u_{nr,1}^{(n)}(\lambda) & \dots & u_{nr,r}^{(n)}(\lambda) \end{vmatrix} \tag{3.1.25}$$

If we take the double-summation and integral signs from the column of the determinant in the expression for $c_j^{(i)}$, outside the determinant bars, and place this column in the first column position of the determinant we obtain

$$c_j^{(i)} = -\sum_{p=1}^{n} \sum_{q=1}^{r} \int_{a_p}^{b_p} \frac{(-1)^{(i-1)r+j-1}}{\Delta(\lambda)}$$

$$\times \left| U_{pq}^{(1)}\; U^{(2)} \dots U_{j1}^{(i)} \dots U^{(n)} \right| f_q^{(p)}(\xi)\, d\xi$$

where

$$U_{pq}^{(1)} = \begin{pmatrix} g_{1q}^{(p)}(\xi, \lambda) & u_{11}^{(1)} & \dots & u_{1r}^{(1)} \\ \dots & \dots & \dots & \dots \\ g_{nr,q}^{(p)}(\xi, \lambda) & u_{nr,1}^{(1)} & \dots & u_{nr,r}^{(1)} \end{pmatrix}$$

$$U_{j1}^{(i)} = \begin{pmatrix} u_{11}^{(i)} & \dots & u_{1,j-1}^{(i)} & u_{1,j+1}^{(i)} & \dots & u_{1r}^{(i)} \\ \dots & \dots & \dots & \dots & \dots & \dots \\ u_{nr,1}^{(i)} & \dots & u_{nr,j-1}^{(i)} & u_{nr,j+1}^{(i)} & \dots & u_{nr,r}^{(i)} \end{pmatrix}$$

Substituting the expression for $c_j^{(i)}$ into the general solution

(3.1.19) and writing the sum obtained in the form of a determinant, we find a solution $y^{(i)}(x, \lambda, f)$ of Problem (3.1.1)-(3.1.2) for $x \in (a_i, b_i)$ in the form*

$$y_k^{(i)}(x, \lambda, f) = \sum_{p=1}^{n} \sum_{q=1}^{r} \int_{a_p}^{b_p} G_{kq}^{(i,p)}(x, \xi, \lambda) f_q^{(p)}(\xi)\, d\xi \tag{3.1.26}$$

where

$$G_{kq}^{(i,p)}(x, \xi, \lambda) = \frac{\Delta_{kq}^{(i,p)}(x, \xi, \lambda)}{\Delta(\lambda)} \tag{3.1.27}$$

where, in turn,

$$\Delta_{kq}^{(i,p)}(x, \xi, \lambda) = \begin{vmatrix} g_{kq}^{(i,p)}(x,\xi,\lambda) & \overbrace{0 \ \dots \ 0}^{(i-1)r} & \dots & y_{k1}^{(i)}(x,\lambda) & \dots & y_{kr}^{(i)}(x,\lambda) & \dots & 0 & \dots & 0 \\ g_{1q}^{(p)}(\xi,\lambda) & u_{11}^{(1)} \ \dots \ u_{1r}^{(1)} & \dots & u_{11}^{(i)} & \dots & u_{1r}^{(i)} & \dots & u_{11}^{(n)} & \dots & u_{1r}^{(n)} \\ \dots & \dots & \dots & \dots & \dots & \dots & \dots & \dots & \dots & \dots \\ g_{nr,q}^{(p)}(\xi,\lambda) & u_{nr,1}^{(1)} \ \dots \ u_{nr,r}^{(1)} & \dots & u_{nr,1}^{(i)} & \dots & u_{nr,r}^{(i)} & \dots & u_{nr,1}^{(n)} & \dots & u_{nr,r}^{(n)} \end{vmatrix} \tag{3.1.28}$$

for $x \in (a_i, b_i)$ and $\xi \in (a_p, b_p)$, where

$$g_{kq}^{(i,p)}(x, \xi, \lambda) = \begin{cases} g_{kq}^{(i)}(x, \xi, \lambda) & \text{for} \quad p = i \\ 0 & \text{for} \quad p \neq i \end{cases} \tag{3.1.29}$$

To derive the basic expansion formula with the aid of the asymptotic formulae (3.1.14), we must find a suitable asymptotic representation for the Green's function $G_{kq}^{(i,p)}(x, \xi, \lambda)$. Let us first consider an asymptotic representation of the denominator $\Delta(\lambda)$ of the function $G_{kq}^{(i,p)}(x, \xi, \lambda)$. Substituting the asymptotic representation (3.1.14) of the functions $y_{ks}^{(i)}(x, \lambda)$ into (3.1.23), we obtain

$$u_{kj}^{(i)}(\lambda) = \sum_{l=1}^{r} \left\{ \alpha_{kl}^{(i)}(\lambda) \left(y_{lj0}^{(i)}(a_i) + \frac{E_{lj}^{(i)}(a_i, \lambda)}{\lambda} \right) \right.$$
$$\left. + \beta_{kl}^{(i)}(\lambda) \exp(\lambda \omega_j^{(i)}) \left(y_{lj0}^{(i)}(b_i) + \frac{E_{lj}^{(i)}(b_i, \lambda)}{\lambda} \right) \right\}$$

* Green's function for systems of linear equations of higher orders can be constructed by reducing the present boundary-value problem to a problem for a first-order system by making a change of derivatives.

where

$$\omega_j^{(i)} = \int_{a_i}^{b_i} \varphi_j^{(i)}(\xi)\, d\xi \tag{3.1.30}$$

Following Birkhoff (see [3a]), we shall denote a sum of the form $\Phi(x) + \frac{E(x, \lambda)}{\lambda}$, where $E(x, \lambda)$ is a bounded function for $|\lambda| \geqslant R$ (where R is a sufficiently large positive number), as follows

$$\Phi(x) + \frac{E(x, \lambda)}{\lambda} = [\Phi(x)]$$

Using Birkhoff's notation, we may write the asymptotic representation of $u_{kl}^{(i)}$ as

$$\begin{aligned} u_{kl}^{(i)} &= \sum_{j=1}^{r} \{\alpha_{kj}^{(i)}(\lambda)\,[y_{jl0}^{(i)}(a_i)] + \beta_{kj}^{(i)}(\lambda)\,[y_{jl0}^{(i)}(b_i)]\, e^{\lambda\omega_l^{(i)}}\} \\ &= \lambda^{\rho_k^{(i)}} \{[A_{kl0}^{(i)}] + [B_{kl0}^{(i)}]\, e^{\lambda\omega_l^{(i)}}\} \end{aligned} \tag{3.1.31}$$

where $A_{kl0}^{(i)}$ and $B_{kl0}^{(i)}$ are positive numbers and $\varrho_k^{(i)}$ is the highest power of λ in the polynomials

$$\alpha_{k1}^{(i)}(\lambda), \ldots, \alpha_{kr}^{(i)}(\lambda), \quad \beta_{k1}^{(i)}(\lambda), \ldots, \beta_{kr}^{(i)}(\lambda) \quad (i = 1, 2, \ldots, n)$$

Substituting (3.1.31) into (3.1.25), we obtain an asymptotic representation of $\Delta(\lambda)$ in the sector (Σ_j) of the form

$$\Delta(\lambda) = \lambda^{\rho}\Delta_0(\lambda) \tag{3.1.32}$$

where

$$\Delta_0(\lambda) = \begin{vmatrix} [A_{11}^{(1)}] + [B_{11}^{(1)}]\, t_1^1 \ldots [A_{1r}^{(1)}] + [B_{1r}^{(1)}]\, t_r^1 \ldots [A_{1r}^{(n)}] + [B_{1r}^{(n)}]\, t_r^n \\ \cdots\cdots\cdots\cdots\cdots\cdots\cdots\cdots\cdots\cdots \\ [A_{nr,1}^{(1)}] + [B_{nr,1}^{(1)}]\, t_1^1 \ldots [A_{nr,r}^{(1)}] + [B_{nr,r}^{(1)}]\, t_r^1 \ldots [A_{nr,r}^{(n)}] + [B_{nr,r}^{(n)}]\, t_r^n \end{vmatrix} \tag{3.1.33}$$

where $t_p^q = e^{\lambda\omega_p^{(q)}}$, $\varrho = \varrho_1 + \ldots + \varrho_{nr}$ ϱ_k is the largest of the numbers $\varrho_k^{(i)}$ (for $i = 1, \ldots, n$), and $A_{kl}^{(i)}$ and $B_{kl}^{(i)}$ are constants, in general, different from the constants $A_{kl0}^{(i)}$ and $B_{kl0}^{(i)}$, (which are zero if $\varrho_k - \varrho_k^{(i)} \neq 0$).

To investigate the asymptotic behaviour of the determinant $\Delta(\lambda)$ and the asymptotic distribution of its zeros, we need to simplify the asymptotic representation of the determinant $\Delta_0(\lambda)$. Hence we consider the set of points in the λ-plane which satisfy the equations

$$\operatorname{Re} \lambda\omega_k^{(i)} = 0 \qquad (k=1, \ldots, r;\ i=1, \ldots, n) \qquad (3.1.34)$$

In accordance with Condition 2, Equations (3.1.34) determine straight lines which do not depend on the index i and which pass through the coordinate origin. If we think of the origin as dividing each of these straight lines into rays, these equations determine 2μ (where $2\mu \leqslant 2r$) distinct rays $d_1, d_2, \ldots, d_{2\mu}$. Let $-\alpha_j + \frac{\pi}{2}$ denote the argument of the ray d_j. Suppose that the rays d_j are situated in such a way that

$$0 \leqslant \alpha_1 < \alpha_2 < \ldots < \alpha_{2\mu} < 2\pi$$

Suppose, finally, that we have a second set of rays d_j' (for $j=1, \ldots, 2\mu$) chosen arbitrarily but distinct from the rays d_j and situated so as to form the sequence

$$d_1',\ d_1,\ d_2',\ d_2,\ \ldots,\ d_{2\mu},\ d_{2\mu}',\ d_1'$$

The rays d_j' (for $j=1, 2, \ldots, 2\mu$) divide the λ-plane into 2μ sectors $(T_1), (T_2), \ldots, (T_{2\mu})$.

Consider one of these sectors (T_j). Let $\omega_{1j}^{(i)}, \ldots, \omega_{\nu_j j}^{(i)}$ (for $i=1, \ldots, n$) represent those of the numbers $\omega_1^{(i)}, \ldots \omega_r^{(i)}$, lying on the straight line through the origin which makes an angle α_j with the positive real axis. On the basis of Condition 2, the arguments of the $\omega_k^{(i)}$ are independent of the index i. Consequently, all the numbers $\omega_{kj}^{(i)}$ (for $k=1, \ldots, \nu_j$) for $i=1, \ldots, n$ lie on the same straight line.

Put

$$\omega_{kj}^{(i)} = \mu_{kj}^{(i)} e^{\alpha_j \sqrt{-1}} \qquad (k=1, \ldots, \nu_j) \qquad (3.1.35)$$

Here, the $\omega_{kj}^{(i)}$ can always be renumbered in such a way that

$$\mu_{1j}^{(i)} < \mu_{2j}^{(i)} < \ldots < \mu_{s_j j}^{(i)} < 0 < \mu_{s_j+1,\,j}^{(i)} < \ldots < \mu_{\nu_j j}^{(i)}$$

If all the $\mu_{kj}^{(i)}$ are positive, we put $s_j = 0$. If all the $\mu_{kj}^{(i)}$ are negative, we put $s_j = \nu_j$. Since $\arg\varphi_k^{(i)}(x)$ is independent of i, s_j is also independent of i.

If we remove the $\omega_{kj}^{(i)}$ (for $k=1, \ldots, \nu_j$) from the set $\{\omega_1^{(i)}, \ldots, \omega_r^{(i)}\}$, the remaining numbers $\omega_k^{(i)}$ can be distributed into two groups $(\omega_k^{(i,\,1)})$ and $(\omega_k^{(i,\,2)})$. The first group includes those $\omega_k^{(i)}$ for which Re $\lambda\omega_k^{(i)} \to -\infty$ in the sector (T_j); the second group includes those for which Re $\lambda\omega_k^{(i)} \to +\infty$.

Let us suppose that the roots of the characteristic equation are numbered in such a way that they are distributed in the sequence

$$\omega_1^{(i,\,1)}, \ldots, \omega_{\varkappa_j}^{(i,\,1)}, \omega_{1j}^{(i)}, \ldots, \omega_{\nu_j j}^{(i)}, \omega_{\varkappa_j+\nu_j+1}^{(i,\,2)}, \ldots, \omega_r^{(i,\,2)} \tag{a}$$

It is clear that, if we take $\exp(\lambda \sum_{i,k} \omega_k^{(i,\,2)})$ (the summation with respect to i and k is over all numbers in the second group) outside the determinant in the expression for $\Delta_0(\lambda)$, we obtain from (3.1.33)

$$\begin{gathered}\Delta_0(\lambda) = \exp(\lambda \sum_{i,k} \omega_k^{(j,\,2)})\, H_j(z) \\ z = \lambda \exp(a_j \sqrt{-1})\end{gathered} \tag{3.1.36}$$

where

$$H_j(z) = [M_{1j}] \exp(m_{1j} z) + \ldots + [M_{\sigma_j j}] \exp(m_{\sigma_j j} z) \tag{3.1.37}$$

$$m_{1j} < m_{2j} < \ldots < m_{\sigma_j j}$$

$$m_{1j} = \begin{cases} \sum_{i=1}^{n} \sum_{k=1}^{s_j} \mu_{kj}^{(i)}, & \text{if} \quad s_j > 0 \\ 0\,, & \text{if} \quad s_j = 0 \end{cases}$$

$$m_{\sigma_j j} = \begin{cases} \sum_{i=1}^{n} \sum_{k=s_j+1}^{\nu_j} \mu_{kj}^{(i)}, & \text{if} \quad s_j < \nu_j \\ 0\,, & \text{if} \quad s_j = \nu_j \end{cases}$$

Furthermore, it is clear that

$$M_{1j} = |M_{\mathrm{I}}^{1j} M_{\mathrm{II}}^{1j}|$$

where

$$M_{\mathrm{I}}^{1j}=\begin{pmatrix} A_{11}^{(1)} & \dots & A_{1\varkappa_j}^{(1)} B_{1,\,\varkappa_j+1}^{(1)} & \dots & B_{1,\,\varkappa_j+s_j}^{(1)} \\ \cdot & \cdot & \cdot & \cdot & \cdot \\ A_{nr,\,1}^{(1)} & \dots & A_{nr,\,\varkappa_j}^{(1)} B_{nr,\,\varkappa_j+1}^{(1)} & \dots & B_{nr,\,\varkappa_j+s_j}^{(1)} \end{pmatrix}$$

$$M_{\mathrm{II}}^{1j}=\begin{pmatrix} A_{1,\,\varkappa_j+s_j+1}^{(1)} & \dots & A_{1,\,\varkappa_j+\nu_j}^{(1)} B_{1,\,\varkappa_j+\nu_j+1}^{(1)} & \dots & B_{1r}^{(1)} & \dots & B_{1r}^{(n)} \\ \cdot & \cdot & \cdot & \cdot & \cdot & \cdot & \cdot \\ A_{nr,\,\varkappa_j+s_j+1}^{(1)} & \dots & A_{nr,\,\varkappa_j+\nu_j}^{(1)} B_{nr,\,\varkappa_j+\nu_j+1}^{(1)} & \dots & B_{nr,\,r}^{(1)} & \dots & B_{nr,\,r}^{(n)} \end{pmatrix}$$

$$M_{\sigma_j j}=|M_{\mathrm{I}}^{\sigma_j}M_{\mathrm{II}}^{\sigma_j}M_{\mathrm{III}}^{\sigma_j}|$$

where

$$M_{\mathrm{I}}^{\sigma_j}=\begin{pmatrix} A_{11}^{(1)} & \dots & A_{1,\,\varkappa_j+s_j}^{(1)} \\ \cdot & \cdot & \cdot \\ A_{nr,\,1}^{(1)} & \dots & A_{nr,\,\varkappa_j+s_j}^{(1)} \end{pmatrix}$$

$$M_{\mathrm{II}}^{\sigma_j}=\begin{pmatrix} B_{1,\,\varkappa_j+s_j+1}^{(1)} & \dots & B_{1r}^{(1)} & \dots & A_{11}^{(n)} & \dots & A_{1,\,\varkappa_j+s_j}^{(n)} \\ \cdot & \cdot & \cdot & \cdot & \cdot & \cdot & \cdot \\ B_{nr,\,\varkappa_j+s_j+1}^{(1)} & \dots & B_{nr,\,r}^{(1)} & \dots & A_{nr,\,1}^{(n)} & \dots & A_{nr,\,\varkappa_j+s_j}^{(n)} \end{pmatrix}$$

$$M_{\mathrm{III}}^{\sigma_j}=\begin{pmatrix} B_{1,\,\varkappa_j+s_j+1}^{(n)} & \dots & B_{1,\,r}^{(n)} \\ \cdot & \cdot & \cdot \\ B_{nr,\,\varkappa_j+s_j+1}^{(n)} & \dots & B_{nr,\,r}^{(n)} \end{pmatrix}$$

Now, we can prove Theorem 7.

Theorem 7 Under Conditions 1–3, if all the numbers $M_{1j}, M_{\sigma_j j}$ (for $j=1,\ 2,\ \dots,\ 2\mu$) are non-zero, the following assertions hold.

1. The characteristic determinant $\Delta(\lambda)$ of the Green's matrix $G(x,\ \xi,\ \lambda)$ of Problem (3.1.1)-(3.1.2) has infinitely many zeros, which may be distributed in 2μ groups. The values of the j group lying in a strip (D_j) of finite width which is parallel to a ray d_j lying within the strip (D_j).
2. If we delete from the λ-plane the interiors of small circles of radius δ with centres at the zeros of the Green's function and at the point $\lambda=0$, then the inequality

$$|\Delta_0(\lambda)\exp(-\lambda\sum_{i,\,h}\omega_h^{(i,\,2)})|\geqslant K_\delta \tag{3.1.38}$$

   where K_δ is a positive number depending only on δ, holds throughout the remainder of the plane.
3. The number of zeros of $\Delta(\lambda)$ which can approach each

other with increasing distance from the coordinate origin is bounded.

The zeros $\lambda_N^{(j)}$ of the function $\Delta(\lambda)$ in the j th group have the asymptotic representation

$$|\lambda_N^{(j)}| = \frac{2N\pi}{m_{\sigma_j j} - m_{1j}}\left(1 + o\left(\frac{1}{N}\right)\right)$$

4. The zeros of the characteristic determinant $\Delta(\lambda)$ are poles of the solution of Problem (3.1.1)-(3.1.2) represented by (3.1.26).

Let us suppose that some zero $\lambda_N^{(j)}$ of the function $\Delta(\lambda)$ is not a pole of the solution of Problem (3.1.1)-(3.1.2) represented by (3.1.26). Then, for $x \in (a_i, b_i)$, we would have the identity

$$\Delta_{kq}^{(i,\,p)}(x, \xi, \lambda_N^{(j)}) \equiv 0 \qquad (p = 1, \ldots, n; \ k, \ q = 1, \ \ldots, \ r)$$

As can be seen from (3.1.28) and (3.1.20), however, the function $\Delta_{kq}^{(i,\,p)}(x, \xi, \lambda_N^{(j)})$ is a linear combination of independent particular solutions

$$y_{k1}^{(i)}(x, \lambda_N^{(j)}), \ \ldots, \ y_{kr}^{(i)}(x, \lambda_N^{(j)})$$

of the homogeneous system (3.1.1a), which contradicts the identity above. This contradiction proves the validity of the fourth assertion of Theorem 7.

Then, it is clear from the asymptotic formulae (3.1.31), (3.1.32), (3.1.35), (3.1.36) and (3.1.37) that, to prove this theorem, it will be sufficient to prove the Lemma 1 below.

Lemma 1 Suppose that $H(z)$ is an analytic function for all z except the infinite point in the z-plane and the point $z=0$. Suppose that $H(z)$ has the following asymptotic representation in a sector R containing the positive half of the imaginary axis of the z-plane

$$H(z) = [M_1]\, e^{m_1 z} + \ldots + [M_\sigma]\, e^{m_\sigma z}$$

where M_i and m_i are constants such that

$$M_1 \neq 0, \qquad M_\sigma \neq 0, \qquad m_1 < m_2 < \ldots < m_\sigma$$

Then, the following assertions hold

1. The equation

$$H(z) \equiv [M_1] e^{m_1 z} + \ldots + [M_\sigma] e^{m_\sigma z} = 0 \qquad (3.1.39)$$

has in the sector R an infinite set of roots z_k (where $|z_1| \leqslant |z_2| \leqslant \ldots$) which are contained in a strip (D_h) of finite width h that does not include the positive half of the imaginary axis of the z-plane. The zeros of $H(z)$ lying in strip (D_h) have the asymptotic representation

$$|z_N| = \frac{2\pi N}{m_\sigma - m_1}\left(1 + O\left(\frac{1}{N}\right)\right)$$

2. In every rectangle (Π_h) of the form

$$|x| \leqslant \frac{h}{2}, \quad y_1 \leqslant y \leqslant y_2 \quad (z = x + \sqrt{-1}y)$$

for sufficiently large positive values of y_1 and y_2, the number N of roots of (3.1.39) lies between the following bounds

$$\frac{1}{2\pi}(m_\sigma - m_1)(y_2 - y_1) - \sigma \leqslant N \leqslant \frac{1}{2\pi}(m_\sigma - m_1)(y_2 - y_1) + \sigma \qquad (3.1.40)$$

3. If we delete the interiors of small circles of radius δ with centres at the zeros z_k from the strip (D_h), the inequality

$$|H(z)| \geqslant K_\delta \qquad (3.1.41)$$

where K_δ is a positive number depending only on δ, holds throughout the remaining part $(D_h^{(\delta)})$ of the strip.

To prove this Lemma, we shall use Lemmas 2, 3 and 4.

Lemma 2 If $f(z)$ is a meromorphic function* within some closed contour c and if $f(z)$ and its derivative $f'(z)$ are continuous on the contour, then the number P of zeros of this function within c (where each zero of multiplicity n is counted

*A single-value function of a complex variable z which has no singularities other than poles in some region of the complex plane is called a meromorphic function in that region.

n times) is given by

$$P=\frac{1}{2\pi}\int_c d\tan^{-1}\frac{Y}{X}=\frac{1}{2\pi}\int_c d\arg f(z)$$

where

$$f(z)=X(x,\ y)+\sqrt{-1}Y(x,\ y)$$

and

$$z=x+\sqrt{-1}y$$

Here, it is assumed that $f(z)$ does not vanish on the contour c.

Lemma 3: Rouché's theorem Suppose that $f(z)$ and $\varphi(z)$ are holomorphic functions within some closed contour c. Suppose also they are continuous on this contour and everywhere on it,

$$|\varphi(z)|<|f(z)|$$

Then, the equations

$$f(z)=0, \qquad f(z)+\varphi(z)=0$$

have the same number of zeros inside c.

Lemma 4 Suppose that $F(z,\ x)$ is a continuous function of its arguments and that it is an analytic function of z for all $x=(x_1,\ \ldots,\ x_n)$ belonging to R (where $a_i\leqslant x_i\leqslant b_i$) in some closed region S of the complex plane. Suppose that, for every x in R, the number of zeros of the function $F(z,\ x)$ in S is less than some positive number N. Suppose, finally, that, for any $x\in R$, z lies at a distance greater than δ (where δ is a sufficiently small positive number) from the zeros of the function of $F(z,\ x)$. Then,

$$|F(z,\ x)|\geqslant K_\delta$$

where K_δ is a positive number depending only on δ.

Proof of Lemma 2 Let us consider an auxiliary function $\psi(z)$ which is holomorphic inside and continuous on c. Obviously, every point a inside c which is neither a zero nor a pole of the function $f(z)$ is a non-singular point of the function

$\psi(z)\frac{f'(z)}{f(z)}$. If a point a is a pole or a zero of the function $f(z)$, then

$$f(z)=(z-a)^{\mu}\Phi(z)$$

in a neighbourhood of that point, where μ is a positive (or negative) number if a is a zero (or pole) of $f(z)$ and $\Phi(z)$ is a holomorphic function in a neighbourhood of the point a which does not vanish at that point. Obviously,

$$\frac{d}{dz}(\ln f(z))=\frac{\mu(z-a)^{\mu-1}\Phi(z)+(z-a)^{\mu}\Phi'(z)}{(z-a)^{\mu}\Phi(z)}$$
$$=\frac{\mu}{z-a}+\frac{\Phi'(z)}{\Phi(z)}$$

Since, on the other hand,

$$\psi(z)=\psi(a)+(z-a)\psi'(a)+\ldots$$

in a neighbourhood of the point a, this point is a pole of the first order of the function $\psi(z)\frac{f'(z)}{f(z)}$ provided $\psi(a)\neq 0$. Therefore, the residue of this function at the point a is equal to $|\mu|\psi(a)$ (or $-|\mu|\psi(a)$) if the point a is a zero (or pole) of order $|\mu|$ of the function $f(z)$.

Since the function $f(z)$ has no zeros on the contour c, we have (from the general residue theorem)

$$\frac{1}{2\pi\sqrt{-1}}\int_c \psi(z)\frac{f'(z)}{f(z)}dz=\sum_k \psi(a_k)-\sum_j \psi(b_j) \quad (3.1.42)$$

Here, the a_k are the zeros of the function $f(z)$, the b_j are the poles of that function, the summation over k is over all the zeros and that over j is over all the poles of the function $f(z)$ which lie inside the contour c. Here, every zero or pole of multiplicity n is counted n times.

In particular, if we put $\psi(z)\equiv 1$, we obtain from (3.1.42)

$$P-Q=\frac{1}{2\pi\sqrt{-1}}\int_c \frac{f'(z)}{f(z)}dz \quad (3.1.43)$$

where P is the number of zeros and Q the number of poles of the function $f(z)$ which lie inside the contour c. Again, the zeros and poles are counted according to their multiplicity.

Since the integrand on the right-hand side of (3.1.43) is

the derivative of $f(z)$ (3.1.43) can be rewritten in the form

$$P-Q=\frac{1}{2\pi\sqrt{-1}}\int_c d\ln f(z) \tag{3.1.43a}$$

Thus,

$$\begin{aligned}\ln f(z) &= \ln|f(z)|\exp(\sqrt{-1}(\arg f(z)+2k\pi))\\ &= \ln|f(z)|+\sqrt{-1}(\arg f(z)+2k\pi),\end{aligned}$$

where k is an arbitrary integer. Therefore, the integral in the right-hand side of (3.1.43a) is equal to the change in the sum

$$\ln|f(z)|+\sqrt{-1}\arg f(z)$$

as z describes the contour c, i.e.

$$\begin{aligned}P-Q &= \frac{1}{2\pi\sqrt{-1}}\int_c d\ln f(z)=\frac{1}{2\pi\sqrt{-1}}\int_c \sqrt{-1}d\arg f(z)\\ &= \frac{1}{2\pi}\int_c d\arg f(z).\end{aligned} \tag{3.1.43b}$$

Or, if we put

$$f(z)=X(x, y)+\sqrt{-1}Y(x, y)$$
$$z=x+\sqrt{-1}y,$$

we obtain

$$X(x, y)=|f(z)|\cos\arg f(z)$$
$$Y(x, y)=|f(z)|\sin\arg f(z)$$

so that

$$\tan\arg f(z)=\frac{Y(x, y)}{X(x, y)}$$

$$\arg f(z)=\tan^{-1}\frac{Y(x, y)}{X(x, y)}$$

Substituting the last expressions into (3.1.43b), we obtain

$$P-Q=\frac{1}{2\pi}\int_c d\arg f(z)=\frac{1}{2\pi}\int_c d\tan^{-1}\frac{Y(x, y)}{X(x, y)} \tag{3.1.44}$$

In particular, if $f(z)$ has no poles within the contour c, the assertion of Lemma 2 follows from (3.1.44).

Proof of Lemma 3 It follows from the hypothesis of the lemma that $f(z)$ does not vanish on the contour c. Consequently, on c,

$$f(z)+\varphi(z)=f(z)\left\{1+\frac{\varphi(z)}{f(z)}\right\}$$

As z describes the closed curve c, the point $w=1+\frac{\varphi(z)}{f(z)}$ describes a closed curve lying entirely inside a circle of unit radius with centre at the point $w=1$ since, in accordance with the hypothesis of the lemma, as z describes c,

$$|w-1|=\left|\frac{\varphi(z)}{f(z)}\right|<1$$

Thus, as z describes the closed contour c, the point w describes a closed contour c_1 lying entirely inside the unit circle with centre at point $w=1$. Consequently, the point $w=0$ lies on c_1. As z describes c, the argument of $1+\frac{\varphi(z)}{f(z)}$ returns to its original value and the change in the argument of $f(z)+\varphi(z)$ is equal to the change in the argument of $f(z)$. On the basis of Lemma 2, the functions $f(z)+\varphi(z)$ and $f(z)$ have the same number of zeros within the contour c.

Proof of Lemma 4 Let S_δ denote that portion of the region S which remains after we delete the interiors of circles of radius δ with centres at the zeros of the function $F(z, x)$ for arbitrary $x \in R$. Since the zeros of the function $F(z, x)$, are finite in number, the region S_δ is closed for arbitrary $x \in R$.

Obviously, for arbitrary fixed $x \in R$, there exists a number C_δ such that, for all $z \in S_\delta$,

$$|F(z, x)| \geqslant C_\delta$$

with equality holding for certain values of $z \in S_\delta$. Thus, the function $C_\delta(x)$ is determined. Since the zeros of the function $F(z, x)$ are continuous, it is clear that $C_\delta(x)$ is a continuous function in the closed region R. Therefore, it attains its greatest lower bound M_δ in that region. Obviously, for certain values of z and x, we have

$$|F(z, x)|=N_\delta$$

Consequently, $N_\delta>0$.

Proof of Lemma 1 Having proved Lemmas 2, 3 and 4 we now prove the validity of 1 for the simplified polynomial $Z(z)$:

$$Z(z) \equiv M_1 e^{m_1 z} + \dots + M_\sigma e^{m_\sigma z} = 0 \qquad (3.1.45)$$

Since $M_1 \neq 0$ and $M_\sigma \neq 0$, we have

$$Z(z) = \begin{cases} M_\sigma e^{m_\sigma z} \left(1 + \frac{1}{M_\sigma} \sum_{i=1}^{\sigma-1} M_i \exp[(m_i - m_\sigma) z]\right) & \text{for } x \geqslant 0 \\ M_1 e^{m_1 z} \left(1 + \frac{1}{M_1} \sum_{i=2}^{\sigma} M_i \exp[(m_i - m_1) z]\right) & \text{for } x \leqslant 0 \end{cases} \qquad (3.1.46)$$

From this, it is clear that a positive constant h can be so chosen that

$$Z(z) \neq 0 \quad \text{for} \quad |x| \geqslant \frac{h}{2}$$

This proves that all the roots of (3.1.45) lie in a strip (D_h) of finite width h:

$$|\operatorname{Re} z| \leqslant \frac{h}{2}$$

Now, it is easy to prove that, in every rectangle (Π_h) of the form

$$|x| \leqslant \frac{h}{2}, \quad y_1 \leqslant y \leqslant y_2$$

N roots of (3.1.45) lie within the following bounds:

$$\frac{1}{2\pi}(m_\sigma - m_1)(y_2 - y_1) - \sigma \leqslant N \leqslant \frac{1}{2\pi}(m_\sigma - m_1)(y_2 - y_1) + \sigma.$$

Specifically, from Lemma 2.

$$N = \frac{1}{2\pi} \int_{\Pi_h} d\theta = \frac{1}{2\pi} \int_{\Pi_g} d\theta = \frac{1}{2\pi} \int_{\Pi_g} d \tan^{-1} \frac{Y(x, y)}{X(x, y)} \qquad (3.1.47)$$

where $Z(z) = |Z| e^{i\theta} = X(x, y) + \sqrt{-1}\, Y(x, y)$, Π_h is the boundary of (Π_h), g is an arbitrary positive number greater than h and $\theta = \arg Z(z)$.

The representation (3.1.46) shows that the portion of the

interval (3.1.47) taken along the vertical side of Π_g is equal to $\frac{1}{2\pi}(m_\sigma - m_1)(y_2 - y_1) + \varepsilon_g$, where $\varepsilon_g \to 0$ as $g \to \infty$. On the other hand, as can be seen from (3.1.47) itself, the portion of this integral taken over each of the horizontal sides of Π_g does not exceed $\frac{\omega+1}{2}$, where ω is the number of real roots of the equation

$$X(x, y) = 0 \qquad (\text{for } y = y_i;\ i = 1, 2)$$

Along each of the horizontal sides of the rectangle Π_g, X is a function only of x $(X = X(x, y_i))$. Consequently, this equation is of the form

$$\varphi(x) = \sum_{i=1}^{\sigma} A_i e^{k_i x} = 0 \tag{3.1.48}$$

where the A_i and k_i are real constants.

It is easy to show by induction that (3.1.48) cannot have more than $\sigma - 1$ real roots. This assertion is clear for $\sigma = 1$. Suppose that it is true for $\sigma - 1$. Obviously, the polynomials $\varphi(x)$ and $\Phi(x) = e^{-k_1 x}\varphi(x)$ have the same number of real roots. On the basis of our assumption, the polynomial

$$\Phi'(x) = A_2(k_2 - k_1)e^{(k_2 - k_1)x} + \ldots + A_\sigma(k_\sigma - k_1)e^{(k_\sigma - k_1)x}$$

cannot have more than $\sigma - 2$ real roots. Therefore, $\Phi(x)$ (or $\varphi(x)$) cannot have more than $\sigma - 1$ real roots. It follows from what has been said that $\omega + 1 \leqslant \sigma$. Therefore, from (3.1.47), we obtain

$$\frac{1}{2\pi}(m_\sigma - m_1)(y_2 - y_1) + \varepsilon_g - \sigma \leqslant N$$
$$\leqslant \frac{1}{2\pi}(m_\sigma - m_1)(y_2 - y_1) + \varepsilon_g + \sigma$$

Since N is independent of g, this inequality implies the validity of the second assertion of Lemma 1 for the polynomial $Z(z)$ for arbitrary y_1 and y_2.

It should be noted that, if the point z describes a rectangle (Π_1) of the form

$$|x| \leqslant \frac{h}{2},\ 2l\pi \leqslant y < 2(l+1)\pi \qquad (l = 1, 2, \ldots)$$

then the values of the exponential polynomial $Z(z)$ (see (3.1.45)) coincide with the values of some exponential polynomial in a rectangle of the form

$$|\operatorname{Re}\zeta| \leqslant \frac{h}{2}, \quad 0 \leqslant \operatorname{Im}\zeta < 2\pi$$

Specifically, if n_i is the integral part of the number $m_i l$, then, for $z \in \Pi_1$, we have

$$Z(z) = \sum_{i=1}^{\sigma} M_i e^{m_i z} = \sum_{i=1}^{\sigma} e^{\xi_i \sqrt{-1}} M_i e^{m_i \zeta} = F(\zeta, \xi_1, \ldots, \xi_\sigma)$$

where $\zeta = x + \sqrt{-1}\eta$, $0 \leqslant \eta < 2\pi$ $(z - 2l\pi\sqrt{-1} = \zeta)$, and the ξ_i are real parameters dependent on l, the values of which fall in the interval $(0, 2\pi)$.

Then, according to Lemma 4, if we delete the interiors of small circles of radius δ with centres at the roots of (3.1.45), or the zeros of the polynomial $Z(z)$, then the inequality

$$|Z(z)| \geqslant N_\delta \tag{3.1.49}$$

where N_δ is a positive number depending only on δ, will be satisfied in the remaining portion of the strip (D_h).

Thus, Lemma 1 is proved for the simplified polynomial $Z(z)$.

Now, to prove Lemma 1 for (3.1.39), we note that, on the boundary of the rectangles

$$|x| \leqslant \frac{h}{2}, \quad 2l\pi \leqslant y \leqslant 2(l+1)\pi \qquad (l = 1, 2, \ldots)$$

the quantity $Z(z)$ does not vanish and, consequently,

$$H(z) = Z(z)\left\{1 + \frac{\psi(z)}{z}\right\} = [Z]$$

where $\frac{\psi(z)}{z} Z(z)$ is an analytic function for $z \neq 0$ or ∞. For sufficiently large h, y_1 and y_2 the inequality

$$\left|\frac{\psi(z)}{z}\right| < 1$$

holds along the boundary Π_h.

Consequently, in accordance with Lemma 3, the functions $H(z)$ and $Z(z)$ have an identical set of zeros within the rectangle Π_h.* This proves assertion 2 of Lemma 1.

To prove assertion 3, we need to use (3.1.49) and the representation

$$H(z)=Z(z)\left\{1+\frac{\psi(z)}{z}\right\}$$

where $\psi(z)$ is a function which is bounded in the strip (D_h) and analytic in that strip except at $z=0$ and the point at infinity.

For the bounded portion $D_{h_1}^{(\delta)}$ of the region $(D_h^{(\delta)})$, there exists, on the basis of the analyticity of $H(z)$ in D_h, a constant $K'_\delta>0$ such that

$$|H(z)|\geqslant K'_\delta$$

According to (3.1.49), however, we have in the region $D_h^{(\delta)}-D_{h1}^{(\delta)}$

$$|H(z)|=|Z(z)|\left|1+\frac{\psi(z)}{z}\right|\geqslant K_\delta\left(1-\frac{|\psi(z)|}{z}\right)$$
$$\geqslant K_\delta\left(1-\frac{c}{|z|}\right)\geqslant\frac{K_\delta}{2}$$

Assertion 1 of Lemma 1 follows from (3.1.40).

Now, to obtain an asymptotic representation for $|z_k^{(j)}|$, out of all the zeros $z_k^{(j)}$ of the function $H_j(z)$, let us draw circles O_δ of radius δ with centres at $z_k^{(\delta)}$. Consider the sequence of rectangles $(\Pi_h^{(\nu)})$, the lower bases of which consist of a segment of the straight line

$$\operatorname{Im} z=y_1$$

and the upper bases of which consist of segments of the straight lines

$$\operatorname{Im} z=y_\nu$$

which do not intersect the circles O_δ. (According to (3.1.40), such straight lines exist.) Here, there exists a constant L such that

$$|y_\nu-y_{\nu+1}|\leqslant L,\quad \lim_{\nu\to\infty} y_\nu=+\infty$$

*The rectangle (Π_h) does not contain the point $z=0$.

Let N_ν denote the number of zeros of $H_j(z)$ lying inside $(\Pi_h^{(\nu)})$. According to the second assertion of the lemma.

$$\frac{1}{2\pi}(m_{\sigma_j j}-m_{1j})(y_\nu-y_1)-\sigma_j \leqslant N_\nu \leqslant \frac{1}{2\pi}(m_{\sigma_j j}-m_{1j})(y_\nu-y_1)+\sigma_j$$

From the inequality, we have

$$N_\nu=\frac{1}{2\pi}(m_{\sigma_j j}-m_{1j})(y_\nu-y_1)+Q_\nu$$

where the Q_ν are bounded by a number which is independent of ν.

Let us now number all the zeros of the function $H_j(z)$ lying inside $(\Pi_h^{(\nu)})$ in increasing order of their absolute values. Then,

$$\operatorname{Im} z_{N_\nu}=y_\nu-C_\nu.$$

where C_ν is a positive constant, depending on ν.

Obviously, the C_ν are bounded by the number L. Then, from the preceding equation, we obtain

$$\begin{aligned}N_\nu&=\frac{1}{2\pi}(m_{\sigma_j j}-m_{1j})(\operatorname{Im} z_{N_\nu}^{(j)}+C_\nu-y_1)+Q_\nu\\&=\frac{1}{2\pi}(m_{\sigma_j j}-m_{1j})\left(\sqrt{|z_{N_\nu}^{(j)}|-(\operatorname{Re} z_{N_\nu}^{(j)})^2}+(C_\nu-y_1)\right)+Q_\nu\\&=\frac{1}{2\pi}(m_{\sigma_j j}-m_{1j})|z_{N_\nu}^{(j)}|\\&\times\left(\sqrt{1-\left(\frac{\operatorname{Re} z_{N_\nu}^{(j)}}{|z_{N_\nu}^{(j)}|}\right)^2}+\frac{C_\nu-y_1}{|z_{N_\nu}^{(j)}|}\right)+Q_\nu\end{aligned}$$

Therefore,

$$\begin{aligned}|z_{N_\nu}^{(j)}|&=\frac{2\pi N_\nu}{m_{\sigma_j j}-m_{1j}}\\&\times\left(\sqrt{1-\frac{(\operatorname{Re} z_{N_\nu}^{(j)})^2}{|z_{N_\nu}^{(j)}|^2}}+\frac{C_\nu-y_1}{|z_{N_\nu}^{(j)}|}+\frac{2\pi Q_\nu}{(m_{\sigma_j j}-m_{1j})|z_{N_\nu}^{(j)}|}\right)^{-1}\end{aligned}$$

Remembering that the real parts of all $z_{N_\nu}^{(j)}$ are bounded ($|\mathrm{Re}\, z_{N_\nu}^{(j)}| \leqslant h$) and that the numbers $C_\nu - y_1$ and Q_ν are bounded, we easily find from the last equation the asymptotic representation

$$|z_{N_\nu}^{(j)}| = \frac{2\pi N_\nu}{m_{\sigma_j j} - m_{1j}} \left(1 + \frac{E(N_\nu)}{N_\nu}\right)$$

where $E(N_\nu)$ is bounded for large N_ν. If we omit the index ν in the last representation, we obtain the asymptotic formula of Lemma 1.

Returning to $\lambda_N^{(j)}$ by using (3.1.36), we have

$$|\lambda_N^{(j)}| = \frac{2\pi N}{m_{\sigma_j j} - m_{1j}} \left(1 + O\left(\frac{1}{N}\right)\right) \tag{3.1.50}$$

Now, to prove the basic theorem of this section, let us study the asymptotic behaviour of the numerator of Green's matrix for large values of λ.

The boundaries of the sectors (T_j) and (Σ_s) divide the entire λ-plane into sectors, which we shall denote by (R_s). Each of the sectors (R_s) lies simultaneously in one of the sectors (Σ_s) and one of the sectors (T_j). Consider one of sectors (R_j) with fixed index j. Denote by $R_j(\delta)$ that portion of this sector which remains when we delete the interiors of small circles of radius δ. Suppose that this sector lies in some sector Σ_s in which, for suitable numbering of the roots of the characteristic equations, the inequalities

$$\begin{gathered} \mathrm{Re}\, \lambda\varphi_1^{(i)}(x) \leqslant \mathrm{Re}\, \lambda\varphi_2^{(i)}(x) \leqslant \ldots \leqslant \mathrm{Re}\, \lambda\varphi_{\tau_j}^{(i)}(x) \leqslant 0 \\ \leqslant \mathrm{Re}\, \lambda\varphi_{\tau_j+1}^{(i)}(x) \leqslant \ldots \leqslant \mathrm{Re}\, \lambda\varphi_r^{(i)}(x). \end{gathered} \tag{3.1.51}$$

where $\tau_j = \varkappa_j + s_j$, hold (see the sequence (a)). Here, in accordance with Condition 2 of this section, τ_j does not depend on the index i.

To obtain an asymptotic representation of the numerator $\Delta_{kl}^{(i,s)}(x, \xi, \lambda)$ (see (3.1.28)) of the Green's function in the sector R_j, let us transform the determinant $\Delta_{kl}^{(i,s)}(x, \xi, \lambda)$. We multiply the columns whose elements are $u_{k1}^{(s)}(\lambda), \ldots, u_{k\tau_j}^{(s)}(\lambda)$ (for $k = 1, \ldots, nr$), respectively, by

$$\frac{1}{2} z_{k1}^{(s)}(\xi, \lambda), \ \ldots, \frac{1}{2} z_{k\tau_j}^{(s)}(\xi, \lambda)$$

and the columns whose elements are $u_{k\tau_j+1}^{(s)}, \ldots, u_{kr}^{(s)}$ by

$$-\frac{1}{2} z_{k\tau_j+1}^{(s)}(\xi, \lambda), \ \ldots, \ -\frac{1}{2} z_{kr}^{(s)}(\xi, \lambda)$$

and then add the resulting columns to the first column. The resulting determinant is denoted by $\Delta_{kl0}^{(i,s)}(x, \xi, \lambda)$ and the elements of the first column of this determinant by

$$g_{kl0}^{(i,s)}(x, \xi, \lambda), \quad g_{1l0}^{(s)}(\xi, \lambda), \ \ldots, \ g_{nr,\,l,\,0}^{(s)}(\xi, \lambda)$$

respectively. In accordance with (3.1.20), (3.1.23), (3.1.24) and (3.1.29), we obtain the following expressions for these elements

$$g_{kl0}^{(i,s)}(x, \xi, \lambda) = \begin{cases} \sum\limits_{p=1}^{\tau_j} y_{kp}^{(i)}(x, \lambda)\, z_{lp}^{(i)}(\xi, \lambda) \\ \qquad \text{for } s = i,\ a_i \leqslant \xi \leqslant x \leqslant b_i \\ -\sum\limits_{p=\tau_j+1}^{r} y_{kp}^{(i)}(x, \lambda)\, z_{lp}^{(i)}(\xi, \lambda) \\ \qquad \text{for } s = i,\ a_i \leqslant x \leqslant \xi \leqslant b_i \\ 0 \qquad \text{for } s \neq i \end{cases} \tag{3.1.52}$$

$$\begin{aligned} g_{kl0}^{(s)}(\xi, \lambda) = & -\sum_{p=1}^{r} \sum_{q=\tau_j+1}^{r} \alpha_{kp}^{(s)}(\lambda)\, y_{pq}^{(s)}(a_s, \lambda)\, z_{lq}^{(s)}(\xi, \lambda) \\ & + \sum_{p=1}^{r} \sum_{q=1}^{\tau_j} \beta_{kp}^{(s)}(\lambda)\, y_{pq}^{(s)}(b_s, \lambda)\, z_{lq}^{(s)}(\xi, \lambda) \end{aligned} \tag{3.1.53}$$

Furthermore, when the determinant $\Delta_{kl0}^{(i,s)}(x, \xi, \lambda)$ is expanded in terms of elements of the first row, we obtain

$$\begin{aligned} \Delta_{kl}^{(i,s)}(x, \xi, \lambda) = \Delta_{kl0}^{(i,s)}(x, \xi, \lambda) = & \ \Delta(\lambda)\, g_{kl0}^{(i,s)}(x, \xi, \lambda) \\ & + \sum_{q=1}^{r} \sum_{p=1}^{nr} y_{kq}^{(i)}(x, \lambda)\, g_{p,\,l,\,0}^{(s)}(\xi, \lambda)\, \Delta_{p,\,(i-1)r+q}(\lambda) \end{aligned} \tag{3.1.54}$$

where $\Delta_{p,\,(i-1)r+q}(\lambda)$ is the cofactor of the element $(p,\ (i-1)r + q)$ in the determinant $\Delta(\lambda)$ and

$$\begin{aligned} G_{kl}^{(i,s)}(x, \xi, \lambda) = & \ g_{kl0}^{(i,s)}(x, \xi, \lambda) \\ & + \frac{1}{\Delta(\lambda)} \sum_{q=1}^{r} \sum_{p=1}^{nr} y_{kq}^{(i)}(x, \lambda)\, g_{pl0}^{(s)}(\xi, \lambda)\, \Delta_{p,\,(i-1)r+q}(\lambda) \end{aligned} \tag{3.1.55}$$

In accordance with Condition 2 of Section 3.1, the arguments of the roots of the characteristic equations (3.1.5) do not depend on x. Consequently, they may be represented in the form

$$\varphi_k^{(i)}(x) = \Pi_k q_k^{(i)}(x) \quad \text{for} \quad x \in [a_i, b_i] \tag{3.1.56}$$

where Π_k is a constant (in general, complex) and $q_k^{(i)}(x) > 0$ for $x \in [a_i, b_i]$.

For convenience, we introduce the following notations:

$$\begin{aligned} \int_{a_i}^{\xi} \varphi_k^{(i)}(t)\,dt &= \int_{a_i}^{\xi} \Pi_k q_k^{(i)}(t)\,dt = \Pi_k \xi_k^{(i)} \\ & \int_{a_i}^{x} \varphi_k^{(i)}(t)\,dt = \Pi_k x_k^{(i)} \\ \int_{a_i}^{b_i} \varphi_k^{(i)}(t)\,dt &= \Pi_k \int_{a_i}^{b_i} q_k^{(i)}(t)\,dt = \Pi_k x_{0k}^{(i)} \end{aligned} \tag{3.1.57}$$

Hence the asymptotic formulae (3.1.14) become

$$y_{ks}^{(i)}(x, \lambda) = e^{\lambda \Pi_s x_s^{(i)}} [y_{ks0}^{(i)}(x)] \tag{3.1.58}$$

By definition of the functions $z_{js}^{(i)}(\xi, \lambda)$, we have the following identities:

$$\sum_{l=1}^{r} y_{kl}^{(i)}(\xi, \lambda)\, z_{jl}^{(i)}(\xi, \lambda) = \delta_{kj} \quad (k = 1, \ldots, r) \tag{3.1.59}$$

where δ_{kj} is Kronecker's symbol

$$\delta_{kj} = \begin{cases} 1 & \text{for } k = j \\ 0 & \text{for } k \neq j \end{cases}$$

If we substitute into (3.1.59) the asymptotic representation of the functions $y_{ks}^{(i)}(\xi, \lambda)$ and write the resulting identities in matrix form, we have

$$\begin{pmatrix} e^{\lambda\Pi_1\xi_1^{(i)}}[y_{110}^{(i)}(\xi)] & \dots & e^{\lambda\Pi_r\xi_r^{(i)}}[y_{1r0}^{(i)}(\xi)] \\ \vdots & & \vdots \\ e^{\lambda\Pi_1\xi_1^{(i)}}[y_{r10}^{(i)}(\xi)] & \dots & e^{\lambda\Pi_r\xi_r^{(i)}}[y_{rr0}^{(i)}(\xi)] \end{pmatrix} \times \begin{pmatrix} z_{j1}^{(i)}(\xi, \lambda) \\ \vdots \\ z_{jr}^{(i)}(\xi, \lambda) \end{pmatrix} = E \begin{pmatrix} \delta_{1j} \\ \vdots \\ \sigma_{rj} \end{pmatrix}$$

where E is the unit matrix. Solving this matrix equation for z, we obtain

$$\begin{pmatrix} z_{j1}^{(i)}(\xi, \lambda) \\ \vdots \\ z_{jr}^{(i)}(\xi, \lambda) \end{pmatrix} = \begin{pmatrix} e^{-\lambda\Pi_1\xi_1^{(i)}}[v_{11}^{(i)}(\xi)] & \dots & e^{-\lambda\Pi_1\xi_1^{(i)}}[v_{r1}^{(i)}(\xi)] \\ \vdots & & \vdots \\ e^{-\lambda\Pi_r\xi_r^{(i)}}[v_{1r}^{(i)}(\xi)] & \dots & e^{-\lambda\Pi_r\xi_r^{(i)}}[v_{rr}^{(i)}(\xi)] \end{pmatrix} \begin{pmatrix} \delta_{1j} \\ \vdots \\ \delta_{rj} \end{pmatrix} \tag{3.1.60}$$

where

$$V^{(i)}(\xi) = \begin{pmatrix} v_{11}^{(i)}(\xi) & \dots & v_{1r}^{(i)}(\xi) \\ \dots & \dots & \dots \\ v_{r1}^{(i)}(\xi) & \dots & v_{rr}^{(i)}(\xi) \end{pmatrix}$$

is the inverse of the matrix

$$Y_0^{(i)}(\xi) = \begin{pmatrix} y_{110}^{(i)}(\xi) & \dots & y_{1r0}^{(i)}(\xi) \\ \dots & \dots & \dots \\ y_{r10}^{(i)}(\xi) & \dots & y_{rr0}^{(i)}(\xi) \end{pmatrix}$$

$$V^{(i)}(\xi)\, Y_0^{(i)}(\xi) = E \tag{3.1.61}$$

From (3.1.60), we obtain for $z_{hs}^{(i)}(\xi, \lambda)$ the following asymptotic representation:

$$z_{ks}^{(i)}(\xi, \lambda) = [v_{ks}^{(i)}(\xi)]\, e^{-\lambda\Pi_s\xi_s^{(i)}} \tag{3.1.62}$$

Now, by using (3.1.58) and (3.1.62), we find from (3.1.52)

the asymptotic representation

$$g_{kl0}^{(i,s)}(x, \xi, \lambda) = \begin{cases} \sum_{p=1}^{\tau_j} [y_{kp0}^{(i)}(x) v_{lp}^{(i)}(\xi)] e^{\lambda \Pi_p (x_p^{(i)} - \xi_p^{(i)})} \\ \qquad \text{for } s=i, \ a_i \leqslant \xi \leqslant x \leqslant b_i \\ -\sum_{k=\tau_j+1}^{r} [y_{kp0}^{(i)}(x) v_{lp}^{(i)}(\xi)] e^{\lambda \Pi_p (x_p^{(i)} - \xi_p^{(i)})} \\ \qquad \text{for } s=i, \ a_i \leqslant x \leqslant \xi \leqslant b_i \\ 0 \qquad \text{for } s \neq i. \end{cases} \tag{3.1.63}$$

Similarly, substituting the asymptotic representations (3.1. 58) and (3.1.62) into (3.1.53), we have

$$g_{kl0}^{(s)}(\xi, \lambda) = \lambda^{\gamma_k^{(s)}} \sum_{p=1}^{r} [M_{kp}^{(s)} v_{lp}^{(s)}(\xi)] w_{p1}^{(s)} \tag{3.1.64}$$

where

$$w_{p1}^{(s)} = \begin{cases} e^{\lambda \Pi_p \left(x_{0p}^{(s)} - \xi_p^{(s)}\right)} & \text{for} \quad p = 1, 2, \dots, \tau_j \\ e^{-\lambda \Pi_p \xi_p^{(s)}} & \text{for} \quad p = \tau_j + 1, \dots, r \end{cases} \tag{3.1.65}$$

$$M_{kp}^{(s)} = \begin{cases} \sum_l d_{kl1}^{(s)} y_{lp0}^{(s)}(a_s) & \text{for} \quad k = 1, \dots, \tau_j, \\ \sum_l d_{kl2}^{(s)} y_{lp0}^{(s)}(b_s) & \text{for} \quad k = \tau_j + 1, \dots, r \end{cases} \tag{3.1.66}$$

$\gamma_k^{(s)}$ is the smallest exponent of λ which appears in the polynomials $\alpha_{k1}^{(s)}(\lambda), \dots, \alpha_{kr}^{(s)}(\lambda), \beta_{k1}^{(s)}(\lambda), \dots, \beta_{kr}^{(s)}(\lambda)$ with non-zero coefficients $d_{kl1}^{(s)}$ and $d_{kl2}^{(s)}$, and the summation over l in (3.1.66) is over all polynomials containing non-zero coefficients of the $\lambda^{\gamma_k^{(s)}}$.

Since there is no row with number p in $\Delta_{p,(i-1)r+k}(\lambda)$ and no column with number $(i-1)r+k$ (containing l to the power $\lambda\omega^{(i)}$), we can obtain the asymptotic formula

$$\Delta_{p,(i-1)r+k}(\lambda) = \begin{cases} \lambda^{\gamma - \gamma_p} e^{\lambda\omega} E_{p,(i-1)r+k}(\lambda) \\ \qquad \text{for } k = 1, \dots, \tau_j \\ \lambda^{\gamma - \gamma_p} e^{\lambda(\omega - \omega_k^{(i)})} E_{p,(i-1)r+k}(\lambda) \\ \qquad \text{for } k = \tau_j + 1, \dots, r \end{cases} \tag{3.1.67}$$

where $\gamma_{p'}$ is the largest of the $\gamma_p^{(i)}$ (for $i=1, \ldots, n$),

$$\gamma=\sum_{p=1}^{nr}\gamma_p, \quad \omega=\sum_{i=1}^{n}\sum_{k=\tau_j+1}^{r}\omega_k^{(i,2)}$$

and the $E_{p,(i-1)r+k}(\lambda)$ are bounded for large values of λ in the sector (R_j).

We denote by $\Omega_{kl}^{(i,s)}(x, \xi, \lambda)$ the second term in the right-hand side of (3.1.55). Substituting into it the asymptotic representations (3.1.58), (3.1.64), (3.1.67) and (3.1.32), we obtain

$$\Omega_{k,l}^{(i,s)}(x, \xi, \lambda) = \sum_{p=1}^{r}\sum_{q=1}^{nr}\sum_{t=1}^{r}[\omega_{kpqtl}^{(i,s)}(x, \xi)]\,\mathscr{E}_{q,(i-1)r+p}(\lambda)\,w_{t1}^{(s)}w_{p2}^{(i)} \tag{3.1.68}$$

where

$$\omega_{kpqtl}^{(i,s)}(x, \xi)=y_{kp0}^{(i)}(x)\,M_{qt}^{(s)}v_{lt}^{(s)}(\xi) \tag{3.1.69}$$

$$\mathscr{E}_{q,(i-1)r+p}(\lambda)=\frac{E_{q,(i-1)r+p}(\lambda)\,\lambda^{\gamma_q^{(s)}-\gamma_q}}{e^{-\lambda\omega}\Delta_0(\lambda)} \tag{3.1.70}$$

$$w_{p2}^{(i)}=\begin{cases} e^{\lambda\Pi_p x_p^{(i)})} & \text{for } p=1, \ldots, \tau_j \\ e^{-\lambda\Pi_p (x_{0p}^{(i)}-x_p^{(i)})} & \text{for } p=\tau_j+1, \ldots, r \end{cases} \tag{3.1.71}$$

Formulae (3.1.63) and (3.1.68) provide an asymptotic representation of the Green's function $G_{kl}^{(i,s)}(x, \xi, \lambda)$ of Problem (3.1.1)-(3.1.2). With the aid of these formulae, we shall prove the theorem on the expansion of an arbitrary vector-valued function, i.e. the theorem on the representability of an arbitrary vector-valued function $f^{(i)}(x)$ in the form of the limit of integrals over expanding closed curves of the solution to Problem (3.1.1)-(3.1.2).

In the proof of the theorem on the expansion of an arbitrary vector-valued function, we shall use the following lemmas.

Lemma 5 Let c be a non-zero constant and let $\mathscr{E}(\lambda, z, x_1, x_2, \ldots, x_n)$ be a function defined for all values of λ on the expanding contours* C_ν in the half-plane

$$\operatorname{Re} \lambda c \leqslant 0$$

for all z in some interval $(0, Z)$ and $x = (x_1, \ldots, x_n)$ in the closed plane D.

Suppose that the function $\mathscr{E}(\lambda, z, x)$ converges uniformly to zero with respect to $x \in D$ and $z \in (0, Z)$ on the contours C_ν

$$|\mathscr{E}(\lambda, z, x)| \leqslant \varepsilon_\nu \text{ on } \Gamma_\nu$$

for all $x \in D$ and $z \in (0, Z)$, where $\varepsilon_\nu \to 0$ as $\nu \to \infty$. Then, the integrals

$$\int_{C_\nu} \mathscr{E}(\lambda, z, x) e^{c\lambda z} d\lambda, \quad \int_{C_\nu} \mathscr{E}(\lambda, z, x) e^{c\lambda(Z-z)} d\lambda$$

approach zero as $\nu \to \infty$ uniformly with respect to $x \in D$ and $z \in (0, Z)$.

Lemma 6 Suppose that $\mathscr{E}(\lambda, z, x)$ is a function defined on the contours C_ν which is uniformly bounded with respect to $x \in D$ and $z \in (0, Z)$ on C_ν. Suppose also that $\psi(z)$ is an arbitrary absolutely integrable function on the interval $(0, Z)$. Under these conditions, the integral

$$\int_\alpha^\beta \psi(z)\, dz \int_{C_\nu} \mathscr{E}(\lambda, z, x) e^{c\lambda z} \frac{d\lambda}{\lambda}$$

converges to zero uniformly w. r. t. $x \in D$, α, $\beta \in (0, Z)$ as $\nu \to \infty$.

Lemma 7 Suppose that c is a non-zero constant and that $\psi(z)$ is an absolutely integrable function on the interval $(0, Z)$. Then, the integral

$$\int_\alpha^\beta \psi(z) e^{c\lambda z} dz$$

*The contours C_ν are assumed to be uniformly dilated, i.e. it is assumed that $\frac{\text{mes } C_\nu}{r_\nu} \leqslant L$, where r_ν is the distance from the coordinate origin to the closest point of the contour C_ν and L is a constant.

approaches zero uniformly with respect to α, $\beta \in (0, Z)$ as $|\lambda|$ is increased provided λ remains in the half-plane

$$\operatorname{Re} c\lambda \leqslant 0 \tag{3.1.72}$$

Proof of Lemma 5 From the hypothesis of the lemma, we have the inequality

$$\begin{aligned}\left|\int_{C_\nu} \mathscr{E}(\lambda, z, x)\, e^{c\lambda z}\, d\lambda\right| &\leqslant \int_{C_\nu} |\mathscr{E}(\lambda, z, x)|\, |e^{c\lambda z}|\, |d\lambda| \\ &\leqslant \varepsilon_\nu \int_{C_\nu} |e^{c\lambda z}|\, |d\lambda|\end{aligned} \tag{3.1.73}$$

Now, to prove Lemmas 5 and 6, let us find a bound for the integral

$$J_\nu = \int_{C_\nu} |e^{c\lambda z}|\, |d\lambda|$$

Suppose that

$$c\lambda = -|c|\,|\lambda|\, e^{\sqrt{-1}\theta} = -re^{\sqrt{-1}\theta}$$

According to the condition of the lemma, as λ is displaced along the contour C_ν in the positive direction, the angle θ increases monotonically in the interval $\left(-\frac{\pi}{2}, \frac{\pi}{2}\right)$. Also,

$$|c|\,|\lambda| = r \geqslant |c|\, r_\nu, \quad |d\lambda| \leqslant r'_\nu\, d\theta$$

where r_ν is the distance from the coordinate origin of the λ-plane to the closest point on C_ν and r'_ν is the greatest distance between points of C_ν. Now, we have

$$\begin{aligned}J_\nu &= \int_{C_\nu} |e^{c\lambda z}|\, |d\lambda| \leqslant r'_\nu \int_{-\frac{\pi}{2}}^{\frac{\pi}{2}} e^{-r_\nu |c| z \cos\theta}\, d\theta \\ &= 2r'_\nu \int_0^{\frac{\pi}{2}} e^{-r_\nu |c| z \cos\theta}\, d\theta = 2r'_\nu \int_0^{\frac{\pi}{2}} e^{-r_\nu |c| z \sin\left(\frac{\pi}{2}-\theta\right)}\, d\theta \leqslant\end{aligned} \tag{3.1.74}$$

$$\leqslant 2r'_\nu \int_0^{\frac{\pi}{2}} e^{-r_\nu |c| z \frac{2}{\pi}\left(\frac{\pi}{2}-\theta\right)} d\theta$$

$$= 2r'_\nu e^{-r_\nu |c| z} \int_0^{\frac{\pi}{2}} e^{\frac{2r_\nu |c| z}{\pi}\theta} d\theta$$

$$= 2r'_\nu e^{-r_\nu |c| z} \frac{\pi}{2r_\nu |c| z} e^{\frac{2r_\nu |c| z}{\pi}\theta}\Big|_0^{\frac{\pi}{2}} \tag{3.1.74 (cont.)}$$

$$= \frac{\pi}{|c|}\frac{r'_\nu}{r_\nu} e^{-r_\nu |c| z} \frac{e^{r_\nu |c| z}-1}{z}$$

$$= \frac{\pi}{|c|}\frac{r'_\nu}{r_\nu} \frac{1-e^{r_\nu |c| z}}{z} < L\frac{1-e^{-r_\nu |c| z}}{z}$$

where L is a constant independent of ν and z. (This is true because, by virtue of the choice of the contour, the ratio $\frac{r'_\nu}{r_\nu}$ remains bounded as ν increases.)

In accordance with (3.1.74), we obtain from (3.1.73)

$$\left|\int_{C_\nu} \mathscr{E}(\lambda, z, x) e^{c\lambda z} d\lambda\right| \leqslant L\varepsilon_\nu \frac{1-e^{-|c| r_\nu z}}{z}$$

The validity of Lemma 5 follows from this last inequality.

Proof of Lemma 6 From the hypothesis of the lemma, the function $\mathscr{E}(\lambda, z, x)$ is uniformly bounded on the curve C_ν. Consequently, there is a constant C such that, in accordance with (3.1.74)

$$\left|\int_\alpha^\beta \psi(z)\, dz \int_{C_\nu} \mathscr{E}(\lambda, z, x) e^{c\lambda z} \frac{d\lambda}{\lambda}\right|$$

$$\leqslant \int_\alpha^\beta |\psi(z)|\, dz \int_{C_\nu} |\mathscr{E}(\lambda, z, x)|\, |e^{c\lambda z}| \frac{|d\lambda|}{|\lambda|} \tag{3.1.75}$$

$$\leqslant \int_\alpha^\beta |\psi(z)|\, dz \int_{C_\nu} C |e^{c\lambda z}| \frac{|d\lambda|}{r_\nu} = \frac{C}{r_\nu}\int_\alpha^\beta |\psi(z)|\, dz \int_{C_\nu} |e^{c\lambda z}|\,|d\lambda|$$

$$\leqslant \frac{C}{r_\nu} L \int_\alpha^\beta \frac{1-e^{-|c| r_\nu z}}{z} |\psi(z)|\, dz$$

Suppose now that δ_ν is a sequence of positive numbers such that

$$\lim_{\nu\to\infty} \delta_\nu = 0, \qquad \lim_{\nu\to\infty} r_\nu\delta_\nu = +\infty \tag{3.1.76}$$

Obviously, for $[\alpha, \beta] + (0, Z)$, we have

$$\begin{aligned}
\int_\alpha^\beta |\psi(z)| \frac{1-e^{-r_\nu |c| z}}{r_\nu z}\,dz &\leqslant \int_0^Z |\psi(z)| \frac{1-e^{-r_\nu |c| z}}{r_\nu z}\,dz \\
&= \int_0^{\delta_\nu} |\psi(z)| \frac{1-e^{-r_\nu |c| z}}{r_\nu z}\,dz + \int_{\delta_\nu}^Z |\psi(z)| \frac{1-e^{-r_\nu |c| z}}{r_\nu z}\,dz \\
&\leqslant \int_0^{\delta_\nu} |\psi(z)| \frac{1-e^{-r_\nu |c| z}}{r_\nu z}\,dz + \frac{1}{r_\nu\delta_\nu}\int_{\delta_\nu}^Z (1-e^{-r_\nu |c| z})\,|\psi(z)|\,dz \\
&\leqslant \frac{1}{r_\nu\delta_\nu}\int_0^Z |\psi(z)|\,dz + \int_0^{\delta_\nu} |\psi(z)| \frac{1-e^{-r_\nu |c| z}}{r_\nu z}\,dz
\end{aligned} \tag{3.1.77}$$

From the hypothesis of the lemma and the second of Conditions (3.1.76), the first term in the right-hand side of (3.1.77) approaches zero as $\nu \to \infty$.

Furthermore, since the ratio

$$\frac{1-e^{-r_\nu z |c|}}{r_\nu z}$$

approaches a finite limit as $r_\nu z \to 0$, there must exist a constant A such that

$$\left| \frac{1-e^{-r_\nu |c| z}}{r_\nu z} \right| \leqslant A$$

for $z \in [0, \delta]$. Consequently, for the second term in the right-hand side of (3.1.77), we have

$$\int_0^{\delta_\nu} |\psi(z)| \frac{1-e^{-r_\nu |c| z}}{r_\nu z}\,dz \leqslant A \int_0^{\delta_\nu} |\psi(z)|\,dz \tag{3.1.78}$$

In accordance with the first of Relations (3.1.76), it follows from (3.1.78) because of the absolute integrability of the function $\psi(z)$ on the interval $(0, Z)$ that

$$\int_0^{\delta_\nu} |\psi(z)| \frac{1-e^{-r_\nu |c| z}}{r_\nu z}\,dz \to 0 \quad \text{as} \quad \nu \to \infty$$

uniformly with respect to α and β in $(0, Z)$.

Then, because of (3.1.77), the conclusion of Lemma 6 follows from inequality (3.1.75).

Proof of Lemma 7 Let η be any arbitrarily small positive number. There exists a step function $\psi_\eta(z)$ such that the interval $[\alpha, \beta]$ can be represented as the union of intervals $[\alpha_k, \beta_k]$ such that, for $z \in [\alpha_k, \beta_k]$,

$$\psi_\eta(z) = \gamma_k$$

and

$$\int_\alpha^\beta |\psi(z) - \psi_\eta(z)|\, dz < \frac{\eta}{2} \tag{3.1.79}$$

For the function $\psi_\eta(z)$, we have

$$\int_\alpha^\beta e^{c\lambda z}\psi_\eta(z)\, dz = \sum_{k=1}^{n} \int_{\alpha_k}^{\beta_k} e^{c\lambda z}\gamma_k\, dz$$

$$= \sum_{k=1}^{n} \gamma_k \frac{e^{c\lambda z}}{c\lambda}\Bigg|_{\alpha_k}^{\beta_k} = \frac{1}{c\lambda}\sum_{k=1}^{n} \gamma_k (e^{c\lambda\beta_k} - e^{c\lambda\alpha_k})$$

It follows from this and from the hypothesis of the lemma that, for sufficiently large $|\lambda|$,

$$\left|\int_\alpha^\beta e^{c\lambda z}\psi_\eta(z)\, dz\right| \leqslant \frac{2n}{|c||\lambda|}\max|\gamma_k| \leqslant \frac{\eta}{2}$$

Therefore, in view of (3.1.79), we have

$$\left|\int_\alpha^\beta e^{c\lambda z}\psi(z)\, dz\right| \leqslant \int_\alpha^\beta |e^{c\lambda z}||\psi(z) - \psi_\eta(z)|\, dz$$

$$+\left|\int_\alpha^\beta \psi_\eta(z)\, e^{c\lambda z}\, dz\right| \leqslant \frac{\eta}{2} + \frac{\eta}{2} = \eta$$

from which the assertion of the lemma follows.

Theorem 8: the expansion theorem Under the conditions of Theorem 7, there exists a sequence of expanding closed contours Γ_ν (for $\nu=1, 2, \ldots$) such that, for every vector-valued function

$$f^{(i)}(x)=\begin{pmatrix} f_1^{(i)}(x) \\ \vdots \\ f_r^{(i)}(x) \end{pmatrix}$$

satisfying the inequality

$$\int_{a_i}^{b_i} |f_k^{(i)}(x)|^2\,dx<\infty \qquad (k=1, \ldots, r;\ i=1, \ldots, n)$$

the integral

$$\begin{aligned} -\frac{1}{2\pi\sqrt{-1}}\int_{\Gamma_\nu} d\lambda \sum_{j=1}^{n}\int_{a_j}^{b_j} G^{(i,j)}(x, \xi, \lambda)\,[f^{(j)}(\xi)]\,d\xi \\ =-\frac{1}{2\pi\sqrt{-1}}\int_{\Gamma_\nu} d\lambda\, y^{(i)}(x, \lambda, [f(x)])\to (a^{(i)}(x))^{-1} f^{(i)}(x) \end{aligned} \tag{3.1.80}$$

as $\nu\to\infty$, where the arrow means convergence in the sense of the metric L_2.

Proof In accordance with Theorem 7, all the zeros of the characteristic determinant, or of $\Delta_0(\lambda)$, lie in a finite number of strips located in sectors (T_j) (for $j=1, \ldots, 2\mu$) parallel to the rays d_j, and including these rays.

It is clear from (3.1.40) that all the zeros of the characteristic determinant $\Delta(\lambda)$ can be surrounded by circles O_δ of small radius δ with centres at the zeros of this determinant and we can choose a sequence of closed expanding contours Γ_ν which do not intersect the circles O_δ. Here, $\text{mes}\,\Gamma_\nu=O(r_\nu)$, where r_ν is the distance of the closest point on the contour Γ_ν to the origin of the λ-plane.

Keeping (3.1.55) in mind, we obtain

$$\int_{\Gamma_\nu} d\lambda \sum_{l=1}^{r}\sum_{s=1}^{n}\int_{a_s}^{b_s} G_{kl}^{(i,s)}(x, \xi, \lambda)\, f_l^{(s)}(\xi)\,d\xi = I_{ki\nu}^{(1)}(x)+I_{ki\nu}^{(2)}(x) \tag{3.1.81}$$

$$I_{ki\nu}^{(1)}(x)=\sum_{(R_m)}\int_{\Gamma_\nu\cap R_m} d\lambda\left\{\sum_{l=1}^{r}\sum_{s=1}^{n}\int_{a_s}^{b_s} g_{kl0}^{(i,s)}(x, \xi, \lambda)\, f_l^{(s)}(\xi)\,d\xi\right\} \tag{3.1.82}$$

$$I_{ki\nu}^{(2)}(x)=\sum_{(R_m)}\int_{\Gamma_\nu\cap R_m} d\lambda \sum_{l=1}^{r}\sum_{s=1}^{n}\int_{a_s}^{b_s} \Omega_{kl}^{(i,s)}(x, \xi, \lambda)\, f_l^{(s)}(\xi)\,d\xi \tag{3.1.83}$$

where the sum $\sum\limits_{(R_m)}$ is taken over all the sectors (R_m), where $\Gamma_\nu \cap R_m$ is that portion of the contour Γ_ν lying in the sector R_m and $\Omega_{kl}^{(i,s)}$ is the second term in the right-hand side of (3.1.55).

Substituting into (3.1.82) the asymptotic representation of $g_{kl0}^{(i,s)}(x, \xi, \lambda)$ in the sector (R_m) which was given by (3.1.63), we obtain

$$I_{ki\nu}^{(1)}(x) = \sum_{(R_m)} \int_{\Gamma_\nu \cap R_m} d\lambda \sum_{l=1}^{r} \left\{ \int_{a_i}^{x} \sum_{q=1}^{\tau m} [y_{kq0}^{(i)}(x)\, v_{lq}^{(i)}(\xi)] \times \exp(\lambda \Pi_q (x_q^{(i)} - \xi_q^{(i)}))\, f_l^{(i)}(\xi)\, d\xi - \int_{x}^{b_i} \sum_{q=\tau m+1}^{r} [y_{kq0}^{(i)}(x)\, v_{lq}^{(i)}(\xi)] \times \exp(\lambda \Pi_q (x_q^{(i)} - \xi_q^{(i)}))\, f_l^{(i)}(\xi)\, d\xi \right\} \tag{3.1.84}$$

Let us denote by $I_{ki\nu}^{(0)}(x)$ the expression obtained from (3.1.84) by omitting the square brackets. In accordance with (3.1.51) and the notations of (3.1.56) and (3.1.57), all the exponential terms in the right-hand side of (3.1.84) have non-positive real parts

$$\operatorname{Re} \lambda \Pi_q (x_q^{(i)} - \xi_q^{(i)}) \leqslant 0$$

Therefore, in accordance with Lemma 6

$$I_{ki\nu}^{(1)}(x) - I_{ki\nu}^{(0)}(x) \longrightarrow 0 \quad \text{as} \quad \nu \longrightarrow \infty \tag{3.1.85}$$

This convergence is uniform in the interval (a_i, b_i).

Furthermore, we note that the integration with respect to λ in the expression for $I_{ki\nu}^{(0)}(x)$ can be carried out. Specifically, in the first term in the right-hand side of (3.1.84), we have

$$\operatorname{Re} \lambda \Pi_q (x_q^{(i)} - \xi_q^{(i)}) \leqslant 0$$

and $\xi_q^{(i)} < x_q^{(i)}$.

Let us use a single numbering system for all the sectors (R_m). Then, for every q, the sum of all those sectors (R_m) in which

$$\operatorname{Re} \lambda \Pi_q \leqslant 0$$

yields some half-plane (which, when we multiply by $\exp\left(\sqrt{-1} \arg \Pi_q\right)$, coincides with the left hand-plane).

Consequently, for these sectors, we have

$$\sum_{(Rm)} \int_{\Gamma_\nu \cap Rm} \exp(\lambda \Pi_q (x_q^{(i)} - \xi_q^{(i)}))\, d\lambda$$

$$= \sum_{(Rm)} \int_{\Gamma_\nu \cap Rm} \exp\left[\lambda (x_q^{(i)} - \xi_q^{(i)}) \,|\Pi_q|\, \exp\left(\sqrt{-1} \arg \Pi_q\right)\right] d\lambda$$

$$= \int_{\sqrt{-1}\, r_\nu}^{-\sqrt{-1}\, r_\nu} \exp[\mu \,|\Pi_q|\, (x_q^{(i)} - \xi_q^{(i)})] \exp\left(-\sqrt{-1} \arg \Pi_q\right) d\mu$$

$$= \exp\left(-\sqrt{-1} \arg \Pi_q\right) \frac{\exp[\mu \,|\Pi_q|\, (x_q^{(i)} - \xi_q^{(i)})]}{|\Pi_q|\, (x_q^{(i)} - \xi_q^{(i)})} \Bigg|_{\sqrt{-1}\, r_\nu}^{-\sqrt{-1}\, r_\nu}$$

$$= \frac{-2\sqrt{-1} \sin r_\nu \,|\Pi_q|\, (x_q^{(i)} - \xi_q^{(i)})}{e^{\sqrt{-1} \arg \Pi_q} \,|\Pi_q|\, (x_q^{(i)} - \xi_q^{(i)})}$$

where r_ν is the distance from the coordinate origin to the closest point of intersection of the contour Γ_ν with the imaginary axis.

Thus, we have

$$\sum_{(Rm)} \int_{\Gamma_\nu \cap Rm} d\lambda \sum_{l=1}^{r} \left\{ \int_{a_i}^{x} \sum_{q=1}^{\tau m} y_{kq0}^{(i)}(x)\, v_{lq}^{(i)}(\xi) \Big| \exp[\lambda \Pi_q (x_q^{(i)} - \xi_q^{(i)})] f_l^{(i)}(\xi)\, d\xi \right\}$$

$$= -2\sqrt{-1} \sum_{l=1}^{r} \sum_{q=1}^{r} y_{kq0}^{(i)}(x) \tag{3.1.86}$$

$$\times \int_{a_i}^{x} v_{lq}^{(i)}(\xi) \frac{\sin r_\nu \,|\Pi_q|\, (x_q^{(i)} - \xi_q^{(i)})}{\Pi_q (x_q^{(i)} - \xi_q^{(i)})} f_l^{(i)}(\xi)\, d\xi$$

Furthermore, the sum of those sectors R_m. in which

$$\operatorname{Re} \lambda \Pi_q \geqslant 0$$

for some q, yields a half-plane (which, when we multiply by $\exp(\sqrt{-1} \arg \Pi_q)$, coincides with the right half-plane). Every q appears only among the terms in the second summation on the right-hand side of (3.1.84)

Therefore, we obtain by similar calculations

$$-\sum_{Rm}\int_{\Gamma_\nu\cap Rm} d\lambda \sum_{l=1}^{r}\int_{x}^{b_i}\sum_{q=\tau m+1}^{r} y_{kq0}^{(i)}(x)\, v_{lq}^{(i)}(\xi)$$

$$\times \exp[\lambda \Pi_q (x_q^{(i)}-\xi_q^{(i)})]\, f_l^{(i)}(\xi)\, d\xi = -2\sqrt{-1}\sum_{l=1}^{r}\sum_{q=1}^{r} y_{kq0}^{(i)}(x) \quad (3.1.87)$$

$$\times \int_{x}^{b_i} v_{lq}^{(i)}(\xi)\, \frac{\sin r_\nu |\Pi_q| (x_q^{(i)}-\xi_q^{(i)})}{\Pi_q (x_q^{(i)}-\xi_q^{(i)})}\, f_l^{(i)}(\xi)\, d\xi$$

Adding (3.1.86) and (3.1.87), we have

$$I_{ki\nu}^{(0)}(x) = -2\sqrt{-1}\sum_{l=1}^{r}\sum_{q=1}^{r} y_{kq0}^{(i)}(x)$$
$$\times \int_{a_i}^{b_i} v_{lq}^{(i)}(\xi)\, \frac{\sin r_\nu |\Pi_q| (x_q^{(i)}-\xi_q^{(i)})}{\Pi_q (x_q^{(i)}-\xi_q^{(i)})}\, f_l^{(i)}(\xi)\, d\xi \quad (3.1.88)$$

Keeping in mind the equality

$$d\xi = \frac{\Pi_q}{\varphi_q^{(i)}(\xi)}\, d\xi_q^{(i)}$$

which was found from the relation

$$\int_{a_i}^{\xi} \varphi_q^{(i)}(t)\, dt = \Pi_q \xi_q^{(i)}$$

we obtain

$$I_{ki\nu}^{(0)}(x) = -2\sqrt{-1}\sum_{l=1}^{r}\sum_{q=1}^{r} y_{kq0}^{(i)}(x)$$
$$\times \int_{a_i}^{b_i} v_{lq}^{(i)}(\xi)\, \frac{\sin r_\nu |\Pi_q| (x_q^{(i)}-\xi_q^{(i)})}{\varphi_q^{(i)}(\xi)\, (x_q^{(i)}-\xi_q^{(i)})}\, f_l^{(i)}(\xi)\, d\xi_q^{(i)} \quad (3.1.89)$$

According to a familiar formula in the theory of the Fourier transformation, the integral on the right-hand side of (3.1.89) converges, for every function

$$f_l^{(i)}(\xi)\, \frac{v_{lq}^{(i)}(\xi)}{\varphi_q^{(i)}(\xi)}$$

in $L_2(a_i, b_i)$, to

$$\pi \frac{v_{lq}^{(i)}(x) f_l^{(i)}(x)}{\varphi_q^{(i)}(x)}$$

in the sense of the metric $L_2(a_i, b_i)$ as $\nu \to \infty$ (see [36], pages 105-110).

Thus, in accordance with (3.1.85), we have

$$I_{kiv}^{(1)}(x) \to -2\sqrt{-1}\,\pi \sum_{l=1}^{r} \sum_{q=1}^{r} y_{kq0}^{(i)}(x) \frac{v_{lq}^{(i)}(x)}{\varphi_q^{(i)}(x)} f_l^{(i)}(x) \quad (3.1.90)$$

in the sense of the metric of $L_2(a_i, b_i)$ as $\nu \to \infty$.

As can be seen from (3.1.51) and Expressions (3.1.65) and (3.1.71), the real parts in the exponentials $w_{t1}^{(s)}$ and $w_{p2}^{(i)}$ are non-positive.

Consequently, from Lemmas 6 and 7,

$$\int_{a_s}^{b_s} [\omega_{kpqtl}^{(i,s)}(x, \xi)]\, w_{t1}^{(s)} f_l^{(s)}(\xi)\, d\xi \to 0 \quad (3.1.91)$$

as $|\lambda| \to \infty$. On the other hand, in accordance with Theorem 7 and the choice of the contours Γ_ν, the functions $\mathscr{E}_{q,(i-1)r+p}(\lambda)$ are uniformly bounded on the contours Γ_ν, as is clear from (3.1.70).

Furthermore, since the exponent of the function $w_{p2}^{(i)}$ has a non-positive real part for every $p = 1, \ldots, r$, the sum of all the $\Gamma_\nu \cap R_m$ yields that portion of the contour Γ_ν which lies in some half-plane in which the real part of the exponent of the function $w_{p2}^{(i)}$ is non-positive for the given number. We will denote this part of the contour by $\Gamma_\nu^{(1)}$. Then, from (3.1.91) it is clear that

$$I_{kiv}^{(2)}(x) = \sum_{R_m} \int_{\Gamma_\nu \cup R_m} d\lambda \sum_{l=1}^{r} \sum_{s=1}^{n} \int_{a_s}^{b_s} \Omega_{kl}^{(i,s)}(x, \xi, \lambda) f_l^{(s)}(\xi)\, d\xi$$

$$= \sum_{l=1}^{r} \sum_{s=1}^{n} \sum_{p=1}^{r} \sum_{q=1}^{nr} \sum_{t=1}^{r} \int_{\Gamma_\nu^{(1)}} w_{p2}^{(i)} \mathscr{E}_{q,(i-1)r+p}(\lambda)\, d\lambda$$

$$\times \int_{a_s}^{b_s} [\omega_{kpqtl}^{(i,s)}(x, \xi)]\, w_{t1}^{(s)} f_l^{(s)}(\xi)\, d\xi$$

converges uniformly to zero within each interval (a_s, b_s) (for $s=1, \ldots, n$) as $\nu \to \infty$.

Thus, from (3.1.81), (3.1.90) and (3.1.83), we have

$$\int_{\Gamma_\nu} d\lambda \sum_{l=1}^{r} \sum_{s=1}^{n} \int_{a_s}^{b_s} G_{kl}^{(i,s)}(x, \xi, \lambda) f_l^{(s)}(\xi)\, d\xi \to -2\pi\sqrt{-1} \sum_{l=1}^{r} \sum_{q=1}^{r} y_{kq0}^{(i)}(x) \frac{v_{lq}^{(i)}(x)}{\varphi_q^{(i)}(x)} f_l^{(i)}(x) \tag{3.1.92}$$

in the sense of $L_2(a_i, b_i)$.

We rewrite these relations in matrix form

$$\int_{\Gamma_\nu} d\lambda \sum_{s=1}^{n} \int_{a_s}^{b_s} G^{(i,s)}(x, \xi, \lambda) f^{(s)}(\xi)\, d\xi \to -2\pi\sqrt{-1}\, Y_0^{(i)}(x) \times \begin{pmatrix} \frac{1}{\varphi_1^{(i)}(x)} & 0 & 0 \ldots & 0 \\ 0 & \frac{1}{\varphi_2^{(i)}(x)} & 0 \ldots & 0 \\ \ldots & \ldots & \ldots & \ldots \\ 0 & 0 & 0 \ldots & \frac{1}{\varphi_r^{(i)}(x)} \end{pmatrix} V^{(i)}(x) f^{(i)}(x) \tag{3.1.93}$$

Consider the equation

$$Y_0^{(i)}(x) \begin{pmatrix} \varphi_1^{(i)}(x) & 0 & 0 \ldots & 0 \\ 0 & \varphi_2^{(i)}(x) & 0 \ldots & 0 \\ \ldots & \ldots & \ldots & \ldots \\ 0 & 0 & 0 \ldots & \varphi_r^{(i)}(x) \end{pmatrix} = a^{(i)}(x) Y_0^{(i)}(x)$$

obtained by substituting (3.1.14) into the homogeneous system corresponding to System (3.1.1) and by equating coefficients of like powers of λ. From this equation, we have

$$(a^{(i)}(x))^{-1} Y_0^{(i)}(x) \begin{pmatrix} \varphi_1^{(i)}(x) & 0 & 0 \ldots & 0 \\ 0 & \varphi_2^{(i)}(x) & 0 \ldots & 0 \\ \ldots & \ldots & \ldots & \ldots \\ 0 & 0 & 0 \ldots & \varphi_r^{(i)}(x) \end{pmatrix} = Y_0^{(i)}(x)$$

If in (3.1.93) we replace $Y_0^{(i)}(x)$ by the left-hand side of this identity and take (3.1.61) into account, we obtain the assertion of the theorem for $[f(x)]$.

As can be seen from the procedure used in proving this theorem, omission of the square brackets leads to a deviation which approaches zero.

Remarks If the function $f_l^{(i)}(x)$ is absolutely continuous on the interval (a_i, b_i) there will be convergence to the limit in (3.1.80) in the usual (pointwise) sense. Specifically, integrating by parts, we obtain

$$I_{kiv}^{(0)}(x)=\sum_{(Rm)}\int_{\Gamma_v\cap Rm} d\lambda \sum_{l=1}^{r}\Big\{\int_{a_i}^{x}\sum_{q=1}^{\tau m} y_{kq0}^{(i)}(x)v_{lq}^{(i)}(\xi)$$

$$\times\exp\Big(\lambda\int_{\xi}^{x}\varphi_q^{(i)}(t)\,dt\Big)f_l^{(i)}(\xi)\,d\xi-\int_{x}^{b_i}\sum_{q=\tau m+1}^{r} y_{kq0}^{(i)}(x)v_{lq}^{(i)}(\xi)$$

$$\times\exp\Big(\lambda\int_{\xi}^{x}\varphi_q^{(i)}(t)\,dt\Big)f_l^{(i)}(\xi)\,d\xi\Big\}$$

$$=\sum_{(Rm)}\int_{\Gamma_v\cap Rm} d\lambda\sum_{l=1}^{r}\Big\{\sum_{q=1}^{\tau m} y_{kq0}^{(i)}(x)\Big[-\frac{1}{\lambda\varphi_q^{(i)}(\xi)}$$

$$\times\exp\Big(\lambda\int_{\xi}^{x}\varphi_q^{(i)}(t)\,dt\Big)v_{lq}^{(i)}(\xi)f_l^{(i)}(\xi)\Big|_{a_i}^{x}$$

$$+\frac{1}{\lambda}\int_{a_i}^{x}\frac{1}{\varphi_q^{(i)}(\xi)}\exp\Big(\lambda\int_{\xi}^{x}\varphi_q^{(i)}(t)\,dt\Big)\frac{d\big(v_{lq}^{(i)}(\xi)f_l^{(i)}(\xi)\big)}{d\xi}\,d\xi\Big] \qquad (3.1.94)$$

$$+\sum_{q=\tau m+1}^{r} y_{kq0}^{(i)}(x)\Big[\frac{1}{\lambda\varphi_q^{(i)}(\xi)}$$

$$\times\exp\Big(\lambda\int_{\xi}^{x}\varphi_q^{(i)}(t)\,dt\Big)v_{lq}^{(i)}(\xi)f_l^{(i)}(\xi)\Big|_{x}^{b_i}$$

$$-\frac{1}{\lambda}\int_{x}^{b_i}\frac{1}{\varphi_q^{(i)}(\xi)}\exp\Big(\lambda\int_{\xi}^{x}\varphi_q^{(i)}(t)\,dt\Big)\frac{d\big(v_{lq}^{(i)}(\xi)f_l^{(i)}(\xi)\big)}{d\xi}\,d\xi\Big]\Big\}$$

$$=\sum_{(Rm)}\int_{\Gamma_v\cap Rm}\frac{d\lambda}{\lambda}\sum_{l=1}^{r}\Big\{\sum_{q=1}^{\tau m} y_{kq0}^{(i)}(x)\Big[\frac{-v_{lq}^{(i)}(x)}{\varphi_q^{(i)}(x)}f_l^{(i)}(x)$$

$$+\frac{1}{\varphi_q^{(i)}(a_i)}\exp\Big(\lambda\int_{a_i}^{x}\varphi_q^{(i)}(t)\,dt\Big)v_{lq}^{(i)}(a_i)f_l^{(i)}(a_i)\Big]+$$

$$+\sum_{q=\tau m+1}^{r} y^{(i)}_{kq0}(x)\Big[\frac{1}{\varphi^{(i)}_q(b_i)}\exp\Big(\lambda\int_{b_i}^{x}\varphi^{(i)}_q(t)\,dt\Big)$$

$$\times v^{(i)}_{lq}(b_i)\,f^{(i)}_l(b_i)-\frac{1}{\varphi^{(i)}_q(x)}v^{(i)}_{lq}(x)\,f^{(i)}_l(x)\Big]\Big\}$$

$$+\sum_{(Rm)}\int_{\Gamma_\nu\cap Rm}\frac{d\lambda}{\lambda}\sum_{l=1}^{r}\Big\{\sum_{q=1}^{\tau m} y^{(i)}_{kq0}(x)\int_{a_i}^{x}\frac{e^{\lambda\int_\xi^x\varphi^{(i)}_q(t)\,dt}}{\varphi^{(i)}_q(\xi)}$$

$$\times\frac{d\big(v^{(i)}_{lq}(\xi)\,f^{(i)}_l(\xi)\big)}{d\xi}\,d\xi-\sum_{q=\tau m+1}^{r} y^{(i)}_{kq0}(x)\int_{x}^{b_i}\frac{\exp\big(\lambda\int_\xi^x\varphi^{(i)}_q(t)\,dt\big)}{\varphi^{(i)}_q(\xi)}$$

$$\times\frac{d\big(v^{(i)}_{lq}(\xi)\,f^{(i)}_l(\xi)\big)}{d\xi}\,d\xi\Big\}$$

$$=-\int_{\Gamma_\nu}\sum_{l=1}^{r}\sum_{q=1}^{r}\frac{y^{(i)}_{kq0}(x)\,v^{(i)}_{lq}(x)}{\varphi^{(i)}_q(x)}f^{(i)}_l(x)\,\frac{d\lambda}{\lambda}$$

$$+\sum_{(Rm)}\int_{\Gamma_\nu\cap Rm}\frac{d\lambda}{\lambda}\sum_{l=1}^{r}\Big\{\sum_{q=1}^{\tau m} y^{(i)}_{kq0}(x)$$

$$\times\int_{a_i}^{x}\frac{\exp\big(\lambda\int_\xi^x\varphi^{(i)}_q(t)\,dt\big)}{\varphi^{(i)}_q(\xi)}\,\frac{d\big(v^{(i)}_{lq}(\xi)\,f^{(i)}_l(\xi)\big)}{d\xi}\,d\xi \tag{3.1.94 (cont.)}$$

$$-\sum_{q=\tau m+1}^{r} y^{(i)}_{kq0}(x)\int_{x}^{b_i}\frac{\exp\big(\lambda\int_\xi^x\varphi^{(i)}_q(t)\,dt\big)}{\varphi^{(i)}_q(\xi)}\,\frac{d\big(v^{(i)}_{lq}(\xi)\,f^{(i)}_l(\xi)\big)}{d\xi}\,d\xi\Big\}$$

$$=-2\pi\sqrt{-1}\sum_{l=1}^{r}\sum_{q=1}^{r}\frac{y^{(i)}_{kq0}(x)\,v^{(i)}_{lq}(x)}{\varphi^{(i)}_q(x)}f^{(i)}_l(x)$$

$$+\sum_{(Rm)}\int_{\Gamma_\nu\cap Rm}\frac{d\lambda}{\lambda}\sum_{l=1}^{r}\Big\{\sum_{q=1}^{\tau m} y^{(i)}_{kq0}(x)$$

$$\times\int_{a_i}^{x}\frac{\exp\big(\lambda\int_\xi^x\varphi^{(i)}_q(t)\,dt\big)}{\varphi^{(i)}_q(\xi)}\,\frac{d\big(v^{(i)}_{lq}(\xi)\,f^{(i)}_l(\xi)}{d\xi}\,d\xi$$

$$-\sum_{q=\tau m+1}^{r} y^{(i)}_{kq0}(x)\int_{x}^{b_i}\frac{\exp\big(\lambda\int_\xi^x\varphi^{(i)}_q(t)\,dt\big)}{\varphi^{(i)}_q(\xi)}\,\frac{d\big(v^{(i)}_{lq}(\xi)\,f^{(i)}_l(\xi)\big)}{d\xi}\,d\xi\Big\}$$

In accordance with Lemma 6, both the summation $\sum\limits_{R_m}$ in the right-hand side of (3.1.94) and the difference $I_{hiv}^{(1)}(x) - I_{hiv}^{(0)}(x)$ approach zero uniformly in the interval (a_i, b_i) as $\nu \to \infty$.

3.2 THEOREM ON THE EXPANSION IN SERIES OF RESIDUES OF SOLUTIONS OF BOUNDARY-VALUE PROBLEMS WITH A PARAMETER FOR SYSTEMS OF ORDINARY DIFFERENTIAL EQUATIONS WITH DISCONTINUOUS COEFFICIENTS

This section is devoted to a proof of the basic theorem on the expansion of an arbitrary vector-valued function $\Phi^{(i)}(x)$ in a series of residues of the solution $v^{(i)}(x, \Phi, \lambda)$ of System (3.2.1) of ordinary linear differential equations with discontinuous coefficients under a boundary condition relating the values of the vector-valued function $v^{(i)}$ at points of discontinuity of the coefficients (see (3.2.16)).

Formula (3.2.16), which is proved in this section, is necessary for obtaining a residue representation of a sufficiently smooth solution of the corresponding mixed problem with boundary condition containing time derivatives of the unknown function (see Theorem 11). It should be noted that (3.2.16) leads directly to a formula giving the expansion of an arbitrary vector-valued function $\Phi_{q-1}^{(i)}(x)$ in a series of residues of the solution of the spectral problem (3.2.7)-(3.2.8). This last formula is a generalisation of the familiar Birkhoff-Tamarkin formula to the case of a system of equations with discontinuous coefficients and with boundary conditions relating the values of the unknown function at points of discontinuity of the coefficients of the system.

We shall consider the problem of finding the solution of the system

$$v_{k+1}^{(i)} - \lambda^m v_k^{(i)} = \Phi_k^{(i)}(x)$$

$$(k = 0, 1, \ldots, q-2)$$

$$\sum_{\substack{mk+l \leq p \\ k \leq q-1}} A_{kl}^{(i)}(x) \frac{d^l v_k^{(i)}}{dx^l} - \lambda^m v_{q-1}^{(i)} = \Phi_{q-1}^{(i)}(x) \tag{3.2.1}$$

$$\text{for } x \in (a_i, b_i)$$

with boundary condition

$$\sum_{i=1}^{n} \sum_{\substack{k\leqslant q-1\\ l\leqslant p-1}} \left\{\alpha_{kl}^{(i)} \frac{d^l v_k^{(i)}}{dx^l}\bigg|_{x=a_i} + \beta_{kl}^{(i)} \frac{d^l v_k^{(i)}}{dx^l}\bigg|_{x=b_i}\right\}$$

$$+\lambda^m \sum_{i=1}^{n} \sum_{l=0}^{p-1} \left\{\alpha_{ql}^{(i)} \frac{d^l v_{q-1}^{(i)}}{dx^l}\bigg|_{x=a_i} + \beta_{ql}^{(i)} \frac{d^l v_{q-1}^{(i)}}{dx^l}\bigg|_{x=b_i}\right\} = 0 \tag{3.2.2}$$

where m, q and p are arbitrary natural numbers satisfying the condition $p=mq$, $A_{kl}^{(i)}(x)$ is an r-dimensional square matrix of the functions $A_{jskl}^{(i)}(x)$ defined on the interval $[a_i, b_i]$, the $\Phi_k^{(i)}(x)$ are r-dimensional vector-valued functions defined on the interval $[a_i, b_i]$, $\alpha_{kl}^{(i)}$ and $\beta_{kl}^{(i)}$ are constant $nrp\times r$ matrices and the (a_i, b_i) (for $i=1, \ldots, n$) are disjoint intervals with common end-points, all contained in $[a_1, b_n]$. We shall call the boundary-value problem (3.2.1)-(3.2.2) a 'spectral problem' (it corresponds to the mixed problem (4.1.5)-(4.1.7) of Section 3.1).

The basic theorem (Theorem 9) of this section is proved by reducing Problem (3.2.1)-(3.2.2) to the spectral problem for a system of first-order equations. To simplify the formulation of Theorem 9, we will make this reduction in advance.

Let us fix s among the numbers $0, 1, \ldots, q-1$. From the first equations of System (3.2.1) for arbitrary natural $k\leqslant q-1$, we have

$$v_k^{(i)} = \begin{cases} \lambda^{m(k-s)} v_s^{(i)} - \lambda^{mk}\left(\lambda^{-m(k+1)}\Phi_k^{(i)}(x) + \ldots + \lambda^{-ms}\Phi_{s-1}^{(i)}(x)\right) \\ \text{for } k<s \\ v_s^{(i)} \\ \text{for } k=s \\ \lambda^{m(k-s)} v_s^{(i)} + \lambda^{mk}\left(\lambda^{-m(s+1)}\Phi_s^{(i)}(x) + \ldots + \lambda^{-mk}\Phi_{k-1}^{(i)}(x)\right) \\ \text{for } k>s \end{cases}$$

Substituting this expression for $v_k^{(i)}$ into the last of Equations (3.2.1) and the boundary condition (3.2.2), we arrive at the problem of finding the solution $v_s^{(i)}$ of the system

$$\sum_{\substack{k\leqslant q-1\\ mk+l\leqslant p}} \lambda^{m(k-s)} A_{kl}^{(i)}(x) \frac{d^l v_s^{(i)}}{dx^l} - \lambda^{m(q-s)} v_s^{(i)} = F_s^{(i)}(x, \Phi, \lambda^m) \quad (3.2.3)$$

with boundary condition

$$\sum_{i=1}^{n} \sum_{k\leqslant q}^{l\leqslant p-1} \lambda^{m(k-s)} \left\{ \alpha_{kl}^{(i)} \frac{d^l v_s^{(i)}}{dx^l}\bigg|_{x=a_i} + \beta_{kl}^{(i)} \frac{d^l v_s^{(i)}}{dx^l}\bigg|_{x=b_i} \right\} = N_{sm}(\Phi, \lambda^m) \quad (3.2.4)$$

where

$$\begin{aligned} F_s^{(i)}(x, \Phi, \lambda^m) = \Phi_{q-1}^{(i)}(x) + \sum_{\substack{k<s\\ mk+l\leqslant p}} \lambda^{mk} A_{kl}^{(i)}(x) \frac{d^l}{dx^l} (\lambda^{-m(k+1)} \Phi_k^{(i)}(x) \\ + \ldots + \lambda^{-ms} \Phi_{s-1}^{(i)}(x)) - \sum_{\substack{q-1\geqslant k>s\\ mk+l\leqslant p}} \lambda^{mk} A_{kl}^{(i)}(x) \\ \times \frac{d^l}{dx^l} (\lambda^{-m(s+1)} \Phi_s^{(i)}(x) + \ldots + \lambda^{-mk} \Phi_{k-1}^{(i)}(x)) \\ + \lambda^{mq} (\lambda^{-m(s+1)} \Phi_s^{(i)}(x) + \ldots + \lambda^{-m(q-1)} \Phi_{q-2}^{(i)}(x)) \end{aligned} \quad (3.2.5)$$

(for $s=q-1$, the last term on the right will be missing) and where

$$\begin{aligned} N_{s,m}(\Phi, \lambda^m) \\ = \sum_{i=1}^{n} \sum_{\substack{l\leqslant p-1\\ 1\leqslant k<s}} \left\{ \alpha_{kl}^{(i)} \frac{d^l}{dx^l} (\lambda^{-m} \Phi_k^{(i)}(x) + \ldots + \lambda^{-m(s-k)} \Phi_{s-1}^{(i)}(x)) \right|_{x=a_i} \\ + \beta_{kl}^{(i)} \frac{d^l}{dx^l} (\lambda^{-m(s-k)} \Phi_{s-1}^{(i)}(x) + \ldots + \lambda^{-m} \Phi_k^{(i)}(x)) \bigg|_{x=b_i} \bigg\} \\ - \sum_{i=1}^{n} \sum_{l\leqslant p-1}^{s<k\leqslant q-2} \left\{ \alpha_{kl}^{(i)} \frac{d^l}{dx^l} (\lambda^{m(k-s-1)} \Phi_s^{(i)}(x) + \ldots + \Phi_{k-1}^{(i)}(x)) \right|_{x=a_i} \\ + \beta_{kl}^{(i)} \frac{d^l}{dx^l} (\lambda^{m(k-s-1)} \Phi_s^{(i)}(x) + \ldots + \Phi_{k-1}^{(i)}(x)) \bigg|_{x=b_i} \bigg\} \\ - \sum_{i=1}^{n} \sum_{l=0}^{p-1} \bigg\{ (\alpha_{q-1l}^{(i)} + \lambda^m \alpha_{ql}^{(i)}) \\ \times \frac{d^l}{dx^l} (\lambda^{m(q-2-s)} \Phi_s^{(i)}(x) + \ldots + \Phi_{q-2}^{(i)}(x)) \bigg|_{x=a_i} \\ + (\beta_{q-1l}^{(i)} + \lambda^m \beta_{ql}^{(i)}) \frac{d^l}{dx^l} (\lambda^{m(q-2-s)} \Phi_s^{(i)}(x) + \ldots + \Phi_{q-2}^{(i)}(x)) \bigg|_{x=b_i} \bigg\} \end{aligned} \quad (3.2.6)$$

We will call Problem (3.2.3)-(3.2.4) the 's-auxiliary spectral problem'.

For $s=0$ we obtain from (3.2.3)-(3.2.4) a zero-auxiliary spectral problem the solution of which will appear in the residue representation of the solution of the mixed problem of Section 4.1 (see 4.1.8).

In connection with this, let us write the zero-auxiliary spectral problem

$$\sum_{\substack{k\leqslant q-1\\ mk+l\leqslant p}} \lambda^{mk} A_{kl}^{(i)}(x) \frac{d^l v_0^{(i)}}{dx^l} - \lambda^p v_0^{(i)} = F_0^{(i)}(x, \Phi, \lambda^m) \quad (3.2.7)$$

$$\sum_{i=1}^{n} \sum_{\substack{k\leqslant q\\ l\leqslant p-1}} \lambda^{mk} \left\{ \alpha_{kl}^{(i)} \frac{d^l v_0^{(i)}}{dx^l}\bigg|_{x=a_i} + \beta_{kl}^{(i)} \frac{d^l v_0^{(i)}}{dx^l}\bigg|_{x=b_i} \right\} = N_{0,m}(\Phi, \lambda^m) \quad (3.2.8)$$

where

$$F_0^{(i)}(x, \Phi, \lambda^m) = \sum_{j=0}^{q-1} \lambda^{m(q-1-j)} \Phi_j^{(i)}(x)$$
$$- \sum_{1\leqslant k\leqslant q-1}^{mk+l\leqslant p} A_{kl}^{(i)}(x) \frac{d^l}{dx^l} (\lambda^{m(k-1)} \Phi_0^{(i)}(x) + \ldots + \Phi_{k-1}^{(i)}(x)) \quad (3.2.9)$$

and

$$N_{0,m}(\Phi, \lambda^m)$$
$$= -\sum_{i=1}^{n} \sum_{\substack{0<k\leqslant q-2\\ l\leqslant p-1}} \left\{ \alpha_{kl}^{(i)} \frac{d^l}{dx^l} (\lambda^{m(k-1)} \Phi_0^{(i)}(x) + \ldots + \Phi_{k-1}^{(i)}(x))\big|_{x=a_i} \right.$$
$$\left. + \beta_{kl}^{(i)} \frac{d^l}{dx^l} (\lambda^{m(k-1)} \Phi_0^{(i)}(x) + \ldots + \Phi_{k-1}^{(i)}(x))\big|_{x=b_i} \right\}$$
$$- \sum_{i=1}^{n} \sum_{l=0}^{p-1} \left\{ (\alpha_{q-1,l}^{(i)} + \lambda^m \alpha_{ql}^{(i)}) \right. \quad (3.2.10)$$
$$\times \frac{d^l}{dx^l} (\lambda^{m(q-2)} \Phi_0^{(i)}(x) + \ldots + \Phi_{q-2}^{(i)}(x))\big|_{x=a_i}$$
$$+ (\beta_{q-1,l}^{(i)} + \lambda^m \beta_{ql}^{(i)})$$
$$\left. \times \frac{d^l}{dx^l} (\lambda^{m(q-2)} \Phi_0^{(i)}(x) + \ldots + \Phi_{q-2}^{(i)}(x))\big|_{x=b_i} \right\}$$

Now, to reduce Problem (3.2.3)-(3.2.4) to the spectral problem for a system of first-order equations, we make the following change of unknown vector-valued functions:

$$\lambda^{-l}\frac{d^l v_s^{(i)}}{dx^l}=w_{sl}^{(i)} \tag{3.2.11}$$

If we make this substitution in System (3.2.3) and the boundary condition (3.2.4), we obtain the spectral problem for a system of first-order equations

$$\begin{gathered}
\frac{dw_{sk}^{(i)}}{dx}-\lambda w_{s,k+1}^{(i)}=0 \quad (k=0, \ldots, p-2) \\
\lambda^{p-1-ms}A_{0p}^{(i)}(x)\frac{dw_{s,p-1}^{(i)}}{dx} \\
+\sum_{\substack{k\leqslant q-1\\ l\leqslant p-1\\ mk+l\leqslant p}}\lambda^{m(k-s)+l}A_{kl}^{(i)}(x)\,w_{sl}^{(i)}-\lambda^{m(q-s)}w_{s0}^{(i)} \\
=F_s^{(i)}(x, \Phi, \lambda^m), \qquad x\in(a_i, b_i)
\end{gathered} \tag{3.2.12}$$

$$\sum_{i=1}^{n}\sum_{\substack{l\leqslant p-1\\ k\leqslant q}}\lambda^{mk+l-ms}\{\alpha_{kl}^{(i)}w_{sl}^{(i)}(a_i)+\beta_{kl}^{(i)}w_{sl}^{(i)}(b_i)\}=N_{sm}(\Phi, \lambda^m) \tag{3.2.13}$$

Suppose that the following conditions are satisfied.

1. The functions $A_{kl}^{(i)}(x)$ are continuous for $x\in[a_i, b_i]$. For $mk+l=p$, these functions have continuous derivatives of first and second orders; for $mk+l=p-1$, they have continuous first derivatives and the determinant of the matrix $A_{0p}^{(i)}(x)$ is non-zero.
2. The roots $\psi_1^{(i)}(x), \psi_2^{(i)}(x), \ldots, \psi_{rp}^{(i)}(x)$ of the characteristic equations

$$\det(\theta^p A_{0p}^{(i)}(x)+\theta^{p-m}A_{1,(q-1)m}^{(i)}(x)+\ldots+\theta^m A_{q-1,m}^{(i)}(x)-E)=0$$
$$(i=1, 2, \ldots, n) \tag{3.2.14}$$

are distinct and non-zero for $x\in(a_i, b_i)$. Both their arguments and the arguments of their differences are independent of x (and hence of the index i).

3. The functions $\Phi_{k-1}^{(i)}(x)$ have continuous derivatives of the first $p-mk$ orders on the interval $[a_i, b_i]$.
4. For sufficiently large λ and for every $s=0, 1, \ldots, q-1$, the following relations hold*

$$\lambda^{m(s+1)-ps}N_{s,m}(\Phi, \lambda^m)=O(1) \tag{3.2.15}$$

*Clearly, if the derivatives of Φ which appear in the expression N_{sm} vanish at the end-points of (a_i, b_i), this condition will be satisfied. Its satisfaction depends both on Φ and on the structure of the boundary condition of the problem.

where $p_s - ms$ is the smallest power of λ in the left-hand side of (3.2.13) with non-zero matrix coefficient.

5. For sufficiently large λ, the rank of the matrix

$$(\alpha_0^{(1)}(\lambda), \ldots, \alpha_{p-1}^{(1)}(\lambda), \ldots, \alpha_0^{(n)}(\lambda), \ldots, \alpha_{p-1}^{(n)}(\lambda)$$
$$\beta_0^{(1)}(\lambda), \ldots, \beta_{p-1}^{(1)}(\lambda), \ldots, \beta_0^{(n)}(\lambda), \ldots, \beta_{p-1}^{(n)}(\lambda))$$

is equal to nrp, where

$$\alpha_j^{(s)}(\lambda) = \sum_{k=0}^{q} \lambda^{mk+j} \alpha_{kj}^{(s)}, \quad \beta_j^{(s)}(\lambda) = \sum_{k=0}^{q} \lambda^{mk+j} \beta_{kj}^{(s)}$$

6. All the numbers M_{1j}, $M_{\sigma_j j}$ for the characteristic determinant $\Delta(\lambda)$ of Problem (3.2.12)-(3.2.13) are non-zero.

Under these conditions, we shall prove the following basic theorem on expansion of an arbitrary vector-valued function.

Theorem 9 Under Conditions 1-6, the formula

$$-\frac{1}{2\pi\sqrt{-1}} \sum_{\nu} \int_{c_\nu} \lambda^{m-1} v_s^{(i)}(x, \Phi, \lambda)\, d\lambda = \Phi_s^{(i)}(x) \qquad (3.2.16)$$

$$(s = 0, \ldots, q-1;\ i = 1, \ldots, n)$$

holds, where $v_s^{(i)}(x, \Phi, \lambda)$ is a solution of Problem (3.2.3)-(3.2.4) and c_ν is a simple closed contour in the λ-plane which encircles only one pole λ_ν of the integrand. The summation with respect to ν is over all poles of this function, and the convergence of the series (3.2.16) is to be understood in the sense of the metric $L_2(a_i, b_i)$.

Proof It is clear from (3.2.5) that the coefficient of the highest power of λ in the expression $\lambda^{ms+1-p} F_s(x, \Phi, \lambda^m)$ is $\Phi_s^{(i)}(x)$. Consequently, by using Birkhoff's notation, when we multiply both sides of the last equation in System (3.2.12) on the left by $\lambda^{ms+1-p}(A_{0p}^{(i)}(x))^{-1}$ we reduce the system to the form

$$\frac{dw_{s,k}^{(i)}}{dx} - \lambda w_{s,k+1}^{(i)} = 0 \qquad (k = 0, \ldots, p-2)$$

$$\frac{dw_{s,p-1}}{dx} + \sum_{\substack{k \le q-1 \\ l \le p-1 \\ mk+l \le p}} \lambda^{mk+l-p+1} (A_{0p}^{(i)}(x))^{-1} A_{kl}^{(i)}(x) w_{sl}^{(i)}$$
$$- \lambda (A_{0p}^{(i)}(x))^{-1} w_{s,0}^{(i)} = \lambda^{-m+1} [(A_{0p}^{(i)}(x))^{-1} \Phi_s^{(i)}(x)] \qquad (3.2.17)$$
$$x \in (a_i, b_i)$$

Furthermore, in accordance with Condition 4, we have

$$\lambda^{m(s+1)-p_s} N_{s,m}(\Phi, \lambda^m) = [R_{s,m}]$$

where the $R_{s,m}$ are constant matrices. Therefore, the boundary condition (3.2.13) can be written

$$\sum_{i=1}^{n} \sum_{\substack{l \leqslant p-1 \\ k \leqslant q \\ p_s \leqslant mk+l}} \lambda^{mk+l-p_s} \{\alpha_{kl}^{(i)} w_{sl}^{(i)}(a_i) + \beta_{kl}^{(i)} w_{sl}^{(i)}(b_i)\} = \lambda^{-m} [R_{s,m}] \tag{3.2.18}$$

Thus, Problem (3.2.12)-(3.2.13) is reduced to the spectral problem (3.2.17)-(3.2.18) for a system of first-order equations. Since the boundary condition (3.2.18) is nonhomogeneous, however, we may not apply to it the result of Section 3.1. Let us therefore consider reducing (3.2.18) to a homogeneous boundary condition. First, we note that, on the basis of Condition 5, we may, for sufficiently large λ, choose numerical columns

$$Z_{s,l,m}^{(i)}(a_i, \lambda) = \lambda^{-m} [C_{s,l,m}^{(i)}], \quad Z_{slm}^{(i)}(b_i, \lambda) = \lambda^{-m} [D_{slm}^{(i)}]$$

satisfying the boundary conditions (3.2.18).

Obviously, the functional columns constructed from these columns

$$Z_{slm}^{(i)}(x, \lambda) = \lambda^{-m} \left\{ [C_{slm}^{(i)}] + \frac{x-a_i}{b_i-a_i} [D_{slm}^{(i)} - C_{slm}^{(i)}] \right\}$$

satisfy (3.2.18). Consequently, the substitution

$$y_{sl}^{(i)} = w_{sl}^{(i)} - Z_{slm}^{(i)}(x, \lambda) \tag{3.2.19}$$

into (3.2.17) and (3.2.18) leads to the problem of finding the solution $y_{sl}^{(i)}$ of the system

$$\frac{dy_{sk}^{(i)}}{dx} - \lambda y_{s,k+1}^{(i)} = \lambda^{-m+1} [Z_{s,k+1,m,0}(x)] \qquad (k = 0, \ldots, p-2)$$

$$\frac{dy_{s,p-1}^{(i)}}{dx} + \sum_{\substack{k \leqslant q-1 \\ l \leqslant p-1 \\ mk+l \leqslant p}} \lambda^{mk+l-p+1} (A_{0p}^{(i)}(x))^{-1} A_{kl}^{(i)}(x) y_{sl}^{(i)} \tag{3.2.20}$$

$$- \lambda (A_{0p}^{(i)}(x))^{-1} y_{s,0}^{(i)} = [f_{s,m}^{(i)}(x)] \lambda^{-m+1}$$

with homogeneous boundary condition

$$\sum_{i=1}^{n} \sum_{\substack{l \leqslant p-1 \\ k \leqslant q \\ p_s \leqslant mk+l}} \lambda^{mk+l-p_s} \{\alpha_{kl}^{(i)} y_{sl}^{(i)}(a_i) + \beta_{kl}^{(i)} y_{sl}^{(i)}(b_i)\} = 0 \tag{3.2.21}$$

where

$$Z_{skm0}^{(i)}(x) = C_{skm}^{(i)} + \frac{x-a_i}{b_i-a_i}(D_{skm}^{(i)} - C_{skm}^{(i)}) \tag{3.2.22}$$

$$\begin{aligned} f_{sm}^{(i)}(x) = (A_{0p}^{(i)}(x))^{-1}\Phi_s^{(i)}(x) + (A_{0p}^{(i)}(x))^{-1} Z_{s0m0}^{(i)}(x) \\ -(A_{0p}^{(i)}(x))^{-1}(A_{q-1,\,m}^{(i)}(x) Z_{smm0}^{(i)}(x) \\ + \ldots + A_{1,(q-1)m}^{(i)}(x) Z_{s,(q-1)m,\,m,\,0}^{(i)}(x)) \end{aligned} \tag{3.2.23}$$

Let us now show that, under Conditions 1-6 of this section, i.e. under the conditions of Theorem 9, all the conditions of Theorem 8 are satisfied for Problem (3.2.20)-(3.2.21). First of all, we note that Problems (3.2.12)-(3.2.13) and (3.2.20)-(3.2.21) have the same characteristic determinant $\Delta(\lambda)$ and the same numbers M_{1j}, $M_{\sigma_j j}$. Consequently, in accordance with Condition 6, the corresponding condition of Theorem 8 is satisfied for Problem (3.2.20)-(3.2.21).

Let us now show that Condition 2 of Theorem 8 is satisfied for Problem (3.2.20)-(3.2.21). For this, it will be sufficient to show that the characteristic equation for System (3.2.20) is equivalent to (3.2.14). This is true because the characteristic equation for (3.2.20) is of the form

$$\det(B^{(i)}(x) - \theta E) = 0 \tag{3.2.24}$$

where E is the unit matrix of appropriate dimensions and $B^{(i)}(x)$ is the square matrix composed of the square $\overline{r}$-dimensional matrix cells $B_{ks}^{(i)}(x)$ (for $k, s = 1, 2, \ldots, p$). Here for $k \neq p$

$$B_{ks}^{(i)}(x) = \begin{cases} e & \text{for } k = s-1 \\ 0 & \text{for } k \neq s-1 \end{cases} \tag{3.2.25}$$

where e is a unit matrix of order r and 0 is the zero matrix of the same order. For the cells in the p th row,

$$\begin{aligned} &B_{p,1}^{(i)}(x) = (A_{0p}^{(i)}(x))^{-1}, \quad B_{p,2}^{(i)} = B_{p,3}^{(i)} = \ldots = B_{p,m}^{(i)} = 0 \\ &B_{p,\,m+1}^{(i)} = -(A_{0p}^{(i)}(x))^{-1} A_{q-1,\,m}^{(i)}(x) \\ &B_{p,\,m+2}^{(i)} = B_{p,\,m+3}^{(i)} = \ldots = B_{p,\,2m}^{(i)} = 0 \\ &\ldots\ldots\ldots\ldots\ldots\ldots\ldots\ldots \\ &B_{p,\,p-m+1}^{(i)}(x) = -(A_{0p}^{(i)}(x))^{-1} A_{1,(q-1)m}^{(i)}(x) \\ &B_{p,\,p-m+2}^{(i)}(x) = B_{p,\,p-m+3}^{(i)}(x) = \ldots = B_{p,\,p}^{(i)}(x) = 0 \end{aligned} \tag{3.2.26}$$

The matrix columns numbered $1, m+1, 2m+1, \ldots, (q-1)m + 1, qm$ of the determinant $\det (B^{(i)}(x) - \theta E)$ are multiplied, respectively, by $1, \theta^m, \theta^{2m}, \ldots, \theta^{(q-1)m}, \theta^{qm-1}$ and added to the last matrix column of that determinant. By successive application of Laplace's theorem to the determinant thus obtained, (3.2.24) is transformed into (3.2.14).

Consequently, in accordance with Theorem 5, Condition 3 of Theorem 8 is satisfied for Problem (3.2.20)-(3.2.21). In accordance with Condition 1 of Theorem 9, Condition 1 of Theorem 8 is satisfied for Problem (3.2.20)-(3.2.21). Thus, Theorem 8 is applicable to this problem.

Applying Theorem 8 to the problem, we see that

$$-\frac{1}{2\pi\sqrt{-1}} \int_{\Gamma_\nu} \lambda^{m-1} \begin{pmatrix} y_{s0}^{(i)}(x, \lambda) \\ \vdots \\ y_{s,p-1}^{(i)}(x, \lambda) \end{pmatrix} d\lambda \to (B^{(i)}(x))^{-1} \times \begin{pmatrix} Z_{s,1,m,0}^{(i)}(x) \\ \vdots \\ Z_{s,p-1,m,0}^{(i)}(x) \\ f_{sm}^{(i)}(x) \end{pmatrix} \tag{3.2.27}$$

as $\nu \to \infty$, where Γ_ν is a sequence of simple expanding closed contours lying at a positive distance from the zeros of the characteristic determinant $\Delta(\lambda)$ of (3.2.20)-(3.2.21).

Suppose that the matrix $(B^{(i)}(x))^{-1}$ consists of square matrix cells $(B^{(i)}(x))_{k,s}^{-1}$ of order r. With the aid of some simple calculations, we see that, for $k \neq 1$

$$(B^{(i)}(x))_{k,s}^{-1} = \begin{cases} e, & \text{for } k = s+1 \\ 0, & \text{for } k \neq s+1 \end{cases}$$

With regard to the cells in the first row,

$$(B^{(i)}(x))_{1,1}^{-1} = \ldots = (B^{(i)}(x))_{1,m-1}^{-1} = 0$$
$$(B^{(i)}(x))_{1,m}^{-1} = A_{q-1,m}^{(i)}(x)$$
$$(B^{(i)}(x))_{1,m+1}^{-1} = \ldots = (B^{(i)}(x))_{1,2m-1}^{-1} = 0$$
$$(B^{(i)}(x))_{1,2m}^{(i)} = A_{q-2,2m}^{(i)}(x)$$
$$(B^{(i)}(x))_{1,p-m+1}^{-1} = \ldots = (B^{(i)}(x))_{1,p-1} = 0$$
$$(B^{(i)}(x))_{1,p}^{-1} = A_{0p}^{(i)}(x)$$

For the right-hand side of (3.2.27), we have

$$(B^{(i)}(x))^{-1}\begin{pmatrix} Z^{(1)}_{s,1,m,0}(x) \\ \vdots \\ Z^{(i)}_{s,p-1,m,0}(x) \\ f^{(i)}_{s,m}(x) \end{pmatrix} = \begin{pmatrix} \Phi^{(i)}_s(x) + Z^{(i)}_{s,0,m,0}(x) \\ Z^{(i)}_{s,1,m,0}(x) \\ \vdots \\ Z^{(i)}_{s,p-1,m,0}(x) \end{pmatrix}$$

Consequently, returning to $w^{(i)}$ in accordance with (3.2.19), we obtain from (3.2.27)

$$-\frac{1}{2\pi\sqrt{-1}}\int_{\Gamma_\nu}\lambda^{m-1}\begin{pmatrix} w^{(i)}_{s,0}(x,\lambda) \\ \vdots \\ w^{(i)}_{s,p-1}(x,\lambda) \end{pmatrix} d\lambda \to \begin{pmatrix} \Phi^{(i)}_s(x) \\ 0 \\ \vdots \\ 0 \end{pmatrix} \qquad (3.2.28)$$

as $\nu \to \infty$

Finally, in accordance with the substitution (3.2.11), we obtain from (3.2.28)

$$\frac{-1}{2\pi\sqrt{-1}}\int_{\Gamma_\nu}\lambda^{m-1}v^{(i)}_s(x,\Phi,\lambda)\,d\lambda \to \Phi^{(i)}_s(x) \quad \text{as} \quad \nu \to \infty$$

where convergence is understood in the sense of $L_2(a_i, b_i)$.

Since $v^{(i)}_s(x, \Phi, \lambda)$ is a meromorphic function of λ, this last formula can also be written in the form (3.2.16), which completes the proof.

A consequence Let us now show that Theorem 9 immediately leads to a theorem on the expansion of an arbitrary vector-valued function $\Phi^{(i)}_{q-1}(x)$ in a series of residues of the solution of the zero-auxiliary spectral problem, i.e. of Problem (3.2.7)-(3.2.8) obtained from (3.2.3)-(3.2.4) for $s=0$.

From the first $q-1$ equations of System (3.2.1) for arbitrary s (where $s = 1, 2, \ldots, q-1$), we obtain, by expressing the $v^{(i)}_s$ in terms of the $v^{(i)}_0$ and substituting the result into (3.2.16),

$$\frac{-1}{2\pi\sqrt{-1}}\sum_\nu\int_{c_\nu}\lambda^{m-1}$$

$$\times\{\lambda^{ms}v^{(i)}_0(x,\Phi,\lambda)+\lambda^{m(s-1)}\Phi^{(i)}_0+\ldots+\Phi^{(i)}_{s-1}\}\,d\lambda$$

$$= -\frac{1}{2\pi\sqrt{-1}}\sum_\nu\int_{c_\nu}\lambda^{m(s+1)-1}v^{(i)}_0(x,\Phi,\lambda)\,d\lambda$$

$$=\Phi^{(i)}_s(x) \quad (s=0,\ldots,q-1) \qquad (3.2.29)$$

Let $G^{(i,j)}(x, \xi, \lambda)$ denote the Green's matrix of the zero-auxiliary spectral problem (3.2.7)-(3.2.8) and let $\Delta^{(i)}(x, \Phi, \lambda)$ denote that solution of the homogeneous system corresponding to System (3.2.7) which satisfies the non-homogeneous boundary conditions (3.2.8). Then, obviously, the solution $v_0^{(i)}(x, \Phi, \lambda)$ of the zero-auxiliary spectral problem (3.2.7)-(3.2.8) can be represented for $x \in (a_i, b_i)$ in the form

$$v_0^{(i)}(x, \Phi, \lambda) = \sum_{j=1}^{n} \int_{a_j}^{b_j} G^{(i,j)}(x, \xi, \lambda) F_0^{(j)}(\xi, \Phi, \lambda^m)\, d\xi + \Delta^{(i)}(x, \Phi, \lambda) \tag{3.2.30}$$

For $\Delta^{(i)}(x, \Phi, \lambda)$, it is easy to obtain a representation in which the nature of the dependence of this function on Φ shows up very clearly. Let the rth-order square matrices

$$V_{0k}^{(i)}(x, \lambda) \quad (k = 1, 2, \ldots, p)$$

denote the set of all independent solutions of the homogeneous system corresponding to System (3.2.7).

Obviously, the general solution of this homogeneous system is of the form

$$v_0^{(i)} = \sum_{k=1}^{p} V_{0k}^{(i)}(x, \lambda)\, c_k^{(i)} \tag{3.2.31}$$

where the $c_k^{(i)}$ are constant vectors of the appropriate dimension.

Substituting the last expression into the boundary condition (3.2.8), we obtain

$$\sum_{i=1}^{n} \sum_{\substack{k \le q \\ l \le p-1}} \lambda^{mk} \sum_{\nu=1}^{p} \left\{ \alpha_{kl}^{(i)} \frac{d^l}{dx^l} V_{0\nu}^{(i)}(x, \lambda) \Big|_{x=a_i} + \beta_{kl}^{(i)} \frac{d^l}{dx^l} V_{0\nu}^{(i)}(x, \lambda) \Big|_{x=b_i} \right\} c_\nu^{(i)} = N_{0,m}(\Phi, \lambda^m) \tag{3.2.32}$$

We introduce the notation

$$\overline{{}_{nrp}\big| L^{(i)}(V_{0\nu}^{(i)}(x, \lambda))}^{\,r} \equiv \sum_{\substack{k \le q \\ l \le p-1}} \left(\alpha_{kl}^{(i)} \frac{d^l}{dx^l} V_{0\nu}^{(i)}(x, \lambda) \Big|_{x=a_i} + \beta_{kl}^{(i)} \frac{d^l}{dx^l} V_{0\nu}^{(i)}(x, \lambda) \Big|_{x=b_i} \right)$$

Here ${}_{nrp}\overset{r}{\ulcorner}$ denotes a matrix with r columns and nrp rows. Obviously, the left-hand side of (3.2.32) can be represented as the product of a matrix consisting of np cells of dimensions $nrp \times r$ and a (numerical) column matrix

$$(L^{(1)}(V_{01}^{(1)}),\ L^{(1)}(V_{02}^{(1)}),\ \ldots,$$

$$L^{(1)}(V_{0p}^{(1)}),\ \ldots,\ L^{(n)}(V_{01}^{(n)}),\ \ldots,\ L^{(n)}(V_{0p}^{(n)}))$$

$$\times \begin{pmatrix} c_1^{(1)} \\ \vdots \\ c_p^{(1)} \\ \vdots \\ c_1^{(n)} \\ \vdots \\ c_p^{(n)} \end{pmatrix} = N_{0m}(\Phi, \lambda)$$

Let $A(\lambda)$ denote the matrix which is multiplied on the left by the numerical column matrix

$$\begin{pmatrix} c_1^{(1)} \\ \vdots \\ c_p^{(n)} \end{pmatrix}$$

Then, the last equation can be written briefly

$$ {}_{nrp}\overset{nrp}{\boxed{A(\lambda)}} \begin{pmatrix} c_1^{(1)} \\ \vdots \\ c_p^{(1)} \\ \vdots \\ c_1^{(n)} \\ \vdots \\ c_p^{(n)} \end{pmatrix} = N_{0,\,m}(\Phi, \lambda)$$

from which it follows that

$$\begin{pmatrix} c_1^{(1)} \\ \cdot \\ \cdot \\ \cdot \\ c_p^{(1)} \\ \cdot \\ \cdot \\ \cdot \\ c_1^{(n)} \\ \cdot \\ \cdot \\ \cdot \\ c_p^{(n)} \end{pmatrix} = A^{-1}(\lambda) N_{0,m}(\Phi, \lambda) \tag{3.2.33}$$

If we divide the matrix $A^{-1}(\lambda)$ vertically into np cells of dimensions $r \times nrp$

$$A^{-1}(\lambda) = \begin{pmatrix} (A^{-1}(\lambda))_{11} \\ \cdot \\ \cdot \\ \cdot \\ (A^{-1}(\lambda))_{p1} \\ \cdot \\ \cdot \\ \cdot \\ (A^{-1}(\lambda))_{1n} \\ \cdot \\ \cdot \\ \cdot \\ (A^{-1}(\lambda))_{pn} \end{pmatrix}$$

then, from (3.2.33), we obtain

$$c_k^{(i)} = (A^{-1}(\lambda))_{ki} N_{0m}(\Phi, \lambda^m)$$

Substituting $c_k^{(i)}$ into (3.2.31), we find the following representation for the solution of $\Delta^{(i)}(x, \Phi, \lambda)$

$$\Delta^{(i)}(x, \Phi, \lambda) = \sum_{k=1}^{p} V_{0k}^{(i)}(x, \lambda)(A^{-1}(\lambda))_{ki} N_{0m}(\Phi, \lambda^m) \tag{3.2.34}$$

We now represent $N_{0m}(\Phi, \lambda^m)$ in the form of products of matrices multiplied by $\Phi^{(s)}(x)$. As can be seen from (3.2.10) if, in the expression for $N_{0,m}(\Phi, \lambda^m)$, we arrange the terms of the sum according to the functions $\Phi_k^{(i)}(x)$, we get

$$N_{0m}(\Phi, \lambda^m) =$$

$$= -\sum_{i=1}^{n}\Big\{\sum_{l=0}^{p-1}\Big(\sum_{k=1}^{q-1}\alpha_{kl}^{(i)}\lambda^{m(k-1)}+\lambda^{m(q-1)}\alpha_{ql}^{(i)}\Big)\frac{d^l}{dx^l}\Phi_0^{(i)}(x)\Big|_{x=a_i}$$

$$+\sum_{l=0}^{p-1}\Big(\sum_{k=1}^{q-1}\beta_{kl}^{(i)}\lambda^{m(k-1)}+\lambda^{m(q-1)}\beta_{ql}^{(i)}\Big)\frac{d^l}{dx^l}\Phi_0^{(i)}(x)\Big|_{x=b_i}$$

$$+\sum_{l=0}^{p-1}\Big(\sum_{k=2}^{q-1}\alpha_{kl}^{(i)}\lambda^{m(k-2)}+\lambda^{m(q-2)}\alpha_{ql}^{(i)}\Big)\frac{d^l}{dx^l}\Phi_1^{(i)}(x)\Big|_{x=a_i} \qquad (3.2.35)$$

$$+\sum_{l=0}^{p-1}\Big(\sum_{k=2}^{q-1}\beta_{kl}^{(i)}\lambda^{m(k-2)}+\lambda^{m(q-2)}\beta_{ql}^{(i)}\Big)\frac{d^l}{dx^l}\Phi_1^{(i)}(x)\Big|_{x=b_i}$$

$$+\ \dots + \sum_{l=0}^{p-1}(\alpha_{q-1\,l}^{(i)}+\lambda^m\alpha_{ql}^{(i)})\frac{d^l}{dx^l}\Phi_{q-2}^{(i)}(x)\Big|_{x=a_i}$$

$$+\sum_{l=0}^{p-1}(\beta_{q-1\,l}^{(i)}+\lambda^m\beta_{ql}^{(i)})\frac{d^l}{dx^l}\Phi_{q-2}^{(i)}(x)\Big|_{x=b_i}\Big\}$$

We introduce the following notations

$$\alpha_1^{(i)}\Big(\lambda, \frac{d}{dx}\Big) = -\Big\{\sum_{l=0}^{p-1}\Big(\sum_{k=1}^{q-1}(\alpha_{kl}^{(i)}\lambda^{m(k-1)}+\lambda^{m(q-1)}\alpha_{ql}^{(i)})\Big)\frac{d^l}{dx^l}$$

$$\sum_{l=0}^{p-1}\Big(\sum_{k=2}^{q-1}(\alpha_{kl}^{(i)}\lambda^{m(k-2)}+\lambda^{m(q-2)}\alpha_{ql}^{(i)})\Big)\frac{d^l}{dx^l}, \qquad (3.2.36)$$

$$\dots, \sum_{l=0}^{p-1}(\alpha_{q-1\,l}^{(i)}+\lambda^m\beta_{ql}^{(i)})\frac{d^l}{dx^l}, \ 0\Big\}$$

$$\beta_1^{(i)}\Big(\lambda, \frac{d}{dx}\Big)$$

$$= -\Big\{ \overline{\Big|_{nrp}\ \sum_{l=0}^{p-1}\Big(\sum_{k=1}^{q-1}\beta_{kl}^{(i)}\lambda^{m(k-1)}+\lambda^{m(q-1)}\beta_{ql}^{(i)}\Big)\frac{d^l}{dx^l}}^{\,r}$$

$$\sum_{l=0}^{p-1}\Big(\sum_{k=2}^{q-1}\beta_{kl}^{(i)}\lambda^{m(k-2)}+\lambda^{m(q-2)}\beta_{ql}^{(i)}\Big)\frac{d^l}{dx^l},$$

$$\dots, \sum_{l=0}^{p-1}(\beta_{q-1,\,l}^{(i)}+\lambda^m\beta_{ql}^{(i)})\frac{d^l}{dx^l}, \ 0\Big\} \qquad (3.2.37)$$

Thus, $\alpha_1^{(i)}\left(\lambda, \frac{d}{dx}\right)$ and $\beta_1^{(i)}\left(\lambda, \frac{d}{dx}\right)$ are $nrp \times qr$ matrices divided horizontally into q cells. Here, the qth cells are zero $nrp \times r$ cells. Using the notations (3.2.36) and (3.2.37), we can write the right-hand side of (3.2.25) in the form of a sum of products of matrices multiplied by vectors $\Phi^{(s)}(x)$ with components $\Phi_0^{(i)}, \ldots, \Phi_{q-1}^{(i)}$:

$$N_{0m}(\Phi, \lambda^m)$$

$$= \sum_{s=1}^{n}\left\{\alpha_1^{(s)}\left(\lambda, \frac{d}{dx}\right)\Phi^{(s)}(x)\Big|_{x=a_s} + \beta_1^{(s)}\left(\lambda, \frac{d}{dx}\right)\Phi^{(s)}(x)\Big|_{x=b_s}\right\}$$

Substituting this into (3.2.34), we obtain

$$\Delta^{(i)}(x, \Phi, \lambda) = \sum_{k=1}^{p} V_{0k}^{(i)}(x, \lambda) \sum_{s=1}^{n} \left\{\alpha_{ki}^{(s)}\left(\lambda, \frac{d}{dx}\right)\Phi^{(s)}(x)\Big|_{x=a_i} + \beta_{ki}^{(s)}\left(\lambda, \frac{d}{dx}\right)\Phi^{(s)}(x)\Big|_{x=b_i}\right\} \quad (3.2.38)$$

where

$$\alpha_{ki}^{(s)}\left(\lambda, \frac{d}{dx}\right) = (A^{-1}(\lambda))_{ki}\,\alpha_1^{(s)}\left(\lambda, \frac{d}{dx}\right)$$

$$\beta_{ki}^{(s)}\left(\lambda, \frac{d}{dx}\right) = (A^{-1}(\lambda))_{ki}\,\beta_1^{(s)}\left(\lambda, \frac{d}{dx}\right)$$

Here, if the matrices $\alpha_{ki}^{(s)}\left(\lambda, \frac{d}{dx}\right)$ and $\beta_{ki}^{(s)}\left(\lambda, \frac{d}{dx}\right)$ are divided horizontally into q cells, then, as can be seen from (3.2.36) and (3.2.37), these last cells will be zero cells.

In connection with this, the solution $\Delta^{(i)}(x, \Phi, \lambda)$ of the homogeneous system corresponding to System (3.2.7) satisfying the non-homogeneous boundary condition (3.2.8) is independent of the component $\Phi_{q-1}^{(i)}(x)$. Therefore, in particular, if we put $\Phi_k^{(i)}(x) \equiv 0$, for $k = 0, 1, \ldots, q-2$, we shall have

$$\Delta^{(i)}(x, \Phi, \lambda) \equiv 0$$

Consequently, in accordance with (3.2.9), we obtain from (3.2.30) the following expression for the solution $v_0^{(i)}(x, \Phi, \lambda)$

of the zero-auxiliary spectral problem

$$v^{(i)}(x, \Phi, \lambda) = \sum_{j=1}^{n} \int_{a_j}^{b_j} G^{(i,j)}(x, \xi, \lambda)\, \Phi_{q-1}^{(j)}(\xi)\, d\xi$$

Substituting this result into (3.2.29), we obtain a formula representing the expansion of an arbitrary vector-valued function $\Phi_{q-1}^{(i)}(x)$ in a series of residues of the solution of the zero-auxiliary spectral problem

$$\frac{-1}{2\pi\sqrt{-1}} \sum_{\nu} \int_{c_\nu} \lambda^{m(s+1)-1}\, d\lambda \sum_{j=1}^{n} \int_{a_j}^{b_j} G^{(i,j)}(x, \xi, \lambda)\, \Phi_{q-1}^{(j)}(\xi)\, d\xi$$
$$= \begin{cases} 0 & \text{for } s < q-1 \\ \Phi_{q-1}^{(i)}(x) & \text{for } s = q-1 \end{cases} \qquad (3.2.39)$$

It is clear from the way in which Theorem 9 was proved that it remains valid even if we put $\Phi_{q-1}^{(i)}(x) \in L_2(a_i, b_i)$.

Thus, Theorem 10 follows directly from Theorem 9.

Theorem 10 If Conditions 1, 2, 5 and 6 of Theorem 9 are satisfied, an arbitrary vector-valued function $\Phi_{q-1}^{(i)}(x) \in L_2(a_i, b_i)$ can be expanded in accordance with (3.2.39) in a series of residues of the solution of Problem (3.2.7), (3.2.8) with $\Phi_k^{(s)}(x) \equiv 0$ (for $k = 0, 1, \ldots, q-2$).

Formula (3.2.39) is a generalisation of the familiar Poincaré-Birkhoff-Tamarkin formula to the case of a system of equations with discontinuous coefficients with boundary conditions given at the points of discontinuity of the coefficients.

In other words, the validity of (3.2.39) was proved by Tamarkin [46] in particular for $n = 1$ (for equations with continuous coefficients), $r = 1$ (for a single equation), and $m = 1$.

This formula was first noted by Poincaré [39] (in connection with the solution of the mixed problem for the heat-flow equation) for the equation

$$(\Delta - \lambda^2)\, u = f(x)$$

Later (1908), Birkhoff [3] proved its validity for Problem

(3.2.7)-(3.2.8) for $n=1, r=1$ when the coefficients in the equation itself (except for the coefficient of v_0) and in the boundary conditions are independent of the parameter λ.

3.3 DERIVATION OF THE SOLUTION OF THE SPECTRAL PROBLEM FOR A SINGLE EQUATION OF HIGHER ORDER WITH DISCONTINUOUS COEFFICIENTS

This section is devoted to a derivation of the formula representing the solution of the spectral problem (a boundary-value problem with a parameter) for a single equation of higher order.

Consider the problem of finding the solution of the equations

$$P_0^{(i)}(x, \lambda)\frac{d^p y^{(i)}}{dx^p} + P_1^{(i)}(x, \lambda)\frac{d^{p-1}y^{(i)}}{dx^{p-1}} + \ldots + P_n^{(i)}(x, \lambda)\, y^{(i)} = F^{(i)}(x, \lambda) \quad (i=1, 2, \ldots, n) \tag{3.3.1}$$

with boundary conditions

$$L_k y \equiv \sum_{i=1}^{n} L_k^{(i)}(y^{(i)}) \equiv \sum_{i=1}^{n}\sum_{l=0}^{p-1}\left\{\alpha_{kl}^{(i)}(\lambda)\frac{d^l y^{(i)}}{dx^l}\bigg|_{x=a_i} + \beta_{kl}^{(i)}(\lambda)\frac{d^l y^{(i)}}{dx^l}\bigg|_{x=b_i}\right\} = N_k(\lambda) \quad (k=1, \ldots, np) \tag{3.3.2}$$

where $P_k^{(i)}(x, \lambda)$ and $F^{(i)}(x, \lambda)$ are continuous functions of x in the interval (a_i, b_i) which depend on a complex parameter λ, where

$$P_0^{(i)}(x, \lambda) \neq 0, \ \alpha_{kl}^{(i)}(\lambda), \ \beta_{kl}^{(i)}(\lambda), \ N_k(\lambda)$$

are functions of the complex parameter λ and the (a_i, b_i) are non-overlapping intervals with common end-points all contained in a finite interval $[a_1, b_n]$.

According to the general theory of ordinary linear differential equations, the homogeneous equation

$$P_0^{(i)}(x, \lambda)\frac{d^p y^{(i)}}{dx^p} + P_1^{(i)}(x, \lambda)\frac{d^{p-1}y^{(i)}}{dx^{p-1}} + \ldots + P_p^{(i)}(x, \lambda)y^{(i)} = 0 \tag{3.3.3}$$

has a fundamental system of particular solutions

$$y_1^{(i)}(x, \lambda), \ y_2^{(i)}(x, \lambda), \ \ldots, \ y_p^{(i)}(x, \lambda) \tag{3.3.4}$$

defined on the interval $[a_i, b_i]$ (see [45]). Then, for $x \in (a_i, b_i)$

$$y^{(i)} = c_1^{(i)} y_1^{(i)}(x, \lambda) + \ldots + c_p^{(i)} y_p^{(i)}(x, \lambda) \tag{3.3.5}$$

is the general solution of (3.3.3).

By the method of variation of parameters, let us construct the general solution of (3.3.1). To do this, we treat the $c_p^{(i)}$ in (3.3.5) as functions of x and look for a solution of (3.3.1) in the form (3.3.5). If we calculate the derivatives of the sum (3.3.5) and substitute them into (3.3.1), we obtain a single relation for determining the unknown functions $c_p^{(i)}(x)$. Consequently, $p-1$ other relations may be chosen arbitrarily. It is convenient to choose them in such a way that all the derivatives of the sum (3.3.5) will have as simple a form as possible. For this it is expedient, when calculating the derivatives of the first $p-1$ orders in the expression (3.3.5), to put in each case the sum of the terms containing the derivatives of the unknown functions $c_k^{(i)}(x)$ equal to zero.

Then, we obtain the following system of equations for determining the $\dfrac{dc_k^{(i)}}{dx}$.

$$\sum_{s=1}^{p} \frac{dc_s^{(i)}}{dx} y_s^{(i)}(x, \lambda) = 0$$

$$\sum_{s=1}^{p} \frac{dc_s^{(i)}}{dx} \frac{dy_s^{(i)}(x,\lambda)}{dx} = 0$$

$$\cdots\cdots\cdots\cdots\cdots\cdots$$

$$\sum_{s=1}^{p} \frac{dc_s^{(i)}}{dx} \frac{d^{p-2} y_s^{(i)}(x, \lambda)}{dx^{p-2}} = 0$$

$$\sum_{s=1}^{p} \frac{dc_s^{(i)}}{dx} \frac{d^{p-1} y_s^{(i)}(x, \lambda)}{dx^{p-1}} = (P_0^{(i)}(x, \lambda))^{-1} F^{(i)}(x, \lambda)$$

From this system, we find the following expressions for the derivatives of the unknown functions $c_s^{(i)}(x)$

$$\frac{dc_s^{(i)}(x)}{dx} = \frac{W_{ps}^{(i)}(x, \lambda)\,(P_0^{(i)}(x, \lambda))^{-1}\, F^{(i)}(x, \lambda)}{W^{(i)}(x, \lambda)} \tag{3.3.6}$$

where $W_{ps}^{(i)}(x, \lambda)$ is the cofactor of the element (p, s) in the

Wronskian determinant

$$W^{(i)}(x, \lambda) = \begin{vmatrix} y_1^{(i)}(x, \lambda) \ldots y_p^{(i)}(x, \lambda) \\ \cdots\cdots\cdots\cdots \\ \dfrac{d^{p-1}y_1^{(i)}(x, \lambda)}{dx^{p-1}} \cdots \dfrac{d^{p-1}y_p^{(i)}(x, \lambda)}{dx^{p-1}} \end{vmatrix}$$

Integrating (3.3.6) from a_i to x, we have

$$c_s^{(i)}(x) - c_s^{(i)}(a_i) = \int_{a_i}^{x} \frac{W_{ps}^{(i)}(\xi, \lambda)}{W^{(i)}(\xi, \lambda)} (P_0^{(i)}(\xi, \lambda))^{-1} F^{(i)}(\xi, \lambda)\, d\xi$$

Substituting this result into (3.3.5), we obtain the following expression for the general solution of the non-homogeneous equation (3.3.1)

$$y^{(i)} = \sum_{s=1}^{p} c_s^{(i)}(a_i)\, y_s^{(i)}(x, \lambda) + \int_{a_i}^{x} \sum_{s=1}^{p} y_s^{(i)}(x, \lambda)\, z_s^{(i)}(\xi, \lambda)\, (P_0^{(i)}(\xi, \lambda))^{-1} F^{(i)}(\xi, \lambda)\, d\xi \tag{3.3.7}$$

where

$$z_s^{(i)}(\xi, \lambda) = \frac{W_{ps}^{(i)}(\xi, \lambda)}{W^{(i)}(\xi, \lambda)} \tag{3.3.8}$$

If we take $x = b_i$ as the lower limit of integration in the identity (3.3.6), we find the expression for the general solution of (3.3.1)

$$y^{(i)} = \sum_{s=1}^{p} c_s^{(i)}(b_i)\, y_s^{(i)}(x, \lambda) + \int_{b_i}^{x} \sum_{s=1}^{p} y_s^{(i)}(x, \lambda)\, z_s^{(i)}(\xi, \lambda) (P_0^{(i)}(\xi, \lambda))^{-1} F^{(i)}(\xi, \lambda)\, d\xi \tag{3.3.9}$$

Adding (3.3.7) and (3.3.9) and dividing by 2, we obtain the following convenient representation for the general solution of the non-homogeneous equation (3.3.1)

$$y^{(i)} = \sum_{s=1}^{p} c_s^{(i)} y_s^{(i)}(x, \lambda) + \int_{a_i}^{b_i} g^{(i)}(x, \xi, \lambda)\, (P_0^{(i)}(\xi, \lambda))^{-1} F^{(i)}(\xi, \lambda)\, d\xi \tag{3.3.10}$$

where

$$c_s^{(i)} = \frac{1}{2}\left(c_s^{(i)}(a_i) + c_s^{(i)}(b_i)\right)$$

and

$$g^{(i)}(x, \xi, \lambda) = \begin{cases} \frac{1}{2}\sum_{s=1}^{p} y_s^{(i)}(x, \lambda)\, z_s^{(i)}(\xi, \lambda) & \text{for } a_i \leqslant \xi \leqslant x \\ -\frac{1}{2}\sum_{s=1}^{p} y_s^{(i)}(x, \lambda)\, z_s^{(i)}(\xi, \lambda) & \text{for } x \leqslant \xi \leqslant b_i \end{cases} \tag{3.3.11}$$

Let us construct the solution of Problem (3.3.1)-(3.3.2). To do this, we assign values to the arbitrary constants $c_s^{(i)}$ in the general solution of (3.3.10) in such a way that (3.3.10) will also satisfy the boundary conditions (3.3.2).

Substituting (3.3.10) into (3.3.2), we find the following system of equations for determining the constants $c_s^{(i)}$

$$\begin{aligned} & L_k^{(1)}(y_1^{(1)}(x, \lambda))\, c_1^{(1)} + \ldots + L_k^{(1)}(y_p^{(1)}(x, \lambda))\, c_p^{(1)} \\ & \ldots\ldots\ldots\ldots\ldots\ldots\ldots\ldots \\ & + L_k^{(n)}(y_1^{(n)}(x, \lambda))\, c_1^{(n)} + \ldots + L_k^{(n)}(y_p^{(n)}(x, \lambda))\, c_p^{(n)} \\ & = N_k(\lambda) - \sum_{j=1}^{n} \int_{a_j}^{b_j} L_k^{(j)}(g^{(j)}(x, \xi, \lambda))_x (P_0^{(j)}(\xi, \lambda))^{-1} F^{(j)}(\xi, \lambda)\, d\xi \\ & (k = 1, 2, \ldots, np) \end{aligned} \tag{3.3.12}$$

where

$$L_k^{(i)}(y_s^{(i)}(x, \lambda)) = \sum_{l=0}^{p-1} \left\{ \alpha_{kl}^{(i)}(\lambda) \left.\frac{d^l y_s^{(i)}(x, \lambda)}{dx^l}\right|_{x=a_i} + \beta_{kl}^{(i)}(\lambda) \left.\frac{d^l y_s^{(i)}(x, \lambda)}{dx^l}\right|_{x=b_i} \right\} \tag{3.3.13}$$

$$L_k^{(j)}(g^{(j)}(x, \xi, \lambda)) = \sum_{l=0}^{p-1} \left\{ \alpha_{kl}^{(j)}(\lambda) \left.\frac{\partial^l g^{(j)}(x, \xi, \lambda)}{\partial x^l}\right|_{x=a_j} + \beta_{kl}^{(j)}(\lambda) \left.\frac{\partial^l g^{(j)}(x, \xi, \lambda)}{\partial x^l}\right|_{x=b_j} \right\} \tag{3.3.14}$$

If we determine the $c_s^{(i)}$ from System (3.3.12), substitute the result in the general solution (3.3.10), and write the sum obtained in the form of a determinant, we obtain

$$y^{(i)}(x,\lambda,F)=\sum_{j=1}^{n}\int_{a_j}^{b_j} G^{(i,j)}(x,\xi,\lambda)\,F^{(j)}(\xi,\lambda)\,d\xi+\Delta^{(i)}(x,N(\lambda),\lambda) \tag{3.3.15}$$
$$x\in(a_i,\,b_i)\qquad(i=1,\,\ldots,\,n)$$

where

$$G^{(i,j)}(x,\,\xi,\,\lambda)=\frac{\Delta^{(i,j)}(x,\,\xi,\,\lambda)}{\Delta(\lambda)}\,(P_0^{(j)}(\xi,\,\lambda))^{-1} \tag{3.3.16}$$

$$\Delta^{(i,j)}(x,\,\xi,\,\lambda)=|U_j^{(1)\ldots(i-1)}(x,\,\xi,\,\lambda)\,U^{(i)}U^{(i+1)}\ldots U^{(n)}| \tag{3.3.17}$$

where

$$U_j^{(1)\ldots(i-1)}=\begin{pmatrix} g^{(i,j)}(x,\xi,\lambda) & \overbrace{0\;\ldots\ldots\ldots\ldots\ldots\;0}^{(i-1)p} \\ L_1^{(j)}(g^{(j)}(x,\xi,\lambda))_x & u_{11}^{(1)}\ldots u_{1p}^{(1)}\ldots u_{11}^{(i-1)}\ldots u_{1p}^{(i-1)} \\ \ldots\ldots\ldots & \ldots\ldots\ldots\ldots\ldots \\ L_{np}^{(j)}(g^{(j)}(x,\xi,\lambda))_x & u_{np,1}^{(1)}\ldots u_{np,p}^{(1)}\ldots u_{np,1}^{(i-1)}\ldots u_{np,p}^{(i-1)} \end{pmatrix}$$

$$U^{(i)}=\begin{pmatrix} y_1^{(i)}\ldots y_p^{(i)} \\ u_{11}^{(i)}\ldots u_{1p}^{(i)} \\ \ldots\ldots\ldots \\ u_{np,1}^{(i)}\ldots u_{np,p}^{(i)} \end{pmatrix},\qquad \underset{(k=1,2,\ldots,n-i)}{U^{i+k}}=\begin{pmatrix} 0\;\ldots\;0 \\ u_{11}^{(i+k)}\ldots u_{1p}^{(i+k)} \\ \ldots\ldots\ldots \\ u_{np,1}^{(i+k)}\ldots u_{np,p}^{(i+k)} \end{pmatrix}$$

where $x\in(a_i,\,b_i)$, $\xi\in(a_j,\,b_j)$,

$$g^{(i,j)}(x,\,\xi,\,\lambda)=\begin{cases} 0 & \text{for}\quad j\neq i \\ g^{(i)}(x,\,\xi,\,\lambda) & \text{for}\quad j=i \end{cases} \tag{3.3.18}$$

$$\Delta(\lambda)=\begin{vmatrix} u_{11}^{(1)}(\lambda)\ldots & u_{1p}^{(1)}(\lambda)\ldots u_{11}^{(n)}(\lambda) & \ldots & u_{1p}^{(n)}(\lambda) \\ \ldots\ldots & \ldots\ldots\ldots & \ldots & \ldots \\ u_{np,1}^{(1)}(\lambda)\ldots & u_{np,p}^{(1)}(\lambda)\ldots u_{np,1}^{(n)}(\lambda) & \ldots & u_{np,p}^{(n)}(\lambda) \end{vmatrix} \tag{3.3.19}$$

$$u_{ks}^{(i)}(\lambda) = L_k^{(i)}(y_s^{(i)}(x, \lambda)) \tag{3.3.20}$$

$$\Delta^{(i)}(x, \lambda, N(\lambda)) =$$

$$\begin{vmatrix} 0 & \overbrace{0 \ldots\ldots\ldots\ldots\ldots\ldots}^{(i-1)p+1} & y_1^{(i)} \ldots y_p^{(i)} & 0 \ldots & \ldots\ldots 0 \\ -N_1 & u_{11}^{(1)} \ldots u_{1p}^{(1)} \ldots u_{11}^{(i-1)} \ldots u_{1p}^{(i-1)} & u_{11}^{(i)} \ldots u_{1p}^{(i)} & u_{11}^{(i+1)} \ldots u_{1p}^{(i+1)} & \ldots u_{11}^{(n)} \ldots u_{1p}^{(n)} \\ -N_2 \ldots & \ldots\ldots\ldots & \ldots\ldots & \ldots\ldots & \ldots\ldots \\ \ldots & \ldots\ldots\ldots & \ldots\ldots & \ldots\ldots & \ldots\ldots \\ -N_{np} & u_{np,1}^{(1)} \ldots u_{np,p}^{(1)} \ldots u_{np,1}^{(i-1)} \ldots u_{np,p}^{(i-1)} & u_{np,1}^{(i)} \ldots u_{np,p}^{(i)} & u_{np,1}^{(i+1)} \ldots u_{np,p}^{(i+1)} & \ldots u_{np,1}^{(n)} \ldots u_{np,p}^{(n)} \end{vmatrix}$$

(3.3.21)

CHAPTER 4

Solution of one-dimensional mixed problems for systems of equations with discontinuous coefficients

4.1 MIXED PROBLEMS WITH BOUNDARY CONDITIONS CONTAINING TIME DERIVATIVES

In this section, we shall consider the one-dimensional* mixed problem of finding the solution of the system

$$\frac{\partial^q u^{(i)}}{\partial t^q} = \sum_{\substack{k \leqslant q-1 \\ mk+l \leqslant p}} A_{kl}^{(i)}(x) \frac{\partial^{k+l} u^{(i)}}{\partial t^k \partial x^l} + f^{(i)}(x, t) \quad \text{for } x \in (a_i, b_i) \qquad (4.1.1)$$

(for $i = 1, 2, \ldots, n$) in a finite interval (a_1, b_n) with boundary condition

$$\sum_{i=1}^{n} \sum_{\substack{k \leqslant q \\ l \leqslant p-1}} \left\{ \alpha_{kl}^{(i)} \frac{\partial^{k+l} u^{(i)}}{\partial t^k \partial x^l} \bigg|_{x=a_i} + \beta_{kl}^{(i)} \frac{\partial^{k+l} u^{(i)}}{\partial t^k \partial x^l} \bigg|_{x=b_i} \right\} = 0 \qquad (4.1.2)$$

*Let us agree to call a mixed problem 'one-dimensional' if the space variable x varies in a one-dimensional region. Otherwise we shall call the problem a 'multi-dimensional' one.

and initial conditions

$$\left.\frac{\partial^k u^{(i)}}{\partial t^k}\right|_{t=0} = \Phi_k^{(i)}(x) \quad \text{for } x \in (a_i, b_i) \quad (i = 1, 2, \ldots, n) \tag{4.1.3}$$

where the (a_i, b_i) are disjoint intervals with common endpoints, the $A_{kl}^{(i)}(x)$ are square matrices of order r, the $\alpha_{kl}^{(i)}$ and the $\beta_{kl}^{(i)}$ are $nrp \times r$ constant matrices and m, p and q are arbitrary natural numbers satisfying the condition $p = mq$. If $p = 1$ in the boundary conditions (4.1.2), we set $mk + l \leqslant p$.

It will be proved in this section that, under certain restrictions, if Problem (4.1.1)-(4.1.3) has a sufficiently smooth solution $u^{(i)}(x, t)$ for $x \in (a_i, b_i)$, it can be represented by (4.1.8), where the expression in the braces in the integrand of the contour integral $\int_{c_\nu}$ is a solution of the 0-auxiliary spectral problem (3.2.7)-(3.2.8) of Section 3.2.

To obtain a residue representation of a sufficiently smooth solution of Problem (4.1.1)-(4.1.3), we transform it into a mixed problem containing only first-order time derivatives, by making a change of time derivatives.

In Problem (4.1.1)-(4.1.3), we make the change

$$\frac{\partial^k u^{(i)}}{\partial t^k} = u_k^{(i)} \quad (k = 0, \ \ldots, \ q-2) \tag{4.1.4}$$

and obtain the mixed problem

$$\begin{gathered} \frac{\partial u_k^{(i)}}{\partial t} = u_{k+1}^{(i)} \quad (k = 0, \ \ldots, \ q-2) \\ \frac{\partial u_{q-1}^{(i)}}{\partial t} = \sum_{\substack{k \leqslant q-1 \\ mk+l \leqslant p}} A_{kl}^{(i)}(x) \frac{\partial^l u_k^{(i)}}{\partial x^l} + f^{(i)}(x, t) \quad \text{for } x \in (a_i, b_i) \end{gathered} \tag{4.1.5}$$

with boundary condition

$$\begin{gathered} \sum_{i=1}^{n} \sum_{\substack{k \leqslant q-1 \\ l \leqslant p-1}} \left\{ \alpha_{kl}^{(i)} \left.\frac{\partial^l u_k^{(i)}}{\partial x^l}\right|_{x=a_i} + \beta_{kl}^{(i)} \left.\frac{\partial^l u_k^{(i)}}{\partial x^l}\right|_{x=b_i} \right\} \\ + \sum_{i=1}^{n} \sum_{l=0}^{p-1} \left\{ \alpha_{ql}^{(i)} \left.\frac{\partial^{l+1} u_{q-1}^{(i)}}{\partial t\, \partial x^l}\right|_{x=a_i} + \beta_{ql}^{(i)} \left.\frac{\partial^{l+1} u_{q-1}^{(i)}}{\partial t\, \partial x^l}\right|_{x=b_i} \right\} = 0 \end{gathered} \tag{4.1.6}$$

and initial conditions

$$u_k^{(i)}(x, 0) = \Phi_k^{(i)}(x) \quad \text{for} \quad x \in (a_i, b_i) \tag{4.1.7}$$
$$(i = 1, \ldots, n; \; k = 0, \ldots, q-1)$$

We shall call Problem (3.2.1)-(3.2.2.) the spectral problem corresponding to the mixed problem (4.1.5)-(4.1.7). It should be noted that the left-hand sides of the equations of the spectral problem are obtained from equations of System (4.1.5) by a formal replacement of the operation of differentiation with respect to time by multiplication by λ^m and that the right-hand sides of the equations of the spectral problem (3.2.1)-(3.2.2) are the corresponding functions $\Phi_k^{(i)}(x)$ in the initial conditions (4.1.7). The boundary condition of the spectral problem (3.2.1)-(3.2.2) is obtained from the boundary condition (4.1.6) of the mixed problem (4.1.5)-(4.1.7) by formally replacing differentiation with respect to time by multiplication by λ^m. The zero-auxiliary spectral problem is obtained from (3.2.1)-(3.2.2) by eliminating all the $v_k^{(i)}$ for $k = 1, 2, \ldots, q-1$. We call the 0-auxiliary spectral problem the spectral problem corresponding to the mixed problem (4.1.1)-(4.1.3).

We note that if the boundary condition (4.1.6) of the mixed problem (4.1.5)-(4.1.7) does not contain a time derivative, i.e. if $\alpha_{ql}^{(i)} = \beta_{ql}^{(i)} = 0$ for all $l = 0, 1, \ldots, p-1$), then the boundary condition of the mixed problem (4.1.5)-(4.1.7) coincides with the boundary condition of the corresponding spectral problem. In this case, the boundary condition (4.1.2) of the mixed problem (4.1.1)-(4.1.3) does not contain the highest-order time derivative, nor does it coincide with the boundary condition of the corresponding spectral problem (3.2.7)-(3.2.8) called the 0-auxiliary spectral problem.

Obviously, the mixed problems (4.1.1)-(4.1.3) and (4.1.5)-(4.1.7) are equivalent. Consequently, if we obtain a residue representation of a sufficiently smooth solution of (4.1.5)-(4.1.7), it is easy to obtain from it a residue representation of a smooth solution of (4.1.1)-(4.1.3). It is by this procedure that the fundamental theorem of this section is proved.

Theorem 11 Suppose that, for every $t \in [0, T]$,

$$\int_{a_i}^{b_i} |f_k^{(i)}(x, t)|^2 \, dx < +\infty \text{ and } \int_0^T \int_{a_i}^{b_i} |f_k^{(i)}(x, t)| \, dx \, dt < +\infty$$
$$(k = 1, \ldots, r; \; i = 1, \ldots, n)$$

and the functions $\Phi_{k-1}^{(i)}(x)$ have continuous derivatives of the first $p-mk$ orders (for $k=1, 2, \ldots, q$) on $[a_i, b_i]$.

Suppose that Conditions 1, 2, 5 and 6 of Theorem 9 (Section 3.2) are satisfied.

Suppose also that the boundary condition (4.1.2) does not contain a time derivative of order q (i.e. the highest time derivative $\alpha_{ql}^{(i)}=\beta_{ql}^{(i)}=0$ for $l=0, \ldots, p-1$ and $i=1, \ldots, n$) and that Problem (4.1.1)-(4.1.3) has a solution $u^{(i)}(x, t)$ for $x \in (a_i, b_i)$ (for $i=1, \ldots, n$) possessing the following properties:

1. The functions $u^{(i)}(x, t), \frac{\partial u^{(i)}(x, t)}{\partial t}, \ldots, \frac{\partial^{q-1} u^{(i)}}{\partial t^{q-1}}$ have derivatives of the first p orders with respect to x in $[a_i, b_i]$ (for $i=1, \ldots, n$). These derivatives of the first $(p-1)$ orders are absolutely continuous with respect to x on $[a_i, b_i]$ and the pth derivatives belong to $L_2(a_i, b_i)$.
2. The derivatives with respect to t of the derivatives $\frac{\partial^{k+l} u^{(i)}}{\partial t^k \partial x^l}$ (for ($k=0, \ldots, q-1$; $l=0, \ldots, p-1$) are summable in the two-dimensional region $0 \leqslant t \leqslant T$, $a_i < x < b_i$ (for $i=1, 2, \ldots, n$) these derivatives $\frac{\partial^{k+l} u^{(i)}}{\partial t^k \partial x^l}$ (for $k=0, \ldots, q-1$; $l=0, \ldots, p-1$) being absolutely continuous with respect to t in the interval $0 \leqslant t \leqslant T$.
3. The functions $\Phi_k^{(i)}$ and $\frac{\partial^k u^{(i)}}{\partial t^k}$ (for $k=0, 1, \ldots, q-2$) satisfy Condition 4 of Theorem 9.

Then this solution is given by

$$u^{(i)}(x, t) = -\frac{1}{2\pi\sqrt{-1}} \sum_{\nu} \int_{c_\nu} \lambda^{m-1} e^{\lambda^m t}\, d\lambda$$

$$\times \left\{ \sum_{j=1}^{n} \int_{a_j}^{b_j} G^{(i,j)}(x, \xi, \lambda) \left(F_0^{(j)}(\xi, \Phi, \lambda^m) \right.\right. \quad (4.1.8)$$

$$\left.\left. + \int_0^t e^{-\lambda^m \tau} f^{(j)}(\xi, \tau)\, d\tau \right) d\xi + \Delta^{(i)}(x, \Phi, \lambda) \right\}$$

where, as before, the expression in the braces with the integral

$$\int_0^t e^{-\lambda^m \tau} f^{(i)}(\xi, \tau)\, d\tau$$

removed is a solution of the 0-auxiliary spectral problem

(3.2.7)-(3.2.8), c_ν is a simple closed curve encircling only one pole λ_ν^m of the integrand, and the summation with respect to ν is over all poles of that function.

Proof Let us write both the mixed problem (4.1.5)-(4.1.7) and the corresponding spectral problem (3.2.1)-(3.2.2) in a more compact form. To do this, we introduce the notations

$$L^{(i)}\left(x, \frac{\partial}{\partial x}\right) = \begin{pmatrix} 0 & E & 0 \\ 0 & 0 & 0 \\ \dots & \dots & \dots \\ 0 & 0 & E \\ \sum_{l=0}^{p} A_{0l}^{(i)}(x)\frac{\partial^l}{\partial x^l} & \sum_{l=0}^{p-m} A_{1l}^{(i)}(x)\frac{\partial^l}{\partial x^l} \dots & \sum_{l=0}^{p-(q-1)m} A_{q-1,l}^{(i)}(x)\frac{\partial^l}{\partial x^l} \end{pmatrix}$$

$$z^{(i)} = \begin{pmatrix} u_0^{(i)} \\ \vdots \\ u_{q-1}^{(i)} \end{pmatrix}, \quad F^{(i)}(x, t) = \begin{pmatrix} 0 \\ \vdots \\ 0 \\ f^{(i)}(x, t) \end{pmatrix}$$

$$\Phi^{(i)}(x) = \begin{pmatrix} \Phi_0^{(i)}(x) \\ \vdots \\ \Phi_{q-1}^{(i)}(x) \end{pmatrix}, \quad y^{(i)} = \begin{pmatrix} v_0^{(i)} \\ \vdots \\ v_{q-1}^{(i)} \end{pmatrix}$$

Here, E denotes the unit matrix of order r and 0 denotes the zero matrix of the same order in the expression for $L^{(i)}\left(x, \frac{\partial}{\partial x}\right)$ but denotes the zero column of dimension r in the expression for $F^{(i)}(x, t)$.

In these notations, in view of the lack of time derivative in the boundary condition, we can write Problem (4.1.5)-(4.1.7) in the form

$$\frac{\partial Z^{(i)}}{\partial t} = L^{(i)}\left(x, \frac{\partial}{\partial x}\right) Z^{(i)} + F^{(i)}(x, t) \text{ for } x \in (a_i, b_i) \quad (i = 1, \dots, n) \tag{4.1.9}$$

$$\sum_{i=1}^{n}\sum_{l=0}^{p-1}\left\{(\alpha_{0l}^{(i)}, \dots, \alpha_{q-1,l}^{(i)})\frac{\partial^l Z^{(i)}}{\partial x^l}\bigg|_{x=a_i} + (\beta_{0l}^{(i)}, \dots, \beta_{q-1,l}^{(i)})\frac{\partial^l Z^{(i)}}{\partial x^l}\bigg|_{x=b_i}\right\} = 0 \tag{4.1.10}$$

$$Z^{(i)}(x, 0) = \Phi^{(i)}(x) \text{ for } x \in (a_i, b_i) \; (i = 1, \dots, n) \tag{4.1.11}$$

The corresponding spectral problem (3.2.1)-(3.2.2) becomes

$$L^{(i)}\left(x, \frac{d}{dx}\right) y^{(i)} - \lambda^m y^{(i)} = \Phi^{(i)}(x) \tag{4.1.12}$$

$$\sum_{i=1}^{n} \sum_{l=0}^{p-1} \left\{ (\alpha_{0l}^{(i)}, \ldots, \alpha_{q-1,l}^{(i)}) \frac{d^l y^{(i)}}{dx^l}\bigg|_{x=a_i} + (\beta_{0l}^{(i)}, \ldots, \beta_{q-1l}^{(i)}) \frac{d^l y^{(i)}}{dx^l}\bigg|_{x=b_i} \right\} = 0 \tag{4.1.13}$$

Let us now find a convenient representation for the solution of Problem (4.1.12)-(4.1.13), in which the way $y^{(i)}$ depends on $\Phi^{(i)}(x)$ shows up clearly.

As we can see, the boundary conditions of the mixed problem (4.1.9)-(4.1.11) and of the spectral problem (4.1.12) -(4.1.13) corresponding to it coincide. If we express all the $v_k^{(i)}$ (for $k=1, \ldots, q-1$) in terms of the $v_0^{(i)}$ and substitute the results into the expression for the $y^{(i)}$, we obtain from the first $q-1$ equations of System (3.2.1)

$$y^{(i)} = \begin{pmatrix} v_0^{(i)} \\ v_1^{(i)} \\ \cdots \\ v_{q-1}^{(i)} \end{pmatrix} = \begin{pmatrix} v_0^{(i)} \\ \lambda^m v_0^{(i)} + \Phi_0^{(i)} \\ \lambda^{2m} v_0^{(i)} + \lambda^m \Phi_0^{(i)} + \Phi_1^{(i)} \\ \cdots\cdots\cdots\cdots \\ \lambda^{m(q-1)} v_0^{(i)} + \lambda^{m(q-2)} \Phi_0^{(i)} \\ + \lambda^{m(q-3)} \Phi_1^{(i)} + \ldots + \Phi_{q-2}^{(i)} \end{pmatrix} \equiv \begin{pmatrix} v_0^{(i)} \\ \lambda^m v_0^{(i)} \\ \lambda^{2m} v_0^{(i)} \\ \cdots \\ \lambda^{m(q-1)} v_0^{(i)} \end{pmatrix} + P(\lambda)\Phi^{(i)}(x) \tag{4.1.14}$$

where

$$P(\lambda) = \begin{pmatrix} 0 & 0 & 0 & \ldots & 0 & 0 \\ E & 0 & 0 & \ldots & 0 & 0 \\ \lambda^m E & E & 0 & \ldots & 0 & 0 \\ \cdots & \cdots & \cdots & \cdots & \cdots & \cdots \\ \lambda^{m(q-2)} E & \lambda^{m(q-3)} E & \lambda^{m(q-4)} E & \ldots & E & 0 \end{pmatrix}.$$

It is clear from the expression for $F_0^{(i)}(\xi, \Phi, \lambda^m)$ that (see (3.2.9)) the right-hand side of (3.2.9) can be represented as the product obtained by multiplying the matrix composed of q^2 matrix cells by the column $\Phi^{(i)}(x)$

$$F_0^{(i)}(\xi, \Phi, \lambda^m) = \Big(\lambda^{m(q-1)}E - \sum_{\substack{1\leq k\leq q-1\\ mk+l\leq p}} \lambda^{m(k-1)} A_{kl}^{(i)}(\xi)\frac{d^l}{d\xi^l}$$

$$\lambda^{m(q-2)}E - \sum_{\substack{2\leq k\leq q-1\\ mk+l\leq p}} \lambda^{m(k-2)} A_{kl}^{(i)}(\xi)\frac{d^l}{d\xi^l}$$

$$\lambda^{m(q-3)}E - \sum_{\substack{3\leq k\leq q-1\\ mk+l\leq p}} \lambda^{m(k-3)} A_{kl}^{(i)}(\xi)\frac{d^l}{d\xi^l}$$

$$\ldots, \lambda^m E - \sum_{l=0}^{m} A_{q-1,l}^{(i)}(\xi)\frac{d^l}{d\xi^l}, E\Big)\Phi^{(i)}\xi$$

If we substitute the following expression for $v_0^{(i)}(x, \Phi, \lambda)$ in (3.2.30), we obtain

$$v_0^{(i)}(x, \Phi, \lambda)$$

$$= \sum_{j=1}^{n}\int_{a_j}^{b_j} G^{(i,j)}(x, \xi, \lambda)\Big(\lambda^{m(q-1)}E - \sum_{\substack{1\leq k\leq q-1\\ mk+l\leq p}} \lambda^{m(k-1)} A_{kl}^{(j)}(\xi)\frac{d^l}{d\xi^l} \tag{4.1.15}$$

$$\ldots, \lambda^m E - \sum_{l=0}^{m} A_{q-1,l}^{(j)}(\xi)\frac{d^l}{d\xi^l}, E\Big)\Phi^{(j)}(\xi)\,d\xi + \Delta^{(i)}(x, \Phi, \lambda)$$

for $x \in (a_i, b_i)$.

Finally, if we substitute (4.1.15) into (4.1.14), we have

$$y^{(i)}(x, \Phi, \lambda) = \sum_{j=1}^{n}\int_{a_j}^{b_j} K^{(i,j)}\Big(x, \xi, \frac{d}{d\xi}, \lambda\Big)\Phi^{(j)}(\xi)\,d\xi \tag{4.1.16}$$

$$+ y_1^{(i)}(x, \Phi, \lambda) + P(\lambda)\Phi^{(i)}(x)$$

where $K^{(i,j)}\Big(x, \xi, \frac{d}{d\xi}, \lambda\Big)$ is a matrix composed of the matrix cells

$$K_{\nu s}^{(i,j)}\left(x, \xi, \frac{d}{d\xi}, \lambda\right) = \lambda^{(\nu-1)m} G^{(i,j)}(x, \xi, \lambda)\left(\lambda^{m(q-s)} E - \sum_{\substack{s \leq k \leq q-1 \\ mk+l \leq p}} \lambda^{m(k-s)} A_{kl}^{(j)}(\xi) \frac{d^l}{d\xi^l}\right),$$

$$(s = 1, 2, \ldots, q-1)$$

$$K_{\nu q}^{(i,j)}\left(x, \xi, \frac{d}{d\xi}, \lambda\right) = \lambda^{(\nu-1)m} G^{(i,j)}(x, \xi, \lambda)$$

$$y_1^{(i)}(x, \Phi, \lambda) = \begin{pmatrix} \Delta^{(i)}(x, \Phi, \lambda) \\ \lambda^m \Delta^{(i)}(x, \Phi, \lambda) \\ \vdots \\ \lambda^{m(q-1)} \Delta^{(i)}(x, \Phi, \lambda) \end{pmatrix}$$

Here, as can be seen from (3.2.38), the dependence of $y_1^{(i)}(x, \Phi, \lambda)$ on Φ is linear

$$y_1^{(i)}(x, c\Phi, \lambda) = c y_1^{(i)}(x, \Phi, \lambda)$$

$$y_1^{(i)}(x, \Phi_1 + \Phi_2, \lambda) = y_1^{(i)}(x, \Phi_1, \lambda) + y_1^{(i)}(x, \Phi_2, \lambda)$$

In this connection, we note that (3.2.16) can be written in the notations that we have been using, as follows

$$-\frac{1}{2\pi\sqrt{-1}} \sum_{\nu} \int_{c_\nu} \lambda^{m-1} \left\{ \sum_{j=1}^{n} \int_{a_j}^{b_j} K^{(i,j)}\left(x, \xi, \frac{d}{d\xi}, \lambda\right) \Phi^{(j)}(\xi)\, d\xi + y_1^{(i)}(x, \Phi, \lambda) \right\} d\lambda = \Phi^{(i)}(x)$$

For an arbitrary vector-valued function $y^{(i)}(x)$ belonging to the domain of definition of the operator defined by Problem (4.1.12)-(4.1.13), i.e. for every vector-valued function $y^{(i)}(x)$ which satisfies the boundary condition (4.1.13) and to which we can apply the differential operator $\left(L^{(i)}\left(x, \frac{d}{dx}\right)\right)$, the following identity holds:

$$y^{(i)}(x) \equiv \sum_{j=1}^{n} \int_{a_j}^{b_j} K^{(i,j)}\left(x, \xi, \frac{d}{d\xi}, \lambda\right)$$

$$\times\left(L^{(j)}\left(\xi, \frac{d}{d\xi}\right) - \lambda^m E\right) y^{(j)}(\xi)\, d\xi + y_1^{(i)}\left(x, \left(L^{(i)}\left(x, \frac{d}{dx}\right)\right.\right. \quad (4.1.17)$$

$$\left.\left. - \lambda^m E\right) y, \lambda\right) + P(\lambda)\left(L^{(i)}\left(x, \frac{d}{dx}\right) - \lambda^m E\right) y^{(i)}(x)$$

Suppose now that λ_ν^m is a pole of order $\varkappa_\nu$ (for $\nu = 1, 2, \ldots$) of the vector-valued function $y^{(i)}(x, \Phi, \lambda)$ defined by (4.1.16).

Let us denote by $F_{k\nu}^{(i)}(x)$ the integral

$$F_{k\nu}^{(i)}(x) \equiv K_{k\nu}^{(i)}(F)$$

$$= -\frac{1}{2\pi\sqrt{-1}} \int_{c_\nu} \lambda^{m(k+1)-1}\, d\lambda \left\{\sum_{j=1}^{n} \int_{a_j}^{b_j} K^{(i,j)}\left(x, \xi, \frac{d}{d\xi}, \lambda\right)\right. \quad (4.1.18)$$

$$\left. \times F^{(j)}(\xi)\, d\xi + y_1^{(i)}(x, F, \lambda)\right\}$$

defined for an arbitrary, sufficiently smooth, vector-valued function $F^{(i)}(x)$ on $[a_i, b_i]$. We note that (3.2.16) can be written in this notation as

$$\sum_\nu \Phi_{0\nu}^{(i)}(x) = \Phi^{(i)}(x)$$

Suppose that $u^{(i)}(x, t)$ is a solution of Problem (4.1.1)-(4.1.3) with the properties enumerated in the formulation of the theorem. Then, the corresponding $Z^{(i)}(x, t)$ constitute a solution of Problem (4.1.9)-(4.1.11) possessing Properties 1 and 2 of the theorem.

If we apply the operator $K_{k\nu}^{(i)}$ to both sides of (4.1.9), we obtain

$$-\frac{1}{2\pi\sqrt{-1}} \int_{c_\nu} \lambda^{m(k+1)-1}\, d\lambda \left\{\sum_{j=1}^{n} \int_{a_j}^{b_j} K^{(i,j)}\left(x, \xi, \frac{d}{d\xi}, \lambda\right)\right.$$

$$\left. \times \frac{\partial}{\partial t} Z^{(j)}(\xi, t)\, d\xi + y_1^{(i)}\left(x, \frac{\partial Z}{\partial t}, \lambda\right)\right\} \quad (4.1.19)$$

$$= -\frac{1}{2\pi\sqrt{-1}} \int_{c_\nu} \lambda^{m(k+1)-1}\, d\lambda \left\{\sum_{j=1}^{n} \int_{a_j}^{b_j} K^{(i,j)}\left(x, \xi, \frac{d}{d\xi}, \lambda\right) \times\right.$$

$$\times L^{(j)}\left(\xi, \frac{\partial}{\partial \xi}\right) Z^{(j)}(\xi, t)\, d\xi + y_1^{(i)}\left(x, L\left(x, \frac{\partial}{\partial x}\right) Z, \lambda\right)\Big\}$$

$$+\frac{-1}{2\pi\sqrt{-1}} \int\limits_{c_\nu} \lambda^{m(k+1)-1}\, d\lambda \left\{\sum_{j=1}^{n} \int\limits_{a_j}^{b_j} K^{(i,j)}\left(x, \xi, \frac{d}{d\xi}, \lambda\right)\right. \qquad (4.1.19)\ \text{(cont.)}$$

$$\times F^{(j)}(\xi, t)\, d\xi + y_1^{(i)}(x, F, \lambda)\Big\}$$

Since all the column components of $F_k^{(j)}(x, t)$ are equal to zero for $k=0, \ldots, q-2$ and $\Delta(x, F, \lambda)$ is independent of the component $F_{q-1}^{(j)}=f^{(j)}(x, t)$ (see (3.2.35) and (3.2.37)), we have

$$y_1^{(i)}(x, F, \lambda) \equiv 0 \qquad (4.1.20)$$

Furthermore, as we can see from (3.2.38), $y_1^{(i)}(x, Z, \lambda)$ depends on Z linearly, so that

$$y_1^{(i)}\left(x, \frac{\partial Z}{\partial t}, \lambda\right) = \frac{\partial}{\partial t} y_1^{(i)}(x, Z, \lambda) \qquad (4.1.21)$$

$$\begin{aligned} & y_1^{(i)}\left(x, L\left(x, \frac{\partial}{\partial x}\right) Z, \lambda\right) \\ & = y_1^{(i)}\left(x, \left(L\left(x, \frac{\partial}{\partial x}\right) - \lambda^m E\right) Z, \lambda\right) + \lambda^m y_1^{(i)}(x, Z, \lambda) \end{aligned} \qquad (4.1.22)$$

In accordance with the hypothesis of the theorem (Property 2), the vector-valued functions $Z^{(i)}(x, t)$ are absolutely integrable with respect to t for every $x \in (a_i, b_i)$ and the derivatives with respect to t of these components are absolutely integrable over the two-dimensional region $0 \leqslant t \leqslant T$, $a_i < x < b_i$.

Consequently, in accordance with the theorem on the possibility of differentiating under the integral sign with respect to a parameter, the differentiation with respect to t in the left-hand side of (4.1.19) can be taken from under the integral signs. Then, since $P(\lambda)$ is analytic throughout the entire λ-plane and by virtue of (4.1.20), (4.1.21) and

(4.1.22), we obtain

$$\frac{\partial}{\partial t}\left\{\frac{-1}{2\pi\sqrt{-1}}\int_{c_\nu}\lambda^{m(k+1)-1}\,d\lambda\left(\sum_{j=1}^{n}\int_{a_j}^{b_j}K^{(i,j)}\left(x,\xi,\frac{d}{d\xi},\lambda\right)\right.\right.$$

$$\left.\left.\times Z^{(j)}(\xi,t)\,d\xi+y_1^{(i)}(x,Z,\lambda)\right)\right\}$$

$$=\frac{-1}{2\pi\sqrt{-1}}\int_{c_\nu}\lambda^{m(k+1)-1}\,d\lambda\left\{\sum_{j=1}^{n}\int_{a_j}^{b_j}K^{(i,j)}\left(x,\xi,\frac{d}{d\xi},\lambda\right)\right.$$

$$\times\left(L^{(j)}\left(\xi,\frac{d}{d\xi}\right)-\lambda^m\right)Z^{(j)}(\xi,t)\,d\xi$$

$$+P(\lambda)\left(L^{(i)}\left(x,\frac{\partial}{\partial x}\right)-\lambda^m E\right)Z^{(i)}(x,t)$$

$$\left.+y_1^{(i)}\left(x,\left(L\left(x,\frac{\partial}{\partial x}\right)-\lambda^m E\right)Z,\lambda\right)\right\} \tag{4.1.23}$$

$$+\frac{-1}{2\pi\sqrt{-1}}\int_{c_\nu}\lambda^{m(k+2)-1}\,d\lambda$$

$$\times\left\{\sum_{j=1}^{n}\int_{a_j}^{b_j}K^{(i,j)}(x,\xi,\lambda)\,Z^{(j)}(\xi,t)\,d\xi+y_1^{(i)}(x,Z,\lambda)\right\}$$

$$-\frac{1}{2\pi\sqrt{-1}}\int_{c_\nu}\lambda^{m(k+1)-1}\,d\lambda\sum_{j=1}^{n}\int_{a_j}^{b_j}K^{(i,j)}\left(x,\xi,\frac{d}{d\xi},\lambda\right)$$

$$\times F^{(j)}(\xi,t)\,d\xi$$

Since the solution $u^{(i)}(x,t)$ of Problem (4.1.1)-(4.1.3) possesses Property 1 owing to the hypothesis of the theorem, the vector-valued function $Z^{(i)}(x,t)$ satisfies the boundary condition (4.1.13) and has derivatives of the first p orders. Consequently, in accordance with (4.1.17), we have

$$Z^{(i)}(x,t)\equiv\sum_{j=1}^{n}\int_{a_j}^{b_j}K^{(i,j)}\left(x,\xi,\frac{d}{d\xi},\lambda\right)$$

$$\times\left(L^{(j)}\left(\xi,\frac{d}{d\xi}\right)-\lambda^m\right)Z^{(j)}(\xi,t)\,d\xi$$

$$+P(\lambda)\left(L^{(i)}\left(x,\frac{\partial}{\partial x}\right)-\lambda^m E\right)Z^{(i)}(x,t)$$

$$+y_1^{(i)}\left(x,\left(L^{(i)}\left(x,\frac{\partial}{\partial x}\right)-\lambda^m E\right)Z,\lambda\right)$$

Then, (4.1.23) can be written in the notations of (4.1.18) as follows:

$$\frac{\partial Z_{k\nu}^{(i)}(x, t)}{\partial t} = Z_{k+1, \nu}^{(i)}(x, t) + F_{k\nu}^{(i)}(x, t) \quad \text{for} \quad x \in (a_i, b_i) \quad (i = 1, 2, \ldots, n) \tag{4.1.24}$$

Applying the operator $K_{k\nu}^{(i)}$ to both sides of the initial conditions (4.1.11), we obtain

$$Z_{k\nu}^{(i)}(x, 0) = \Phi_{k\nu}^{(i)}(x) \quad \text{for} \quad x \in (a_i, b_i) \; (i = 1, \ldots, n) \tag{4.1.25}$$

Since λ_ν^m is a pole of order $\varkappa_\nu$ of the vector-valued function defined by (4.1.16), we have

$$-\frac{1}{2\pi\sqrt{-1}} \int_{c_\nu} \lambda^{m-1} (\lambda^m - \lambda_\nu^m)^{\varkappa_\nu} \, d\lambda \times \left\{ \sum_{j=1}^{n} \int_{a_j}^{b_j} K^{(i,j)}\left(x, \xi, \frac{d}{d\xi}, \lambda\right) Z^{(j)}(\xi, t) \, d\xi + y_1^{(i)}(x, Z, \lambda) \right\} \tag{4.1.26}$$

$$= \sum_{k=0}^{\varkappa_\nu} \binom{\varkappa_\nu}{k} (-\lambda_\nu^m)^{\varkappa_\nu - k} Z_{k,\nu}^{(i)}(x, t) \equiv 0$$

From this identity, we can determine the vector-valued function $Z_{\varkappa_\nu, \nu}^{(i)}(x, t)$ in terms of the remaining ones

$$Z_{0,\nu}^{(i)}(x, t), \; Z_{1\nu}^{(i)}(x, t), \ldots, Z_{\varkappa_\nu - 1, \nu}^{(i)}(x, t) \tag{4.1.27}$$

Consequently, Problem (4.1.24)-(4.1.25) for $k = 0, 1, \ldots \varkappa_\nu - 1$ is a Cauchy problem for the system with unknowns (4.1.27). In other words, (4.1.24)-(4.1.25) show that the vector-valued functions (4.1.27) constitute a solution of the Cauchy problem (4.1.24)-(4.1.25).

It can be directly verified that

$$Z_{k\nu 0}^{(i)}(x, t) = -\frac{1}{2\pi\sqrt{-1}} \int_{c_\nu} \lambda^{m(k+1)-1} d\lambda \times \left\{ \sum_{j=1}^{n} \int_{a_j}^{b_j} K^{(i,j)}\left(x, \xi, \frac{\partial}{\partial \xi}, \lambda\right) (\Phi^{(j)}(\xi) \exp(\lambda^m t) \right. \tag{4.1.28}$$

$$+\int_0^t \exp(\lambda^m(t-\tau))\,F^{(j)}(\xi,\tau)\,d\tau)\,d\xi \;+\exp(\lambda^m t)\,y_1^{(i)}(x,\Phi,\lambda)\Big\}$$

$$(k=0,\,\ldots,\,\varkappa_\nu-1;\quad i=1,\,\ldots,\,n;\quad \nu=1,\,2,\,\ldots) \qquad (4.1.28)\ \text{(cont.)}$$

is a solution of Problem (4.1.24)-(4.1.25). Specifically, in accordance with the hypothesis of the theorem, the right-hand side of the above equation can be differentiated with respect to t under the integral signs. Therefore,

$$\frac{\partial Z_{k\nu 0}^{(i)}}{\partial t} \equiv -\frac{1}{2\pi\sqrt{-1}}\int_{c_\nu} \lambda^{m(k+2)-1}\,d\lambda$$

$$\times\Big\{\sum_{j=1}^{n}\int_{a_j}^{b_j} K^{(i,j)}\Big(x,\,\xi,\,\frac{\partial}{\partial\xi},\,\lambda\Big)\,(\Phi^{(j)}(\xi)\exp(\lambda^m t)$$

$$+\int_0^t \exp(\lambda^m(t-\tau))\,F^{(j)}(\xi,\tau)d\tau)\,d\xi+\exp(\lambda^m t)\,y_1^{(i)}(x,\Phi,\lambda)\Big\} \qquad (4.1.29)$$

$$-\frac{1}{2\pi\sqrt{-1}}\int_{c_\nu}\lambda^{m(k+1)-1}d\lambda$$

$$\times\Big\{\sum_{j=1}^{n}\int_{a_j}^{b_j} K^{(i,j)}\Big(x,\,\xi,\,\frac{\partial}{\partial\xi},\,\lambda\Big)\,F^{(j)}(\xi,\,t)\,d\xi\Big\}$$

Since $y_1^{(i)}(x,\Phi,\lambda)$ is independent of the component $\Phi_{q-1}^{(i)}(x)$ and since all the vector-valued components of the vector-valued function $F^{(j)}(x,t)$ with the exception of the component $f^{(i)}(x,t)$ vanish identically, we have

$$y_1^{(i)}(x,\,F,\,\lambda)\equiv 0$$

Consequently, in the notation of (4.1.18), we obtain from (4.1.29)

$$\frac{\partial Z_{k\nu 0}^{(i)}(x,\,t)}{\partial t} \equiv Z_{k+1,\nu 0}^{(i)}(x,\,t)+F_{k\nu}^{(i)}(x,\,t)$$

Thus, we have shown that the functions (4.1.28) satisfy the equations in (4.1.24).

Furthermore, using the notation of (4.1.18), we see by

letting $t \to 0$ in (4.1.28) that

$$Z_{k\nu 0}^{(i)}(x, 0) \equiv -\frac{1}{2\pi\sqrt{-1}} \int_{c_\nu} \lambda^{m(k+1)-1} d\lambda$$

$$\times \left\{ \sum_{j=1}^{n} \int_{a_j}^{b_j} K^{(i,j)}\left(x, \xi, \frac{\partial}{\partial \xi}, \lambda\right) (\Phi^{(j)}(\xi)\, d\xi + y_1^{(i)}(x, \Phi, \lambda)) \right\}$$

$$= \Phi_{k\nu}^{(i)}(x)$$

i.e. the functions (4.1.28) satisfy Conditions (4.1.25).

Because of the uniqueness of the solution of the Cauchy problem (4.1.24)-(4.1.25), we conclude that

$$Z_{k\nu}^{(i)}(x, t) = Z_{k\nu_0}^{(i)}(x, t) \tag{4.1.30}$$

In accordance with the hypothesis of the theorem, the solution $u^{(i)}(x, t)$ of (4.1.1)-(4.1.3) possesses Property 3 in the statement of the theorem. This means that the components $Z^{(i)}(x, t)$ satisfy Condition 4 of Theorem 9.

Thus, if we take for $\Phi^{(i)}(x)$ the vector-valued function $Z^{(i)}(x, t)$, all the hypotheses of Theorem 9 will be satisfied. Consequently, if we apply Theorem 9 to the vector-valued function $Z^{(i)}(x, t)$, we obtain in the notation of (4.1.18)

$$Z^{(i)}(x, t) = \sum_{\nu=1}^{\infty} Z_{0\nu}^{(i)}(x, t) \tag{4.1.31}$$

Finally, on the basis of (4.1.28) and (4.1.30), we obtain from (4.1.31)

$$Z^{(i)}(x, t) = -\frac{1}{2\pi\sqrt{-1}} \sum_{\nu=1}^{\infty} \int_{c_\nu} [\lambda^{m-1} d\lambda$$

$$\times \left\{ \sum_{j=1}^{n} \int_{a_j}^{b_j} K^{(i,j)}\left(x, \xi, \frac{d}{d\xi}, \lambda\right) (\Phi^{(j)}(\xi) \exp(\lambda^m t) \right. \tag{4.1.32}$$

$$+ \int_0^t \exp(\lambda^m (t-\tau)) F^{(j)}(\xi, \tau)\, d\tau)\, d\xi$$

$$\left. + \exp(\lambda^m t)\, y_1^{(i)}(x, \Phi, \lambda) \right\}$$

To complete the proof of the theorem, we need only note, that in accordance with the notations which we have introduced, the function

$$u^{(i)}(x, t) = u_0^{(i)}(x, t)$$

is the first-column component of the vector-valued function $Z^{(i)}(x, t)$, obtained from (4.1.32) by singling out the first-column component of the integrand. For this, we have to apply the first row of the matrix

$$K^{(i, j)}\left(x, \xi, \frac{\partial}{\partial \xi}, \lambda\right)$$

to the column

$$\left(\Phi^{(j)}(\xi) \exp(\lambda^m t) + \int_0^t \exp(\lambda^m (t-\tau)) F^{(j)}(\xi, \tau)\, d\tau\right)$$

writing it in detail in terms of the column components

$$\left(\Phi_k^{(j)}(\xi) \exp(\lambda^m t) + \int_0^t \exp(\lambda^{m(t-\tau)}) F_k^{(j)}(\xi, \tau)\, d\tau\right)$$

$$(k = 0, 1, \ldots, q-1)$$

and keeping in mind the fact that $F_k^{(j)}(x, t) \equiv 0$ for $k=0,1, 2, \ldots, q-2$.

Thus, by taking the column component $u_0^{(i)}$ in (4.1.32), we obtain (4.1.8), which completes the proof.

Remark 1 It can be directly verified that (4.1.8) gives a formal solution of Problem (4.1.1)-(4.1.3) for the more general case in which the boundary condition (4.1.2) also contains derivatives with respect to t of order q, i.e. $\alpha_{ql}^{(i)} \neq 0$ and $\beta_{ql}^{(i)} \neq 0$. However, in this case, as can be seen from (4.1.5) -(4.1.7), the substitution (4.1.4) does not lead to the mixed problem with separable variables x and t. In other words, in the mixed problem (4.1.5)-(4.1.7) obtained from the substitution (4.1.4), the boundary condition (4.1.6) still contains a time derivative and, consequently, the boundary condition (3.2.2) of the corresponding spectral problems (3.2.1)-(3.2.2) does not coincide with the boundary condition (4.1.6) of (4.1.5)-(4.1.7). Hence, in the general case ($\alpha_{ql}^{(i)} \neq 0$, $\beta_{ql}^{(i)} \neq 0$), we cannot use the method followed in this section to prove the representability of a sufficiently smooth solution of the problem (4.1.1)-(4.1.3) in the form (4.1.8).

In this connection, we must consider (4.1.8) again when $\alpha_{ql}^{(i)} \neq 0$ and $\beta_{ql}^{(i)} \neq 0$. In other words, if the boundary condition (4.1.2) of (4.1.1)-(4.1.3) contains time derivatives of the highest order, we have to show that, under certain restrictions on the given conditions of the problem, the function defined by (4.1.8) is a solution in some sense or other of Problem (4.1.1)-(4.1.3).

To understand better the structure of (4.1.8), it will be useful to show that the function defined by (4.1.8) is a formal solution of (4.1.1)-(4.1.3) even in the case in which the boundary condition (4.1.2) contains the time derivative of highest order. We shall consider this in two stages. First, let us show that the vector-valued functions

$$u^{(i,1)}(x, t) = -\frac{1}{2\pi\sqrt{-1}} \sum_{\nu} \int_{c_\nu} \lambda^{m-1} \exp(\lambda^m t)\, d\lambda \times \left\{ \sum_{j=1}^{n} \int_{a_j}^{b_j} G^{(i,j)}(x, \xi, \lambda)\, F_0^{(j)}(\xi, \Phi, \lambda^m) d\xi + \Delta^{(i)}(x, \Phi, \lambda) \right\} \tag{4.1.33}$$

for $x \in (a_i, b_i)$ (where $i = 1, \ldots, n$) formally satisfy the homogeneous system corresponding to (4.1.1), the boundary conditions (4.1.2) and the initial conditions (4.1.3). Then, we shall have to show that, for certain restrictions on the vector-valued function $f^{(i)}(x, t)$, the vector-valued functions

$$u^{(i,2)}(x, t) = -\frac{1}{2\pi\sqrt{-1}} \sum_{\nu} \int_{c_\nu} \lambda^{m-1} d\lambda \times \sum_{j=1}^{n} \int_{a_j}^{b_j} G^{(i,j)}(x, \xi, \lambda) \int_0^t \exp(\lambda^m (t-\tau))\, f^{(j)}(\xi, \tau)\, d\tau\, d\xi \tag{4.1.34}$$

formally satisfy the non-homogeneous system (4.1.1), the boundary conditions (4.1.2) and the homogeneous initial conditions.

We note that the expression in braces in the integrand over the closed contour c_ν in the right-hand side of (4.1.33) is a solution (determined by (3.2.30)) of the 0-auxiliary spectral problem (3.2.7)-(3.2.8). Therefore, provided that the termwise differentiation of (4.1.33) is possible a sufficient number of times, we have, since $F_0^{(i)}(x, \Phi, \lambda^m)$ is analytic in the entire λ-plane,

$$\sum_{\substack{k \leqslant q-1 \\ mk+l \leqslant p}} A_{kl}^{(i)}(x) \frac{\partial^{k+l} u^{(i,1)}(x,t)}{\partial t^k \partial x^l} - \frac{\partial^q u^{(i,1)}}{\partial t^q}$$

$$\equiv \Big(\sum_{\substack{k \leqslant q-1 \\ mk+l \leqslant p}} A_{kl}^{(i)}(x) \frac{\partial^{k+l}}{\partial t^k \partial x^l} - \frac{\partial^q}{\partial t^q} \Big) \frac{-1}{2\pi \sqrt{-1}}$$

$$\times \sum_{\nu} \int_{c_\nu} \lambda^{m-1} \exp(\lambda^m t)\, d\lambda v_0^{(i)}(x, \Phi, \lambda)$$

$$\equiv \frac{-1}{2\pi\sqrt{-1}} \sum_{\nu} \int_{c_\nu} \lambda^{m-1} d\lambda \Big\{ \sum_{\substack{k \leqslant q-1 \\ mk+l \leqslant p}} \lambda^{mk} A_{kl}^{(i)}(x) \frac{\partial^l v_0^{(i)}(x, \Phi, \lambda)}{\partial x^l}$$

$$- \lambda^p v_0^{(i)}(x, \Phi, \lambda) \Big\} \exp(\lambda^m t)$$

$$\equiv \frac{-1}{2\pi\sqrt{-1}} \sum_{\nu} \int_{c_\nu} \lambda^{m-1} d\lambda \exp(\lambda^m t) F_0^{(i)}(x, \Phi, \lambda^m) \equiv 0$$

Furthermore, substituting (4.1.33) into the boundary condition (4.1.2) and bearing in mind (3.2.8) and (3.2.30), we obtain, since $N_{0,m}(\Phi, \lambda^m)$ is analytic in the entire λ-plane (see (3.2.10))

$$\sum_{i=1}^{n} \sum_{\substack{k \leqslant q \\ l \leqslant p-1}} \Big\{ \alpha_{kl}^{(i)} \frac{\partial^{k+l} u^{(i,1)}}{\partial t^k \partial x^l} \Big|_{x=a_i} + \beta_{kl}^{(i)} \frac{\partial^{k+l} u^{(i,1)}}{\partial t^k \partial x^l} \Big|_{x=b_i} \Big\}$$

$$= \frac{-1}{2\pi\sqrt{-1}} \sum_{i=1}^{n} \sum_{\substack{k \leqslant q \\ l \leqslant p-1}} \Big\{ \alpha_{kl}^{(i)} \frac{\partial^{k+l}}{\partial t^k \partial x^l} \sum_{\nu} \int_{c_\nu} \lambda^{m-1} \exp(\lambda^m t)\, d\lambda$$

$$\times v_0^{(i)}(x, \Phi, \lambda) \Big|_{x=a_i} + \beta_{kl}^{(i)} \frac{\partial^{k+l}}{\partial t^k \partial x^l} \sum_{\nu} \int_{c_\nu} \lambda^{m-1}$$

$$\times \exp(\lambda^m t)\, d\lambda v_0^{(i)}(x, \Phi, \lambda) \Big|_{x=b_i} \Big\} = \frac{-1}{2\pi\sqrt{-1}} \sum_{\nu} \int_{c_\nu}$$

$$\times \lambda^{m-1} \exp(\lambda^m t)\, d\lambda \sum_{i=1}^{n} \sum_{\substack{k \leqslant q \\ l \leqslant p-1}} \Big\{ \lambda^{mk} \alpha_{kl}^{(i)} \frac{\partial^l v_0^{(i)}(x, \Phi, \lambda)}{\partial x^l} \Big|_{x=a_i}$$

$$+ \lambda^{mk} \beta_{kl}^{(i)} \frac{\partial^l v_0^{(i)}(x, \Phi, \lambda)}{\partial x^l} \Big|_{x=b_i} \Big\}$$

$$= \frac{-1}{2\pi\sqrt{-1}} \sum_{\nu} \int_{c_\nu} \lambda^{m-1} \exp(\lambda^m t)\, d\lambda N_{0,m}(\Phi, \lambda^m) = 0$$

Finally, assuming the possibility of termwise differentiation with respect to t of the series (4.1.33) in the interval $[0, T]$, we have, in accordance with (3.2.29),

$$\left.\frac{\partial^s u^{(i,1)}}{\partial t^s}\right|_{t=0} = -\frac{1}{2\pi\sqrt{-1}} \sum_{\nu} \int_{c_\nu} \lambda^{m-1+ms} v_0^{(i)}(x, \Phi, \lambda)\, d\lambda = \Phi_s^{(i)}(x)$$

$$\text{for } s = 0, 1, \ldots, q-1$$

Let us now verify the second assertion. If we substitute (4.1.34) into (4.1.1) and keep in the mind the possibility of termwise differentiation of the series, we obtain

$$\begin{aligned}
&\sum_{\substack{k \le q-1 \\ mk+l \le p}} A_{kl}^{(i)}(x) \frac{\partial^{k+l} u^{(i,2)}}{\partial t^k \partial x^l} - \frac{\partial^q u^{(i,2)}}{\partial t^q} \equiv \frac{-1}{2\pi\sqrt{-1}} \sum_{\nu} \int_{c_\nu} \lambda^{m-1}\, d\lambda \\
&\times \Big\{ \sum_{\substack{k \le q-1 \\ mk+l \le p}} A_{kl}^{(i)}(x) \frac{\partial^l}{\partial x^l} \sum_{j=1}^{n} \int_{a_j}^{b_j} G^{(i,j)}(x, \xi, \lambda) \\
&\times \frac{\partial^k}{\partial t^k} \int_0^t \exp(\lambda^m (t-\tau)) f^{(j)}(\xi, \tau)\, d\tau\, d\xi \\
&- \sum_{j=1}^{n} \int_{a_j}^{b_j} G^{(i,j)}(x, \xi, \lambda) \frac{\partial^q}{\partial t^q} \int_0^t \exp(\lambda^m (t-\tau)) \\
&\times f^{(j)}(\xi, \tau)\, d\tau\, d\xi \Big\} = \frac{-1}{2\pi\sqrt{-1}} \sum_{\nu} \int_{c_\nu} \lambda^{m-1}\, d\lambda \\
&\times \Big\{ \sum_{\substack{k \le q-1 \\ mk+l \le p}} A_{kl}^{(i)}(x) \frac{\partial^l}{\partial x^l} \sum_{j=1}^{n} \int_{a_j}^{b_j} G^{(i,j)}(x, \xi, \lambda) \\
&\times \Big(\lambda^{mk} \int_0^t \exp[\lambda^m (t-\tau)] f^{(j)}(\xi, \tau)\, d\tau \\
&+ \lambda^{m(k-1)} f^{(j)}(\xi, t) + \lambda^{m(k-2)} \frac{\partial f^{(j)}(\xi, t)}{\partial t} \\
&+ \ldots + \frac{\partial^{k-1} f^{(j)}(\xi, t)}{\partial t^{k-1}} \Big) d\xi - \sum_{j=1}^{n} \int_{a_j}^{b_j} G^{(i,j)}(x, \xi, \lambda) \\
&\times \Big(\lambda^{mq} \int_0^t \exp[\lambda^m (t-\tau)] f^{(j)}(\xi, \tau)\, d\tau + \lambda^{m(q-1)} f^{(j)}(\xi, t) \\
&+ \lambda^{m(q-2)} \frac{\partial f^{(j)}(\xi, t)}{\partial t} + \ldots + \frac{\partial^{q-1} f^{(j)}(\xi, t)}{\partial t^{q-1}} \Big) d\xi \Big\} =
\end{aligned} \tag{4.1.35}$$

$$
\begin{aligned}
&= \frac{-1}{2\pi\sqrt{-1}} \sum_{\nu} \int_{c_\nu} \lambda^{m-1}\, d\lambda \Big\{ \sum_{\substack{k \leq q-1 \\ mk+l \leq p}} \lambda^{mk} A_{kl}^{(i)}(x) \frac{\partial^l}{\partial x^l} - \lambda^p E \Big\} \\
&\quad \times \sum_{j=1}^{n} \int_{a_j}^{b_j} G^{(i,j)}(x, \xi, \lambda) \int_0^t \exp[\lambda^m (t-\tau)]\, f^{(j)}(\xi, \tau)\, d\tau\, d\xi \\
&+ \sum_{\substack{k \leq q-1 \\ mk+l \leq p}} A_{kl}^{(i)}(x) \frac{\partial^l}{\partial x^l} \sum_{s=0}^{k-1} \Big(\frac{-1}{2\pi\sqrt{-1}} \sum_{\nu} \int_{c_\nu} \lambda^{m-1+m(k-1-s)}\, d\lambda \\
&\quad \times \sum_{j=1}^{n} \int_{a_j}^{b_j} G^{(i,j)}(x, \xi, \lambda) \frac{\partial^s f^{(j)}(\xi, t)}{\partial t^s}\, d\xi \Big) \\
&- \sum_{s=1}^{q-1} \Big(\frac{-1}{2\pi\sqrt{-1}} \sum_{\nu} \int_{c_\nu} \lambda^{\overbrace{m-1+m(q-1-s)}^{m(q-s)-1}}\, d\lambda \\
&\quad \times \sum_{j=1}^{n} \int_{a_j}^{b_j} G^{(i,j)}(x, \xi, \lambda) \frac{\partial^s f^{(j)}(\xi, t)}{\partial t^s}\, d\xi \Big) \\
&+ \frac{1}{2\pi\sqrt{-1}} \sum_{\nu} \int_{c_\nu} \lambda^{\overbrace{m-1-m(q-1)}^{mq-1}} \\
&\quad \times \sum_{j=1}^{n} \int_{a_j}^{b_j} G^{(i,j)}(x, \xi, \lambda) f^{(j)}(\xi, t)\, d\xi
\end{aligned}
\qquad \text{(4.1.35) (cont.)}
$$

It is clear that

$$
\sum_{j=1}^{n} \int_{a_j}^{b_j} G^{(i,j)}(x, \xi, \lambda) \int_0^t \exp[\lambda^m (t-\tau)]\, f^{(j)}(\xi, \tau)\, d\tau\, d\xi
$$

is a solution of the system

$$
\sum_{\substack{k \leq q-1 \\ mk+l \leq p}} \lambda^{mk} A_{kl}^{(i)}(x) \frac{\partial^l v_0^{(i)}}{\partial x^l} - \lambda^p v_0^{(i)}
= \int_0^t \exp[\lambda^m (t-\tau)]\, f^{(i)}(x, \tau)\, d\tau
$$

Consequently, we have

$$\left(\sum_{\substack{k \leq q-1 \\ mk+l \leq p}} \lambda^{mk} A_{kl}^{(i)}(x) \frac{\partial^l}{\partial x^l} - \lambda^p E \right)$$

$$\times \sum_{j=1}^{n} \int_{a_j}^{b_j} G^{(i,j)}(x, \xi, \lambda) \int_0^t \exp[\lambda^m (t-\tau)] f^{(j)}(\xi, \tau)\, d\tau\, d\xi$$

$$\equiv \int_0^t \exp[\lambda^m (t-\tau)] f^{(i)}(x, \tau)\, d\tau$$

Since the right-hand side of this identity is analytic throughout the entire λ-plane, we conclude that the sum of the first series with respect to ν in the right-hand side of (4.1.35) vanishes identically. With regard to the second and third series over ν in the large parentheses under the summation over s in the right-hand side of (4.1.35), its sum is also identically equal to zero because of (3.2.39). According to this same formula, the sum of the fourth series in the right-hand side of (4.1.35) is equal to $-f^{(i)}(x, t)$. Thus, from (4.1.35), we obtain

$$\sum_{\substack{k \leq q-1 \\ mk+l \leq p}} A_{kl}^{(i)}(x) \frac{\partial^{k+l} u^{(i,2)}}{\partial t^k \partial x^l} - \frac{\partial^q u^{(i,2)}}{\partial t^q} \equiv -f^{(i)}(x, t)$$

Substituting (4.1.34) into (4.1.2) and taking into account the possibility of termwise differentiation of the series, we obtain

$$\sum_{i=1}^{n} \sum_{\substack{k \leq q \\ l \leq p-1}} \left\{ \alpha_{kl}^{(i)} \frac{\partial^{k+l} u^{(i,2)}}{\partial t^k \partial x^l}\Big|_{x=a_i} + \beta_{kl}^{(i)} \frac{\partial^{k+l} u^{(i,2)}}{\partial t^k \partial x^l}\Big|_{x=b_i} \right\}$$

$$= \frac{-1}{2\pi\sqrt{-1}} \sum_{\nu} \int_{c_\nu} \lambda^{m-1}\, d\lambda \tag{4.1.36}$$

$$\times \sum_{i=1}^{n} \sum_{\substack{k \leq q \\ l \leq p-1}} \left\{ \alpha_{kl}^{(i)} \lambda^{mk} \frac{\partial^l}{\partial x^l} \sum_{j=1}^{n} \int_{a_j}^{b_j} G^{(i,j)}(x, \xi, \lambda) \right.$$

$$\times \int_0^t \exp[\lambda^m (t-\tau)] f^{(j)}(\xi, \tau)\, d\tau\, d\xi\, \Big|_{x=a_i} +$$

$$+\beta_{kl}^{(i)}\lambda^{mk}\frac{\partial^l}{\partial x^l}\sum_{j=1}^{n}\int_{a_j}^{b_j}G^{(i,j)}(x,\xi,\lambda)$$

$$\times\int_0^t \exp[\lambda^m(t-\tau)]\,f^{(j)}(\xi,\tau)\,d\tau\,d\xi\,|_{x=b_i}\}$$

$$+\sum_{i=1}^{n}\sum_{\substack{k\leq q\\ l\leq p-1}}\alpha_{kl}^{(i)}\frac{\partial^l}{\partial x^l}\sum_{s=0}^{k-1}\left\{\frac{-1}{2\pi\sqrt{-1}}\sum_{\nu}\int_{c_\nu}\lambda^{m-1+m(k-1-s)}\,d\lambda\right.$$

$$\left.\times\sum_{j=1}^{n}\int_{a_j}^{b_j}G^{(i,j)}(x,\xi,\lambda)\frac{\partial^s f^{(j)}(\xi,t)}{\partial t^s}\,d\xi\right|_{x=a_i}\Bigg\} \tag{4.1.36 (cont.)}$$

$$+\sum_{i=1}^{n}\sum_{\substack{k\leq q\\ l\leq p-1}}\beta_{kl}^{(i)}\frac{\partial^l}{\partial x^l}\sum_{s=0}^{k-1}\left\{\frac{-1}{2\pi\sqrt{-1}}\sum_{\nu}\int_{c_\nu}\lambda^{m-1+m(k-1-s)}\,d\lambda\right.$$

$$\left.\times\sum_{j=1}^{n}\int_{a_j}^{b_j}G^{(i,j)}(x,\xi,\lambda)\frac{\partial^s f^{(j)}(\xi,t)}{\partial t^s}\,d\xi\right|_{x=b_i}\Bigg\}$$

Since

$$\sum_{j=1}^{n}\int_{a_j}^{b_j}G^{(i,j)}(x,\xi,\lambda)\int_0^t\exp[\lambda^m(t-\tau)]\,f^{(j)}(\xi,\tau)\,d\tau\,d\xi$$

is a solution of the system

$$\sum_{\substack{k\leq q-1\\ mk+l\leq p}}\lambda^{mk}A_{kl}^{(i)}(x)\frac{\partial^l v_0^{(i)}}{\partial x^l}-\lambda^p v_0^{(i)}$$

$$=\int_0^t\exp[\lambda^m(t-\tau)]\,f^{(i)}(x,\tau)\,d\tau$$

which satisfies the homogeneous boundary condition

$$\sum_{i=1}^{n}\sum_{\substack{k\leq q\\ l\leq p-1}}\lambda^{mk}\left\{\alpha_{kl}^{(i)}\frac{d^l v_0^{(i)}}{dx^l}\bigg|_{x=a_i}+\beta_{kl}^{(i)}\frac{d^l v_0^{(i)}}{dx^l}\bigg|_{x=b_i}\right\}=0$$

the sum of the first series over ν in the right-hand side of (4.1.36) is zero.

Furthermore, on the basis of (3.2.29), i.e. in accordance

with Theorem 10, we have

$$\frac{-1}{2\pi\sqrt{-1}}\sum_{\nu}\int_{c_\nu}\lambda^{m-1+m(k-1-s)}\,d\lambda \times\sum_{j=1}^{n}\int_{a_j}^{b_j}G^{(i,j)}(x,\xi,\lambda)\frac{\partial^s f^{(j)}(\xi,t)}{\partial t^s}\,d\xi \quad (4.1.37)$$

$$=\begin{cases} f^{(i)}(x,t) & \text{for } s=0,\ k=q \\ 0 & \text{for } s\neq 0 \text{ and arbitrary } k\leqslant q \end{cases}$$

In accordance with (4.1.37), we obtain from (4.1.36)

$$\sum_{i=1}^{n}\sum_{\substack{k\leqslant q\\ l\leqslant p-1}}\left\{\alpha_{kl}^{(i)}\frac{\partial^{k+l}u^{(i,2)}}{\partial t^k\,\partial x^l}\bigg|_{x=a_i}+\beta_{kl}^{(i)}\frac{\partial^{k+l}u^{(i,2)}}{\partial t^k\,\partial x^l}\bigg|_{x=b_i}\right\}$$
$$=\sum_{i=1}^{n}\sum_{l=0}^{p-1}\left\{\alpha_{ql}^{(i)}\frac{\partial^l f^{(i)}(x,t)}{\partial x^l}\bigg|_{x=a_i}+\beta_{ql}^{(i)}\frac{\partial^l f^{(i)}(x,t)}{\partial x^l}\bigg|_{x=b_i}\right\} \quad (4.1.38)$$

Thus, we conclude from (4.1.38) that, in the general case in which the boundary condition (4.1.2) of the mixed problem (4.1.1)-(4.1.3) contains the time derivative of highest order ($\alpha_{ql}^{(i)}\neq 0$, $\beta_{ql}^{(i)}\neq 0$) but the remaining conditions of Theorem 11 are satisfied, (4.1.8) yields a formal solution of (4.1.1)-(4.1.3) if $f^{(i)}(x, t)$ satisfies the boundary condition

$$\sum_{i=1}^{n}\sum_{l=0}^{p-1}\left\{\alpha_{ql}^{(i)}\frac{\partial^l f^{(i)}(x,t)}{\partial x^l}\bigg|_{x=a_i}+\beta_{ql}^{(i)}\frac{\partial^l f^{(i)}(x,t)}{\partial x^l}\bigg|_{x=b_i}\right\}=0 \quad (4.1.39)$$

Remark 2 If the given conditions of Problem (4.1.1)-(4.1.3) are sufficiently smooth, we can show by the method of [40b] that, for problems of a very broad class, the vector-valued functions $u^{(i)}(x, t)$ represented by (4.1.8) are a solution of the corresponding mixed problem of the type (4.1.1)-(4.1.3). *Example* In the study of subterranean hydromechanics in connection with the investigation of the hydrodynamic parameters of a layer, the mixed problem arises for the equation

$$\frac{\partial^2 u}{\partial t^2}+\delta c^2\frac{\partial u}{\partial t}=c^2\left(\frac{\partial^2 u}{\partial x^2}+\frac{1}{x}\frac{\partial u}{\partial x}\right) \quad (4.1.40)$$

with boundary conditions*

$$\left(\frac{\partial u}{\partial x}\right)_{x=a}+\alpha\left(\frac{\partial u}{\partial t}\right)_{x=a}=0, \quad u(b, t)=\beta \qquad (4.1.41)$$

and initial conditions

$$u(x, 0)=\Phi_0(x), \quad \left.\frac{\partial u}{\partial t}\right|_{t=0}=\Phi_1(x) \qquad (4.1.42)$$

where δ, c. α and β are constants.

Since $\frac{1}{c^2}$ is small, the term $\frac{1}{c^2}\frac{\partial^2 u}{\partial t^2}$ is discarded in the book by Charnii ([51], pages 118-132) in (4.1.40); then, the corresponding problem for the heat-flow equation is solved. Here, with the aid of some devices used by Carslaw for solving several one-dimensional heat-flow-theory problems (see [19]), the solution of the problem obtained can be represented in the form of a contour integral.

It should be pointed out that discarding the term $\frac{1}{c^2}\frac{\partial^2 u}{\partial t^2}$ leads to a large error, as is easily seen by calculating the first term in the residue representations of the solution of this problem.

The example considered (4.1.40)-(4.1.42) corresponds physically to the fact that the inertial force of the liquid (see [51], pages 98-99) is taken into account, in contrast with the problem solved in Charnii's book.

Let us show that if the functions $\Phi_0''(x)$ and $\Phi_1(x)$ are continuous on an interval $[a, b]$ and if $\Phi_0(b)=0$, then all the hypotheses of Theorem 11 are satisfied for this problem. Specifically, for this problem, we have

$$m=1, \quad p=q=2$$

Obviously, Conditions 1 and 3 of Theorem 9 are satisfied for Problem (4.1.40)-(4.1.42). It is clear that Condition 2 is satisfied from the characteristic equation

$$\theta^2-1=0$$

of the corresponding spectral problem.

*Clearly, the substitutions $u-\beta=v$ leads to the same mixed problem but the boundary conditions lead to homogeneous boundary conditions. Therefore, we can take $\beta = 0$ without loss of generality.

Replacement of the time derivative with respect to u in (4.1.4) by u_1 leads to the mixed problem

$$\frac{\partial u_0}{\partial t}=u_1$$

$$\frac{\partial u_1}{\partial t}+\delta c^2 u_1=\varkappa\left(\frac{\partial^2 u_0}{\partial x^2}+\frac{1}{x}\frac{\partial u_0}{\partial x}\right)$$

$$\left.\frac{\partial u_0}{\partial x}\right|_{x=a}+\alpha u_1(a,t)=0, \quad u_0(b,t)=0$$

$$u_0(x,0)=\Phi_0(x), \quad u_1(x,0)=\Phi_1(x)$$

for a first-order system in the time derivatives.

The corresponding spectral problem is of the form

$$v_1-\lambda v_0=\Phi_0(x)$$

$$\varkappa\left(\frac{d^2 v_0}{dx^2}+\frac{1}{x}\frac{dv_0}{dx}\right)-\delta c^2 v_1-\lambda v_1=\Phi_1(x)$$

$$\left.\frac{dv_0}{dx}\right|_{x=a}+\alpha v_1(a)=0, \quad v_0(b)=0$$

The 0-auxiliary problem is written

$$\varkappa\left(\frac{d^2 v_0}{dx^2}+\frac{1}{x}\frac{dv_0}{dx}\right)-(\lambda^2+\delta c^2\lambda)\,v_0$$

$$=(\lambda+\delta c^2)\,\Phi_0(x)+\Phi_1(x)=F_0(x,\Phi,\lambda)$$

$$\left.\frac{dv_0}{dx}\right|_{x=a}+\alpha\lambda v_0(a)=-\alpha\Phi_0(a), \quad v_0(b)=0$$

Making the substitution (3.2.11) in this problem

$$\left(w_{00}=v_0,\ w_{01}=\lambda^{-1}\frac{dv_0}{dx}\right)$$

we get the following spectral problem for a system of first-order equations

$$\frac{dw_{00}}{dx}=\lambda w_{01}$$

$$\varkappa\left(\frac{dw_{01}}{dx}+\frac{1}{x}w_{01}\right)-(\lambda+\delta c^2)\,w_{00}=\frac{\Phi_1(x)}{\lambda}+\left(1+\frac{\delta c^2}{\lambda}\right)\Phi_0(x)$$

$$w_{00}(b)=0 \tag{4.1.43}$$

$$w_{01}(a)+\alpha w_{00}(a)=-\frac{\alpha\Phi_0(a)}{\lambda}$$

As can be seen from the boundary conditions (4.1.43), $p_0=1$ and (3.2.15) with $s=0$ takes the form

$$\lambda^{1-1} N_{0,1}(\Phi, \lambda)=\begin{pmatrix} 0 \\ -\alpha\Phi_0(a) \end{pmatrix}=O(1) \qquad (4.1.44)$$

The 1-auxiliary problem is

$$\varkappa\left(\frac{1}{\lambda}\frac{d^2 v_1}{dx^2}+\frac{1}{x}\frac{dv_1}{dx}\right)-\lambda\left(1+\frac{\delta c^2}{\lambda}\right)v_1$$
$$=\Phi_1(x)+\frac{\varkappa}{\lambda}\left(\frac{d^2\Phi_0}{dx^2}+\frac{1}{x}\frac{d\Phi_0}{dx}\right)$$
$$\frac{1}{\lambda}\frac{d}{dx}(v_1-\Phi_0(x))|_{x=a}+\alpha v_1(a)=0, \quad \frac{v_1(b)-\Phi_0(b)}{\lambda}=0$$

If we make the substitution (3.2.11), the boundary conditions of this problem lead to the following conditions

$$w_{01}(b)=\Phi_0(b)$$
$$\lambda(w_{11}(a)+\alpha w_{01}(a))=\Phi_0'(a)$$

From this it is clear that if $\Phi_0(b)=0$, then $p_1=1$ and (3.2.15) with $s=1$ for the problem in question takes the form

$$\lambda^{1-1} N_{1,1}(\Phi, \lambda)=\begin{pmatrix} 0 \\ \Phi_0'(a) \end{pmatrix}=O(1) \quad . \qquad (4.1.45)$$

Thus, as can be seen from (4.1.44) and (4.1.45), Condition 4 of Theorem 9 is satisfied for the mixed problem (4.1.40)-(4.1.42) in question if $\Phi_0(b)=0$.

Condition 5 of Theorem 9 for Problem (4.1.40)-(4.1.42) reduces to the requirement that, for sufficiently large λ,

$$\operatorname{rank}\begin{pmatrix} \alpha\lambda & \lambda & 0 & 0 \\ \lambda & 0 & 0 & 0 \end{pmatrix}=2$$

which obviously is the case.

Finally, Condition 6 of Theorem 9 is also satisfied for (4.1.40)-(4.1.42), as can easily be seen by obtaining an asymptotic representation of the characteristic determinant of the Green's function (to which matter we shall return).

Furthermore, we note that the boundary conditions of the

mixed problem (4.1.40)-(4.1.42) do not contain the highest time derivative.

Thus, we have the conditions under which Theorem 11 can be applied to the problems in question. Thus, the solution $u(x, t)$ of the mixed problem (4.1.40)-(4.1.42) possessing Properties* 1-3 listed in the statement of Theorem 11 is represented by the formula

$$u(x, t) = \frac{-1}{2\pi\sqrt{-1}} \sum_{\nu} \int_{c_\nu} d\lambda e^{\lambda t} \left\{ \int_a^b G(x, \xi, \lambda)\left((\lambda + \delta c^2)\Phi_0(\xi) + \Phi_1(\xi)\right) + \Delta(x, \Phi, \lambda) \right\} \qquad (4.1.46)$$

where

$$G(x, \xi, \lambda) = \frac{1}{\Delta(\lambda)} \begin{vmatrix} g(x, \xi, \lambda) & I_0(\mu x) & K_0(\mu x) \\ \left.\frac{\partial g(x, \xi, \lambda)}{\partial x}\right|_{x=a} + \alpha\lambda g(a, \xi, \lambda) & \left.\frac{dI_0(\mu x)}{dx}\right|_{x=a} + \alpha\lambda I_0(\mu a) & \left.\frac{dK_0(\mu x)}{dx}\right|_{x=a} + \alpha\lambda K_0(\mu a) \\ g(b, \xi, \lambda) & I_0(\mu b) & K_0(\mu b) \end{vmatrix}$$

$$\Delta(x, \Phi, \lambda) = \frac{1}{\Delta(\lambda)} \begin{vmatrix} 0 & I_0(\mu x) & K_0(\mu x) \\ \alpha\Phi_0(a) & \left.\frac{dI_0(\mu x)}{dx}\right|_{x=a} + \alpha\lambda I_0(\mu a) & \left.\frac{dK_0(\mu x)}{dx}\right|_{x=a} + \alpha\lambda K_0(\mu a) \\ 0 & I_0(\mu b) & K_0(\mu b) \end{vmatrix}$$

$$g(x, \xi, \lambda) = \begin{cases} +\frac{1}{2\delta(\xi, \lambda)}\{I_0(\mu x)K_0(\mu\xi) - I_0(\mu\xi)K_0(\mu x)\} & \text{for } a \leqslant \xi \leqslant x \\ -\frac{1}{2\delta(\xi, \lambda)}\{I_0(\mu x)K_0(\mu\xi) - I_0(\mu\xi)K_0(\mu x)\} & \text{for } x \leqslant \xi \leqslant b \end{cases}$$

$\delta(\xi, \lambda)$ is the Wronskian determinant of the Bessel functions

$$I_0(\mu\xi),\ K_0(\mu\xi) \qquad \left(\mu = \sqrt{\varkappa^{-1}(\lambda^2 + \delta c^2)}\right),$$

$$\Delta(\lambda) = \begin{vmatrix} \left.\frac{dI_0(\mu x)}{dx}\right|_{x=a} + \alpha\lambda I_0(\mu a) & \left.\frac{dK_0(\mu x)}{dx}\right|_{x=a} + \alpha\lambda K_0(\mu a) \\ I_0(\mu b) & K_0(\mu b) \end{vmatrix}$$

*$u(x, t)$ possesses Property 3 if $u(a, t)$, $\left.\frac{\partial u}{\partial x}\right|_{x=a}$, $u(b, t)$ are bounded.

Using the asymptotic representations of functions $I_0(\mu x)$ and $K_0(\mu x)$ and of their derivatives, we easily obtain the following asymptotic representation (for large values of λ)

$$\Delta(\lambda)=\frac{c}{2\sqrt{ab}}\left\{\left[\alpha+\frac{1}{c}\right]e^{-\frac{\lambda}{c}(b-a)}+\left[\frac{1}{c}-\alpha\right]e^{\frac{\lambda}{c}(b-a)}\right\}$$

If we use a fundamental system of particular solutions of the homogeneous equation of the spectral problem that admit asymptotic representations of the form (2.3.13), we obtain the following asymptotic representation for the determinant $\Delta(\lambda)$

$$\Delta(\lambda)=-\frac{ic}{2}\sqrt{\frac{a}{b}}\left\{\left[\frac{1}{c}+\alpha\right]e^{-\frac{\lambda}{c}(b-a)}+\left[\frac{1}{c}-\alpha\right]e^{\frac{\lambda}{c}(b-a)}\right\}$$

From this it is clear that the numbers σ, M_1 and M_σ which appear in the statement of Theorem 9 are in the present case

$$\sigma=2,\quad M_1=\frac{1}{c}+\alpha,\quad M_2=\alpha-\frac{1}{c}$$

These numbers are non-zero, as we would expect from the physical meanings of α and c.

4.2 MIXED PROBLEMS WITH BOUNDARY CONDITIONS CONTAINING NO TIME DERIVATIVES

If there are no time derivatives in the boundary condition of Problem (4.1.1)-(4.1.3) of the preceding section, it turns out that the residue formula representing a sufficiently smooth solution of the problem and the method of obtaining this formula are considerably simplified. In this case, we are able to avoid use of Theorem 9 and need only use Theorem 10 on the expansion of functions in a series of residues according to a formula of the same type as the Poincaré-Birkhoff formula.

This section is devoted to finding a residue representation of a sufficiently smooth solution of mixed problems of a general nature with boundary conditions not containing a time derivative.

Consider the mixed problem for the solution of the system

$$\sum_{k=0}^{q} A_k^{(i)}\left(x, \frac{\partial}{\partial x}\right)\frac{\partial^k u^{(i)}}{\partial t^k} = f^{(i)}(x, t) \quad \text{for} \quad x \in (a_i, b_i)$$
$$\left(A_q^{(i)}\left(x, \frac{\partial}{\partial x}\right) = 1; \quad i = 1, 2, \ldots, n\right) \tag{4.2.1}$$

with boundary condition

$$\sum_{i=1}^{n}\sum_{l=0}^{p-1}\left\{\alpha_l^{(i)}\frac{\partial^l u^{(i)}}{\partial x^l}\bigg|_{x=a_i} + \beta_l^{(i)}\frac{\partial^l u^{(i)}}{\partial x^l}\bigg|_{x=b_i}\right\} = 0 \tag{4.2.2}$$

and initial conditions

$$\frac{\partial^k u^{(i)}}{\partial t^k}\bigg|_{t=0} = \Phi_k^{(i)}(x) \quad \text{for} \quad x \in (a_i, b_i)$$
$$(i = 1, \ldots, n; \quad k = 0, \ldots, q-1) \tag{4.2.3}$$

where $A_k^{(i)}\left(x, \frac{\partial}{\partial x}\right)$ is an r-dimensional square matrix of linear differential operators of orders not exceeding p (where p is the order of the derivative with respect to x in (4.2.1)), $\alpha_l^{(i)}$ and $\beta_l^{(i)}$ are constant $nrp \times r$ matrices and $f^{(i)}(x, t)$ and $\Phi_k^{(i)}(x)$ are vector-valued functions of appropriate dimensions defined on $[a_i, b_i]$ (for $i = 1, 2, \ldots, n$).

We shall refer to the problem of solving the system

$$\sum_{k=0}^{q}\lambda^k A_k^{(i)}\left(x, \frac{d}{dx}\right)v^{(i)} = F^{(i)}(x)$$
$$x \in (a_i, b_i) \quad (i = 1, 2, \ldots, n) \tag{4.2.4}$$

with boundary condition

$$\sum_{i=1}^{n} L^{(i)}(v^{(i)}) = \sum_{i=1}^{n}\sum_{l=0}^{p-1}\left\{\alpha_l^{(i)}\frac{d^l v^{(i)}}{dx^l}\bigg|_{x=a_i} + \beta_l^{(i)}\frac{d^l v^{(i)}}{dx^l}\bigg|_{x=b_i}\right\} = 0 \tag{4.2.5}$$

as the spectral problem of the corresponding mixed problem (4.2.1)-(4.2.3).

By making a substitution of the derivatives, we can reduce (4.2.4) to a system of first-order differential equations.* Here, if the coefficients in (4.2.4) are continuous

*It is convenient to make the substitution

$$\frac{dv^{(i)}}{dx} = v^{(i, 1)}, \quad \frac{dv^{(i, k)}}{dx} = v^{(i, k+1)}$$

on the interval $[a_i, b_i]$ and if the coefficient of the highest derivative on this interval is the inverse matrix, then, when the substitution of the derivatives is made, the resulting first-order system will have a fundamental system of particular solutions. The matrix of the solutions will be a square matrix of order rp. If we divide this matrix into r^2 square cells, we obtain p matrix cells

$$Y_1^{(i)}(x, \lambda), \ldots, Y_p^{(i)}(x, \lambda) \tag{4.2.6}$$

in the first row. Obviously, the remaining rows of cells of the fundamental matrix are made up of the respective derivatives of System (4.2.6).

Thus, we can easily arrange for the matrix of fundamental solutions of the system of first-order equations obtained from (4.2.4) by making a substitution of derivatives to have the form

$$V^{(i)}(x, \lambda) = \begin{pmatrix} Y_1^{(i)}(x, \lambda) & Y_2^{(i)}(x, \lambda) & \ldots & Y_p^{(i)}(x, \lambda) \\ \frac{dY_1^{(i)}(x, \lambda)}{dx} & \frac{dY_2^{(i)}(x, \lambda)}{dx} & \ldots & \frac{dY_p^{(i)}(x, \lambda)}{dx} \\ \ldots & \ldots & \ldots & \ldots \\ \frac{d^{p-1}Y_1^{(i)}(x, \lambda)}{dx^{p-1}} & \frac{d^{p-1}Y_2^{(i)}(x, \lambda)}{dx^{p-1}} & \ldots & \frac{d^{p-1}Y_p^{(i)}(x, \lambda)}{dx^{p-1}} \end{pmatrix} \tag{4.2.7}$$

Obviously, every matrix $Y_k^{(i)}(x, \lambda)$ (for $k = 1, \ldots, p$) is a solution of the homogeneous system

$$\sum_{k=0}^{q} \lambda^k A_k^{(i)}\left(x, \frac{d}{dx}\right) v^{(i)} \equiv 0 \quad (i = 1, \ldots, n) \tag{4.2.8}$$

corresponding to System (4.2.4).

Let us denote the determinant of the matrix (4.2.7) by $W^{(i)}(x, \lambda)$. Obviously, this is the Wronskian determinant for the corresponding first-order system.

The general solution of the homogeneous system is of the form

$$v^{(i)} = Y_1^{(i)}(x, \lambda) c_1^{(i)} + \ldots + Y_p^{(i)}(x, \lambda) c_p^{(i)} \tag{4.2.9}$$

where the $c_k^{(i)}$ are r-dimensional columns of arbitrary constants.

Since the homogeneous first-order system obtained from (4.2.8) by making a substitution of derivatives is equivalent to (4.2.8), the general solution of System (4.2.8) is also represented by (4.2.9).

The general solution of the non-homogeneous system (4.2.4) can be constructed by the method of variation of the parameters $c_k^{(i)}$. To do this, we rewrite (4.2.8) in the form

$$\frac{d^p v^{(i)}}{dx^p} + P_1(x, \lambda)\frac{d^{p-1}v^{(i)}}{dx^{p-1}} + \ldots + P_p(x, \lambda)\, v^{(i)} = 0 \qquad (4.2.10)$$

Furthermore, we have

$$\frac{dv^{(i)}}{dx} = \sum_{k=1}^{p} \frac{dY_k^{(i)}(x, \lambda)}{dx} c_k^{(i)} + \sum_{k=1}^{p} Y_k^{(i)}(x, \lambda)\frac{dc_k^{(i)}}{dx}$$

If we put

$$\sum_{k=1}^{p} Y_k^{(i)}(x, \lambda)\frac{dc_k^{(i)}}{dx} = 0$$

we obtain from the preceding equation

$$\frac{d^2v^{(i)}}{dx^2} = \sum_{k=1}^{p} \frac{d^2Y_k^{(i)}(x, \lambda)}{dx^2} c_k^{(i)} + \sum_{k=1}^{p} \frac{dY_k^{(i)}(x, \lambda)}{dx}\frac{dc_k^{(i)}}{dx}$$

Suppose now that

$$\sum_{k=1}^{p} \frac{dY_k^{(i)}(x, \lambda)}{dx}\frac{dc_k^{(i)}}{dx} = 0$$

By continuing this process, on the $(p-1)$th step, we get

$$\frac{d^{p-1}v^{(i)}}{dx^{p-1}} = \sum_{k=1}^{p} \frac{d^{p-1}Y_k^{(i)}(x, \lambda)}{dx^{p-1}} c_k^{(i)} + \sum_{k=1}^{p} \frac{d^{p-2}Y_k^{(i)}(x, \lambda)}{dx^{p-2}}\frac{dc_k^{(i)}}{dx}$$

Finally, by putting

$$\sum_{k=1}^{p} \frac{d^{p-2}Y_k^{(i)}}{dx^{p-2}}\frac{dc_k^{(i)}}{dx} = 0$$

we obtain the following expression for the p-th derivative from the penultimate equation:

$$\frac{d^p v^{(i)}}{dx^p} = \sum_{k=1}^{p} \frac{d^p Y_k^{(i)}}{dx^p} c_k^{(i)} + \sum_{k=1}^{p} \frac{d^{p-1} Y_k^{(i)}}{dx^{p-1}} \frac{dc_k^{(i)}}{dx}$$

By substituting the derivatives of $\frac{d^s v^{(i)}}{dx^s}$ thus obtained into non-homogeneous system (4.2.4) and re-grouping, we obtain

$$\sum_{k=1}^{p} \frac{d^{p-1} Y_k^{(i)}}{dx^{p-1}} \frac{dc_k^{(i)}}{dx} + \sum_{k=1}^{p} \left\{ \frac{d^p Y_k^{(i)}}{dx^p} + P_1(x, \lambda) \frac{d^{p-1} Y_k^{(i)}}{dx^{p-1}} + \dots \right. \tag{4.2.11}$$

$$\left. \dots + P_p(x, \lambda) Y_k^{(i)}(x, \lambda) \right\} c_k^{(i)} = (B^{(i)}(x))^{-1} F^{(i)}(x)$$

where $B^{(i)}(x)$ is the matrix coefficient of the p-th derivative in the left-hand side of (4.2.4).

Since the $Y_k^{(i)}$ satisfies (4.2.8) or (4.2.10), the expression in the braces on the left-hand side of (4.2.11) is identically zero. Consequently, combining the equations obtained from (4.2.11) with the equations found earlier, we arrive at the following system of equations in $\frac{dc_k^{(i)}}{dx}$:

$$\left.\begin{aligned} &\sum_{k=1}^{p} Y_k^{(i)}(x, \lambda) \frac{dc_k^{(i)}}{dx} = 0 \\ &\sum_{k=1}^{p} \frac{dY_k^{(i)}(x, \lambda)}{dx} \frac{dc_k^{(i)}}{dx} = 0 \\ &\dots\dots\dots\dots \\ &\sum_{k=1}^{p} \frac{d^{p-2} Y_k^{(i)}}{dx^{p-2}} \frac{dc_k^{(i)}}{dx} = 0 \\ &\sum_{k=1}^{p} \frac{d^{p-1} Y_k^{(i)}(x, \lambda)}{dx^{p-1}} \frac{dc_k^{(i)}}{dx} = (B^{(i)}(x))^{-1} F^{(i)}(x) \end{aligned}\right\} \tag{4.2.12}$$

System (4.2.12) can be rewritten in matrix form

$$\begin{pmatrix} Y_1^{(i)}(x, \lambda) & \dots & Y_p^{(i)}(x, \lambda) \\ \frac{dY_1^{(i)}(x, \lambda)}{dx} & \dots & \frac{dY_p^{(i)}(x, \lambda)}{dx} \\ \dots & \dots & \dots \\ \frac{d^{p-1} Y_1^{(i)}(x, \lambda)}{dx^{p-1}} & \dots & \frac{d^{p-1} Y_p^{(i)}(x, \lambda)}{dx^{p-1}} \end{pmatrix} \begin{pmatrix} \frac{dc_1^{(i)}}{dx} \\ \frac{dc_2^{(i)}}{dx} \\ \vdots \\ \frac{dc_p^{(i)}}{dx} \end{pmatrix} = \begin{pmatrix} 0 \\ \vdots \\ 0 \\ (B^{(i)}(x))^{-1} F^{(i)}(x) \end{pmatrix}$$

From this we obtain

$$\begin{pmatrix} \frac{dc_1^{(i)}}{dx} \\ \vdots \\ \frac{dc_p^{(i)}}{dx} \end{pmatrix} = (V^{(i)}(x, \lambda))^{-1} \begin{pmatrix} 0 \\ \vdots \\ 0 \\ (B^{(i)}(x))^{-1} F^{(i)}(x) \end{pmatrix} \tag{4.2.13}$$

Let $Q_\nu^{(i)}(x, \lambda)$ denote the r-th-order matrix obtained by taking the transpose of the matrix composed of the co-factors of the elements of the matrix

$$\frac{d^{p-1} Y_\nu^{(i)}(x, \lambda)}{dx^{p-1}}$$

in the Wronskian determinant $W^{(i)}(x, \lambda)$.

We introduce the notation

$$z_\nu^{(i)}(x, \lambda) = \frac{Q_\nu^{(i)}(x, \lambda)}{W^{(i)}(x, \lambda)} \tag{4.2.14}$$

Then, it follows from (4.2.13) that

$$\frac{dc_\nu^{(i)}}{dx} = z_\nu^{(i)}(x, \lambda)\,(B^{(i)}(x))^{-1} F^{(i)}(x) \tag{4.2.15}$$

Integrating from a_i to x, we obtain

$$c_\nu^{(i)}(x) = c_\nu^{(i)}(a_i) + \int_{a_i}^{x} z_\nu^{(i)}(\xi, \lambda)\,(B^{(i)}(\xi))^{-1} F^{(i)}(\xi)\, d\xi$$

Substituting this result into (4.2.9), we obtain the following representation for the general solution of System (4.2.4)

$$v^{(i)} = \sum_{\nu=1}^{p} Y_\nu^{(i)}(x, \lambda) \Big\{ c_\nu^{(i)}(a_i) + \int_{a_i}^{x} z_\nu^{(i)}(\xi, \lambda)\,(B^{(i)}(\xi))^{-1} F^{(i)}(\xi)\, d\xi \Big\} \tag{4.2.16}$$

If we take

$$x = b_i$$

as constant limit of integration in the identity (4.2.15), we have

$$c_\nu^{(i)}(x) = c_\nu^{(i)}(b_i) + \int_{b_i}^{x} z_\nu^{(i)}(\xi, \lambda)\,(B^{(i)}(\xi))^{-1} F^{(i)}(\xi)\, d\xi$$

Substitution into (4.2.9) yields

$$v^{(i)} = \sum_{\nu=1}^{p} Y_\nu^{(i)}(x, \lambda)\left\{c_\nu^{(i)}(b_i) + \int_{b_i}^{x} z_\nu^{(i)}(\xi, \lambda)(B^{(i)}(\xi))^{-1}F^{(i)}(\xi)\,d\xi\right\} \tag{4.2.17}$$

Adding (4.2.16) and (4.2.17) and dividing the result by 2, we obtain the following representation for the general solution of System (4.2.4)

$$v^{(i)} = \sum_{\nu=1}^{p} Y_\nu^{(i)}(x, \lambda)\, c_\nu^{(i)} + \int_{a_i}^{b_i} g^{(i)}(x, \xi, \lambda)(B^{(i)}(\xi))^{-1}F^{(i)}(\xi)\,d\xi \tag{4.2.18}$$

where

$$c_\nu^{(i)} = \frac{c_\nu^{(i)}(a_i) + c_\nu^{(i)}(b_i)}{2}$$

$$g^{(i)}(x, \xi, \lambda) = \begin{cases} \dfrac{1}{2}\displaystyle\sum_{\nu=1}^{p} Y_\nu^{(i)}(x, \lambda)\, z_\nu^{(i)}(\xi, \lambda) & \text{for } a_i \leqslant \xi \leqslant x \leqslant b_i \\ -\dfrac{1}{2}\displaystyle\sum_{\nu=1}^{p} Y_\nu^{(i)}(x, \lambda)\, z_\nu^{(i)}(\xi, \lambda) & \text{for } a_i \leqslant x \leqslant \xi \leqslant b_i \end{cases} \tag{4.2.19}$$

The representation (4.2.18) is convenient in constructing Green's matrix since the right-hand side contains a definite integral. Now, we choose the constants $c_\nu^{(i)}$ in such a way that (4.2.18) will be a solution of the boundary-value problem (4.2.4)-(4.2.5).

Let us suppose that Problem (4.2.4)-(4.2.5) has a solution that is valid for all except countably - many complex values of λ, which are assumed to be poles of that solution. We will now formally construct this solution. By substituting (4.2.18) into the boundary condition (4.2.5), we obtain

$$\sum_{=1}^{n}\sum_{\nu=1}^{p} L^{(i)}(Y_\nu^{(i)}(x, \lambda))\, c_\nu^{(i)} = -\sum_{i=1}^{n}\int_{a_i}^{b_i} L^{(i)}(g^{(i)}(x, \xi, \lambda))_x (B^{(i)}(\xi))^{-1}F^{(i)}(\xi)\,d\xi \tag{4.2.20}$$

From this, we get*

$$\begin{pmatrix} c_1^{(1)} \\ \vdots \\ c_p^{(1)} \\ \vdots \\ c_1^{(n)} \\ \vdots \\ c_p^{(n)} \end{pmatrix} = -A^{-1}(\lambda) \sum_{j=1}^{n} \int_{a_j}^{b_j} L^{(j)}(g^{(j)}(x, \xi, \lambda))_x \times (B^{(j)}(\xi))^{-1} F^{(j)}(\xi)\, d\xi \tag{4.2.21}$$

where

$$A(\lambda) = (L^{(1)}(Y_1^{(1)}), \ldots, L^{(1)}(Y_p^{(1)}) \ldots, L^{(n)}(Y_1^{(n)}), \ldots, L^{(n)}(Y_p^{(n)})) \tag{4.2.22}$$

is a characteristic matrix of order nrp composed of the $nrp \times r$ matrix cells

$$L^{(i)}(Y_\nu^{(i)}(x, \lambda))$$

$$(i = 1, \ldots, n; \quad \nu = 1, \ldots, p)$$

Let us divide the matrix $A^{-1}(\lambda)$ into $(np)^2$ cells and the matrix $L^{(j)}(g^{(j)}(x, \xi, \lambda))_x$ vertically into np cells.

$$A^{-1}(\lambda) = \begin{pmatrix} B_{11}^{(1)}(\lambda) & \ldots & B_{1,np}^{(1)}(\lambda) \\ \cdot & \cdots & \cdot \\ B_{p1}^{(1)}(\lambda) & \ldots & B_{p,np}^{(1)}(\lambda) \\ \cdot & \cdots & \cdot \\ B_{11}^{(n)}(\lambda) & \ldots & B_{1,np}^{(n)}(\lambda) \\ \cdot & \cdots & \cdot \\ B_{p1}^{(n)}(\lambda) & \ldots & B_{p,np}^{(n)}(\lambda) \end{pmatrix} \tag{4.2.23}$$

$$L^{(j)}(g^{(j)}(x, \xi, \lambda)) = \begin{pmatrix} L_1^{(j)}(g(x, \xi, \lambda)) \\ \cdots \\ L_{np}^{(j)}(g(x, \xi, \lambda)) \end{pmatrix} \tag{4.2.24}$$

*We assume the existence of a matrix $A^{-1}(\lambda)$ for all complex λ except for a countable set of values which are assumed to be poles of the solution of Problem (4.2.4) – (4.2.5).

If we substitute the representations (4.2.23) and (4.2.24) into (4.2.21) and equate corresponding cells (according to their vertical positions), we obtain

$$c_{\nu}^{(i)} = \sum_{k=1}^{np} \sum_{j=1}^{n} \int_{a_j}^{b_j} B_{\nu k}^{(i)}(\lambda) L_k^{(j)} (g^{(j)}(x, \xi, \lambda))_x (B^{(j)}(\xi))^{-1} F^{(j)}(\xi)\, d\xi$$

Substituting these values of $c_{\nu}^{(i)}$ into the general solution (4.2.18), we obtain the following representation for the solution $v^{(i)}(x, F, \lambda)$ of Problem (4.2.4)-(4.2.5) for $x \in (a_i, b_i)$

$$v^{(i)}(x, F, \lambda) = \sum_{j=1}^{n} \int_{a_j}^{b_j} \Big\{ \sum_{\nu=1}^{p} \sum_{k=1}^{np} Y_{\nu}^{(i)}(x, \lambda) B_{\nu k}^{(i)}(\lambda) \times L_k^{(j)} (g^{(j)}(x, \xi, \lambda))_x (B^{(j)}(\xi))^{-1} \Big\} F^{(j)}(\xi)\, d\xi + \int_{a_i}^{b_i} g^{(i)}(x, \xi, \lambda) (B^{(i)}(\xi))^{-1} F^{(i)}(\xi)\, d\xi \qquad (4.2.25)$$

Finally, if we introduce the notation

$$G^{(i,j)}(x, \xi, \lambda) = \Big\{ g^{(i,j)}(x, \xi, \lambda) + \sum_{\nu=1}^{p} \sum_{k=1}^{np} Y_{\nu}^{(i)}(x, \lambda) \times B_{\nu k}^{(i)}(\lambda) L_k^{(j)} (g^{(j)}(x, \xi, \lambda))_x \Big\} (B^{(j)}(\xi))^{-1} \qquad (4.2.26)$$

we can write (4.2.25) in the form

$$v^{(i)}(x, F, \lambda) = \sum_{j=1}^{n} \int_{a_j}^{b_j} G^{(i,j)}(x, \xi, \lambda) F^{(j)}(\xi)\, d\xi \qquad (4.2.27)$$

where

$$g^{(i,j)}(x, \xi, \lambda) = \begin{cases} g^{(i)}(x, \xi, \lambda) & \text{for } j = i \\ 0 & \text{for } j \neq i \end{cases} \qquad (4.2.28)$$

The matrix defined by (4.2.26) is called the Green's matrix of (4.2.4)-(4.2.5). In other words, the Green's matrix of the boundary-value problem (4.2.4)-(4.2.5) is the matrix by means of which the solution of this problem is represented in the form (4.2.27).

Suppose that the Green's matrix of Problem (4.2.4)-(4.2.5) exists and is a meromorphic function of the parameter λ. Suppose that the following formula* holds for every vector-valued function $F^{(i)}(x) \in L_2(a_i, b_i)$:

$$\frac{-1}{2\pi\sqrt{-1}} \sum_{\nu} \int_{c_\nu} \lambda^s \, d\lambda \sum_{j=1}^{n} \int_{a_j}^{b_j} G^{(i,j)}(x, \xi, \lambda) F^{(j)}(\xi) \, d\xi = \begin{cases} 0 & \text{for } s < q-1 \\ F^{(i)}(x) & \text{for } s = q-1 \end{cases} \tag{4.2.29}$$

where c_ν is, as before, a simple closed contour encircling only one pole λ_ν of the vector-valued function (4.2.27) and where the summation with respect to ν is over all poles of that vector-valued problem.

Then, we have the following theorem.

Theorem 12 Suppose that the components of a vector-valued function

$$A_k^{(i)}\left(x, \frac{\partial}{\partial x}\right) \Phi_s^{(i)}(x) \quad (s = 0, 1, \ldots, k-1; \; k = 0, \ldots, q-1)$$

are continuous on an interval $[a_i, b_i]$ that the components of a vector-valued function $f^{(i)}(x, t)$ belong to the space $L_2(a_i, b_i)$ for $t \in [0, T]$, and that they are absolutely integrable in the two-dimensional region $0 \leqslant t \leqslant T$, $a_i < x < b_i$.

Suppose that Problem (4.2.1)-(4.2.3) has a solution $u^{(i)}(x, t)$ for $x \in (a_i, b_i)$ possessing the following properties.

1. The components of the vector-valued function

$$\frac{\partial^s}{\partial t^s} A_k^{(i)}\left(x, \frac{\partial}{\partial x}\right) \times u^{(i)}(x, t)$$

for $s \leqslant k-1$ are absolutely integrable with respect to t over the interval $[0, T]$ for all $x \in (a_i, b_i)$, and the components of the vector-valued function

$$\frac{\partial^k}{\partial t^k} A_k^{(i)}\left(x, \frac{\partial}{\partial x}\right) u^{(i)}(x, t)$$

* For simplicity, convergence of the series (4.2.29) is understood, as before, in the sense of the matrix $L_2(a_i, b_i)$.

(for $k=1, 2, \ldots, q$) are summable in the two-dimensional region $0 \leqslant t \leqslant T$, $a_i < x < b_i$ (for $i=1, 2, \ldots, n$). The components of the vector-valued function

$$\frac{\partial^k}{\partial t^k} A_k^{(i)}\left(x, \frac{\partial}{\partial x}\right) \times u^{(i)}(x, t) \in L_2(a_i, b_i)$$

for all $t \in [0, T]$ for ($k=1, \ldots, q-1$).

Then, this solution can be represented by the formula*

$$u^{(i)}(x, t) = \frac{-1}{2\pi\sqrt{-1}} \sum_{\nu} \int_{c_\nu} e^{\lambda t}\, d\lambda \sum_{j=1}^{n} \int_{a_j}^{b_j} G^{(i, j)}(x, \xi, \lambda) \times \left\{F_0^{(j)}(\xi, \Phi, \lambda) + \int_0^t e^{-\lambda\tau} f^{(j)}(\xi, \tau)\, d\tau\right\} d\xi \tag{4.2.30}$$

where

$$F_0^{(j)}(\xi, \Phi, \lambda) = \sum_{k=1}^{q} A_k^{(j)}\left(\xi, \frac{\partial}{\partial \xi}\right) \{\Phi_{k-1}^{(j)}(\xi) + \ldots + \lambda^{k-1}\Phi_0^{(j)}(\xi)\} \tag{4.2.31}$$

Proof By hypothesis, the solution $v^{(i)}(x, F, \lambda)$ of the spectral problem (4.2.4)-(4.2.5) for $x \in (a_i, b_i)$ and for every non-eigenvalue λ is represented by (4.2.7). Therefore, for every vector-valued function $v^{(i)}(x)$ (for $i=1, \ldots, n$) which is p times continuously differentiable on (a_i, b_i) and which satisfies the boundary condition (4.2.5), the identity

$$v^{(i)}(x) = \sum_{k=0}^{q} \lambda^k \sum_{j=1}^{n} \int_{a_j}^{b_j} G^{(i, j)}(x, \xi, \lambda) \times A_k^{(j)}\left(\xi, \frac{\partial}{\partial \xi}\right) v^{(j)}(\xi)\, d\xi \tag{4.2.32}$$

holds for every

$$x \in (a_i, b_i) \quad (i=1, 2, \ldots, n)$$

Let $u^{(i)}(x, t)$ (for $i=1, 2, \ldots, n$) be a solution of Problem (4.2.1)-(4.2.3) possessing Properties 1 and 2 of the theorem. Then, it reduces (4.2.1) to an identity. We rewrite

*It is convenient to use the formula obtained from (4.2.30) by the substitution $\lambda = \mu^2$.

this identity in the form

$$\sum_{k=0}^{q}\left(\frac{\partial^k}{\partial t^k}-\lambda^k\right)A_k^{(i)}\left(x,\frac{\partial}{\partial x}\right)u^{(i)}(x, t)$$

$$+\sum_{k=0}^{q}\lambda^k A_k^{(i)}\left(x,\frac{\partial}{\partial x}\right)u^{(i)}(x, t)\equiv f^{(i)}(x, t)$$

Applying the operator

$$R_\lambda^{(i)}(F)\equiv\sum_{j=1}^{n}\int_{a_j}^{b_j}G^{(i,j)}(x, \xi, \lambda)F^{(j)}(\xi)\,d\xi \qquad (4.2.33)$$

to both sides of this identity, we obtain

$$\sum_{j=1}^{n}\int_{a_j}^{b_j}G^{(i,j)}(x, \xi, \lambda)$$

$$\times\sum_{k=0}^{q}\left(\frac{\partial^k}{\partial t^k}-\lambda^k\right)A_k^{(j)}\left(\xi,\frac{\partial}{\partial \xi}\right)u^{(j)}(\xi, t)\,d\xi$$

$$+\sum_{j=1}^{n}\int_{a_j}^{b_j}G^{(i,j)}(x, \xi, \lambda)\sum_{k=0}^{q}\lambda^k A_k^{(j)}\left(\xi,\frac{\partial}{\partial \xi}\right)u^{(j)}(\xi, t)\,d\xi$$

$$\equiv\sum_{j=1}^{n}\int_{a_j}^{b_j}G^{(i,j)}(x, \xi, \lambda)f^{(j)}(\xi, t)\,d\xi$$

Since $u^{(i)}(x, t)$ satisfies the boundary solution (4.2.5), it follows that the boundary condition of the mixed problem in question does not contain time derivatives. Therefore, it coincides with the boundary condition of the mixed problem (4.2.1)-(4.2.3), and the second summation with respect to j in the left-hand side of this last identity is, in accordance with the identity (4.2.32), equal to $u^{(i)}(x, t)$.

On the other hand, according to the hypothesis of the theorem, $u^{(i)}(x, t)$ possesses Property 1. This makes it possible for us to take the differentiation with respect to time in the last identity outside the integrals with respect to ξ.

Consequently, in accordance with (4.2.32), we obtain from

the last identity

$$\sum_{k=1}^{q}\left(\frac{\partial^k}{\partial t^k}-\lambda^k\right)\sum_{j=1}^{n}\int_{a_j}^{b_j} G^{(i,j)}(x,\xi,\lambda) \times A_k^{(j)}\left(\xi,\frac{\partial}{\partial\xi}\right)u^{(j)}(\xi,t)\,d\xi+u^{(i)}(x,t) \equiv \sum_{j=1}^{n}\int_{a_j}^{b_j} G^{(i,j)}(x,\xi,\lambda)\,f^{(j)}(\xi,t)\,d\xi$$

Obviously, this identity can also be written in the form

$$\left(\frac{\partial}{\partial t}-\lambda\right)w^{(i)}(x,t,\lambda) \equiv \sum_{j=1}^{n}\int_{a_j}^{b_j} G^{(i,j)}(x,\xi,\lambda)\,f^{(j)}(\xi,t)\,d\xi-u^{(i)}(x,t) \tag{4.2.34}$$

where

$$w^{(i)}(x,t,\lambda) = \sum_{k=1}^{q}\left(\frac{\partial^{k-1}}{\partial t^{k-1}}+\lambda\frac{\partial^{k-2}}{\partial t^{k-2}}+\ldots+\lambda^{k-1}\right)\sum_{j=1}^{n}\int_{a_j}^{b_j} G^{(i,j)}(x,\xi,\lambda) \times A_k^{(j)}\left(\xi,\frac{\partial}{\partial\xi}\right)u^{(j)}(\xi,t)\,d\xi \tag{4.2.35}$$

If we multiply both sides of (4.2.34) by $e^{-\lambda t}$ and integrate from 0 to t, we obtain

$$w^{(i)}(x,t,\lambda)=w^{(i)}(x,0,\lambda)\,e^{\lambda t}-\int_0^t e^{\lambda(t-\tau)}u^{(i)}(x,\tau)\,d\tau + \sum_{j=1}^{n}\int_{a_j}^{b_j} G^{(i,j)}(x,\xi,\lambda)\int_0^t e^{\lambda(t-\tau)}f^{(j)}(\xi,\tau)\,d\tau\,d\xi$$

Integrating both sides of this identity over the contour c_ν

and summing over all ν (i.e. over all the poles of $G^{(i,j)}(x, \xi, \lambda)$), we have

$$\sum_{\nu} \int_{\nu} w^{(i)}(x, t, \lambda)\, d\lambda = \sum_{\nu} \int_{c_\nu} \Big\{ e^{\lambda t} w^{(i)}(x, 0, \lambda) + \sum_{j=1}^{n} \int_{a_j}^{b_j} G^{(i,j)}(x, \xi, \lambda) \int_0^t e^{\lambda(t-\tau)} f^{(j)}(\xi, \tau)\, d\tau\, d\xi \Big\} d\lambda \tag{4.2.36}$$

Bearing in mind the initial conditions (4.2.3) and Property 1 of the solution $u^{(i)}(x, t)$ of Problem (4.2.1)-(4.2.3), we obtain from (4.2.35)

$$\begin{aligned} w^{(i)}&(x, 0, \lambda) \\ &= \sum_{j=1}^{n} \int_{a_j}^{b_j} G^{(i,j)}(x, \xi, \lambda) \sum_{k=1}^{q} A_k^{(j)}\left(\xi, \frac{\partial}{\partial \xi}\right) \left\{ \frac{\partial^{k-1} u^{(j)}(\xi, t)}{\partial t^{k-1}} \Big|_{t=0} \right. \\ &\qquad \left. + \lambda \frac{\partial^{k-2} u^{(j)}(\xi, t)}{\partial t^{k-2}} \Big|_{t=0} + \ldots + \lambda^{k-1} u^{(j)}(\xi, 0) \right\} d\xi \\ &= \sum_{j=1}^{n} \int_{a_j}^{b_j} G^{(i,j)}(x, \xi, \lambda) \sum_{k=1}^{q} A_k^{(j)}\left(\xi, \frac{\partial}{\partial \xi}\right) \\ &\qquad \times \{\Phi_{k-1}^{(j)}(\xi) + \lambda \Phi_{k-2}^{(j)}(\xi) + \ldots + \lambda^{k-1} \Phi_0^{(j)}(\xi)\}\, d\xi \end{aligned}$$

Substituting this result into (4.2.36) and remembering (4.2.35) and Property 1 in the statement of the theorem, we obtain

$$\begin{aligned} &\sum_{\nu} \int_{c_\nu} d\lambda \sum_{j=1}^{n} \int_{a_j}^{b_j} G^{(i,j)}(x, \xi, \lambda) \sum_{k=1}^{q} A_k^{(j)}\left(\xi, \frac{\partial}{\partial \xi}\right) \left\{ \lambda^{k-1} u^{(j)}(\xi, t) \right. \\ &\left. + \lambda^{k-2} \frac{\partial u^{(j)}(\xi, t)}{\partial t} + \ldots + \lambda \frac{\partial^{k-2} u^{(j)}(\xi, t)}{\partial t^{k-2}} + \frac{\partial^{k-1} u^{(j)}(\xi, t)}{\partial t^{k-1}} \right\} d\xi \\ &= \sum_{\nu} \int_{c_\nu} e^{\lambda t}\, d\lambda \sum_{j=1}^{n} \int_{a_j}^{b_j} G^{(i,j)}(x, \xi, \lambda) \left\{ \sum_{k=1}^{q} A_k^{(j)}\left(\xi, \frac{\partial}{\partial \xi}\right) (\Phi_{k-1}^{(j)}(\xi) \right. \\ &\left. + \lambda \Phi_{k-2}^{(j)}(\xi) + \ldots + \lambda^{k-1} \Phi_0^{(j)}(\xi)) + \int_0^t e^{-\lambda \tau} f^{(j)}(\xi, \tau)\, d\tau \right\} d\xi \end{aligned} \tag{4.2.37}$$

From Property 2 of the theorem and (4.2.29), we have

$$\sum_{\nu}\int_{c_\nu} d\lambda \sum_{j=1}^{n}\int_{a_j}^{b_j} G^{(i,j)}(x,\xi,\lambda)\, A_k^{(j)}\left(\xi,\frac{\partial}{\partial\xi}\right)\frac{\partial^{k-s}u^{(j)}(\xi,t)}{\partial t^{k-s}}\lambda^{s-1}d\xi \tag{4.2.38}$$

$$=\begin{cases} 0 & \text{for } k\leqslant q,\ s<q \\ -2\pi\sqrt{-1}A_q^{(i)}\left(x,\frac{\partial}{\partial x}\right)u^{(i)}(x,t) & \text{for } k=q,\ s=q\end{cases}$$

Since $A_q^{(i)}\left(x,\frac{\partial}{\partial x}\right)=1$, we obtain from (4.2.37) by virtue of (4.2.38)

$$-2\pi\sqrt{-1}\,u^{(i)}(x,t)$$

$$=\sum_{\nu}\int_{c_\nu} e^{\lambda t}\,d\lambda\sum_{j=1}^{n}\int_{a_j}^{b_j} G^{(i,j)}(x,\xi,\lambda)\left\{\sum_{k=1}^{q} A_k^{(j)}\left(\xi,\frac{\partial}{\partial\xi}\right)\right.$$

$$\left.\times(\Phi_{k-1}^{(j)}(\xi)+\ldots+\lambda^{k-1}\Phi_0^{(j)}(\xi))+\int_0^t e^{-\lambda\tau}f^{(j)}(\xi,\tau)\,d\tau\right\}d\xi$$

This completes the proof of the theorem.

Example 1 Consider the problem

$$\frac{\partial^2 u}{\partial t^2}=\sqrt{-1}\frac{\partial^4 u}{\partial x^4}+(1-\sqrt{-1})\frac{\partial^3 u}{\partial t\,\partial x^2}+f(x,t)$$

$$\left.\frac{\partial^k u}{\partial x^k}\right|_{x=0}-\left.\frac{\partial^k u}{\partial x^k}\right|_{x=1}=0 \qquad (k=0,1,2,3)$$

$$u(x,0)=\Phi_0(x),\quad \left.\frac{\partial u}{\partial t}\right|_{t=0}=\Phi_1(x)$$

Let us set up the spectral problem by the same method used for Problem (4.2.4)-(4.2.5)

$$\sqrt{-1}y^{(4)}+(1-\sqrt{-1})\lambda^2 y''-\lambda^4 y=F(x)$$

$$y^{(k)}(0)-y^{(k)}(1)=0 \quad (k=0,1,2,3)$$

The characteristic equation is of the form, see (3.2.14),

$$\sqrt{-1}\theta^4+(1-\sqrt{-1})\theta^2-1=0$$

The roots of this equation are

$$\theta_1 = 1, \quad \theta_2 = -1, \quad \theta_3 = \frac{\sqrt{2}}{2}(1+\sqrt{-1})$$

$$\theta_4 = -\frac{\sqrt{2}}{2}(1+\sqrt{-1})$$

It is clear that all the conditions of Theorem 10 are satisfied for this example. The functions $e^{\theta_i \lambda x}$ (for $i=1, 2, 3, 4$) constitute a complete system of independent solutions of the corresponding homogeneous differential equation. Let us solve by the usual method the corresponding spectral problem

$$y(x, \lambda) = \int_0^1 G(x, \xi, \lambda) F(\xi)\, d\xi$$

where

$$G(x, \xi, \lambda) = \frac{g(x, \xi, \lambda)}{\sqrt{-1}}$$

$$+ \frac{1}{4\sqrt{2}(1+\sqrt{-1})\lambda^3} \left\{ \frac{\exp(\lambda x) D_1(\xi, \lambda) + \exp(\lambda(1-x)) D_2(\xi, \lambda)}{e^{\lambda}-1} \right.$$

$$+ \frac{\exp\left[\frac{\sqrt{2}}{2}(1+\sqrt{-1})\lambda x\right] D_3(\xi, \lambda)}{\exp\left[\frac{\sqrt{2}}{2}(1+\sqrt{-1})\lambda\right]-1}$$

$$\left. + \frac{\exp\left[\frac{\sqrt{2}}{2}(1+\sqrt{-1})\lambda(1-x)\right] D_4(\xi, \lambda)}{\exp\left[\frac{\sqrt{2}}{2}(1+\sqrt{-1})\lambda\right]-1} \right\}$$

$$D_1(\xi, \lambda) = \frac{1}{1-\sqrt{-1}} \left\{ -\sqrt{2}(1+\sqrt{-1})(1+e^{-\lambda}) \exp(\lambda\xi) \right.$$

$$+ ((\sqrt{2}-1)\sqrt{-1}-1)\left(1+\exp\left(\frac{\sqrt{2}}{2}(1+\sqrt{-1})\lambda\right)\right) \exp$$

$$\times \left[-\frac{\sqrt{2}}{2}(1+\sqrt{-1})\lambda\xi\right] + (\sqrt{-2}+1+\sqrt{-1})$$

$$\left. \times \left(\exp\left[\frac{\sqrt{2}}{2}(1+\sqrt{-1})\lambda\xi\right] + \exp\left[\frac{\sqrt{2}}{2}(1+\sqrt{-1})\lambda(\xi-1)\right]\right) \right\}$$

$$D_2(\xi, \lambda) = \frac{-1}{1-\sqrt{-1}} \left\{ \sqrt{2}(1+\sqrt{-1})(1+e^{\lambda}) e^{-\lambda\xi} \right.$$

$$-(1+(1+\sqrt{2})\sqrt{-1})\left(\exp\left[-\frac{\sqrt{2}}{2}(1+\sqrt{-1})\lambda\xi\right] + \right.$$

$$+\exp\left[\frac{\sqrt{2}}{2}(1+\sqrt{-1})\lambda(1-\xi)\right]\Big)+(1+(1-\sqrt{2})\sqrt{-1})$$

$$\times\left(\exp\left[\frac{\sqrt{2}}{2}(1+\sqrt{-1})\lambda\xi\right]+\exp\left[\frac{\sqrt{2}}{2}(1+\sqrt{-1})\lambda(\xi-1)\right]\right)\Big\}$$

$$D_3(\xi,\lambda)=-\frac{1}{\sqrt{2}(1-\sqrt{-1})}\Big\{(\sqrt{2}(\sqrt{-1}-1)+2)(1+e^{\lambda})e^{-\lambda\xi}$$

$$+(\sqrt{2}(\sqrt{-1}-1)-2)(1+e^{-\lambda})e^{\lambda\xi}+2\sqrt{2}$$

$$\times\left(\exp\left[\frac{\sqrt{2}}{2}(1+\sqrt{-1})\lambda\xi\right]+\exp\left[\frac{\sqrt{2}}{2}(1+\sqrt{-1})\lambda(\xi-1)\right]\right)\Big\}$$

$$D_4(\xi,\lambda)=\frac{1}{\sqrt{2}(1-\sqrt{-1})}\Big\{(2-\sqrt{2}(\sqrt{-1}-1))(1+e^{\lambda})e^{-\lambda\xi}$$

$$-(2+\sqrt{2}(\sqrt{-1}-1))(1+e^{-\lambda})e^{\lambda\xi}$$

$$-2\sqrt{2}\Big(\exp\left[-\frac{\sqrt{2}}{2}(1+\sqrt{-1})\lambda\xi\right]$$

$$+\exp\left[\frac{\sqrt{2}}{2}(1+\sqrt{-1})\lambda(1-\xi)\right]\Big)\Big\}$$

$$\Delta(\lambda)=4\sqrt{2}\lambda^6(1-e^{\lambda})(1-e^{-\lambda})\left(1-\exp\left[\frac{\sqrt{2}}{2}(1+\sqrt{-1})\lambda\right]\right)$$

$$\times\left(1-\exp\left[-\frac{\sqrt{2}}{2}(1+\sqrt{-1})\lambda\right]\right)$$

$$g(x,\xi,\lambda)=\pm\frac{1}{4\sqrt{2}(1-\sqrt{-1})\lambda^6}$$

$$\times\begin{vmatrix} e^{\theta_1\lambda x} & e^{\theta_2\lambda x} & e^{\theta_3\lambda x} & e^{\theta_4\lambda x} \\ (\theta_1\lambda)^2 e^{\theta_1\lambda\xi} & (\theta_2\lambda)^2 e^{\theta_2\lambda\xi} & (\theta_3\lambda)^2 e^{\theta_3\lambda\xi} & (\theta_4\lambda)^2 e^{\theta_4\lambda\xi} \\ \theta_1\lambda e^{\theta_1\lambda\xi} & \theta_2\lambda e^{\theta_2\lambda\xi} & \theta_3\lambda e^{\theta_3\lambda\xi} & \theta_4\lambda e^{\theta_4\lambda\xi} \\ e^{\theta_1\lambda\xi} & e^{\theta_2\lambda\xi} & e^{\theta_3\lambda\xi} & e^{\theta_4\lambda\xi} \end{vmatrix},$$

where, in the last equation, the plus sign is taken for $0\leqslant\xi\leqslant x\leqslant 1$ and the minus sign is taken for $0\leqslant x\leqslant\xi\leqslant 1$. It is easy to see that

$$F_0(\xi,\Phi,\lambda^2)=\lambda^2\Phi_0(\xi)+\Phi_1(\xi)+(1-\sqrt{-1})\frac{d^2\Phi_0(\xi)}{d\xi^2}$$

Clearly from the expression for $G(x,\xi,\lambda)$, the numbers

$$\lambda_k=2k\pi\sqrt{-1}\quad(k=0,\ \pm1,\ \pm2,\ \dots)$$

$$\lambda_k=\sqrt{2}\,k\pi(1+\sqrt{-1})\quad(k=0,\ \pm1,\ \pm2,\ \dots)$$

are poles of the solution of the spectral problem.

In accordance with Theorem 12, a sufficiently smooth solution of the mixed problem can be represented by (4.2.30). If we substitute the expressions for $G(x, \xi, \lambda)$ and $F_0(\xi, \Phi, \lambda^2)$ into (4.2.30) and calculate the residues, we obtain the following representation of the solution of the problem in question

$$u(x, t) = \frac{1}{4\sqrt{2}(1+\sqrt{-1})} \sum_{\substack{k=-\infty \\ k \neq 0}}^{\infty} \left\{ \frac{\exp(-4k^2\pi^2 t + 2k\pi\sqrt{-1}\,x)}{4k^2\pi^2} \right.$$

$$\times \int_0^1 \left(D_1(\xi, 2k\pi\sqrt{-1}) + D_2(\xi, -2k\pi\sqrt{-1}) \right) \Big[-4k^2\pi^2 \Phi_0(\xi)$$

$$+ \Phi_1(\xi) + (1-\sqrt{-1}) \frac{d^2}{d\xi^2} \Phi_0(\xi) + \int_0^t e^{4k^2\pi^2\tau} f(\xi, \tau)\, d\tau \Big]\, d\xi$$

$$+ \frac{\exp(4k^2\pi^2\sqrt{-1}\,t + 2k\pi\sqrt{-1}\,x)}{2\sqrt{2}\,k^2\pi^2(1-\sqrt{-1})} \int_0^1 \Big(D_3(\xi, 2k\pi(1+\sqrt{-1}))$$

$$+ D_4(\xi, -\sqrt{2k\pi}(1+\sqrt{-1})) \Big) \Big[4k^2\pi^2\sqrt{-1}\,\Phi_0(\xi) + \Phi_1(\xi)$$

$$+ (1-\sqrt{-1}) \frac{d^2}{d\xi^2} \Phi_0(\xi)$$

$$\left. + \int_0^t \exp(-4k^2\pi^2\sqrt{-1}\,\tau) f(\xi, \tau)\, d\tau \Big]\, d\xi \right\} + u_0(x, t)$$

where $u_0(x, t)$ is a residue at the pole $\lambda = 0$.

Example 2 Consider the mixed problem

$$\frac{\partial^2 u}{\partial t^2} + a \frac{\partial^4 u}{\partial x^4} = f(x, t)$$

$$L_k u \equiv \left. \frac{\partial^k u}{\partial x^k} \right|_{x=0} - 2 \left. \frac{\partial^k u}{\partial x^k} \right|_{x=1} = 0 \quad (k = 0, 1, 2, 3)$$

$$u(x, 0) = \Phi_0(x), \quad \left. \frac{\partial u}{\partial t} \right|_{t=0} = \Phi_1(x)$$

It is clear that the corresponding spectral problem is not self-adjoint. Consequently, the eigenfunctions are not orthogonal and the problem cannot be solved by the usual Fourier method. However, all the conditions of Theorem 12 are satisfied for the spectral problem. Thus, the solution of this problem can be represented in the form (4.2.30).

A fundamental system of particular solutions of the homogeneous equation of the spectral problem is of the form

$$y_k(x)=e^{\lambda\varepsilon_k x}$$

where ε_k is one of the fourth roots of $-\frac{1}{a}$.

$$\varepsilon_k=\frac{1}{\sqrt[4]{|a|}}\exp\left\{\sqrt{-1}\,\frac{\left(\arg\frac{-1}{a}+2k\pi\right)}{4}\right\}\ (k=0,\ 1,\ 2,\ 3)$$

$$L_s y_k=y_k^{(s)}(0)-2y_k^{(s)}(1)=(\lambda\varepsilon_k)^s\,(1-2e^{\lambda\varepsilon_k})$$

For the characteristic determinant $\Delta(\lambda)$, we obtain

$$\begin{vmatrix} 1-2e^{\lambda\varepsilon_1} & 1-2e^{\lambda\varepsilon_2} & 1-2e^{\lambda\varepsilon_3} & 1-2e^{\lambda\varepsilon_4} \\ \lambda\varepsilon_1(1-2e^{\lambda\varepsilon_1}) & \lambda\varepsilon_2(1-2e^{\lambda\varepsilon_2}) & \lambda\varepsilon_3(1-2e^{\lambda\varepsilon_3}) & \lambda\varepsilon_4(1-2e^{\lambda\varepsilon_4}) \\ (\lambda\varepsilon_1)^2(1-2e^{\lambda\varepsilon_1}) & (\lambda\varepsilon_2)^2(1-2e^{\lambda\varepsilon_2}) & (\lambda\varepsilon_3)^2(1-2e^{\lambda\varepsilon_3}) & (\lambda\varepsilon_4)^2(1-2e^{\lambda\varepsilon_4}) \\ (\lambda\varepsilon_1)^3(1-2e^{\lambda\varepsilon_1}) & (\lambda\varepsilon_2)^3(1-2e^{\lambda\varepsilon_2}) & (\lambda\varepsilon_3)^3(1-2e^{\lambda\varepsilon_3}) & (\lambda\varepsilon_4)^3(1-2e^{\lambda\varepsilon_4}) \end{vmatrix}$$

For the poles of the solution of the spectral problem, we have

$$\lambda_{nk}=\frac{1}{\varepsilon_k}\left(\ln\left|\frac{1}{2}\right|+2n\pi\sqrt{-1}\right)$$

$$=\left(\ln\frac{1}{2}+2n\pi\sqrt{-1}\right)\exp\left[-\frac{1}{4}\sqrt{-1}\left(\arg\frac{-1}{a}+2k\pi\right)\right]$$

$$(k=0,\ 1,\ 2,\ 3;\ n=0,\ \pm1,\ \pm2,\ \pm3,\ \pm4,\ \ldots)$$

When we have calculated the residue by (4.2.30), the terms of the series will contain a factor of the form $\exp(\lambda_{nk}^2 t)$. Then, for the series of residues to converge, it is necessary that the Re λ_{nk}^2 be bounded for all integral n. As we can see from the expression for λ_{nk}, this is possible only when

$$\cos\left(\frac{1}{2}\arg\frac{-1}{a}+k\pi\right)\geqslant 0\quad\text{for}\quad k=0,\ 1,\ 2,\ 3$$

Therefore

$$\cos\left(\frac{1}{2}\arg\frac{-1}{a}\right)=\cos\left(\frac{1}{2}\arg\frac{-1}{a}+2\pi\right)\geqslant 0$$

$$\cos\left(\frac{1}{2}\arg\frac{-1}{a}+\pi\right)=\cos\left(\frac{1}{2}\arg\frac{-1}{a}+3\pi\right)=-\cos\left(\frac{1}{2}\arg\frac{-1}{a}\right)\geqslant 0$$

However, this is possible only if

$$\cos\left(\frac{1}{2}\arg\frac{-1}{a}\right)=0$$

or

$$\frac{1}{2}\arg\frac{-1}{a}=\pm\frac{\pi}{2}, \quad \arg\frac{-1}{a}=\pm\pi$$

This means that $\frac{-1}{a}<0$, i.e. that $a>0$. We conclude that, for the mixed problem to be correctly formulated, it is necessary that $a>0$.

Example 3 Consider the problem for heat-flow in a non-homogeneous cylinder

$$\frac{\partial u^{(i)}}{\partial t}=\varkappa^{(i)}\left(\frac{\partial^2 u^{(i)}}{\partial x^2}+\frac{1}{x}\frac{\partial u^{(i)}}{\partial x}\right)+f^{(i)}(x,t) \text{ for } x\in(a_{i-1},b_{i-1})\ (a_0>0)$$

$$\left.\frac{\partial u^{(i)}}{\partial x}\right|_{x=a_i}+h^{(i)}\{u^{(i+1)}(a_i,t)-u^{(i)}(a_i,t)\}=0$$

$$\left.\frac{\partial u^{(i)}}{\partial x}\right|_{x=a_{i-1}}+e^{(i-1)}\{u^{(i)}(a_{i-1},t)-u^{(i-1)}(a_{i-1},t)\}=0$$

$$(u_0(a_0,t)=u_4(a_4,t)=0)$$

$$u^{(i)}(x,0)=\Phi^{(i)}(x) \quad \text{for} \quad x\in(a_{i-1},b_{i-1}) \quad (i=1,2,3)$$

where $\varkappa^{(i)}$, $h^{(i)}$, and $e^{(i-1)}$ are constants and the (a_{i-1},b_{i-1}) (for $i=1, 2, 3$) are non-overlapping intervals with common end-points $(0<a_0<b_0=a_1<b_1=a_2<b_2=a_3)$.

The corresponding spectral problem is of the form (where $p=2$, $q=1$, $m=2$)

$$\varkappa^{(i)}\left(\frac{d^2 v^{(i)}}{dx^2}+\frac{1}{x}\frac{dv^{(i)}}{dx}\right)-\lambda^2 v^{(i)}=\Phi^{(i)}(x) \text{ for } x\in(a_{i-1},b_{i-1})$$

$$\left.\frac{dv^{(i)}}{dx}\right|_{x=a_i}+h^{(i)}\{v^{(i+1)}(a_i)-v^{(i)}(a_i)\}=0$$

$$\left.\frac{dv^{(i)}}{dx}\right|_{x=a_{i-1}}+e^{(i-1)}\{v^{(i)}(a_{i-1})-v^{(i-1)}(a_{i-1})\}=0 \quad (i=1,2,3)$$

The conditions of Theorem 12 are satisfied for this

spectral problem. Therefore, a solution of the mixed problem posed can, if it is sufficiently smooth on the interval $[a_i, b_i]$, be represented in the form (4.2.30), where

$$F_0^{(j)}(\xi, \Phi, \lambda) = \Phi^{(j)}(\xi)$$

4.3 THE MIXED PROBLEM WITH SEPARABLE VARIABLES

In the preceding sections we examined mixed problems for systems of equations with time-constant coefficients.

The residue method enables us to obtain an explicit representation of the solution of mixed problems with separable variables even in the case in which the coefficients of the differential (with respect to time) operator are dependent on the time and the coefficients of the differential (with respect to space) operator depend on the space variable.

In this case, the problem of finding the integrand in the residue formula reduces to solving a boundary-value problem and the Cauchy problem with a parameter for systems of ordinary differential equations.

Consider the mixed problem

$$M\left(t, \frac{\partial}{\partial t}\right) u^{(i)} = L^{(i)}\left(x, \frac{\partial}{\partial x}\right) u^i + f^{(i)}(x, t) \qquad (4.3.1)$$

$$\sum_{i=1}^{n} \sum_{j=0}^{p-1} \left\{\alpha_j^{(i)} \frac{\partial^j u^{(i)}}{\partial x^j}\Big|_{x=a_i} + \beta_j^{(i)} \frac{\partial^j u^{(i)}}{\partial x^j}\Big|_{x=b_i}\right\} = 0 \qquad (4.3.2)$$

$$\frac{\partial^k u^{(i)}}{\partial t^k}\Big|_{t=0} = \Phi_k^{(i)}(x) \quad \text{for } x \in (a_i, b_i) \quad (i = 1, \ldots, n) \qquad (4.3.3)$$

where $M\left(t, \frac{\partial}{\partial t}\right) = \sum_{k=0}^{q} B_k(t) \frac{\partial^{q-k}}{\partial t^{q-k}}$, the $B_k(t)$ are square matrices of order r of functions of t on $[0, T]$ (we recall that $\det B_0(t) \neq 0$ on $[0, T]$), $L^{(i)}\left(x, \frac{\partial}{\partial x}\right) = \sum_{k=0}^{p} A_k^{(i)}(x) \frac{\partial^{p-k}}{\partial x^{p-k}}$, the $A_k^{(i)}(x)$ are square matrices of order r which are continuous functions of x on $[a_i, b_i]$, $\det A_0^{(i)}(x) \neq 0$ for $x \in [a_i, b_i]$, $\alpha_j^{(i)}$ and

$\beta_j^{(i)}$ are constant $nrp \times r$ matrices and $f^{(i)}(x, t)$ and $\Phi_k^{(i)}(x)$ (for $(i = 1, \ldots, n)$ are vector-valued functions of the corresponding dimensions.

We set up the spectral problem corresponding to Problem (4.3.1)-(4.3.3) according to the rule

$$L^{(i)}\left(x, \frac{d}{dx}\right) v^{(i)} - \mu^p v^{(i)} = f^{(i)}(x)$$
$$x \in (a_i, b_i) \quad (i = 1, \ldots, n) \tag{4.3.4}$$

$$\sum_{i=1}^{n} \sum_{j=0}^{p-1} \left\{ \alpha_j^{(i)} \frac{d^j v^{(i)}}{dx^j} \Big|_{x=a_i} + \beta_j^{(i)} \frac{d^j v^{(i)}}{dx^j} \Big|_{x=b_i} \right\} = 0 \tag{4.3.5}$$

If $G^{(i, j)}(x, \xi, \lambda)$ (where $\lambda = \mu^p$ for $x \in (a_i, b_i)$ and $\xi \in (a_j, b_j)$) is the Green's matrix of the spectral problem (4.3.4)-(4.3.5) and if $v^{(i)}(x, \lambda)$ is its solution, then for $x \in (a_i, b_i)$, we have

$$v^{(i)}(x, \lambda) = \sum_{j=1}^{n} \int_{a_j}^{b_j} G^{(i, j)}(x, \xi, \lambda) f^{(j)}(\xi)\, d\xi$$

From this formula, we get the identity

$$\left(L^{(i)}\left(x, \frac{d}{dx}\right) - \lambda\right) \sum_{j=1}^{n} \int_{a_j}^{b_j} G^{(i, j)}(x, \xi, \lambda) f^{(j)}(\xi)\, d\xi \equiv f^{(i)}(x) \tag{4.3.6}$$

Furthermore, it is clear that, for every vector-valued function $v^{(i)}(x)$, which satisfies boundary condition (4.3.5),

$$\sum_{j=1}^{n} \int_{a_j}^{b_j} G^{(i, j)}(x, \xi, \lambda) \left(L^{(j)}\left(\xi, \frac{d}{d\xi}\right) - \lambda \right) v^{(j)}(\xi)\, d\xi \equiv v^{(i)}(x) \tag{4.3.7}$$

To solve the basic problems of this section, let us first consider the solution of the corresponding Cauchy problem

$$M\left(t, \frac{d}{dt}\right) y^{(i)} - \lambda y^{(i)} = f^{(i)}(x, t) \tag{4.3.8}$$

$$\frac{d^k y^{(i)}}{dt^k}\Big|_{t=0} = \Phi_k^{(i)}(\xi) \tag{4.3.9}$$

Suppose that $y_1(t, \lambda), \ldots, y_q(t, \lambda)$, where the $y_k(t, \lambda)$ are r-th-order square matrices, constitute a complete system of independent solutions of the equation

$$M\left(t, \frac{\partial}{\partial t}\right) y - \lambda y = 0$$

which satisfy the initial conditions

$$\left.\frac{d^k y}{dt^k}\right|_{t=0} = \begin{cases} E & \text{for } k = j-1 \\ 0 & \text{for } k \neq j-1 \end{cases} \tag{4.3.10}$$

Let us denote by $\delta(t, \lambda)$ the determinant

$$\delta(t, \lambda) = \begin{vmatrix} \frac{d^{q-1} y_1(t, \lambda)}{dt^{q-1}} & \cdots & \frac{d^{q-1} y_q(t, \lambda)}{dt^{q-1}} \\ \cdots & \cdots & \cdots \\ y_1(t, \lambda) & \cdots & y_q(t, \lambda) \end{vmatrix}$$

Suppose that $Z_\nu(t, \lambda)$ is the adjoint matrix of the matrix $y_\nu(t, \lambda)$ (where $\nu = 1, \ldots, q$) for each $y_\nu(t, \lambda)$ in the determinant $\delta(t, \lambda)$.

Then, the solution $y^{(i)}(t, \xi, \lambda)$ of Problem (4.3.8)-(4.3.9) is given by

$$y^{(i)}(t, \xi, \lambda) = \sum_{k=1}^{q} y_k(t, \lambda) \Phi_k^{(i)}(\xi) + \int_0^t K(t, \tau, \lambda) f^{(i)}(\xi, \tau)\, d\tau$$

where

$$K(t, \tau, \lambda) = \sum_{k=1}^{q} \frac{y_k(t, \lambda) Z_k(\tau, \lambda)}{\delta(\tau, \lambda)} B_0^{-1}(\tau)$$

We shall now prove Theorem 13.

Theorem 13 Suppose that the conditions of Theorem 10 are satisfied for the spectral problem (4.3.4)-(4.3.5), that the operator $M\left(t, \frac{\partial}{\partial t}\right)$ commutes with $G^{(i, j)}(x, \xi, \lambda)$, and that Problem (4.3.1)-(4.3.3) for

$$\int_0^T \int_{a_i}^{b_i} |f_k^{(i)}(x, t)|\, dx\, dt < +\infty \quad (i = 1, \ldots, n, \quad k = 1, \ldots, r)$$

has a solution $u^{(i)}(x, t)$ possessing the following properties.

1. $u^{(i)}, \frac{\partial u^{(i)}}{\partial t}, \ldots, \frac{\partial^{q-1} u^{(i)}}{\partial t^{q-1}}$ are absolutely continuous with respect to $t \in [0, T]$ for $a_i < x < b_i$ and are bounded in the region

$$a_i \leqslant x \leqslant b_i, \ 0 \leqslant t \leqslant T$$

2. $\frac{\partial^q u^{(i)}}{\partial t^q}$ is absolutely integrable over the region

$$a_i < x < b_i, \ 0 \leqslant t \leqslant T \quad (i = 1, \ldots, n)$$

3. On $[a_i, b_i]$, the vector-valued functions

$$u^{(i)}, \frac{\partial u^{(i)}}{\partial x}, \ldots, \frac{\partial^{p-1} u^{(i)}}{\partial x^{p-1}}$$

are absolutely continuous for $0 \leqslant t \leqslant T$ and $\frac{\partial^p u^{(i)}}{\partial x^p}$ is square-summable (for $i = 1, \ldots, n$).

Then, this solution can be represented by

$$u^{(i)}(x, t) = \frac{-1}{2\pi \sqrt{-1}} \sum_{\nu} \int_{c_\nu} d\lambda \sum_{j=1}^{n} \times \int_{a_j}^{b_j} G^{(i, j)}(x, \xi, \lambda) \left\{ \sum_{k=1}^{q} y_k(t, \lambda) \Phi_k^{(j)}(\xi) + \int_0^t K(t, \tau, \lambda) f^{(j)}(\xi, \tau)\, d\tau \right\} d\xi \quad \text{for } x \in (a_i, b_i)$$

where the c_ν denotes as before a closed contour in the λ-plane which encircles only one pole λ_ν of the solution of Problem (4.3.4)-(4.3.5) and the summation with respect to ν is over all poles of that solution.

Proof According to Theorem 10, we have the following formula for the vector-valued function $f^{(i)}(x) \in L_2(a_i, b_i)$ for ($i = 1, \ldots, n$):

$$\frac{-1}{2\pi \sqrt{-1}} \sum_{\nu} \int_{c_\nu} \left\{ \sum_{j=1}^{n} \int_{a_j}^{b_j} G^{(i, j)}(x, \xi, \lambda) f^{(j)}(\xi)\, d\xi \right\} d\lambda = f^{(i)}(x) \quad (4.3.11)$$

for $x \in (a_i, b_i)$. Suppose that $F^{(i)}(x) \in L_2(a_i, b_i)$ (for $i = 1, \ldots, n$).

Let $F_{k\nu}^{(i)}(x)$ denote the integral

$$K_{k\nu}^{(i)}(F) \equiv F_{k\nu}^{(i)}(x)$$

$$= \frac{-1}{2\pi\sqrt{-1}} \int_{c_\nu} \lambda^k \, d\lambda \sum_{j=1}^{n} \int_{a_j}^{b_j} G^{(i,j)}(x, \xi, \lambda) F^{(j)}(\xi) \, d\xi$$

Under hypotheses 1 and 2, we have whenever $s \leqslant q$

$$\frac{\partial^s}{\partial t^s} \int_{c_\nu} \lambda^k \, d\lambda \sum_{j=1}^{n} \int_{a_j}^{b_j} G^{(i,j)}(x, \xi, \lambda) u^{(j)}(\xi, t) \, d\xi$$

$$= \int_{c_\nu} \lambda^k \, d\lambda \sum_{j=1}^{n} \int_{a_j}^{b_j} G^{(i,j)}(x, \xi, \lambda) \frac{\partial^s u^j(\xi, t)}{\partial t^s} \, d\xi$$

Consequently,

$$\begin{aligned} &\int_{c_\nu} \lambda^k \, d\lambda \sum_{j=1}^{n} \int_{a_j}^{b_j} G^{(i,j)}(x, \xi, \lambda) M\left(t, \frac{\partial}{\partial t}\right) u^{(j)}(\xi, t) \, d\xi \\ &= M\left(t, \frac{\partial}{\partial t}\right) \int_{c_\nu} \lambda^k \sum_{j=1}^{n} \int_{a_j}^{b_j} G^{(i,j)}(x, \xi, \lambda) u^{(j)}(\xi, t) \, d\xi \, d\lambda \end{aligned} \tag{4.3.12}$$

Furthermore, by hypothesis 1, when $s \leqslant q-1$, we have

$$\begin{aligned} &\int_{c_\nu} \lambda^s \, d\lambda \sum_{j=1}^{n} \int_{a_j}^{b_j} G^{(i,j)}(x, \xi, \lambda) \frac{\partial^s u^{(j)}(\xi, t)}{dt^s} \, d\xi \Big|_{t \to 0} \\ &\to \int_{c_\nu} \lambda^s \, d\lambda \sum_{j=1}^{n} \int_{a_j}^{b_j} G^{(i,j)}(x, \xi, \lambda) \Phi^{(j)}(\xi) \, d\xi \end{aligned} \tag{4.3.13}$$

Finally, from Property 3, we obtain, taking (4.3.7) into consideration,

$$\begin{aligned} &\sum_{j=1}^{n} \int_{a_j}^{b_j} G^{(i,j)}(x, \xi, \lambda) L^{(j)}\left(\xi, \frac{\partial}{\partial \xi}\right) u^{(j)}(\xi, t) \, d\xi \\ &= u^{(i)}(x, t) + \lambda \sum_{j=1}^{n} \int_{a_j}^{b_j} G^{(i,j)}(x, \xi, \lambda) u^{(j)}(\xi, t) \, d\xi \end{aligned} \tag{4.3.14}$$

If we apply the operator $K^{(i)}_{k\nu}$ to both sides of (4.3.1)-(4.3.3) and take account of (4.3.12)-(4.3.14), we obtain the identities

$$M\left(t, \frac{\partial}{\partial t}\right) u^{(i)}_{k\nu} = u^{(i)}_{k+1\nu} + f^{(i)}_{k\nu}(x, t) \quad \text{for } x \in (a_i, b_i) \tag{4.3.15}$$

$$u^{(i)}_{k\nu}(x, 0) = \Phi^{(i)}_{k\nu}(x) \quad \text{for } x \in (a_i, b_i) \quad (i = 1, \ldots, n) \tag{4.3.16}$$

It is clear from the identity

$$-\frac{1}{2\pi\sqrt{-1}} \int_{c_\nu} (\lambda - \lambda_\nu)^{\varkappa_\nu} d\lambda \sum_{j=1}^{n} \int_{a_j}^{b_j} G^{(i,j)}(x, \xi, \lambda)\, u^{(j)}(\xi, t)\, d\xi$$

$$= \sum_{k=0}^{\varkappa_\nu} \binom{\varkappa_\nu}{k} (-\lambda_\nu)^{\varkappa_\nu - k} u^{(i)}_{k\nu}(x, t) \equiv 0$$

that the vector-valued functions $u^{(i)}_{\varkappa_\nu \nu}(x, t)$ can be expressed in terms of

$$u^{(i)}_{0\nu}(x, t), \ \ldots, \ u^{(i)}_{\varkappa_\nu - 1\nu}(x, t) \tag{4.3.17}$$

Consequently, for $k = 0, 1, \ldots, x_\nu - 1$, (4.3.15)-(4.3.16) represent the Cauchy problem for the system with unknowns (4.3.17).

Using (4.3.7) and (4.3.12)-(4.3.14), we can verify directly that

$$u^{(i)}_{k\nu_0}(x, t)$$

$$= \frac{-1}{2\pi\sqrt{-1}} \int_{c_\nu} \lambda^k d\lambda \sum_{j=1}^{n} \int_{a_j}^{b_j} G^{(i,j)}(x, \xi, \lambda) \Big\{ \sum_{k=1}^{q} y_k(t, \lambda)\, \Phi^{(i)}_k(\xi)$$

$$+ \int_0^t K(t, \tau, \lambda)\, f^{(j)}(\xi, \tau)\, d\tau \Big\}\, d\xi \tag{4.3.18}$$

is a solution of Problem (4.3.15)-(4.3.16).

Noting (4.3.18) and the uniqueness of the solution of the Cauchy problem (4.3.15)-(4.3.16) and applying (4.3.11) to the solution $u^{(i)}(x, t)$ of Problem (4.3.1)-(4.3.3), using the notation for $F^{(i)}_{k\nu}(x)$, we complete the proof of Theorem 13.

A similar theorem can be proved for a more general system of the form

$$M_1\left(t, \frac{\partial}{\partial t}\right) u^{(i)} = M_2\left(t, \frac{\partial}{\partial t}\right) L^{(i)}\left(x, \frac{\partial}{\partial x}\right) u^{(i)} + f^{(i)}(x,t) \quad (4.3.19)$$

where $M_1\left(t, \frac{\partial}{\partial t}\right)$ and $M_2\left(t, \frac{\partial}{\partial t}\right)$ are linear differential operators, the coefficients in which are square matrices of order r which depend continuously on t.

Let q denote the order of one of these differential operators and assume that the order of the other does not exceed q. The coefficients of the highest derivatives are assumed to have inverses. The expression $L^{(i)}\left(x, \frac{\partial}{\partial x}\right)$ has the same meaning as above.

Consider System (4.3.19) with boundary condition (4.3.2) and initial conditon (4.3.3).

By repetition of the outline followed above, we can prove Theorem 14.

Theorem 14 Suppose that the conditions of Theorem 10 are satisfied for the spectral problem (4.3.4) and (4.3.5), that operators $M_1\left(t, \frac{\partial}{\partial t}\right)$ and $M_2\left(t, \frac{\partial}{\partial t}\right)$ commute with $G^{(i,j)}(x, \xi, \lambda)$, and that the problem defined by (4.3.19), (4.3.2) and (4.3.3) for $f^{(i)}(x, t) \in L_2$

$$\int_0^T \int_{a_i}^{b_i} |f_k^{(i)}(x, t)|\, dx\, dt < +\infty \quad (i = 1, \ldots, n;\; k = 1, 2, \ldots, r)$$

has a solution $u^{(i)}(x, t)$ possessing Properties 1, 2 and 3 of Theorem 13. Then, this solution can be represented by the formula

$$u^{(i)}(x, t) = \frac{-1}{2\pi\sqrt{-1}} \sum_\nu \int_{c_\nu} d\lambda \sum_{j=1}^{n} \int_{a_j}^{b_j} G^{(i,j)}(x, \xi, \lambda) \times y^{(j)}(\xi, t, \lambda, f, \varphi)\, d\xi \quad (4.3.20)$$

where $y^{(i)}(\xi, t, \lambda, f, \varphi)$ is a solution of the Cauchy problem

$$M_1\left(t, \frac{\partial}{\partial t}\right) y^{(i)} = \lambda M_2\left(t, \frac{\partial}{\partial t}\right) y^{(i)} + f^{(i)}(\xi, t) \quad (4.3.21)$$

$$\left.\frac{d^k y^{(i)}}{dt^k}\right|_{k=0} = \Phi_k^{(i)}(\xi) \quad (k=0,\ 1,\ \ldots,\ q-1) \tag{4.3.22}$$

Proof If we apply the operator $K_{k\nu}^{(i)}$ to both sides of (4.3.19) and (4.3.3) and take into account (4.3.12) for the operators M_1 and M_2, and also (4.3.13)-(4.3.14), we obtain

$$M_1\left(t, \frac{\partial}{\partial t}\right) u_{k\nu}^{(i)} = M_2\left(t, \frac{\partial}{\partial t}\right) u_{k+1\nu}^{(i)} + f_{k\nu}^{(i)}(x,\ t) \tag{4.3.23}$$

$$u_{k\nu}^{(i)}(x,\ 0) = \Phi_{k\nu}^{(i)}(x) \tag{4.3.24}$$

Furthermore, in view of the (4.3.7) and (4.3.12) for the operators M_1, M_2 and (4.3.13)-(4.3.14), it, can be directly verified that

$$u_{k\nu 0}^{(i)}(x,\ t) = \frac{-1}{2\pi\sqrt{-1}} \int_{c_\nu} \lambda^k\, d\lambda \sum_{j=1}^{n} \int_{a_j}^{b_j} G^{(i,\ j)}(x,\ \xi,\ \lambda) \times y^{(j)}(\xi,\ t,\ \lambda,\ f,\ \Phi)\, d\xi$$

is a solution of the Cauchy problem (4.3.23)-(4.3.24), where $y^{(i)}(\xi, t, \lambda, f, \Phi)$ is a solution of (4.3.21)-(4.3.22).

From the uniqueness of the solution of (4.3.23)-(4.3.24) and on the basis of (4.3.11), we conclude that the solution of the problem (4.3.19), (4.3.2) and (4.3.3) can be represented in the form (4.3.20), which completes the proof.

The uniqueness of the solutions of the problems considered in Sections 3.1, 3.2 and 3.3 follows from Theorems 11-14.

In conclusion, we note that, if the orders of the poles of the solutions of the spectral problems in Sections 1.1, 1.2 and 1.3 are bounded, it can be shown by the use of asymptotic representations of the solution of these spectral problems outside a δ-neighbourhood of the spectrum that the mixed problems considered in this chapter are correctly formulated [40b].

CHAPTER 5

Residue method for solving multi-dimensional mixed problems

In Section 5.1 it will be shown that, assuming the validity of (5.1.11), the residue-method procedure of Section 4.1 can easily be extended to multi-dimensional mixed problems.

As shown in Chapter 4, the residue method yields explicit representations of solutions of one-dimensional mixed problems of broad classes. Here, to construct the solutions of these problems we reduce them to the corresponding spectral problems, which are easily solved since they are associated with ordinary differential equations. Therefore, if the space variables in a multi-dimensional mixed problem are separable, it is simple to reduce it to a problem with a smaller number of independent variables. In Section 5.2 the residue method of separating the variables is given. This method is a generalisation of the method used for separating variables in the case of non-orthogonal eigenfunctions and associated functions of boundary-value problems.

In Section 5.3 we prove the validity of (5.3.6) for a certain class of multi-dimensional spectral problems with separable variables using the residue method described in Section 5.2. In Section 5.4, we apply the methods and results of the first three sections to the solutions of certain illustrative problems taken from the theory of subterranean hydromechanics. These examples constitute a generalisation of the hydrodynamic problem considered in Section 4.1 (see Example 1) to the case of a layer which is vertically non-homogeneous. Here, the non-homogeneity is assumed to be continuous.

5.1 PROCEDURE FOR SOLVING MULTI-DIMENSIONAL MIXED PROBLEMS

Consider the problem of finding the solution of the System of differential equations

$$\frac{\partial^q u}{\partial t^q} = \sum_{\substack{k \leqslant q-1 \\ mk+l \leqslant p}} A_{kl_1 \ldots l_n}(x) \frac{\partial^{k+l} u}{\partial t^k \partial x_1^{l_1} \ldots \partial x_n^{l_n}} + f(x, t) \qquad (5.1.1)$$

in a bounded region D of points $x = (x_1, \ldots, x_n)$ with boundary conditions of the type

$$\lim_{x \to y} \sum_{k=0}^{q} \frac{\partial^k}{\partial t^k} B_k\left(y, \frac{\partial}{\partial x}\right) u(x, t) = 0 \quad y \in \Gamma \qquad (5.1.2)$$

and initial conditions

$$\left. \frac{\partial^k u}{\partial t^k} \right|_{t=0} = \Phi_k(x) \qquad (k = 0, \ldots, q-1) \qquad (5.1.3)$$

Here, Γ is the boundary of D; $p = mq$, where m and q are natural numbers; the $A_{kl_1 \ldots l_n}(x)$ are sufficiently smooth rth-order square matrices in D; the $B_k\left(y, \frac{\partial}{\partial x}\right)$ are rth-order square matrices of linear differential operators with respect to x with coefficients depending on $y \in \Gamma$; $f(x, t)$ and $\Phi_k(x)$ are rth-order sufficiently smooth vector-valued functions in D.

In a similar way to the one-dimensional case, the substitution $\frac{\partial^k u}{\partial t^k} = u_k(x)$ (for $k = 0, \ldots, q-1$) leads to the problem

$$\begin{aligned} \frac{\partial u_k}{\partial t} &= u_{k+1} \qquad (k = 0, \ldots, q-2) \\ \frac{\partial u_{q-1}}{\partial t} &= \sum_{\substack{k \leqslant q-1 \\ mk+l \leqslant p}} A_{kl_1 \ldots l_n}(x) \frac{\partial^l u_k}{\partial x_1^{l_1} \ldots \partial x_n^{l_n}} + f(x, t) \end{aligned} \qquad (5.1.4)$$

$$\lim_{x\to y}\left\{\sum_{k=0}^{q-1} B_k\left(y, \frac{\partial}{\partial x}\right) u_k(x, t) + B_q\left(y, \frac{\partial}{\partial x}\right)\frac{\partial u_{q-1}(x, t)}{\partial t}\right\} = 0, \quad y\in\Gamma \tag{5.1.5}$$

$$u_k(x, 0) = \Phi_k(x) \quad (k = 0, \ldots, q-1) \tag{5.1.6}$$

We shall refer to the problem of finding the solution of the system

$$\left.\begin{aligned} & v_{k+1}(x) - \lambda^m v_k(x) = \Phi_k(x) \quad (k = 0, \ldots, q-2) \\ & \sum_{\substack{k\leqslant q-1\\ mk+l\leqslant p}} A_{kl_1\ldots l_n}(x)\frac{\partial^l v_k}{\partial x_1^{l_1}\ldots\partial x_n^{l_n}} - \lambda^m v_{q-1}(x) = \Phi_{q-1}(x)\end{aligned}\right\} \tag{5.1.7}$$

with boundary condition

$$\lim_{x\to y}\left\{\sum_{k=0}^{q-1} B_k\left(y, \frac{\partial}{\partial x}\right) v_k + \lambda^m B_q\left(y, \frac{\partial}{\partial x}\right) v_{q-1}(x)\right\} = 0, \quad y\in\Gamma \tag{5.1.8}$$

as the spectral problem corresponding to the Problem (5.1.4)-(5.1.6).

From the first $q-2$ equations of System (5.1.7), we find

$$v_k = \lambda^{mk} v_0 + \lambda^{m(k-1)}\Phi_0(x) + \ldots + \Phi_{k-1}(x)$$

Substituting this into (5.1.7) and (5.1.8), we obtain the spectral problem corresponding to Problem (5.1.1)-(5.1.3)

$$\sum_{\substack{k\leqslant q-1\\ mk+l\leqslant p}} \lambda^{mk} A_{kl_1\ldots l_n}(x)\frac{\partial^l v_0}{\partial x_1^{l_1}\ldots\partial x_n^{l_n}} - \lambda^p v_0 = F_0(x, \Phi, \lambda^m) \tag{5.1.9}$$

$$\lim_{x\to y}\left\{\sum_{k=0}^{q-1} \lambda^{mk} B_k\left(y, \frac{\partial}{\partial x}\right) v_0(x) + \lambda^p B_q\left(y, \frac{\partial}{\partial x}\right) v_0(x)\right\} = N_{0m}(\Phi, \lambda^m) \tag{5.1.10}$$

where

$$F_0(x, \Phi, \lambda^m) = \sum_{k=0}^{q-1} \lambda^{m(q-1-k)} \Phi_k(x)$$

$$- \sum_{\substack{1 \leq k \leq q-1 \\ mk+l \leq p}} A_{kl_1 \ldots l_n}(x) \frac{\partial^l}{\partial x_1^{l_1} \ldots \partial x_n^{l_n}} \left(\sum_{s=0}^{k-1} \lambda^{m(k-1-s)} \Phi_s(x) \right)$$

$$N_{0m}(\Phi, \lambda^m)$$

$$= -\sum_{k=0}^{q-1} B_k\left(y, \frac{\partial}{\partial y}\right)(\lambda^{m(k-1)} \Phi_0(y) + \ldots + \Phi_{k-1}(y))$$

$$- \lambda^m B_q\left(y, \frac{\partial}{\partial y}\right)(\lambda^{m(q-2)} \Phi_0(y) + \ldots + \Phi_{q-2}(y)), \quad y \in \Gamma$$

Let $\Phi_0(x), \ldots, \Phi_{q-1}(x)$ be vector-valued functions defined in a closed region D such that $\Phi_{k-1}(x) \in C^{(p-mk)}$ (where $C^{(k)}$ denotes the set of vector-valued functions with continuous derivatives of the first k orders in D). We denote by $\mathfrak{N}$ the set of vector-valued functions with coefficients $\Phi_{k-1}(x)$ (where $(\Phi_{k-1}(x) \in C^{(p-mk)}$ for $k = 1, \ldots, q$). Suppose that, for any arbitrary element $\mathfrak{N}$, Problem (5.1.7)-(5.1.8) has a unique solution $v_k(x, \Phi, \lambda)$ (for $k = 0, \ldots, q-1$) which is a meromorphic function of the parameter λ. Suppose also that an arbitrary element $\mathfrak{N}$ can be expanded in a series according to the formula

$$-\frac{1}{2\pi\sqrt{-1}} \sum_{\nu} \int_{c_\nu} \lambda^{m-1} v_k(x, \Phi, \lambda)\, d\lambda = \Phi_k(x) \qquad (5.1.11)$$

$$(k = 0, \ldots, q-1)$$

where c_ν is a closed contour encircling only one pole of the function in the integrand and the summation with respect to ν is over all poles of that function.

With these assumptions, it can be shown, by the method used to prove Theorem 9, that a sufficiently smooth solution $u(x, t)$ of the mixed problem (5.1.1)-(5.1.3) for $B_q\left(y, \frac{\partial}{\partial x}\right) = 0$ can be represented by

$$u(x, t) = \frac{-1}{2\pi\sqrt{-1}} \sum_{\nu} \int_{c_\nu} \lambda^{m-1} e^{\lambda^m t}\, d\lambda$$

$$\times \left\{ \int_D G(x, \xi, \lambda)(F_0(\xi, \Phi, \lambda^m) \qquad (5.1.12)$$

$$+ \int_0^t e^{-\lambda^m \tau} f(\xi, \tau)\, d\tau)\, d_\xi D + \Delta(x, \Phi, \lambda) \right\}$$

where $G(x, \xi, \lambda)$ is the Green's matrix of Problem (5.1.9)-(5.1.10) and $\Delta(x, \Phi, \lambda)$ is the solution of the homogeneous problem corresponding to System (5.1.9) with boundary condition (5.1.10). Formula (5.1.12) gives a formal solution of Problem (5.1.1)-(5.1.3) in the more general case in which

$$B_q\left(y, \frac{\partial}{\partial x}\right) \neq 0$$

According to Section 3.2, if we assume that

$$N_{0m}(\Phi, \lambda^m) = 0$$

(5.1.11) implies the validity of the formula

$$-\frac{1}{2\pi\sqrt{-1}} \sum_{\nu} \int_{c_\nu} \lambda^{m(s+1)-1} d\lambda \int_D G(x, \xi, \lambda) \Phi_{q-1}(\xi) d_\xi D = \begin{cases} 0 & \text{for } s < q-1 \\ \Phi_{q-1}(x) & \text{for } s = q-1 \end{cases} \tag{5.1.13}$$

Finally, we note that if the boundary condition (5.1.2) contains no differentiation with respect to time ($B_k \equiv 0$ for $k \neq 0$) then it can be shown, by the method used in proving Theorem 12, that by assuming (5.1.13) is valid, a sufficiently smooth solution $u(x, t)$ of Problem (5.1.1)-(5.1.3) can be represented by the formula

$$u(x, t) = \frac{-1}{2\pi\sqrt{-1}} \sum_{\nu} \int_{c_\nu} \lambda^{m-1} e^{\lambda^m t} d\lambda \int_D G(x, \xi, \lambda) \times \left(F_0(\xi, \Phi, \lambda^m) + \int_0^t e^{-\lambda^m \tau} f(\xi, \tau) d\tau\right) d_\xi D \tag{5.1.14}$$

Thus, the validation of the residue formulae (5.1.12) and (5.1.14) reduces essentially to proving (5.1.11) for the spectral problem (5.1.7)-(5.1.8).

In this connection, Section 5.3 is devoted to a proof of (5.1.13) for a class of multi-dimensional spectral problems with separable variables.

5.2 RESIDUE METHOD OF SEPARATING VARIABLES

Suppose that we have the differential equation

$$L_1\left(x^*, \frac{\partial}{\partial x^*}, \frac{\partial}{\partial t}\right)u + a(x^*)\, L_2\left(x^{**}, \frac{\partial}{\partial x^{**}}\right)u = f(x, t) \qquad (5.2.1)$$

applying to a bounded n-dimensional region D which is the Cartesian product of regions D_1 and D_2 described, respectively, by the points $x^* = (x_1, \ldots, x_{n_0})$ and $x^{**} = (x_{n_0+1}, \ldots, x_n)$, where $L_1\left(x^*, \frac{\partial}{\partial x^*}, \frac{\partial}{\partial t}\right)$ and $L_2\left(x^{**}, \frac{\partial}{\partial x^{**}}\right)$ are linear differential operators with respect to x^* and t on the one hand and x^{**} on the other with coefficients depending on x^* and x^{**} and where $a(x^*)$ is a function of the point x^*. We denote the boundary of the region D_i by Γ_i (for $i = 1, 2$). Consider the mixed problem of solving (5.2.1) with boundary conditions

$$\lim_{x^* \to y^*} B_1\left(y^*, \frac{\partial}{\partial x^*}, \frac{\partial}{\partial t}\right) u(x, t) = 0, \qquad y^* \in \Gamma_1 \qquad (5.2.2)$$

$$\lim_{x^{**} \to y^{**}} B_2\left(y^{**}, \frac{\partial}{\partial x^{**}}\right) u(x, t) = 0, \qquad y^{**} \in \Gamma_2 \qquad (5.2.3)$$

and initial conditions

$$\left.\frac{\partial^k u}{\partial t^k}\right|_{t=0} = \Phi_k(x) \qquad (k = 0, \ldots, q-1) \qquad (5.2.4)$$

where B_1 and B_2 are the linear differential operators with respect to x^* and t in the first case and x^{**} in the second with coefficients depending respectively on y^* and y^{**} and where q is the order of the highest derivative with respect to t in (5.2.1).

Suppose that the following conditions are satisfied.

1. The boundary-value problem

$$L_2\left(x^{**}, \frac{\partial}{\partial x^{**}}\right) w - \lambda w = h(x^{**}) \qquad (5.2.5)$$

$$\lim_{x^{**} \to y^{**}} B_2\left(y^{**}, \frac{\partial}{\partial x^{**}}\right) w(x^{**}) = 0, \quad y^{**} \in \Gamma_2 \qquad (5.2.6)$$

has a unique solution which is meromorphic with respect to λ; for an arbitrary function $h(x^{**}) \in L_2(D_2)$ the formula

$$-\frac{1}{2\pi\sqrt{-1}} \sum_{\nu} \int_{c_\nu} d\lambda \int_{D_2} G(x^{**}, \xi^{**}, \lambda)\, h(\xi^{**})\, d_{\xi^{**}} D_2 = h(x^{**}) \tag{5.2.7}$$

holds, where $G(x^{**}, \xi^{**}, \lambda)$ are the Green's functions of Problem (5.2.5)-(5.2.6) and the remaining notations are as indicated above.

2. The mixed problem

$$L_1\left(x^*, \frac{\partial}{\partial x^*}, \frac{\partial}{\partial t}\right) v + a(x^*)\lambda v = f(x^*, \xi^{**}, t) \tag{5.2.8}$$

$$\lim_{x^* \to y^*} B_1\left(y^*, \frac{\partial}{\partial x^*}, \frac{\partial}{\partial t}\right) v(x^*, \xi^{**}, t, \lambda) = 0, \quad y^* \in \Gamma_1 \tag{5.2.9}$$

$$\left.\frac{\partial^k v}{\partial t^k}\right|_{t=0} = \Phi_k(x^*, \xi^{**}) \quad (k = 0, \ldots, q-1) \tag{5.2.10}$$

has a solution $v(x^*, \xi^{**}, t, \lambda)$ which is analytic with respect to λ in some neighbourhood of every pole λ_ν of the function $G(x^{**}, \xi^{**}, \lambda)$; also, it $\lambda = 0$ is a pole of the function G, then $\int_{c_0} v(x, \lambda)\, d\lambda = 0$.

Suppose now that Problem (5.2.1)-(5.2.4) has a solution $u(x, t)$ for sufficiently smooth functions $f(x, t)$ and $\Phi_k(x)$. Let us look for this solution in the form of a series

$$u(x, t) = \frac{-1}{2\pi\sqrt{-1}} \sum_{\nu} \int_{c_\nu} d\lambda \int_{D_2} G(x^{**}, \xi^{**}, \lambda) \times v(x^*, \xi^{**}, t, \lambda)\, d_{\xi^{**}} D_2 \tag{5.2.11}$$

When we substitute (5.2.11) into (5.2.1), (5.2.2) and (5.2.4) and assume the validity of termwise application of the operators L_1, B_1 and $\frac{\partial^k}{\partial t^k}$ (for $k = 0, \ldots, q-1$) to the terms of the series (5.2.11), we obtain in accordance with (5.2.7)

$$\sum_\nu \int_{c_\nu} d\lambda \left\{a(x^*)\, v(x, t, \lambda) + \int_{D_2} G(x^{**}, \xi^{**}, \lambda) \right.$$
$$\left. \times \left(L_1\left(x^*, \frac{\partial}{\partial x^*}, \frac{\partial}{\partial t}\right) v + a(x^*)\,\lambda v\right) d_{\xi^{**}} D_2\right\}$$
$$= \sum_\nu \int_{c_\nu} d\lambda \int_{D_2} G(x^{**}, \xi^{**}, \lambda)\, f(x^*, \xi^{**}, t)\, d_{\xi^{**}} D_2$$

$$\sum_\nu \int_{c_\nu} d\lambda \int_{D_2} G(x^{**}, \xi^{**}, \lambda) \tag{5.2.12}$$
$$\times \lim_{\substack{x^* \to y^* \\ y^* \in \Gamma_1}} B_1\left(y^*, \frac{\partial}{\partial x^*}, \frac{\partial}{\partial t}\right) v(x^*, \xi^{**}, t)\, d_{\xi^{**}} D_2 = 0$$

$$\sum_\nu \int_{c_\nu} d\lambda \int_{D_2} G(x^{**}, \xi^{**}, \lambda) \left.\frac{\partial^k v(x^*, \xi^{**}, t, \lambda)}{\partial t^k}\right|_{t=0} d_{\xi^{**}} D_2$$
$$= \sum_\nu \int_{c_\nu} d\lambda \int_{D_2} G(x^{**}, \xi^{**}, \lambda)\, \Phi_k(x^*, \xi^{**})\, d_{\xi^{**}} D_2$$

When Condition 2 is satisfied, it is clear that

$$\int_{c_\nu} v(x, t, \lambda) = 0$$

for all poles λ_ν of the function G. Consequently, under the assumptions made, for (5.2.12) to be satisfied, it will be sufficient to take for v in (5.2.11) the solution of Problem (5.2.8)-(5.2.10). For such a choice of v, the function $u(x, t)$ defined by (5.2.11) is a formal solution of (5.2.1)-(5.2.4).

Thus, the variables in Problem (5.2.1)-(5.2.4) are separable and solution of this problem is reduced formally to solving Problem (5.2.8)-(5.2.10), which is of the same type for the region D_1, but with a smaller number of dimensions.

We introduce the notation

$$G_{\nu j}(F) \equiv F_\nu^{(j)}(x^{**}) \tag{5.2.13}$$
$$= \frac{-1}{2\pi\sqrt{-1}} \int_{c_\nu} \lambda^j\, d\lambda \int_{D_2} G(x^{**}, \xi^{**}, \lambda)\, F(\xi^{**})\, d_{\xi^{**}} D_2$$

To show the validity of the residue method of separating the variables, let us prove the following theorem.

Theorem 15 Suppose that Conditions 1 and 2 of this section are satisfied. Suppose also that, for sufficiently smooth functions $f(x, t)$ and $\Phi_k(x)$ defined in D, Problem (5.2.1)-(5.2.4) has a sufficiently smooth solution $u(x, t)$ (requiring a sufficiently smooth solution ensures the validity of the operations carried out in the proof of the theorem). Suppose finally that the mixed problem

$$L_1\left(x^*, \frac{\partial}{\partial x^*}, \frac{\partial}{\partial t}\right) w_{j\nu} + a(x^*)\, w_{j+1\nu} = f_\nu^{(j)}(x, t) \qquad (j = 0, 1, \ldots, \varkappa_\nu - 1) \tag{5.2.14}$$

(where $\varkappa_\nu$ is the order of the pole λ_ν),

$$\sum_{k=0}^{\varkappa_\nu} \binom{\varkappa_\nu}{k} (-\lambda_\nu)^k w_{\varkappa_\nu - k,\, \nu} = 0 \tag{5.2.15}$$

$$\lim_{x^* \to y^*} B_1\left(y^*, \frac{\partial}{\partial x^*}, \frac{\partial}{\partial t}\right) w_{j\nu}(x, t) = 0, \quad y^* \in \Gamma_1$$
$$\left.\frac{\partial^k w_{j\nu}}{\partial t^k}\right|_{t=0} = \Phi_{k\nu}^{(j)}(x) \tag{5.2.16}$$

$$(k = 0, \ldots, q-1; \quad j = 0, \ldots, \varkappa_\nu - 1) \tag{5.2.17}$$

has a unique solution for every pole λ_ν. Then $u(x, t)$ can be represented by (5.2.11).

Proof If we apply the operator $G_{\nu j}$ to both sides of (5.2.1), (5.2.2) and (5.2.4), we see that the functions $u_\nu^{(j)}(x, t)$ (for $j = 0, \ldots, \varkappa_\nu - 1$) satisfy (5.2.14), (5.2.16) and (5.2.17). With regard to (5.2.15), we need only note that it is another form of writing the identity

$$\frac{-1}{2\pi\sqrt{-1}} \int_{c_\nu} (\lambda - \lambda_\nu)^{\varkappa_\nu} d\lambda \int_{D_2} G(x^{**}, \xi^{**}, \lambda) \times u(x^*, \xi^{**}, t)\, d_{\xi^{**}} D_2 \equiv 0$$

Suppose also that $v(x^*, \xi^{**}, t, \lambda)$ is a solution of Problem (5.2.8)-(5.2.10) which is analytic with respect to λ in some neighbourhood of every non-zero pole λ_ν of the function

$G(x^{**}, \xi^{**}, \lambda)$ and that

$$\int_{c_0} v \, d\lambda = 0$$

if $\lambda = 0$ is a pole of the function G.

It can be directly verified that the functions

$$w_{j\nu} = \frac{-1}{2\pi\sqrt{-1}} \int_{c_\nu} \lambda^j \, d\lambda \int_{D_2} G(x^{**}, \xi^{**}, \lambda) v(x^*, \xi^{**}, t, \lambda) \, d_{\xi^{**}} D_2 \qquad (5.2.18)$$

$$(j = 0, \ldots, \varkappa_\nu - 1)$$

constitute a solution of Problem (5.2.14)-(5.2.17). By virtue of Condition 2 of the first section, we conclude that

$$w_{j\nu}(x, t) = u_\nu^{(j)}(x, t) \qquad (5.2.19)$$

In accordance with Theorem 1 and the Relations (5.2.13), (5.2.18) and (5.2.19), we obtain (5.2.11) for $j = 0$, which completes the proof.

Theorem 16 Suppose that Condition 1 of this section is satisfied and that (5.2.1)-(5.2.4) has a sufficiently smooth solution $u(x, t)$ for sufficiently smooth given functions $f(x, t)$ and $\Phi_h(x, t)$. Suppose finally that, for every λ_ν of the function $G(x^{**}, \xi^{**}, \lambda)$, Problem (5.2.14)-(5.2.17) has a unique solution $w_{j\nu}$ (for $j = 0, \ldots, \varkappa_\nu - 1$). Then, the solution $u(x, t)$ is given by

$$u(x, t) = \sum_\nu w_{0\nu}(x, t) = \sum_\nu u_\nu^{(0)}(x, t) \qquad (5.2.20)$$

The proof of this theorem is indicated by the procedure followed in proving Theorem 15.

Remark 1 If λ_ν is a simple pole of function $G(x^{**}, \xi^{**}, \lambda)$, the condition of uniqueness of the solution to Problem (5.2.14)-(5.2.17) is, because of the equivalence of Problems (5.2.14)-(5.2.17) and (5.2.21)-(5.2.23), replaced with the condition of uniqueness of the solution to the problem

$$L_1\left(x^*, \frac{\partial}{\partial x^*}, \frac{\partial}{\partial t}\right) w_0 + a(x^*) \lambda_\nu w_0 = f_\nu^{(0)}(x, t) \qquad (5.2.21)$$

$$\lim_{x^* \to y^*} B_1 \left(y^*, \frac{\partial}{\partial x^*}, \frac{\partial}{\partial t} \right) w_0(x, t) = 0, \ y^* \in \Gamma_1 \qquad (5.2.22)$$

$$\left. \frac{\partial^k w_0}{\partial t^k} \right|_{t=0} = \Phi_{k\nu}^{(0)}(x) \qquad (5.2.23)$$

Remark 2 It is clear from the line of reasoning followed that the method described above of separating the variables can also be applied to boundary-value problems. This means, in particular, that the operator L_1 may fail to contain time derivatives, in which case no longer Condition (5.2.4) holds.

As the following example shows, Condition 2 of this section may not hold for certain problems.

Let $u_1(x, y)$ and $u_2(x, y)$ denote solutions of the two equations

$$\frac{\partial^2 u}{\partial x^2} + \frac{\partial^2 u}{\partial y^2} = f_1(x, y)$$

$$\frac{\partial^2 u}{\partial x^2} - \frac{\partial^2 u}{\partial y^2} = f_2(x, y)$$

respectively, both satisfying the boundary conditions

$$u(0, y) = u(a, y) = u(x, 0) = u(x, b) = 0$$

Let $G_a(x, \xi, \lambda)$ denote the Green's function of the boundary-value problem

$$\frac{d^2 X}{dx^2} - \lambda X = f(x) \qquad X(0) = X(a) = 0$$

We have

$$G_a(x, \xi, \lambda) = \frac{\Delta_a(x, \xi, \lambda)}{\Delta_a(\lambda)}$$

where

$$\Delta_a(x, \xi, \lambda) = \begin{vmatrix} g(x, \xi, \lambda) & e^{\sqrt{\lambda} x} & e^{-\sqrt{\lambda} x} \\ g(0, \xi, \lambda) & 1 & 1 \\ g(a, \xi, \lambda) & e^{\sqrt{\lambda} a} & e^{-\sqrt{\lambda} a} \end{vmatrix}$$

$$g(x, \xi, \lambda) = \begin{cases} \dfrac{1}{2\sqrt{\lambda}} \sinh \sqrt{\lambda}\,(x - \xi) & \text{for } 0 \leqslant \xi \leqslant x \leqslant a \\ \dfrac{-1}{2\sqrt{\lambda}} \sinh \sqrt{\lambda}\,(x - \xi) & \text{for } 0 \leqslant x \leqslant \xi \leqslant a \end{cases}$$

$$\Delta_a(\lambda) = e^{-\sqrt{\lambda} a} - e^{\sqrt{\lambda} a}$$

As can be seen from these formulae, the poles of G_a are the numbers

$$\lambda_k = -\frac{(k\pi)^2}{a^2} \qquad (k=0, \pm 1, \pm 2, \ldots)$$

Also, all the poles are simple. If we follow the above scheme for finding the functions $u_i(x, y)$ (for $i=1, 2$) in the form of a series

$$u_i(x, y) = -\frac{1}{2\pi\sqrt{-1}} \sum_{\nu} \int_{c_\nu} d\lambda \int_0^a G_a(x, \xi, \lambda)\, v_i(\xi, y, \lambda)\, d\xi$$

corresponding to (5.2.11), we obtain the problems

$$\frac{d^2 v_1}{dy^2} + \lambda v_1 = f_1(\xi, y), \quad v_1(\xi, 0, \lambda) = v_1(\xi, b, \lambda) = 0$$

$$\frac{d^2 v_2}{dy^2} - \lambda v_2 = f_2(\xi, y), \quad v_2(\xi, 0, \lambda) = v_2(\xi, b, \lambda) = 0$$

corresponding to Problem (5.2.8)-(5.2.10).

Obviously, the numbers belonging to the sequences

$$\lambda_\nu^{(1)} = \left(\frac{\nu\pi}{b}\right)^2, \quad \lambda_\nu^{(2)} = -\left(\frac{\nu\pi}{b}\right)^2 \quad (\nu = 0, \pm 1, \pm 2, \ldots)$$

will be poles of functions $v_1(\xi, y, \lambda)$ and $v_2(\xi, y, \lambda)$, respectively. Comparison of the numbers λ_ν, $\lambda_\nu^{(1)}$ and $\lambda_\nu^{(2)}$ shows that the non-zero poles of G_a cannot coincide with the poles v_1 and that

$$\int_{c_0} v_1(\xi, y, \lambda)\, d\lambda = 0$$

whereas the poles of the function G_a coincide with the poles of v_2 for $a=b$. Consequently, Condition 2 is not satisfied and the above scheme of separating the variables cannot be used in the present case. It might be noted that this indicates the possibility of correct formulation of the second of the boundary-value problems in this example.

Finally, we consider a problem of the type (5.2.1)-(5.2.4) which admits complete separation of the space variables.

Consider the following boundary-value problem:

$$\sum_{i=1}^{n-1} c_i(x_n) L_i\left(x_i, \frac{\partial}{\partial x_i}\right) u + c_n(x_n) L_n\left(x_n, \frac{\partial}{\partial x_n}, \frac{\partial}{\partial t}\right) u = f(x, t) \tag{5.2.24}$$

$$Q_{ij}(u) \equiv \sum_{k=1}^{N_j} \left\{ \alpha_{ik}^{(j)} \frac{\partial^{k-1} u}{\partial x_j^{k-1}} \bigg|_{x=a_j} + \beta_{ik}^{(j)} \frac{\partial^{k-1} u}{\partial x_j^{k-1}} \bigg|_{x=b_j} \right\} = 0$$
$$(i = 1, 2, \ldots, N_j, \; j = 1, 2, \ldots, n) \quad (5.2.25)$$

$$\frac{\partial^k u}{\partial t^k}\bigg|_{t=0} = \Phi_k(x) \quad (k = 0, 1, \ldots, q-1) \quad (5.2.26)$$

Here, the L_i are linear differential operators of orders N_i with respect to x_i for $i = 1, \ldots, n-1$ and with respect to x and t for $i = n$; the coefficients in these operators are independent of the x_i; q is the order of the highest derivative with respect to t in L_n; $\alpha_{ik}^{(j)}$ and $\beta_{ik}^{(j)}$ are constants for $j = 1, \ldots, n-1$); for $j = n$, they are, in general, linear differential operators with respect to t of orders not exceeding q and the coefficients in them are constants.

Let $G_i(x_i, \xi_i, \lambda_i)$ denote the Green's function of the boundary-value problem

$$L_i\left(x_i, \frac{\partial}{\partial x_i}\right) X - \lambda_i X = f(x_i)$$
$$Q_{ij}(X) = 0 \quad (i = 1, \ldots, N_j; \; j = 1, 2, \ldots, n-1)$$

Suppose also that $f(x_i) \in L_2(a_i, b_i)$ can be expanded in a series of residues of the solution of this boundary-value problem. Then, by $n-1$ applications of the scheme shown above for separating the variables for a formal solution $u(x, t)$ of Problem (5.2.24)-(5.2.26), we obtain the following representation:

$$u(x, t) = \left(\frac{-1}{2\pi\sqrt{-1}}\right)^{n-1} \sum_{k_1, \ldots, k_{n-1}} \left(\prod_{i=1}^{n-1} \int_{c_{k_i}} d\lambda_i \int_{a_i}^{b_i} G_i(x_i, \xi_i, \lambda_i) \times u_{n-1}(\xi^*, x_n, \lambda^*)\, d\xi_i \right) \quad (5.2.27)$$

where $\xi^* = (\xi_1, \ldots, \xi_{n-1})$, $\lambda^* = (\lambda_1, \ldots, \lambda_{n-1})$ and u_{n-1} is a solution of the problem

$$c_n(x_n) L_n\left(x_n, \frac{\partial}{\partial x_n}, \frac{\partial}{\partial t}\right) u_{n-1} + \sum_{k=1}^{n-1} c_k(x_n) \lambda_k u_{n-1} = f(\xi^*, x_n, t) \quad (5.2.28)$$

$$Q_{in}(u_{n-1})=0 \quad (i=1, \dots, N_n) \tag{5.2.29}$$

$$\left.\frac{\partial^k u_{n-1}}{\partial t^k}\right|_{t=0}=\Phi_k(\xi^*, x_n) \tag{5.2.30}$$

We introduce the notations

$$G_s(F)\equiv F_{k_s}^{(j_s)}(x)=\frac{-1}{2\pi\sqrt{-1}}\int_{c_{k_s}}\lambda_s^{j_s}\,d\lambda_s\int_{a_s}^{b_s}G_s(x_s, \xi_s, \lambda_s)$$

$$\times F(x_1, \dots, x_{s-1}, \xi_s, x_{s+1}, \dots, x_n)\,d\xi_s \quad (s=1, \dots, n-1)$$

$$F_{k_1\dots k_s}^{(j_1,\dots,j_s)}(x)=G_s(F_{k_1\dots k_{s-1}}^{(j_1,\dots,j_{s-1})}(x))$$

To show the validity of (5.2.27), one can prove (by the method shown in the proof of Theorem 16) the following theorem.

Theorem 17 Suppose that the hypotheses just enumerated are satisfied, that Problem (5.2.24)-(5.2.26) has a sufficiently smooth solution $u(x, t)$ and that the following conditions are satisfied.

1. Problem (5.2.28)-(5.2.30) has a unique solution $u_{n-1}(\xi^*, x_n, \lambda)$, which is analytic with respect to $\lambda_1, \dots, \lambda_{n-1}$ in in a sufficiently small neighbourhood of every point $(\lambda_1^{(k_1)}, \dots, \lambda_{n-1}^{(k_{n-1})})$ such that $\lambda_s^{(k)}\neq 0$ (where s is one of the integers $1, \dots, n-1$) and

$$\int_{c_0}\lambda_s^{N_s-1}u_{n-1}\,d\lambda_s=0$$

if $\lambda_s=0$ is a pole of the function $G_s(x_s, \xi_s, \lambda_s)$.

2. The problem

$$c_n(x_n)L_n\left(x_n, \frac{\partial}{\partial x_n}, \frac{\partial}{\partial t}\right)v_{k_j}$$
$$+c_1(x_n)v_{k_j+l_1}+\dots+c_n(x_n)v_{k_j+l_n}=f_k^{(j)}(x)$$

$$\sum_{p=0}^{\varkappa_{k_s}}\binom{\varkappa_{k_s}}{p}(-\lambda_s^{(k_s)})^p v_{k_{j_1},\dots,j_{s-1},\varkappa_{k_s}-p,j_{s+1},\dots,j_{n-1}}=0$$
$$(s=1, \dots, n-1)$$

$$Q_{in}(v_{k_j})=0$$

$$\left.\frac{\partial^s v_{k_j}}{\partial t^s}\right|_{t=0}=\Phi_k^{(j)}(x) \quad (s=0, \dots, q-1)$$

has a unique solution v_{k_j} for every point

$$(\lambda_1^{(k_1)}, \ldots, \lambda_{n-1}^{(k_{n-1})})$$

where

$$j=(j_1, \ldots, j_{n-1}),\ k=(k_1, \ldots, k_{n-1}),\ l_1=(1, 0, \ldots, 0)$$
$$\ldots, l_n=(0, \ldots, 0, 1),\ j_s=0, \ldots, \varkappa_{k_s}-1,\ s=1, \ldots, n-1$$

and $\varkappa_{k_s}$ is the order of the pole $\lambda_s^{(k_s)}$ of the function $G_s(x_s, \xi_s, \lambda_s)$. Then, $u(x, t)$ is given by (5.2.27).

5.3 FORMULA FOR EXPANDING AN ARBITRARY FUNCTION IN A SERIES OF RESIDUES OF A SOLUTION OF A CERTAIN CLASS OF MULTI-DIMENSIONAL SPECTRAL PROBLEMS

Consider the differential equation

$$L_1\left(x^*, \frac{\partial}{\partial x^*}, \lambda\right) v + a(x^*) L_2\left(x^{**}, \frac{\partial}{\partial x^{**}}\right) v = f(x) \qquad (5.3.1)$$

applicable in a bounded n-dimensional region D of the point $x=(x_1, \ldots, x_n)$, which is the Cartesian product of the regions D_1 and D_2 defined, respectively, by the points $x^*=(x_1, \ldots, x_{n_0})$, and $x^{**}=(x_{n_0+1}, \ldots, x_n)$, where L_1 and L_2 are linear differential operators with respect to x^* and x^{**}, respectively. To be more definite, let us assume that L_1 is of the form

$$L_1\left(x^*, \frac{\partial}{\partial x^*}, \lambda\right)$$
$$= \sum_{\substack{k\leqslant q-1\\ mk+l\leqslant p}} \lambda^{mk} A_{kl_1 \ldots l_{n_0}}(x^*) \frac{\partial^l}{\partial x_1^{l_1} \ldots \partial x_{n_0}^{l_{n_0}}} - \lambda^p$$

where m and q are natural numbers such that $p=mq$. As before, we denote the boundary of the region D_i by Γ_i (for $(i=1, 2)$.

Consider the problem of finding the solution of (5.3.1) with boundary conditions

$$\lim_{x^*\to y^*} \sum_{k=0}^{q} \lambda^{mk} B_k\left(y^*, \frac{\partial}{\partial x^*}\right) v(x) = 0, \quad y^* \in \Gamma_1 \qquad (5.3.2)$$

$$\lim_{x^{**}\to y^{**}} C\left(y^{**}, \frac{\partial}{\partial x^{**}}\right) v(x) = 0, \quad y^{**} \in \Gamma_2 \qquad (5.3.3)$$

where $B_k\left(y^*, \frac{\partial}{\partial x^*}\right)$ and $C\left(y^{**}, \frac{\partial}{\partial x^{**}}\right)$ are linear differential operators with respect to x^* and x^{**} respectively, the coefficients in which are independent of $y^* \in \Gamma_1$ and $y^{**} \in \Gamma_2$.

Suppose that the following conditions are satisfied.

1. Problem (5.3.1)-(5.3.3) has a unique solution $v(x, f, \lambda)$ which is meromorphic with respect to λ for every $f(x) \in L_2(D)$.
2. The equation

$$L_2\left(x^{**}, \frac{\partial}{\partial x^{**}}\right) z - \mu z = \Phi(x^{**})$$

with boundary condition (5.3.3) has a unique solution $z(x^{**}, \Phi, \mu)$ for every $\Phi(x^{**}) \in L_2(D_2)$; the solution is meromorphic with respect to μ. Also

$$\Phi(x^{**}) = \frac{-1}{2\pi\sqrt{-1}} \sum_{\nu} \int_{c_\nu} d\mu \int_{D_2} G_2(x^{**}, \xi^{**}, \mu)\, \Phi(\xi^{**})\, d_{\xi^{**}} D_2$$

where $G_2(x^{**}, \xi^{**}, \mu)$ is the Green's function of that boundary-value problem.

3. The equation

$$L_1\left(x^*, \frac{\partial}{\partial x^*}, \lambda\right) w + a(x^*)\, \mu_\nu w = \psi(x^*)$$

with boundary condition (5.3.2) has a unique solution $w(x^*, \psi, \mu_\nu, \lambda)$ for every $\psi(x^*) \in L_2(D_1)$; the solution is meromorphic with respect to λ. The function $\psi(x^*)$ can be expanded in a series according to the formula

$$\frac{-1}{2\pi\sqrt{-1}} \sum_{k} \int_{d_{\nu k}} \lambda^{m(s+1)-1}\, d\lambda \int_{D_1} G_1(x^*, \xi^*, \mu_\nu, \lambda) \times \psi(\xi^*)\, d_{\xi^*} D_1 = \begin{cases} 0 & \text{for } s < q-1 \\ \psi(x^*) & \text{for } s = q-1 \end{cases}$$

Here, $G_1(x^*, \xi^*, \mu_\nu, \lambda)$ is the Green's function of this boundary-value problem, $d_{\nu k}$ is a simple closed contour in the λ-plane which encircles only one pole $\lambda_{\nu k}$ of the function $G_1(x^*, \xi^*, \mu_\nu, \lambda)$ (namely, the pole corresponding to the pole μ_ν of the function $G_2(x^{**}, \xi^{**}, \mu)$ and the summation with respect to k is over all poles of the functions in the integrand.

Theorem 18 Suppose that Conditions 1, 2 and 3 above are satisfied and that all poles μ_ν (for $\nu=1, 2, \ldots$) of the function $G_2(x^{**}, \xi^{**}, \mu)$ are simple. Suppose finally that, for some λ and $f(x) \in L_2(D)$, Problem (5.3.1)-(5.3.3) has a sufficiently smooth solution $v(x, f, \lambda)$. Then, this solution is given by

$$v(x, f, \lambda) = \frac{-1}{2\pi\sqrt{-1}} \sum_{\nu=1}^{\infty} \int_{c_\nu} d\mu \int_{D_2} G_2(x^{**}, \xi^{**}, \mu) \int_{D_1} G_1(x^*, \xi^*, \mu_\nu, \lambda) f(\xi)\, d_\xi D \tag{5.3.4}$$

and $\lambda \neq \lambda_{\nu k}$.

Proof Let us denote by $F_{\nu j}(x)$ the integral

$$G_{\nu j}^{(2)}(F) \equiv F_{\nu j}(x) = \frac{-1}{2\pi\sqrt{-1}} \int_{c_\nu} \mu^j\, d\mu \int_{D_2} G_2(x^{**}, \xi^{**}, \mu) F(\xi^{**})\, d_{\xi^{**}} D_2$$

Let $v(x, \lambda)$ be a sufficiently smooth solution of Problem (5.3.1)-(5.3.3). Applying the operator $G_{\nu 0}^{(2)}$ to both sides of (5.3.1) and (5.3.2), we obtain

$$\begin{gathered} L_1\left(x^*, \frac{\partial}{\partial x^*}, \lambda\right) v_{\nu 0} + a(x^*)\, v_{\nu 1}(x, \lambda) = f_{\nu 0}(x) \\ \lim_{x^* \to y^*} \sum_{k=0}^{q} \lambda^{m_k} B_k\left(y^*, \frac{\partial}{\partial x^*}\right) v_{\nu 0}(x, \lambda) = 0, \qquad y^* \in \Gamma \end{gathered} \tag{5.3.5}$$

According to the hypothesis of the theorem, all poles μ_ν of the function $G_2(x^{**}, \xi^{**}, \mu)$ are simple. Consequently,

$$v_{\nu 1}(x, \lambda) = \mu_\nu v_{\nu 0}(x, \lambda)$$

Substituting this into (5.3.5), we get

$$\begin{gathered} L_1\left(x^*, \frac{\partial}{\partial x^*}, \lambda\right) v_{\nu 0}(x, \lambda) + a(x^*)\, \mu_\nu v_{\nu 0}(x, \lambda) = f_{\nu 0}(x) \\ \lim_{x^* \to y^*} \sum_{k=0}^{q} \lambda^{m_k} B_k\left(y^*, \frac{\partial}{\partial x^*}\right) v_{\nu 0}(x, \lambda) = 0, \quad y^* \in \Gamma_1 \end{gathered}$$

In accordance with Condition 3, it follows from these identities that

$$\lambda \neq \lambda_{\nu k} \qquad (\nu, k = 1, 2, \ldots)$$

and

$$v_{\nu 0}(x, \lambda) = \int_{D_1} G_1(x^*, \xi^*, \mu_\nu, \lambda) f_\nu(\xi^*, x^{**})\, d_{\xi^*} D_1$$

$$= \frac{-1}{2\pi\sqrt{-1}} \int_{c_\nu} d\mu \int_{D_2} G_2(x^{**}, \xi^{**}, \mu)\, d_{\xi^{**}} D_2$$

$$\times \int_{D_1} G_1(x^*, \xi^*, \mu_\nu, \lambda) f(\xi)\, d_{\xi^*} D_1$$

Finally, according to Condition 2, we obtain (5.3.4) from the last equation, which completes the proof.

Remark 1 It follows from Theorem 18 that all poles of the function $v(x, \lambda)$ are exhausted by the numbers

$$\lambda_{\nu k}\ (\nu, k = 1, 2, 3, \ldots)$$

Remark 2 This same theorem can be proved for a boundary condition of the form (5.3.3) which depends on λ,

$$C = C\left(y^{**}, \frac{\partial}{\partial x^{**}}, \lambda\right)$$

Now, with the aid of Theorem 18, we can prove Theorem 19 below.

Theorem 19 Under the hypotheses of Theorem 18, the following formula holds for every function $f(x) \in L_2(D)$

$$\frac{-1}{2\pi\sqrt{-1}} \sum_{i=1}^{\infty} \sum_{j=1}^{\infty} \int_{d_{ij}} \lambda^{m(s+1)-1} v(x, \lambda)\, d\lambda$$

$$= \frac{-1}{2\pi\sqrt{-1}} \sum_{i=1}^{\infty} \sum_{j=1}^{\infty} \int_{d_{ij}} \lambda^{m(s+1)-1} d\lambda \int_{D} G(x, \xi, \lambda) f(\xi)\, d_\xi D \qquad (5.3.6)$$

$$= \begin{cases} 0 & \text{for } s < q-1 \\ f(x) & \text{for } s = q-1 \end{cases}$$

where $G(x, \xi, \lambda)$ is the Green's function of Problem (5.3.1)-(5.3.3) and the double summation with respect to i and j is over all poles λ_{ij} of that function.

Proof In accordance with Theorem 18, we have

$$\int_{d_{ij}} \lambda^{m(s+1)-1} v(x, \lambda)\, d\lambda$$

$$= \int_{d_{ij}} \lambda^{m(s+1)-1}\, d\lambda \left\{ \frac{-1}{2\pi\sqrt{-1}} \sum_{\nu=1}^{\infty} \int_{c_\nu} d\mu \int_{D_2} G_2(x^{**}, \xi^{**}, \mu) \right.$$

$$\left. \times\, d_{\xi^{**}}D_2 \int_{D_1} G_1(x^*, \xi^*, \mu_\nu, \lambda) f(\xi)\, d_{\xi^*}D_1 \right\} \qquad (5.3.7)$$

since d_{ij} is a sufficiently small closed contour, all terms in the series in the braces on the right-hand side of (5.3.7) are analytic functions of λ except for the term

$$\frac{-1}{2\pi\sqrt{-1}} \int_{c_i} d\mu \int_{D_2} G_2(x^{**}, \xi^{**}, \mu)\, d_{\xi^{**}}D_2$$

$$\times \int_{D_1} G_1(x^*, \xi^*, \mu_i, \lambda) f(\xi)\, d_{\xi^*}D_1$$

Consequently, the integral over the contour d_{ij} of the sum of the remaining terms in this series is equal to zero. Therefore, from (5.3.7), we obtain

$$\int_{d_{ij}} \lambda^{m(s+1)-1} v(x, \lambda)\, d\lambda$$

$$= \frac{-1}{2\pi\sqrt{-1}} \int_{d_{ij}} \lambda^{m(s+1)-1} d\lambda \int_{c_i} d\mu \int_{D_2} G_2(x^{**}, \xi^{**}, \mu)\, d_{\xi^{**}}D_2$$

$$\times \int_{D_1} G_1(x^*, \xi^*, \mu_i, \lambda) f(\xi)\, d_{\xi^*}D_1$$

Summing over all i and j, we have

$$\frac{-1}{2\pi\sqrt{-1}} \sum_{i=1}^{\infty} \sum_{j=1}^{\infty} \int_{d_{ij}} \lambda^{m(s+1)-1} v(x, \lambda)\, d\lambda$$

$$= \frac{-1}{2\pi\sqrt{-1}} \sum_{i=1}^{\infty} \int_{c_i} d\mu \int_{D_2} G_2(x^{**}, \xi^{**}, \mu)\, d_{\xi^{**}}D_2$$

$$\times \left\{ \frac{-1}{2\pi\sqrt{-1}} \sum_{j=1}^{\infty} \int_{d_{ij}} \lambda^{m(s+1)-1} d\lambda \right.$$

$$\left. \times \int_{D_1} G_1(x^*, \xi^*, \mu_i, \lambda) f(\xi)\, d_{\xi^*}D_1 \right\}$$

In accordance with Condition 3, the summation inside the braces on the right-hand side of this last equation is equal to zero for $s<q-1$ and equal to $f(x^*, \xi^{**})$ for $s=q-1$. Therefore, on the basis of Condition 2, we obtain (5.3.6) from this last equation, which completes the proof.

5.4 PROBLEMS IN SUBTERRANEAN HYDROMECHANICS

The following problems in subterranean hydrodynamics are generalisations of the problems listed in Example 1 of Chapter A and Example 1 of Section 6.1 to the case of three-dimensional regions (with the time variable not considered) for a circular layer which is non-homogeneous in the vertical direction.

Reasoning similar to that of Charnii [51] indicates that the physical problem formulated in the seventh chapter of his book for the case of a non-homogeneous circular layer with allowance made for the force of inertia reduces to solving the equation

$$\frac{\partial^2 u}{\partial t^2}+\nu^2 a(y)\frac{\partial u}{\partial t}=\nu^2\left(\frac{\partial^2 u}{\partial x^2}+\frac{1}{x}\frac{\partial u}{\partial x}+\frac{\partial^2 u}{\partial y^2}\right)+\nu^2 b(y)\frac{\partial u}{\partial y} \quad (5.4.1)$$

with boundary conditions

$$\left.\frac{\partial u}{\partial x}\right|_{x=a}+\alpha(y)\left.\frac{\partial u}{\partial t}\right|_{x=a}=0,\ u(b,\ y,\ t)=\beta(y) \quad (5.4.2)$$

$$\left.\frac{\partial u}{\partial y}\right|_{y=0}=\left.\frac{\partial u}{\partial y}\right|_{y=h}=0 \quad (5.4.3)$$

and initial conditions

$$u(x,\ y,\ 0)=\Phi_0(x,\ y),\ \left.\frac{\partial u}{\partial t}\right|_{t=0}=\Phi_1(x,\ y) \quad (5.4.4)$$

If we neglect the inertial force of the liquid, we arrive at the mixed problem

$$\frac{\partial u}{\partial t}=\varkappa(y)\left(\frac{\partial^2 u}{\partial x^2}+\frac{1}{x}\frac{\partial u}{\partial x}+\frac{\partial^2 u}{\partial y^2}\right)+c(y)\frac{\partial u}{\partial y} \quad (5.4.5)$$

$$\left.\frac{\partial u}{\partial x}\right|_{x=a}+\alpha(y)\left.\frac{\partial u}{\partial t}\right|_{x=a}=0,\ u(b,\ y,\ t)=\beta(y) \quad (5.4.6)$$

$$\left.\frac{\partial u}{\partial y}\right|_{y=0}=\left.\frac{\partial u}{\partial y}\right|_{y=h}=0 \tag{5.4.7}$$

$$u(x, y, 0)=\Phi_0(x, y) \tag{5.4.8}$$

where $u(x, y, t)$ is the pressure at the point (x, y) at the instant t, ν is the velocity of sound,

$$a(y)=\frac{m\mu}{kK},\ b(y)=\frac{\mu}{k}\frac{\partial}{\partial y}\left(\frac{k}{\mu}\right),\ \alpha(y)=\frac{f_k\mu}{2\pi ah\gamma_0 k}$$

h is the thickness of the layer, f is the area of the annular section of the gap between the settling and rising tubes and

$$\varkappa(y)=\frac{kK_1K_s}{\mu(m_0K_s+K_1)},\ c(y)=\frac{K_sK_1}{m_0K_s+K_1}\frac{\partial}{\partial y}\left(\frac{k}{\mu}\right)$$

Here, m, k, K_s, and m_0 are physical quantities characterising the filtration properties of the stratum, and K_1 and μ characterise the physical properties of the liquid.

Example 1 Consider Problem (5.4.1)-(5.4.4). First, let us give a residue formula representing the solution of this problem by assuming that $b(y)=0$ and $a(y)$, $\alpha(y)$ and $\beta(y)$ are constants. With these assumptions, (5.4.1) becomes

$$\frac{\partial^2 u}{\partial t^2}+\nu^2 a\frac{\partial u}{\partial t}=\nu^2\left(\frac{\partial^2 u}{\partial x^2}+\frac{1}{x}\frac{\partial u}{\partial x}+\frac{\partial^2 u}{\partial y^2}\right) \tag{5.4.9}$$

If $u_1(x, y)$ is a solution of this equation which does not depend on t and which satisfies Conditions (5.4.2) and (5.4.3), then we can reduce Problem (5.4.1)-(5.4.4) to the same problem with homogeneous boundary conditions corresponding to Conditions (5.4.2) and (5.4.3) by making the substitution $v=u-u_1$. Therefore, we can take $\beta=0$ without loss of generality.

Let us denote by $G(y, \eta, \lambda)$ the Green's function of the boundary-value problem

$$\frac{d^2Y}{dy^2}-\lambda Y=f(y),\quad Y'(0)=Y'(h)=0$$

Obviously, the conditions of Theorem 10, Section 3.2 are satisfied for this spectral problem. Consequently, Condition 1 of Theorem 16 is satisfied. It remains to show that the problem corresponding to Problem (5.2.14)-(5.2.17) has a unique solution. Then, by finding $w_{0\nu}$ in the form of an integral residue, we can use (5.2.11) to obtain a solution of Problem (5.4.1)-(5.4.4). First, let us find

$$G(y, \eta, \lambda) = g(y, \eta, \lambda)$$
$$\frac{\cosh(\sqrt{\lambda}(y-h))\cosh(\sqrt{\lambda}\eta)+\cosh(\sqrt{\lambda}y)\cosh(\sqrt{\lambda}(\eta-h))}{2\sqrt{\lambda}\sinh\sqrt{\lambda}h} \tag{5.4.10}$$

where

$$g(y, \eta, \lambda) = \begin{cases} -\dfrac{1}{2\sqrt{\lambda}}\sinh(\sqrt{\lambda}(\eta-y)) \text{ for } 0\leqslant\eta\leqslant y \\ \dfrac{1}{2\sqrt{\lambda}}\sinh(\sqrt{\lambda}(\eta-y)) \text{ for } y\leqslant\eta\leqslant h \end{cases}$$

As can be seen from (5.4.10), the poles of $G(y, \eta, \lambda)$ are the numbers

$$\lambda_k = -\left(\frac{k\pi}{h}\right)^2 (k=0, \pm 1, \pm 2, \ldots)$$

It is clear that all the poles λ_k (for $k=0, \pm 1, \pm 2, \ldots$) are simple. Then, in accordance with the remark to Theorem 16, the last condition of Theorem 16 reduces to the condition that the problem

$$\frac{\partial^2 w_{0k}}{\partial t^2} + \nu^2 a \frac{\partial w_{0k}}{\partial t} = \nu^2\left(\frac{\partial^2 w_{0k}}{\partial x^2} + \frac{1}{x}\frac{\partial w_{0k}}{\partial x} + \lambda_k w_{0k}\right) \tag{5.4.11}$$

$$\left.\frac{\partial w_{0k}}{\partial x}\right|_{x=a} + \alpha \left.\frac{\partial w_{0k}}{\partial t}\right|_{x=a} = 0, \quad w_{0k}(b, y, t) = 0 \tag{5.4.12}$$

$$w_{0k}(x, y, 0) = \Phi_{0k}^{(0)}(x, y), \quad \left.\frac{\partial w_{0k}}{\partial t}\right|_{t=0} = \Phi_{1k}^{(0)}(x, y) \tag{5.4.13}$$

where, in the notation (5.2.13),

$$\Phi_{ik}^{(0)}(x, y) = \frac{-1}{2\pi\sqrt{-1}}\int_{c_k} d\lambda \int_0^h G(y, \eta, \lambda)\,\Phi_i(x, \eta)\,d\eta$$

has a unique solution.

Substituting the expression for $G(y, \eta, \lambda)$ given by (5.4.10) into this last formula, we obtain

$$\Phi_{ik}^{(0)}(x, y) = \frac{4}{h} \cos \frac{k\pi}{h} \int_0^h \Phi_i(x, \eta) \cos \frac{k\pi}{h} \eta \, d\eta \quad (k = 1, 2, \ldots)$$

$$\Phi_{i0}^{(0)}(x, y) = \frac{2}{h} \int_0^h \Phi_i(x, \eta) \, d\eta \quad (i = 0, 1)$$

However, as shown in Example 1 of Chapter 4, Problem (5.4.11)-(5.4.13) satisfies all the conditions of Theorem 11 (see Chapter 4) for $(k = 0, \pm 1, \ldots)$ if $\Phi_0(x, y)$ and $\Phi_1(x, y)$ are sufficiently smooth and if $\Phi_0(b, y) = 0$ (where $p = q = 2$ and $m = 1$). Consequently, its solution is unique and is given by

$$w_{0k}(x, y, t) = \frac{-1}{2\pi\sqrt{-1}} \sum_s \int_{d_{sk}} e^{\mu t} d\mu \left\{ \int_a^b G_1(x, \xi, \lambda_k, \mu) (\Phi_{1k}^{(0)}(\xi, y) + (\mu + \nu^2 a) \Phi_{0k}^{(0)}(\xi, y)) \, d\xi + \Delta_k(x, y, \Phi, \mu) \right\} \quad (5.4.14)$$

where $G_1(x, \xi, \lambda_k, \mu)$ is the Green's function of the spectral problem

$$\nu^2 \left(\frac{d^2 X_k}{dx^2} + \frac{1}{x} \frac{dX_k}{dx} + \lambda_k X_k \right) - (\mu^2 - a\nu^2 \mu) X_k = (\mu + a\nu^2) \Phi_{0k}^{(0)}(x, y) + \Phi_{1k}^{(0)}(x, y) \quad (5.4.15)$$

$$\left. \frac{dX_k}{dx} \right|_{x=a} + a\mu X_k(a) = -a \left. \frac{\partial \Phi_{01}^{(0)}(x, y)}{\partial x} \right|_{x=a}, \quad X_k(b) = 0, \quad (5.4.16)$$

corresponding to Problem (5.4.11)-(5.4.13) with the corresponding homogeneous boundary conditions, $\Delta_k(x, y, \Phi, \mu)$ is the solution of the homogeneous equation (5.4.15) with boundary conditions (5.4.16) and d_{sk} is a closed contour in the μ-plane encircling only one pole μ_{sk} (for $s = 1, 2, \ldots$) of the function in the integrand.

Then, in accordance with Theorem 16, the solution of (5.4.1)-(5.4.4) can be constructed from (5.2.11) in the form

$$u(x, y, t) = \sum_{k=0}^{\infty} w_{0k}(x, y, t) \quad (5.4.17)$$

where w_{0k} is given by (5.4.14).

The case of variable coefficients $a(y)$ and $b(y)$ is of interest. In this case, as shown in Section 5.1, the solution of Problem (5.4.1)-(5.4.4) can be constructed from (5.1.12) by assuming that the relevant formula of type (5.1.11) is valid.

It should be noted that, if we apply the method of separation of variables (see Section 5.2) to the solution of the corresponding spectral problem for constants $\alpha(y)=\alpha$, then the construction of the solution of the corresponding spectral problem is indeed reduced to solving two boundary-value problems for ordinary differential equations.

Specifically, consider the spectral problem

$$\nu^2\left(\frac{\partial^2 v}{\partial x^2}+\frac{1}{x}\frac{\partial v}{\partial x}+\frac{\partial^2 v}{\partial y^2}\right)+\nu^2 b(y)\frac{\partial v}{\partial y}-(\lambda^2+\lambda\nu^2 a(y))\,v$$
$$=\sum_{i=0}^{1}\lambda^{1-i}\Phi_i(x, y)+\nu^2 a(y)\,\Phi_0(x, y) \qquad (5.4.18)$$

$$\left.\frac{\partial v}{\partial x}\right|_{x=a}+\alpha\lambda v(a, y)=-\alpha\Phi_0(a, y),\ v(b, y)=0 \qquad (5.4.19)$$

$$\left.\frac{\partial v}{\partial y}\right|_{y=0}=\left.\frac{\partial v}{\partial y}\right|_{y=h}=0 \qquad (5.4.20)$$

corresponding to the mixed problem (5.4.1)-(5.4.4). Suppose that $G_1(x, \xi, \lambda, \mu)$ is the Green's function of the spectral problem

$$\frac{d^2X}{dx^2}+\frac{1}{x}\frac{dX}{dx}-\mu X=f(x), \qquad \frac{dX(a)}{dx}+\alpha\lambda X(a)=0,\ X(b)=0$$

Let us obtain a formal solution of Problem (5.4.18)-(5.4.20) with corresponding homogeneous boundary conditions using the method of separation of variables in the form

$$v(x, y, \lambda)$$
$$=\frac{-1}{2\pi\sqrt{-1}}\sum_s\int_{c_s}d\mu\int_a^b G_1(x, \xi, \lambda, \mu)\,v_1(\xi, y, \lambda, \mu)\,d\xi \qquad (5.4.21)$$

Substituting (5.4.21) into (5.4.18) and (5.4.20) and equating the right and left sides of the resulting equations, we arrive at the spectral problem

$$\nu^2\left(\frac{d^2v_1}{dy^2}+\mu v_1\right)+\nu^2 b(y)\frac{dv_1}{dy}-(\lambda^2+\lambda\nu^2 a(y))\,v_1 =\sum_{i=0}^{1}\lambda^{1-i}\Phi_i(\xi,\ y)+\nu^2 a(y)\,\Phi_0(\xi,\ y)$$

$$\left.\frac{dv_1}{dy}\right|_{y=0}=\left.\frac{dv_1}{dy}\right|_{y=h}=0$$

If $G_2(y,\ \eta,\ \mu,\ \lambda)$ is the Green's function of this problem, we shall have

$$v_1(\xi,\ y,\ \lambda,\ \mu) =\int_0^h G_2(y,\ \eta,\ \mu,\ \lambda)\left\{\sum_{i=0}^{1}\lambda^{1-i}\Phi_i(\xi,\ \eta)+\nu^2 a(\eta)\,\Phi_0(\xi,\ \eta)\right\}d\eta$$

If we substitute this into (5.4.21), we obtain

$$v(x,\ y,\ \lambda) =\int_a^b\int_0^h G(x,\ y,\ \xi,\ \eta,\ \lambda)\left\{\sum_{i=0}^{1}\lambda^{1-i}\Phi_i(\xi,\ \eta)+\nu^2 a(\eta)\,\Phi_0(\xi,\ \eta)\right\}d\xi\,d\eta$$

where

$$G(x,\ y,\ \xi,\ \eta,\ \lambda)=\frac{-1}{2\pi\sqrt{-1}}\sum_s\int_{c_s} d\mu G_1(x,\ \xi,\ \lambda,\ \mu)\,G_2(y,\ \eta,\ \mu,\ \lambda)$$

Now, let $T(y,\ \eta,\ \lambda,\ \mu)$ denote the Green's function of the spectral problem

$$\nu^2 Y''+\nu^2 b(y)\,Y'+\lambda\nu^2 a(y)\,Y=h(y)$$
$$Y'(0)=Y'(h)=0$$

By parting the variables, we seek the solution $\Delta(x,\ y, \Phi,\ \lambda)$ of the corresponding homogeneous equation (5.4.18) with boundary conditions (5.4.19) and (5.4.20) in the form of a series

$$\Delta(x,\ y,\ \Phi,\ \lambda) =\frac{-1}{2\pi\sqrt{-1}}\sum_h\int_{d_k} T(y,\ \eta,\ \lambda,\ \mu)\,Z(x,\ \eta,\ \lambda,\ \mu)\,d\eta \qquad (5.4.22)$$

For the function $\Phi_0(a, \eta)$, we have the expansion

$$\Phi_0(a, y) = \frac{-1}{2\pi\sqrt{-1}} \sum_k \int_{d_k} T(y, \eta, \lambda, \mu)\, \Phi_0(a, \eta)\, d\eta \quad (5.4.23)$$

Substituting (5.4.22) and (5.4.23) into the corresponding homogeneous equation (5.4.18) and the boundary condition (5.4.19), and separating the variables (see Section 5.2), we arrive at the spectral problem

$$\nu^2\left(\frac{d^2Z}{dx^2} + \frac{1}{x}\frac{dZ}{dx}\right) - \lambda^2 Z + \mu Z = 0$$

$$\frac{dZ(a)}{dx} + \alpha\lambda Z(a) = -\alpha\Phi_0(a, \eta)$$

$$Z(b) = 0,$$

Example 2 Consider the mixed problem (5.4.5)-(5.4.8). Let us first take the case in which $c(y) = 0$ and $\varkappa$ and α are constants. In this case, (5.4.5) is of the form

$$\frac{\partial u}{\partial t} = \varkappa\left(\frac{\partial^2 u}{\partial x^2} + \frac{1}{x}\frac{\partial u}{\partial x} + \frac{\partial^2 u}{\partial y^2}\right) \quad (5.4.24)$$

As before, we assume that $\beta(y) = 0$.

For the example in question, the first spectral problem corresponding to Problem (5.2.5)-(5.2.6) is exactly as in the preceding example. Obviously, Condition 1 of Theorem 16 is satisfied for this problem. It remains to show that the last condition of Theorem 16 is satisfied. This condition is equivalent in the present example to the uniqueness of the solution of the mixed problem

$$\frac{\partial w_{0k}}{\partial t} = \varkappa\left(\frac{\partial^2 w_{0k}}{\partial x^2} + \frac{1}{x}\frac{\partial w_{0k}}{\partial x} + \lambda_k w_{0k}\right) \quad (5.4.25)$$

$$\left.\frac{\partial w_{0k}}{\partial x}\right|_{x=a} + \alpha\left.\frac{\partial w_{0k}}{\partial t}\right|_{x=a} = 0, \quad w_{0k}(b, y, t) = 0 \quad (5.4.26)$$

$$w_{0k}(x, y, 0) = \Phi_{0k}^{(0)}(x, y) \quad (5.4.27)$$

for all k, where $\Phi_{0k}^{(0)}(x, y)$ is defined as in the preceding example.

We shall prove that the solution of Problem (5.4.25)-(5.4.27) is unique by a well-known method [54].

Let us show that the solution of Problem (5.4.25)-(5.4.27) with homogeneous initial conditions vanishes identically. (For simplicity, we shall omit the subscript to letter w.)

Suppose that $t_1 > 0$. Multiplying (5.4.25) by x gives us

$$x\frac{\partial w}{\partial t} = \varkappa\left(\frac{\partial}{\partial x}\left(x\frac{\partial w}{\partial x}\right) + \lambda_k x w\right) \tag{5.4.28}$$

If we multiply (5.4.28) by w and integrate the resulting equation with respect to t from 0 to t_1, we obtain

$$\int_0^{t_1} dt \int_a^b w\left\{x\frac{\partial w}{\partial t} - \varkappa\left(\frac{\partial}{\partial x}\left(x\frac{\partial w}{\partial x}\right) + \lambda_k x w\right)\right\} dx = 0$$

Integrating this last equation by parts gives

$$\int_a^b \left(\frac{xw^2(x, t_1)}{2} - \frac{xw^2(x, 0)}{2}\right) dx - \int_0^{t_1} \varkappa x w \frac{\partial w}{\partial x}\bigg|_a^b dt + \int_0^{t_1} dt \int_a^b \left(\varkappa x\left(\frac{\partial w}{\partial x}\right)^2 - \varkappa\lambda_k x w^2\right) dx = 0 \tag{5.4.29}$$

Remembering that

$$w(x, 0) = 0 \quad w(b, t_1) = 0$$

we obtain from (5.4.29)

$$\int_a^b xw^2(x, t_1)\, dx + \int_0^{t_1} \varkappa a w(a, t)\left(-\alpha\frac{\partial w}{\partial t}\right)_{x=a} dt + \int_0^{t_1} dt \int_a^b \left(\varkappa x\left(\frac{\partial w}{\partial x}\right)^2 - \varkappa\lambda_k x w^2\right) dx = 0$$

or

$$\int_a^b xw^2(x, t_1)\, dx - \frac{\alpha a \varkappa}{2}\left(w^2(a, t_1) - w^2(a, 0)\right) + \int_0^{t_1} dt \int_a^b \left(\varkappa x\left(\frac{\partial w}{\partial x}\right)^2 - \varkappa\lambda_k x w^2\right) dx = 0$$

Remembering that

$$w(a, 0)=0, \ \alpha<0, \ \varkappa>0, \ a>0, \ \lambda_k \leqslant 0$$

we conclude from the last equation that

$$w(x, t_1) \equiv 0$$

which completes the proof.

In accordance with Theorem 11, the solution $w_{0k}(x, y, t)$ of Problem (5.4.25)-(5.4.27) is given by

$$w_{0k}(x, y, t)$$

$$= -\frac{1}{2\pi\sqrt{-1}} \sum_s \int_{c_{sk}} e^{\mu^2 t} d\mu \int_a^b G(x, \xi, \lambda_k, \mu) \Phi_{0k}^{(0)}(\xi, y) \, d\xi$$

where c_{sk} is a closed contour encircling only one pole μ_{sk} and the summation with respect to s is over all poles of the solution of the spectral problem

$$x\left(\frac{d^2X}{dx^2}+\frac{1}{x}\frac{dX}{dx}+\lambda_k X\right)-\mu^2 X=\Phi_{0k}^{(0)}(x, y)$$

$$\frac{dX(a)}{dx}+\alpha\mu^2 X(a)=0, \quad X(b)=0$$

corresponding to Problem (5.4.25)-(5.4.27).

Thus, the solution $u(x, y, t)$ of Problem (5.4.5)-(5.4.8) is, in accordance with Theorem 16, given by

$$u(x, y, t)$$

$$=\frac{-1}{2\pi\sqrt{-1}} \sum_{k=0}^{\infty} \sum_s \int_{c_{sk}} e^{\mu^2 t} d\mu \int_a^b G(x, \xi, \lambda_k, \mu) \Phi_{0k}^{(0)}(\xi, y) \, d\xi$$

$$=\frac{-1}{2\pi\sqrt{-1}} \left\{ \sum_s \int_{c_{s0}} e^{\mu^2 t} d\mu \int_a^b G(x, \xi, \lambda_0, \mu) \frac{2}{h} \int_0^h \Phi_0(\xi, \eta) \, d\eta \right.$$

$$+\frac{4}{h} \sum_{k=1}^{\infty} \sum_s \cos\frac{k\pi}{h} y \int_{c_{sk}} e^{\mu^2 t} d\mu$$

$$\left. \times \int_a^b G(x, \xi, \lambda_k, \mu) \int_0^h \Phi_0(\xi, \eta) \cos\frac{k\pi}{h} \eta \, d\eta \right\}$$

In analogy with what was done in the case of Example 1, we can use the method of separation of variables (see Section 5.2) to construct the Green's function of the spectral problem corresponding to Problem (5.4.5)-(5.4.8) for the case of variable $\varkappa(y)$ and $c(y)$ and constant α.

Part Two

THE CONTOUR-INTEGRAL METHOD

CHAPTER 6

Contour-integral method of solving one-dimensional mixed problems for second-order equations with discontinuous coefficients

6.1 EQUATIONS CONTAINING ONLY FIRST-ORDER TIME DERIVATIVES

Consider the mixed problem of solving the equations

$$\frac{\partial v^{(i)}}{\partial t}=c_{02}^{(i)}(x)\frac{\partial^2 v^{(i)}}{\partial x^2}+c_{01}^{(i)}(x)\frac{\partial v^{(i)}}{\partial x}+c_{00}^{(i)}(x)v^{(i)}+f^{(i)}(x,\ t) \tag{6.1.1}$$

$$x\in(a_i,\ b_i)\ \ (i=1,\ 2,\ \ldots,\ n)$$

with boundary conditions

$$\sum_{i=1}^{n}\sum_{l=0}^{1}\left\{\alpha_{sl}^{(i)}\left(\frac{\partial}{\partial t}\right)\frac{\partial^l v^{(i)}}{\partial x^l}\bigg|_{x=a_i}+\beta_{sl}^{(i)}\left(\frac{\partial}{\partial t}\right)\frac{\partial^l v^{(i)}}{\partial x^l}\bigg|_{x=b_i}\right\}=\gamma_s \tag{6.1.2}$$

$$(s=1,\ 2,\ \ldots,\ 2n)$$

and initial conditions

$$v^{(i)}(x,\ 0)=\Phi^{(i)}(x),\quad x\in(a_i,\ b_i)\quad (i=1,\ \ldots,\ n) \tag{6.1.3}$$

where the (a_i, b_i) are disjoint intervals with common endpoints, $\alpha_{sl}^{(i)}(z)$ and $\beta_{sl}^{(i)}(z)$ are first-degree polynomials in z,

$$\alpha_{sl}^{(i)}(z)=\sum_{k=0}^{1}\alpha_{slk}^{(i)}z^k, \quad \beta_{sl}^{(i)}(z)=\sum_{k=0}^{1}\beta_{slk}^{(i)}z^k$$

γ_s, $\alpha_{slk}^{(i)}$ and $\beta_{slk}^{(i)}$ are constants and $c_{0s}^{(i)}(x)$ are in general complex functions.

Let us suppose that the following conditions are satisfied.

A. The functions $c_{0k}^{(i)}(x)$ are $2-k$ times (for $k=0, 1, 2$) continuously differentiable on the interval $[a_i, b_i]$; also, $c_{02}^{(i)}(x)$ does not vanish, and the arguments of the θ-roots

$$\varphi_1^{(i)}(x)=\sqrt{\frac{1}{c_{02}^{(i)}(x)}}, \quad \varphi_2^{(i)}(x)=-\sqrt{\frac{1}{c_{02}^{(i)}(x)}}$$

of the equation $\theta^2-\dfrac{1}{c_{02}^{(i)}(x)}=0$ are independent of x and of the index i.*

B. Suppose that

$$A_{ks}^{(i)}(\lambda)=\sum_{l=0}^{1}\alpha_{kl}^{(i)}(\lambda^2)(\lambda\varphi_s^{(i)}(a_i))^l \quad B_{ks}^{(i)}(\lambda)=\sum_{l=0}^{1}\beta_{kl}^{(i)}(\lambda^2)(\lambda\varphi_s^{(i)}(b_i))^l$$

It is assumed that the determinants

$$\begin{vmatrix} B_{11}^{(1)}(\lambda) & A_{12}^{(1)}(\lambda) & B_{11}^{(2)}(\lambda) & A_{12}^{(2)}(\lambda) & \ldots B_{11}^{(n)}(\lambda) & A_{12}^{(n)}(\lambda) \\ \cdots & \cdots & \cdots & \cdots & \cdots & \cdots \\ B_{2n,1}^{(1)}(\lambda) & A_{2n,2}^{(1)}(\lambda) & B_{2n,1}^{(2)}(\lambda) & A_{2n,2}^{(2)}(\lambda) & \ldots B_{2n,1}^{(n)}(\lambda) & A_{2n,2}^{(n)}(\lambda) \end{vmatrix}$$

$$\begin{vmatrix} A_{11}^{(1)}(\lambda) & B_{12}^{(1)}(\lambda) & A_{11}^{(2)}(\lambda) & B_{12}^{(2)}(\lambda) & \ldots A_{11}^{(n)}(\lambda) & B_{12}^{(n)}(\lambda) \\ \cdots & \cdots & \cdots & \cdots & \cdots & \cdots \\ A_{2n,1}^{(1)}(\lambda) & B_{2n,2}^{(1)}(\lambda) & A_{2n,1}^{(2)}(\lambda) & B_{2n,2}^{(2)}(\lambda) & \ldots A_{2n,1}^{(n)}(\lambda) & B_{2n,2}^{(n)}(\lambda) \end{vmatrix}$$

are polynomials in λ, all of the same degree d and none of them identically zero. All determinants of order $2n$ composed of other combinations of the columns

$$\begin{pmatrix} A_{1s}^{(k)}(\lambda) \\ \cdot \\ \cdot \\ \cdot \\ A_{2n,s}^{(k)}(\lambda) \end{pmatrix}, \quad \begin{pmatrix} B_{1s}^{(k)}(\lambda) \\ \cdot \\ \cdot \\ \cdot \\ B_{2n,s}^{(k)}(\lambda) \end{pmatrix} \quad (k=1, \ldots, n;\ s=1, 2)$$

*Clearly, for this it is necessary and sufficient that $c_{02}^{(i)}(x) = c\omega^{(i)}(x)$, where $\omega^{(i)}(x) > 0$, and c is a constant.

are polynomials of degree not exceeding d. All determinants of order $2n-1$ composed of elements of the matrix

$$\begin{pmatrix} A_{11}^{(1)}(\lambda) & A_{12}^{(1)}(\lambda) & \ldots A_{11}^{(n)}(\lambda) & A_{12}^{(n)}(\lambda) & B_{11}^{(1)}(\lambda) & B_{12}^{(1)}(\lambda) & \ldots B_{11}^{(n)}(\lambda) & B_{12}^{(n)}(\lambda) \\ \cdots & \cdots & \cdots & \cdots & \cdots & \cdots & \cdots & \cdots \\ A_{2n,1}^{(1)}(\lambda) & A_{2n,2}^{(1)}(\lambda) & \ldots A_{2n,1}^{(n)}(\lambda) & A_{2n,2}^{(n)}(\lambda) & B_{2n,1}^{(1)}(\lambda) & B_{2n,2}^{(1)}(\lambda) & \ldots B_{2n,1}^{(n)}(\lambda) & B_{2n,2}^{(n)}(\lambda) \end{pmatrix}$$

are also polynomials of degree not exceeding d.

6.2 ASYMPTOTIC REPRESENTATION OF THE SOLUTION OF A SPECTRAL PROBLEM OUTSIDE A δ-NEIGHBOURHOOD OF THE SPECTRUM

According to a rule given in [40d], we set up the spectral problem corresponding to Problem (6.1.1)-(6.1.3)

$$c_{02}^{(i)}(x)\frac{d^2y^{(i)}}{dx^2}+c_{01}^{(i)}(x)\frac{dy^{(i)}}{dx}+c_{00}^{(i)}(x)y^{(i)}-\lambda^2y^{(i)}=\Phi^{(i)}(x) \qquad (6.2.1)$$

$$\sum_{i=1}^{n}\sum_{l=0}^{1}\left\{\alpha_{sl}^{(i)}(\lambda^2)\frac{d^ly^{(i)}}{dx^l}\bigg|_{x=a_i}+\beta_{sl}^{(i)}(\lambda^2)\frac{d^ly^{(i)}}{dx^l}\bigg|_{x=b_i}\right\}=\gamma_s$$
$$(i=1,2,\ldots,n;\ s=1,2,\ldots,2n) \qquad (6.2.2)$$

For simplicity in writing, we introduce the notation

$$L_s^{(i)}(y^{(i)})\equiv\sum_{l=0}^{1}\left\{\alpha_{sl}^{(i)}(\lambda^2)\frac{d^ly^{(i)}}{dx^l}\bigg|_{x=a_i}+\beta_{sl}^{(i)}(\lambda^2)\frac{d^ly^{(i)}}{dx^l}\bigg|_{x=b_i}\right\} \qquad (6.2.3)$$

Suppose that $y_s^{(i)}(x,\lambda)$ (for $s=1,\ 2$) is a fundamental system of particular solutions of the homogeneous equation corresponding to (6.2.1). By the method of variation of parameters, we then obtain for the general solution of the non-homogeneous equation (6.2.1) the following representation:

$$y^{(i)}=B_{11}^{(i)}y_1^{(i)}(x,\lambda)+B_{21}^{(i)}y_2^{(i)}(x,\lambda)$$
$$+\int_a^x\frac{y_1^{(i)}(x,\lambda)W_{21}^{(i)}(\xi,\lambda)+y_2^{(i)}(x,\lambda)W_{22}^{(i)}(\xi,\lambda)}{c_{02}^{(i)}(\xi)W^{(i)}(\xi,\lambda)}\Phi^{(i)}(\xi)\,d\xi \qquad (6.2.4)$$

where the $B_{k1}^{(i)}$ (for $k=1,2$) are arbitrary constants, where

$$W^{(i)}(\xi, \lambda) = \begin{vmatrix} y_1^{(i)}(\xi, \lambda) & y_2^{(i)}(\xi, \lambda) \\ \dfrac{dy_1^{(i)}(\xi, \lambda)}{d\xi} & \dfrac{dy_2^{(i)}(\xi, \lambda)}{d\xi} \end{vmatrix} \qquad (6.2.5)$$

and $W_{21}^{(i)}(\xi, \lambda)$ and $W_{22}^{(i)}(\xi, \lambda)$ are the cofactors of the corresponding elements in the Wronskian determinant (6.2.5).

When we use the method of variation of parameters, if we take as lower limit of integration the right-hand endpoint of the interval (a_i, b_i), we obtain the following representation for the general solution of (6.2.1)

$$y^{(i)} = B_{12}^{(i)} y_1^{(i)}(x, \lambda) + B_{22}^{(i)} y_2^{(i)}(x, \lambda) + \int_{b_i}^{x} \frac{y_1^{(i)}(x, \lambda) W_{21}^{(i)}(\xi, \lambda) + y_2^{(i)}(x, \lambda) W_{22}^{(i)}(\xi, \lambda)}{c_{02}^{(i)}(\xi) W^{(i)}(\xi, \lambda)} \Phi^{(i)}(\xi)\, d\xi \qquad (6.2.6)$$

where the $B_{k2}^{(i)}$ (for $k = 1, 2$) are arbitrary constants.

Adding (6.2.4) and (6.2.6) and dividing by 2, we obtain a convenient representation for the general solution (6.2.1)

$$y^{(i)}(x, \lambda) = B_1^{(i)} y_1^{(i)}(x, \lambda) + B_2^{(i)} y_2^{(i)}(x, \lambda) + \int_{a_i}^{b_i} g^{(i)}(x, \xi, \lambda) \frac{\Phi^{(i)}(\xi)}{c_{02}^{(i)}(\xi)}\, d\xi \qquad (6.2.7)$$

where

$$B_1^{(i)} = \frac{B_{11}^{(i)} + B_{12}^{(i)}}{2}, \qquad B_2^{(i)} = \frac{B_{21}^{(i)} + B_{22}^{(i)}}{2}$$

$$g^{(i)}(x, \xi, \lambda) = \begin{cases} \dfrac{1}{2W^{(i)}(\xi, \lambda)} \begin{vmatrix} y_1^{(i)}(\xi, \lambda) & y_2^{(i)}(\xi, \lambda) \\ y_1^{(i)}(x, \lambda) & y_2^{(i)}(x, \lambda) \end{vmatrix} & \text{for } a_i \leqslant \xi \leqslant x \\ -\dfrac{1}{2W^{(i)}(\xi, \lambda)} \begin{vmatrix} y_1^{(i)}(\xi, \lambda) & y_2^{(i)}(\xi, \lambda) \\ y_1^{(i)}(x, \lambda) & y_2^{(i)}(x, \lambda) \end{vmatrix} & \text{for } x \leqslant \xi \leqslant b_i \end{cases} \qquad (6.2.8)$$

Substituting the general solution (6.2.7) into the boundary conditions (6.2.2), we obtain a system of equations for determining the constants $B_k^{(i)}$ (for $k = 1, 2$, and $i = 1, \ldots, n$)

$$u_{s1}^{(1)}(\lambda)B_1^{(1)}+u_{s2}^{(1)}(\lambda)B_2^{(1)}+\ldots+u_{s1}^{(n)}(\lambda)B_1^{(n)}+u_{s2}^{(n)}(\lambda)B_2^{(n)}$$
$$=\gamma_s-\sum_{i=1}^{n}\int_{a_i}^{b_i}L_s^{(i)}(g^{(i)}(x,\xi,\lambda))_x\,\frac{\Phi^{(i)}(\xi)}{c_{02}^{(i)}(\xi)}\,d\xi\quad(s=1,\ldots,2n)\tag{6.2.9}$$

where

$$u_{sk}^{(i)}(\lambda)=L_s^{(i)}(y_k^{(i)}(x,\lambda))$$
$$(i=1,\ldots,n;\quad s=1,\ldots,2n;\quad k=1,2)\tag{6.2.10}$$

and $L_s^{(i)}(g^{(i)})_x$ is the result obtained by applying the operator $L_s^{(i)}$ to $g^{(i)}$ as to a function of x.

When we determine the constants $B_k^{(i)}$ (for $k=1, 2$, and $i=1,\ldots,n$) from System (6.2.9), substitute them into the general solution (6.2.7) and write the resulting sum in the form of a determinant of order $2n+1$, we obtain the following formula for the solution of Problem (6.2.1)-(6.2.2)

$$y^{(i)}(x,\lambda)=\frac{\Delta^{(i)}(x,\lambda)}{\Delta(\lambda)}+\sum_{j=1}^{n}\int_{a_j}^{b_j}\frac{\Delta^{(i,j)}(x,\xi,\lambda)}{\Delta(\lambda)}\,\frac{\Phi_j(\xi)}{c_{02}^{(j)}(\xi)}\,d\xi\tag{6.2.11}$$

$$\Delta^{(i)}(x,\lambda)=$$
$$\begin{vmatrix} 0 & 0 & 0 & \ldots & 0 & 0 & y_1^{(i)} & y_2^{(i)} & \ldots & 0 & 0\\ -\gamma_1 & u_{11}^{(1)} & u_{12}^{(1)} & \ldots & u_{11}^{(i-1)} & u_{12}^{(i-1)} & u_{11}^{(i)} & u_{12}^{(i)} & \ldots & u_{11}^{(n)} & u_{12}^{(n)}\\ \cdots & \cdots & \cdots & \cdots & \cdots & \cdots & \cdots & \cdots & \cdots & \cdots & \cdots\\ -\gamma_{2n} & u_{2n,1}^{(1)} & u_{2n,2}^{(1)} & \ldots & u_{2n,1}^{(i-1)} & u_{2n,2}^{(i-1)} & u_{2n,1}^{(i)} & u_{2n,2}^{(i)} & \ldots & u_{2n,1}^{(n)} & u_{2n,2}^{(n)} \end{vmatrix}\tag{6.2.12}$$

$$\Delta^{(i,j)}(x,\xi,\lambda)=$$
$$\begin{vmatrix} g^{(i,j)}(x,\xi,\lambda) & 0 & 0 & \ldots y_1^{(i)}(x,\lambda) & y_2^{(i)}(x,\lambda) & \ldots & 0 & 0\\ L_1^{(j)}(g^{(j)})_x & u_{11}^{(1)}(\lambda) & u_{12}^{(1)}(\lambda) & \ldots u_{11}^{(i)}(\lambda) & u_{12}^{(i)}(\lambda) & \ldots & u_{11}^{(n)}(\lambda) & u_{12}^{(n)}(\lambda)\\ \cdots & \cdots & \cdots & \cdots & \cdots & \cdots & \cdots & \cdots\\ L_{2n}^{(j)}(g^{(j)})_x & u_{2n,1}^{(1)}(\lambda) & u_{2n,2}^{(1)}(\lambda) & \ldots u_{2n,1}^{(i)}(\lambda) & u_{2n,2}^{(i)}(\lambda) & \ldots & u_{2n,1}^{(n)}(\lambda) & u_{2n,2}^{(n)}(\lambda) \end{vmatrix}\tag{6.2.13}$$

$$g^{(i,j)}(x,\xi,\lambda)=\begin{cases} g^{(i)}(x,\xi,\lambda) & \text{for } j=i\\ 0 & \text{for } j\neq i\end{cases}\tag{6.2.14}$$

$$\Delta(\lambda)=\begin{vmatrix} u_{11}^{(1)}(\lambda) & u_{12}^{(1)}(\lambda) & \ldots & u_{11}^{(n)}(\lambda) & u_{12}^{(n)}(\lambda)\\ \cdot & \cdot & \ldots & \cdot & \cdot\\ \cdot & \cdot & \ldots & \cdot & \cdot\\ u_{2n,1}^{(1)}(\lambda) & u_{2n,2}^{(1)}(\lambda) & \ldots & u_{2n,1}^{(n)}(\lambda) & u_{2n,2}^{(n)}(\lambda) \end{vmatrix}\tag{6.2.15}$$

The function

$$G^{(i,j)}(x, \xi, \lambda) = \frac{\Delta^{(i,j)}(x, \xi, \lambda)}{\Delta(\lambda)} \tag{6.2.16}$$

is called the Green's function of Problem (6.2.1)-(6.2.2). With the aid of it, we can write the solution $y^{(i)}$ of Problem (6.2.1)-(6.2.2) with corresponding homogeneous boundary conditions in the form

$$y^{(i)}(x, \lambda) = \sum_{j=1}^{n} \int_{a_j}^{b_j} G^{(i,j)}(x, \xi, \lambda) \frac{\Phi^{(j)}(\xi)}{c_{02}^{(j)}(\xi)} d\xi \tag{6.2.17}$$

To obtain an asymptotic representation of the solution (6.2.11) of Problem (6.2.1)-(6.2.2), we use the following theorem of Tamarkin [46a].

Theorem 20 Suppose that we have the differential equation

$$\frac{d^n y}{dx^n} + P_1(x, \lambda) \frac{d^{n-1} y}{dx^{n-1}} + \ldots + P_n(x, \lambda) y = 0 \tag{6.2.18}$$

the coefficients in which have an expansion of the form

$$P_i(x, \lambda) = \sum_{\nu=0}^{\infty} \lambda^{i-\nu} p_{i\nu}(x), \qquad x \in [a, b]$$

for

$$|\lambda| \geqslant R \tag{6.2.19}$$

where R is a sufficiently large positive number. Suppose also that the following three conditions are satisfied.

1. At least one of the functions $p_{i0}(x)$ (for $i = 1, \ldots, n$) is not identically zero on the interval $[a, b]$.
2. The functions $p_{i\nu}(x)$ (for $\nu = 0, 1, 2, \ldots$) are continuous and uniformly bounded on $[a, b]$. The functions $\frac{dp_{i0}(x)}{dx}$ and $p_{i1}(x)$ (for $i = 1, \ldots, n$) are once continuously differentiable on $[a, b]$.
3. The θ-roots of the characteristic equation

$$f(\theta) = \theta^n + p_{10}(x)\theta^{n-1} + \ldots + p_{n-10}(x)\theta + p_{n0}(x) = 0 \tag{6.2.20}$$

are distinct for all $x \in [a, b]$.

Let Ω denote an unbounded portion of the region (6.2.19) in which the inequalities

$$\operatorname{Re}\lambda\varphi_1(x) \leqslant \operatorname{Re}\lambda\varphi_2(x) \leqslant \ldots \leqslant \operatorname{Re}\lambda\varphi_n(x) \qquad (6.2.21)$$

are satisfied for a suitable numbering of the roots $\varphi_1(x), \ldots, \varphi_n(x)$ of the characteristic equation (6.2.20).

Under the above conditions, (6.2.18) has a fundamental system of particular solutions $y_s(x, \lambda)$ (for $s = 1, \ldots, n$) which together with their first $n-1$ derivatives, have asymptotic representations of the form

$$\frac{d^m y_s(x, \lambda)}{dx^m}$$

$$= \lambda^m \left\{\eta_{s0m}(x) + \frac{\eta_{s1m}(x)}{\lambda} + \frac{E_{sm}(x, \lambda)}{\lambda^2}\right\} \exp\left\{\lambda \int_a^x \varphi_s(\xi)\, d\xi\right\} \quad (6.2.22)$$

$$(m = 0, \ldots, n-1)$$

The coefficients $\eta_{skm}(x)$ can be obtained by differentiating

$$\left\{\eta_{s00}(x) + \frac{\eta_{s10}(x)}{\lambda}\right\} \exp\left\{\lambda \int_a^x \varphi_s(\xi)\, d\xi\right\}$$

and expanding the result in decreasing powers of λ. Furthermore, on the interval $[a, b]$, the functions $\eta_{sk0}(x)$ have continuous derivatives of the first $2-k$ orders (for $k = 0, 1$), the $E_{sm}(x, \lambda)$ are continuous with respect to x and bounded for $\lambda \in \Omega$, and the functions $\eta_{s00}(x)$ are given by

$$\eta_{s00}(x) = \frac{1}{\sqrt{f'(\varphi_s)}} \exp\left\{-\int_a^x \frac{f_1(\varphi_s)}{\left.\dfrac{df(\theta)}{d\theta}\right|_{\theta=\varphi_s(\xi)}} d\xi\right\} \qquad (6.2.23)$$

where

$$f_1(\theta) = p_{11}(x)\,\theta^{n-1} + p_{21}(x)\,\theta^{n-2} + \ldots + p_{n-11}(x)\,\theta + p_{n1}(x)$$

In accordance with Condition A of Section 6.1, the argument of the θ-roots of the characteristic equation

$$f(\theta) = \theta^2 - \frac{1}{c_{02}^{(i)}(x)} = 0 \qquad (6.2.24)$$

are independent both of x and the index i. Consequently, $c_{02}^{(i)}(x)$ is a function of the form

$$c_{02}^{(i)}(x) = |c_{02}^{(i)}(x)|\, c$$

where

$$c = \exp\left(\sqrt{-1}\arg c_{02}^{(i)}(x)\right) = e^{\sqrt{-1}\gamma}$$

Therefore, the characteristic equation (6.2.24) has the roots

$$\begin{aligned} \theta_1^{(i)} &= \frac{1}{\sqrt{|c_{02}^{(i)}(x)|}} \exp\left(-\sqrt{-1}\frac{\gamma}{2}\right) \\ \theta_2^{(i)} &= -\frac{1}{\sqrt{|c_{02}^{(i)}(x)|}} \exp\left(-\sqrt{-1}\frac{\gamma}{2}\right) \end{aligned} \tag{6.2.25}$$

On the basis of Condition A of Section 6.1, the set of values λ satisfying the equation

$$\operatorname{Re} \lambda\theta_1^{(i)} = \operatorname{Re} \lambda\theta_2^{(i)} \tag{6.2.26}$$

constitutes a straight line passing through the coordinate origin of the λ-plane. To see this, note that (6.2.26) is equivalent to

$$\frac{1}{\sqrt{|c_{02}^{(i)}(x)|}} \cos\left(-\frac{\gamma}{2} + \arg\lambda\right) = 0$$

which, in accordance with Condition A, leads to the equation

$$\cos\left(-\frac{\gamma}{2} + \arg\lambda\right) = 0$$

Therefore, we have

$$\arg\lambda = \pm\frac{\pi}{2} + \frac{\gamma}{2}$$

This last equation is the equation of the straight line referred to above (see Fig. 2). This straight line divides the λ-plane into two half-planes Π_1 and Π_2. (In the figure, Π_2 is shown by the shading.)

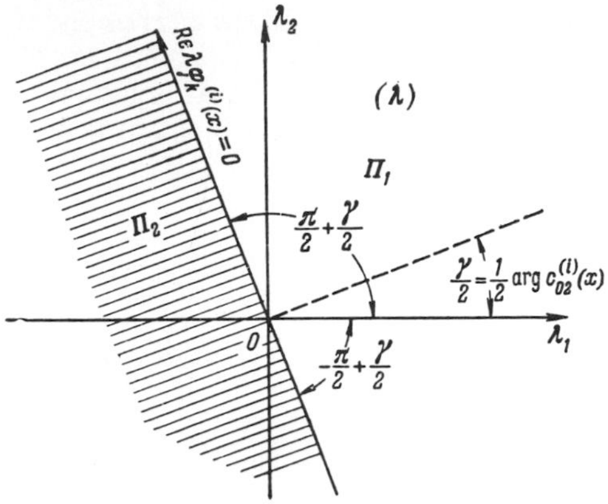

Fig. 2

It is clear that

$$\operatorname{Re}\lambda\theta_1^{(i)}=\frac{|\lambda|}{\sqrt{|c_{02}^{(i)}(x)|}}\cos\left(-\frac{\gamma}{2}+\arg\lambda\right)$$
$$\operatorname{Re}\lambda\theta_2^{(i)}=-\frac{|\lambda|}{\sqrt{|c_{02}^{(i)}x|}}\cos\left(-\frac{\gamma}{2}+\arg\lambda\right) \tag{6.2.27}$$

As can be seen from these relations, in Π_2 we have the inequalities $\operatorname{Re}\lambda\theta_1^{(i)}\leqslant 0$, and $\operatorname{Re}\lambda\theta_2^{(i)}\geqslant 0$. Consequently, if the roots (6.2.25) of the characteristic equation are numbered in such a way that

$$\varphi_1^{(i)}(x)=\theta_1^{(i)},\quad \varphi_2^{(i)}(x)=\theta_2^{(i)}$$

then the inequalities

$$\operatorname{Re}\lambda\varphi_1^{(i)}(x)\leqslant\operatorname{Re}\lambda\varphi_2^{(i)}(x) \tag{6.2.28}$$

will be satisfied in the half-plane Π_2.

It is clear from (6.2.27) that for (6.2.28) to be maintained in the half-plane Π_1, the roots (6.2.25) of the characteristic equation (6.2.24) should be numbered as

$$\varphi_1^{(i)}(x)=\theta_2^{(i)},\qquad \varphi_2^{(i)}(x)=\theta_1^{(i)}$$

Thus, for homogeneous equations corresponding to (6.2.1), all the conditions of Theorem 20 are satisfied. Consequently, these equations have a fundamental system of particular solutions $y_1^{(i)}(x, \lambda)$ and $y_2^{(i)}(x, \lambda)$ with asymptotic representations

$$\frac{d^m y_s^{(i)}(x, \lambda)}{dx^m} = \lambda^m \left\{ \eta_{s0m}^{(i)}(x) + \frac{\eta_{s1m}^{(i)}(x)}{\lambda} + \frac{E_{sm}^{(i)}(x, \lambda)}{\lambda^2} \right\} \exp\left\{ \lambda \int_{a_i}^{x} \varphi_s^{(i)}(\xi)\, d\xi \right\} \quad (6.2.29)$$

$$(m = 0, 1, 2)$$

both in the half-plane Π_2 and in the half-plane Π_1, where

$$\begin{gathered} \eta_{s0m}^{(i)}(x) = (\varphi_s^{(i)}(x))^m \eta_{s0}^{(i)}(x) \\ \eta_{s0}^{(i)}(x) = \frac{1}{\sqrt{2\varphi_s^{(i)}(x)}} \exp\left(- \int_{a_i}^{x} \frac{c_{01}^{(i)}(\xi)}{2c_{02}^{(i)}(\xi)}\, d\xi \right) \end{gathered} \quad (6.2.30)$$

$$\eta_{s1m}^{(i)}(x) = \begin{cases} \eta_{s1}^{(i)}(x) & \text{for} \quad m = 0 \\ \varphi_s^{(i)}(x)\, \eta_{s1}^{(i)}(x) + \dfrac{d\eta_{s0}^{(i)}}{dx} & \text{for} \quad m = 1 \\ \dfrac{\eta_{s1}^{(i)}(x) - c_{01}^{(i)}(x)\, \varphi_s^{(i)}(x) \eta_{s0}^{(i)}(x)}{c_{02}^{(i)}(x)} & \text{for} \quad m = 2 \end{cases} \quad (6.2.31)$$

On the interval $[a_i, b_i]$, the functions $\eta_{sk}^{(i)}(x)$ have continuous derivatives of the first $2-k$ orders (for $k = 0, 1$) and the $E_{s\,m}^{(i)}(x, \lambda)$ are continuous with respect to x and bounded for large values of λ. Here, it should be pointed out that the asymptotic formula (6.2.29) is obtained for $m = 2$ from the homogeneous equation corresponding to Equation (6.2.1) by substituting into it the representations (6.2.29) for $m = 0, 1$.

With the aid of the (6.2.29), we can derive asymptotic formulae for the elements $u_{kj}^{(i)}(\lambda)$ of the determinant (6.2.15). If we substitute (6.2.29) into (6.2.10) and keep (6.2.3) in mind, we obtain the asymptotic formulae

$$
\left.\begin{aligned}
u_{k1}^{(i)}(\lambda) &= A_{k1}^{(i)}(\lambda)\,[\eta_{10}^{(i)}(a_i)] \\
&\quad + B_{k1}^{(i)}(\lambda)\,[\eta_{10}^{(i)}(b_i)]\exp\left(-\lambda\frac{\omega^{(i)}}{\sqrt{c}}\right) \\
u_{k2}^{(i)}(\lambda) &= A_{k2}^{(i)}(\lambda)\,[\eta_{20}^{(i)}(a_i)] \\
&\quad + B_{k2}^{(i)}(\lambda)\,[\eta_{20}^{(i)}(b_i)]\exp\left(\lambda\frac{\omega^{(i)}}{\sqrt{c}}\right)
\end{aligned}\right. \tag{6.2.32}
$$

which are valid in the half-plane Π_1, where an expression of the form $[\psi]$ denotes the sum $\psi+\frac{E(\lambda)}{\lambda}$. Here, the function $E(\lambda)$ is bounded for large values of λ and

$$
\omega^{(i)} = \int_{a_i}^{b_i} \frac{1}{\sqrt{|c_{02}^{(i)}(x)|}}\,dx \tag{6.2.33}
$$

Substituting (6.2.32) into (6.2.15) and expanding the resulting determinant into the sum of $2n$th-order determinants in which all the exponentials can be taken outside the determinants since they are common factors of the elements of the columns, we obtain

$$
\Delta(\lambda) = M_1(\lambda)\,e^{m_1\frac{\lambda}{\sqrt{c}}} + M_2(\lambda)\,e^{m_2\frac{\lambda}{\sqrt{c}}} + \ldots + M_\sigma(\lambda)\,e^{m_\sigma\frac{\lambda}{\sqrt{c}}} \tag{6.2.34}
$$

where

$$
\left.\begin{aligned}
m_1 &= -(\omega^{(1)}+\omega^{(2)}+\ \ldots\ +\omega^{(n)}) \\
m_\sigma &= (\omega^{(1)}+\omega^{(2)}+\ \ldots\ +\omega^{(n)})
\end{aligned}\right\} \tag{6.2.35}
$$

$$
M_\sigma(\lambda) = K_\sigma \begin{vmatrix}
A_{11}^{(1)}(\lambda) & B_{12}^{(1)}(\lambda) & A_{11}^{(2)}(\lambda) & B_{12}^{(2)}(\lambda) \ldots & A_{11}^{(n)}(\lambda) & B_{12}^{(n)}(\lambda) \\
\cdot & \cdot & \cdot & \cdot & \cdot & \cdot \\
A_{2n,1}^{(1)}(\lambda) & B_{2n,2}^{(1)}(\lambda) & A_{2n,1}^{(2)}(\lambda) & B_{2n,2}^{(2)}(\lambda) \ldots & A_{2n,1}^{(n)}(\lambda) & B_{2n,2}^{(n)}(\lambda)
\end{vmatrix} \tag{6.2.36}
$$

$$
M_1(\lambda) = K_1 \begin{vmatrix}
B_{11}^{(1)}(\lambda) & A_{12}^{(1)}(\lambda) & \ldots & B_{11}^{(n)}(\lambda) & A_{12}^{(n)}(\lambda) \\
\cdot & \cdot & \cdot & \cdot & \cdot \\
B_{2n,1}^{(1)}(\lambda) & A_{2n,2}^{(1)}(\lambda) & \ldots & B_{2n,1}^{(n)}(\lambda) & A_{2n,2}^{(n)}(\lambda)
\end{vmatrix} \tag{6.2.37}
$$

$$M_s(\lambda) = K_s P_s(\lambda) \qquad (s \neq 1, \sigma) \tag{6.2.38}$$

$$\left.\begin{aligned} K_1 &= [\eta_{10}^{(1)}(b_1)]\,[\eta_{20}^{(1)}(a_1)]\,\ldots\,[\eta_{10}^{(n)}(b_n)]\,[\eta_{20}^{(n)}(a_n)] \\ K_\sigma &= [\eta_{10}^{(1)}(a_1)]\,[\eta_{20}^{(1)}(b_1)]\,\ldots\,[\eta_{10}^{(n)}(a_n)]\,[\eta_{20}^{(n)}(b_n)] \end{aligned}\right\} \tag{6.2.39}$$

The $P_s(\lambda)$ are $2n$th-order determinants made up of all possible combinations of the columns of the matrix

$$\begin{pmatrix} A_{11}^{(1)}(\lambda) & A_{12}^{(1)}(\lambda) \ldots & A_{11}^{(n)}(\lambda) & A_{12}^{(n)}(\lambda) & B_{11}^{(1)}(\lambda) & B_{12}^{(1)}(\lambda) \ldots & B_{11}^{(n)}(\lambda) & B_{12}^{(n)}(\lambda) \\ \cdots & \cdots & \cdots & \cdots & \cdots & \cdots & \cdots & \cdots \\ A_{2n,1}^{(1)}(\lambda) & A_{2n,2}^{(1)}(\lambda) \ldots & A_{2n,1}^{(n)}(\lambda) & A_{2n,2}^{(n)}(\lambda) & B_{2n,1}^{(1)}(\lambda) & B_{2n,2}^{(1)}(\lambda) \ldots & B_{2n,1}^{(n)}(\lambda) & B_{2n,2}^{(n)}(\lambda) \end{pmatrix} \tag{6.2.40}$$

and K_s is a product of n factors consisting of all possible combinations of the expressions

$$[\eta_{ks}^{(i)}(a_i)], \quad [\eta_{ks}^{(i)}(b_i)]$$

The terms of the polynomial (6.2.34) are arranged in order of increase of the numbers m_k

$$m_1 < m_2 < \ldots < m_\sigma \tag{6.2.41}$$

In accordance with Condition A of Section 6.1, the determinants in the right-hand side of (6.2.36) and (6.2.37) are polynomials of the same degree d and are not identically zero; the determinants $P_s(\lambda)$ (where $s \neq 1, \sigma$) are polynomials of degree not exceeding d. Therefore, if we denote by l_1 and l_σ, respectively, the coefficients of highest powers of λ in the polynomials obtained by expanding the determinants (6.2.36) and (6.2.37), we have

$$M_s(\lambda) = \lambda^d [M_s] \tag{6.2.42}$$

where

$$\begin{aligned} M_1 &= l_1 \eta_{10}^{(1)}(b_1)\, \eta_{20}^{(1)}(a_1)\, \ldots\, \eta_{10}^{(n)}(b_n)\, \eta_{20}^{(n)}(a_n) \\ M_\sigma &= l_\sigma \eta_{10}^{(1)}(a_1)\, \eta_{20}^{(1)}(b_1)\, \ldots\, \eta_{10}^{(n)}(a_n)\, \eta_{20}^{(n)}(b_n) \end{aligned}$$

and M_s (for $s \neq 1, \sigma$) are constants.

As can be seen from (6.2.30), M_1 and M_σ are non-zero

$$M_1 \neq 0, \quad M_\sigma \neq 0 \tag{6.2.43}$$

Substituting (6.2.42) into (6.2.34), we obtain

$$\Delta(\lambda) = \lambda^d H(z) \tag{6.2.44}$$

where

$$H(z) = [M_1]\, e^{m_1 z} + [M_2]\, e^{m_2 z} + \ldots + [M_\sigma]\, e^{m_\sigma z} \tag{6.2.45}$$

$$z = \frac{\lambda}{\sqrt{c}} \tag{6.2.46}$$

With regard to the exponential polynomial with asymptotically constant analytic coefficients in Section 3.1, we have proved Lemma 1.

Lemma 1 If $H(z)$ is an analytic function in some infinite strip of the z-plane with boundaries parallel to the imaginary axis, then, when Conditions (6.2.41) and (6.2.43) are satisfied, the function $H(z)$ has a countable set of zeros. All the zeros of this function lie in a strip D_h bounded by the width with centre at the coordinate origin in the z-plane the boundaries of which are parallel to the imaginary axis.

If we denote by N the number of zeros $H(z)$ located within the rectangle defined by the inequalities

$$\begin{gathered} -\frac{h}{2} \leqslant \operatorname{Re} z \leqslant +\frac{h}{2} \\ y_1 \leqslant \operatorname{Im} z \leqslant y_2 \end{gathered} \tag{6.2.47}$$

(where y_1 and y_2 are real numbers), then

$$\begin{aligned} &\frac{1}{2\pi}(m_\sigma - m_1)(y_2 - y_1) - \sigma \leqslant N \\ &\leqslant \frac{1}{2\pi}(m_\sigma - m_1)(y_2 - y_1) + \sigma \end{aligned} \tag{6.2.48}$$

If we delete from the strip D_h the interiors of small circles Q_{δ_h}, then the inequality

$$|H(z)| \geqslant C_\delta$$

where $C_\delta > 0$ and depends on the choice of δ, is satisfied in the remaining portion $D_h(\delta)$ of the strip D_h.

If the zeros z_k (for $k = 1, 2, \ldots$) of the function $H(z)$ are numbered in increasing order of their absolute values, then the following asymptotic representation holds for them

$$|z_k| = \frac{2k\pi}{m_\sigma - m_1}\left(1 + O\left(\frac{1}{k}\right)\right)$$

Obviously, (6.2.46) maps the strip D_h in the z-plane into a strip D_{h1} in the λ-plane in which all the assertions of Lemma 1 with regard to the function $\lambda^{-d}\Delta(\lambda)$ remain valid, since the strip D_{h1} is obtained from the strip D_h by a rotation around the coordinate origin through an angle

$$\frac{\gamma}{2} = \frac{1}{2}\arg c_{02}^{(i)}(x)$$

Thus, from Lemma 1 we have Theorem 21.

Theorem 21 Under Conditions A and B of Section 6.1, all the zeros of the function $\Delta(\lambda)$ are located in the strip D_{h1}. The number N of zeros of the function $\lambda^{-d}\Delta(\lambda)$ which are located within the rectangle of the strip D_{h1} corresponding to the rectangle (6.2.47) of the strip D_h satisfies (6.2.48).

If we delete from the λ-plane the interiors of small circles $Q_{\delta k}^{(1)}$ with centres at the zeros λ_k of the function $\Delta(\lambda)$, then the inequality

$$\left|H\left(\frac{\lambda}{\sqrt{c}}\right)\right| = |\lambda^{-d}\Delta(\lambda)| \geqslant C_\delta > 0$$

will be satisfied in the remaining portion of the λ-plane.

If the zeros λ_k of the function $\Delta(\lambda)$ are numbered in increasing order of their absolute values, then the following asymptotic representation holds for them

$$|\lambda_k| = \frac{2k\pi}{m_\sigma - m_1}\left(1 + O\left(\frac{1}{k}\right)\right) \qquad (6.2.49)$$

Now, to obtain an asymptotic representation of the first term in the right-hand side of (6.2.11), we expand the determinant in its numerator in terms of elements of the first row and first column,

$$\Delta^{(i)}(x,\lambda)=y_1^{(i)}(x,\lambda)\sum_{k=1}^{2n}\gamma_k\Delta_{k,\,2i-1}(\lambda)$$
$$+y_2^{(i)}(x,\lambda)\sum_{k=1}^{2n}\gamma_k\Delta_{k,\,2i}(\lambda) \tag{6.2.50}$$

Here, $\Delta_{k,\,s}(\lambda)$ denotes the cofactor of the corresponding element of the determinant $\Delta(\lambda)$.

It follows from (6.2.50) that, to obtain the asymptotic representation $\Delta^{(i)}(x, \lambda)$, we need to have the asymptotic representation for $\Delta_{k,\,2i-1}(\lambda)$ and $\Delta_{k,\,2i}(\lambda)$.

We note that to solve the spectral problem (6.2.1)-(6.2.2), it is important to obtain such representations in which the elements that increase in the half-planes Π_1 and Π_2 are singled out. We call such representations 'asymptotic representations'.

The elements $u_{ks}^{(i)}(\lambda)$ of the determinant $\Delta(\lambda)$ have asymptotic representations of the form (6.2.32). Obviously,

$$\operatorname{Re}\lambda\frac{\omega^{(i)}}{\sqrt{c}}=|\lambda|\,\omega^{(i)}\cos\left(-\frac{\gamma}{2}+\arg\lambda\right) \tag{6.2.51}$$

From Equation (6.2.51), we see that the real part of $\lambda\frac{\omega^{(i)}}{\sqrt{c}}$ is negative in Π_1 and positive in Π_2. Consequently, in Π_2 tne exponential function $\left(-\lambda\frac{\omega^{(i)}}{\sqrt{c}}\right)$ decreases and $\exp\left(\lambda\frac{\omega^{(i)}}{\sqrt{c}}\right)$ increases as $|\lambda|\to+\infty$. In Π_1, the function $\exp\left(-\lambda\frac{\omega^{(i)}}{\sqrt{c}}\right)$ increases and $\exp\left(\lambda\frac{\omega^{(i)}}{\sqrt{c}}\right)$ decreases. It should be noted in this connection that there are no elements of the form

$$A_{k2}^{(i)}(\lambda)\,[\eta_{20}^{(i)}(a_i)]$$
$$+\,B_{k2}^{(i)}(\lambda)\,[\eta_{20}^{(i)}(b_i)]\exp\left(\frac{\lambda\omega^{(i)}}{\sqrt{c}}\right)$$

in $\Delta_{k,\,2i}(\lambda)$. Therefore, when we substitute the expressions for the elements $u_{k1}^{(i)}(\lambda)$ and $u_{k2}^{(i)}(\lambda)$ given by (6.2.32) into

$\Delta_{k,\,2i-1}(\lambda)$ and $\Delta_{k,\,2i}(\lambda)$ and then we represent the resulting determinant in the form of the sum of $(2n-1)$th-order determinants (in which the exponential functions, being common factors of elements of the columns, can be taken outside the determinants), we obtain, keeping in mind Condition B of Section 6.1, the following inequalities

$$|\Delta_{k,\,2i-1}(\lambda)| \leqslant C|\lambda|^d \left|\exp\left[\frac{\lambda}{\sqrt{c}}\sum_{j=1}^{n}\omega^{(j)}\right]\right|$$

$$|\Delta_{k,\,2i}(\lambda)| \leqslant C|\lambda|^d \left|\exp\left[\frac{\lambda}{\sqrt{c}}\left(\sum_{j=1}^{n}\omega^{(j)}-\omega^{(i)}\right)\right]\right|$$

which are valid in the half-plane Π_1, where C is a constant. In the notations of (6.2.35), these inequalities can be written

$$\left.\begin{aligned} &|\Delta_{k,\,2i-1}(\lambda)| \leqslant C|\lambda|^d \left|\exp\left(m_\sigma\frac{\lambda}{\sqrt{c}}\right)\right| \\ &|\Delta_{k,\,2i}(\lambda)| \leqslant C|\lambda|^d \left|\exp\left((m_\sigma-\omega^{(i)})\frac{\lambda}{\sqrt{c}}\right)\right| \end{aligned}\right\} \qquad (6.2.52)$$

Since we take $\theta_1^{(i)}(x)$ for $\varphi_1^{(i)}(x)$ and $\theta_2^{(i)}(x)$ for $\varphi_2^{(i)}(x)$ (see (6.2.25)) in the half-plane Π_2, we have the following asymptotic representations for $u_{k1}^{(i)}(\lambda)$ and $u_{k2}^{(i)}(\lambda)$:

$$u_{k1}^{(i)}(\lambda) = A_{k1}^{(i)}(\lambda)\,[\eta_{10}^{(i)}(a_i)] + B_{k1}^{(i)}(\lambda)\,[\eta_{10}^{i}(b_i)]\,e^{\lambda\frac{\omega^{(i)}}{\sqrt{c}}}$$

$$u_{k2}^{(i)}(\lambda) = A_{k2}^{(i)}(\lambda)[\,\eta_{20}^{(i)}(a_i)] + B_{k2}^{(i)}(\lambda)\,[\eta_{20}^{(i)}(b_i)]\,e^{-\lambda\frac{\omega^{(i)}}{\sqrt{c}}}$$

In connection with this, we obtain the following inequalities in the half-plane Π_2

$$\left.\begin{aligned} &|\Delta_{k,\,2i-1}(\lambda)| \leqslant C|\lambda|^d \left|e^{m_1\frac{\lambda}{\sqrt{c}}}\right| \\ &|\Delta_{k,\,2i}(\lambda)| \leqslant C|\lambda|^d \left|\exp\left((m_1+\omega^{(i)})\frac{\lambda}{\sqrt{c}}\right)\right| \end{aligned}\right\} \qquad (6.2.53)$$

Bearing in mind (6.2.44)-(6.2.46), we get the following inequality from (6.2.50) with the aid of the asymptotic representations (6.2.29) and inequalities (6.2.52)

$$\left|\frac{1}{\Delta(\lambda)}\frac{d^m\Delta^{(i)}(x,\lambda)}{dx^m}\right|$$

$$=\left|\lambda^m[\eta_{10m}^{(i)}(x)]\exp\left(\lambda\int_{a_i}^{x}\varphi_1^{(i)}(\xi)\,d\xi\right)\sum_{k=1}^{2n}\gamma_k\frac{\Delta_{k,\,2i-1}(\lambda)}{\Delta(\lambda)}\right.$$

$$\left.+\lambda^m[\eta_{20m}^{(i)}(x)]\exp\left(\lambda\int_{a_i}^{x}\varphi_2^{(i)}(\xi)\,d\xi\right)\sum_{k=1}^{2n}\gamma_k\frac{\Delta_{k,\,2i}(\lambda)}{\Delta(\lambda)}\right|$$

$$\leqslant 2n\max|\gamma_k|C|\lambda|^m\left\{\frac{\left|\lambda^d e^{m_\sigma\frac{\lambda}{\sqrt{c}}}\right|}{|\Delta(\lambda)|}|[\eta_{10m}^{(i)}(x)]|\right. \tag{6.2.54}$$

$$\times\left|\exp\left(\lambda\int_{a_i}^{x}\varphi_1^{(i)}(\xi)\,d\xi\right)\right|+\frac{\left|\lambda^d\exp\left[(m_\sigma-\omega^{(i)}),\frac{\lambda}{\sqrt{c}}\right]\right|}{|\Delta(\lambda)|}|[\eta_{20m}^{(i)}(x)]|$$

$$\left.\times\left|\exp\left(\lambda\int_{a_i}^{x}\varphi_2^{(i)}(\xi)\,d\xi\right)\right|\right\}$$

$$\leqslant 2n\max|\gamma_k|C|\lambda|^m\left\{\frac{\left|e^{m_\sigma\frac{\lambda}{\sqrt{c}}}\right|}{\left|H\left(\frac{\lambda}{\sqrt{c}}\right)\right|}C_1\left|\exp\left(\lambda\int_{a_i}^{x}\varphi_1^{(i)}(\xi)\,d\xi\right)\right|\right.$$

$$\left.+\frac{\left|e^{m_\sigma\frac{\lambda}{\sqrt{c}}}\right|}{\left|H\left(\frac{\lambda}{\sqrt{c}}\right)\right|}C_2\left|\exp\left(-\lambda\int_{x}^{b_i}\varphi_2^{(i)}(\xi)\,d\xi\right)\right|\right\}$$

which is valid in Π_1. Here, the C_k are constants and

$$\varphi_1^{(i)}(x)=-\left(\sqrt{c\,|\,c_{02}^{(i)}(x)\,|}\right)^{-1},\quad \varphi_2^{(i)}(x)=\left(\sqrt{c\,|\,c_{02}^{(i)}(x)\,|}\right)^{-1}$$

$$\lambda\int_{a_i}^{x}\varphi_2^{(i)}(\xi)\,d\xi-\frac{\lambda\omega^{(i)}}{\sqrt{c}}=-\lambda\int_{x}^{b_i}\varphi_2^{(i)}(\xi)\,d\xi$$

Similarly, with the aid of the asymptotic representations (6.2.29) and inequalities (6.2.53), we obtain from (6.2.50) the inequality

$$\left|\frac{1}{\Delta(\lambda)}\frac{d^m\Delta^{(i)}(x,\lambda)}{dx^m}\right| \leqslant 2n\max|\gamma_k|C|\lambda|^m\left\{\frac{\left|\lambda^d e^{m_1\frac{\lambda}{\sqrt{c}}}\right|}{|\Delta(\lambda)|}\right.$$

$$\times|[\eta_{10m}^{(i)}(x)]|\left|\exp\left(\lambda\int_{a_i}^{x}\varphi_1^{(i)}(\xi)\,d\xi\right)\right|$$

$$\left.+\frac{\left|\lambda^d\exp\left[(m_1+\omega^{(i)})\frac{\lambda}{\sqrt{c}}\right]\right|}{|\Delta(\lambda)|}|[\eta_{20m}^{(i)}(x)]|\left|\exp\left(\lambda\int_{a_i}^{x}\varphi_2^{(i)}(\xi)\,d\xi\right)\right|\right\} \quad (6.2.55)$$

$$\leqslant 2n\max|\gamma_k|C|\lambda|^m\left\{\frac{\left|e^{m_1\frac{\lambda}{\sqrt{c}}}\right|}{\left|H\left(\frac{\lambda}{\sqrt{c}}\right)\right|}C_1\exp\left(\lambda\int_{a_i}^{x}\varphi_1^{(i)}(\xi)\,d\xi\right)\right.$$

$$\left.+\frac{\left|e^{m_1\frac{\lambda}{\sqrt{c}}}\right|}{\left|H\left(\frac{\lambda}{\sqrt{c}}\right)\right|}C_2\exp\left(-\lambda\int_{x}^{b_i}\varphi_2^{(i)}(\xi)\,d\xi\right)\right\}$$

which is valid in Π_2. Here,

$$\varphi_1^{(i)}(x)=-\left(\sqrt{c\,|c_{02}^{(i)}(x)|}\right)^{-1},\quad \varphi_2^{(i)}(x)=\left(\sqrt{c\,|c_{02}^{(i)}(x)|}\right)^{-1}$$

$$\omega^{(i)}\frac{\lambda}{\sqrt{c}}+\lambda\int_{a_i}^{x}\varphi_2^{(i)}(\xi)\,d\xi=-\lambda\int_{x}^{b_i}\varphi_2^{(i)}(\xi)\,d\xi$$

If we delete from the λ-plane the interiors of small circles $Q_{\delta k}^{(1)}$ of radius δ with centres at the zeros $\Delta(\lambda)$, then, in accordance with Theorem 21, the inequality

$$\frac{\left|e^{m_\sigma\frac{\lambda}{\sqrt{c}}}\right|}{\left|H\left(\frac{\lambda}{\sqrt{c}}\right)\right|}\leqslant C_{1\delta} \quad (6.2.56)$$

where $C_{1\delta}$ is a number depending only on δ, is satisfied in the remaining part of Π_1.

Similarly, if we delete from the λ-plane the interiors of circles $Q_{\delta k}^{(1)}$, the inequality

$$\frac{\left| e^{m_1 \frac{\lambda}{\sqrt{c}}} \right|}{\left| H\left(\frac{\lambda}{\sqrt{c}}\right) \right|} \leqslant C_{1\delta} \tag{6.2.57}$$

will be satisfied in the remaining portion of the half-plane Π_2. Thus, from inequalities (6.2.54), (6.2.55), (6.2.66) and (6.2.67), we have Theorem 22.

Theorem 22 Suppose that Conditions A and B of Section 6.1 are satisfied. Then, the inequality

$$\left| \frac{1}{\Delta(\lambda)} \frac{d^m \Delta^{(i)}(x, \lambda)}{dx^m} \right| \leqslant |\lambda|^m \max_{1 \leqslant k \leqslant 2n} |\gamma_k| \left\{ L_{1\delta} \left| \exp\left(\lambda \int_{a_i}^{x} \varphi_1^{(i)}(\xi)\, d\xi\right) \right| + L_{2\delta} \left| \exp\left(-\lambda \int_{x}^{b_i} \varphi_2^{(i)}(\xi)\, d\xi\right) \right| \right\} \tag{6.2.58}$$

where $L_{1\delta}$ and $L_{2\delta}$ are numbers depending only on δ, will be satisfied in the portion of the λ-plane which remains when the interiors of small circles $Q_{\delta k}^{(1)}$ are deleted from it. Here, the roots (6.2.25) of the characteristic equation (6.2.24) are so numbered that the inequalities

$$\operatorname{Re} \lambda \varphi_1^{(i)}(x) \leqslant 0, \quad \operatorname{Re} \lambda \varphi_2^{(i)}(x) \geqslant 0$$

are satisfied both in Π_1 and Π_2.

Let us now find a suitable asymptotic representation of the second term in the right-hand side of (6.2.11) representing the solution of the spectral problem (6.2.1)-(6.2.2). Clearly, to do this, it will be sufficient to obtain a suitable asymptotic representation of the determinants $\Delta^{(i,j)}(x, \xi, \lambda)$ (see 6.2.13)). We have asymptotic representations for all elements of this determinant except the elements of the first column. As can be seen from (6.2.8) and (6.2.13), to get an asymptotic representation of the determinant $\Delta^{(i,j)}(x, \xi, \lambda)$ we need first to obtain such a representation for $g^{(i,j)}(x, \xi, \lambda)$. In this connection, we have to find asymptotic representations for the functions

$$
\begin{aligned}
z_1^{(i)}(\xi, \lambda) &= \frac{W_{21}^{(i)}(\xi, \lambda)}{W^{(i)}(\xi, \lambda)} = \frac{-y_2^{(i)}(\xi, \lambda)}{W^{(i)}(\xi, \lambda)} \\
z_2^{(i)}(\xi, \lambda) &= \frac{W_{22}^{(i)}(\xi, \lambda)}{W^{(i)}(\xi, \lambda)} = \frac{y_1^{(i)}(\xi, \lambda)}{W^{(i)}(\xi, \lambda)}
\end{aligned}
\tag{6.2.59}
$$

Keeping (6.2.5) in mind and substituting (6.2.29) into (6.2.59), we obtain, after some simple rearrangements, the asymptotic representations

$$
\begin{aligned}
z_1^{(i)}(\xi, \lambda) &= \frac{1}{\lambda} \exp\left(-\lambda \int_{a_i}^{\xi} \varphi_1^{(i)}(z)\, dz \right) \\
&\quad \times \left\{ \zeta_{10}^{(i)}(\xi) + \frac{\zeta_{11}^{(i)}(\xi)}{\lambda} + \frac{E_1^{(i)}}{\lambda^2} \right\} \\
z_2^{(i)}(\xi, \lambda) &= \frac{1}{\lambda} \exp\left(-\lambda \int_{a_i}^{\xi} \varphi_2^{(i)}(z)\, dz \right) \\
&\quad \times \left\{ \zeta_{20}^{(i)}(\xi) + \frac{\zeta_{21}^{(i)}(\xi)}{\lambda} + \frac{E_2^{(i)}}{\lambda^2} \right\}
\end{aligned}
\tag{6.2.60}
$$

which are valid both in Π_1 and in Π_2. Here, for Π_1, the roots of (6.2.25) are so numbered that

$$
\varphi_1^{(i)}(\xi) = -\left(\sqrt{c\,|c_{02}^{(i)}(\xi)|} \right)^{-1}, \quad \varphi_2^{(i)}(\xi) = \left(\sqrt{c\,|c_{02}^{(i)}(\xi)|} \right)^{-1}
$$

For Π_2, we obtain

$$
\varphi_1^{(i)}(\xi) = \left(\sqrt{c\,|c_{02}^{(i)}(\xi)|} \right)^{-1}, \quad \varphi_2^{(i)}(\xi) = -\left(\sqrt{c\,|c_{02}^{(i)}(\xi)|} \right)^{-1}
$$

where

$$
\begin{aligned}
&\zeta_{s0}^{(i)}(\xi) = (2\varphi_s^{(i)}(\xi)\, \eta_{s0}^{(i)}(\xi))^{-1} \qquad (s = 1,\ 2) \\
&\zeta_{11}^{(i)}(\xi) = \eta_{10}^{(i)}(\xi) \left\{ \eta_{21}^{(i)}(\xi) \left(\eta_{11}^{(i)}(\xi) + \frac{d\eta_{10}^{(i)}(\xi)}{d\xi} \right) \right. \\
&\qquad \left. - \eta_{11}^{(i)}(\xi) \left(\eta_{21}^{(i)}(\xi) + \frac{d\eta_{20}^{(i)}(\xi)}{d\xi} \right) \right\} (2\varphi_1^{(i)}(\xi)\, \eta_{10}^{(i)}(\xi)\, \eta_{20}^{(i)}(\xi))^{-2} \\
&\qquad - \eta_{21}^{(i)}(\xi)\, (2\varphi_1^{(i)}(\xi)\, \eta_{10}^{(i)}(\xi)\, \eta_{20}^{(i)}(\xi))^{-1} \\
&\zeta_{21}^{(i)}(\xi) = \eta_{10}^{(i)}(\xi) \left\{ \eta_{21}^{(i)}(\xi) \left(\eta_{11}^{(i)}(\xi) + \frac{d\eta_{10}^{(i)}(\xi)}{d\xi} \right) \right. \\
&\qquad \left. - \eta_{11}^{(i)}(\xi) \left(\eta_{21}^{(i)}(\xi) + \frac{d\eta_{20}^{(i)}(\xi)}{d\xi} \right) \right\} (2\varphi_2^{(i)}(\xi)\, \eta_{10}^{(i)}(\xi)\, \eta_{20}^{(i)}(\xi))^{-2} \\
&\qquad + \eta_{11}^{(i)}(\xi)\, (2\varphi_2^{(i)}(\xi)\, \eta_{10}^{(i)}(\xi)\, \eta_{20}^{(i)}(\xi))^{-1}
\end{aligned}
\tag{6.2.60a}
$$

From these formulae, it is clear that the functions $\zeta_{sk}^{(i)}(\xi)$ are $2-k$ times (for $k=0$, 1 and $s=1$, 2) continuously differentiable on the interval $[a_i, b_i]$.

In the notations of (6.2.59), (6.2.8) can be written in the form

$$g^{(i)}(x, \xi, \lambda) = \begin{cases} \frac{1}{2}\{y_1^{(i)}(x, \lambda)\, z_1^{(i)}(\xi, \lambda) + y_2^{(i)}(x, \lambda)\, z_2^{(i)}(\xi, \lambda)\} \\ \qquad\qquad\qquad\qquad \text{for } a_i \leqslant \xi \leqslant x \\ -\frac{1}{2}\{y_1^{(i)}(x, \lambda)\, z_1^{(i)}(\xi, \lambda) + y_2^{(i)}(x, \lambda)\, z_2^{(i)}(\xi, \lambda)\} \\ \qquad\qquad\qquad\qquad \text{for } x \leqslant \xi \leqslant b_i \end{cases} \tag{6.2.61}$$

The asymptotic representations of the elements of the first row of the determinant (6.2.13), which were obtained by means of (6.2.22), (6.2.60) and (6.2.61), contain exponential functions of quantities with non-negative real parts. Consequently, they may increase as $|\lambda| \to +\infty$, which may interfere with the convergence of the contour integrals, as we shall see in Section 6.3. In this connection with this, let us transform the determinant (6.2.13) in such a way that the first column of the resulting determinant does not contain exponential functions of quantities with non-negative real parts. To do this, we multiply the columns

$$\begin{pmatrix} u_{11}^{(j)}(\lambda) \\ \vdots \\ u_{2n,1}^{(j)}(\lambda) \end{pmatrix}, \quad \begin{pmatrix} u_{12}^{(j)}(\lambda) \\ \vdots \\ u_{2n,2}^{(j)}(\lambda) \end{pmatrix}$$

of the determinant (6.2.13) by $\frac{1}{2} z_1^{(j)}(\xi, \lambda)$ and $-\frac{1}{2} z_2^{(j)}(\xi, \lambda)$, respectively, and add the result to the first column. We denote the resulting determinant by $\Delta_0^{(i, j)}(x, \xi, \lambda)$. In accordance with properties of determinants, we have

$$\Delta^{(i, j)}(x, \xi, \lambda) = \Delta_0^{(i, j)}(x, \xi, \lambda)$$

We denote the elements of the first column of the determinant $\Delta_0^{(i, j)}(x, \xi, \lambda)$, respectively, by

$$g_0^{(i, j)}(x, \xi, \lambda), \quad g_{10}^{(j)}(\xi, \lambda), \; \ldots, \; g_{2n, 0}^{(j)}(\xi, \lambda)$$

From (6.2.61) and (6.2.14), we have

$$g_0^{(i,\,i)}(x,\,\xi,\,\lambda)=g^{(i)}(x,\,\xi,\,\lambda)+\frac{1}{2}\{y_1^{(i)}(x,\,\lambda)\,z_1^{(i)}(\xi,\,\lambda)$$

$$-\,y_2^{(i)}(x,\,\lambda)\,z_2^{(i)}(\xi,\,\lambda)\}=\begin{cases} y_1^{(i)}(x,\,\lambda)\,z_1^{(i)}(\xi,\,\lambda) & \text{for } a_i\leqslant\xi\leqslant x\leqslant b_i \\ -\,y_2^{(i)}(x,\,\lambda)\,z_2^{(i)}(\xi,\,\lambda) & \text{for } a_i\leqslant x\leqslant\xi\leqslant b_i \end{cases}$$

$$g_0^{(i,\,j)}(x,\,\xi,\,\lambda)=\begin{cases} y_1^{(j)}(x,\,\lambda)\,z_1^{(i)}(\xi,\,\lambda) & \text{for } a_i\leqslant\xi\leqslant x\leqslant b_i,\ j=i \\ -\,y_2^{(i)}(x,\,\lambda)\,z_2^{(i)}(\xi,\,\lambda) & \text{for } a_i\leqslant x\leqslant\xi\leqslant b_i,\ j=i \\ 0 & \text{for } j\neq i, \end{cases}$$

(6.2.62)

$$g_{k0}^{(j)}(\xi,\,\lambda)=L_k^{(j)}(g^{(j)}(x,\,\xi,\,\lambda))_x+\frac{1}{2}\,u_{k1}^{(j)}(\lambda)\,z_1^{(j)}(\xi,\,\lambda)-\frac{1}{2}\,u_{k2}^{(j)}(\lambda)\,z_2^{(j)}(\xi,\,\lambda)$$

$$\begin{aligned}
&=-\frac{1}{2}\sum_{l=0}^{1}\alpha_{kl}^{(j)}(\lambda^2)\left.\frac{d^l y_1^{(j)}(x,\,\lambda)}{dx^l}\right|_{x=a_j} z_1^{(j)}(\xi,\,\lambda)\\
&\quad-\frac{1}{2}\sum_{l=0}^{1}\alpha_{kl}^{(j)}(\lambda^2)\left.\frac{d^l y_2^{(j)}(x,\,\lambda)}{dx^l}\right|_{x=a_j} z_2^{(j)}(\xi,\,\lambda)\\
&\quad+\frac{1}{2}\sum_{l=0}^{1}\beta_{kl}^{(j)}(\lambda^2)\left.\frac{d^l y_1^{(j)}(x,\,\lambda)}{dx^l}\right|_{x=b_j} z_1^{(j)}(\xi,\,\lambda)\\
&\quad+\frac{1}{2}\sum_{l=0}^{1}\beta_{kl}^{(j)}(\lambda^2)\left.\frac{d^l y_2^{(j)}(x,\,\lambda)}{dx^l}\right|_{x=b_j} z_2^{(j)}(\xi,\,\lambda)\\
&\quad+\frac{1}{2}\sum_{l=0}^{1}\alpha_{kl}^{(j)}(\lambda^2)\left.\frac{d^l y_1^{(j)}(x,\,\lambda)}{dx^l}\right|_{x=a_j} z_1^{(j)}(\xi,\,\lambda) \qquad (6.2.63)\\
&\quad+\frac{1}{2}\sum_{l=0}^{1}\beta_{kl}^{(j)}(\lambda^2)\left.\frac{d^l y_1^{(j)}(x,\,\lambda)}{dx^l}\right|_{x=b_j} z_1^{(j)}(\xi,\,\lambda)\\
&\quad-\frac{1}{2}\sum_{l=0}^{1}\alpha_{kl}^{(j)}(\lambda^2)\left.\frac{d^l y_2^{(j)}(x,\,\lambda)}{dx^l}\right|_{x=a_j} z_2^{(j)}(\xi,\,\lambda)\\
&\quad-\frac{1}{2}\sum_{l=0}^{1}\beta_{kl}^{(j)}(\lambda^2)\left.\frac{d^l y_2^{(j)}(x,\,\lambda)}{dx^l}\right|_{x=b_j} z_2^{(j)}(\xi,\,\lambda)\\
&=-\sum_{l=0}^{1}\alpha_{kl}^{(j)}(\lambda^2)\left.\frac{d^l y_2^{(j)}(x,\,\lambda)}{dx^l}\right|_{x=a_j} z_2^{(j)}(\xi,\,\lambda)\\
&\quad+\sum_{l=0}^{1}\beta_{kl}^{(j)}(\lambda^2)\left.\frac{d^l y_1^{(j)}(x,\,\lambda)}{dx^l}\right|_{x=b_j} z_1^{(j)}(\xi,\,\lambda)
\end{aligned}$$

Substituting (6.2.29) and (6.2.60) into (6.2.62), we obtain the asymptotic representation

$$\frac{\partial^m g_0^{(i,\,i)}(x,\xi,\lambda)}{\partial x^m} = \begin{cases} \lambda^{m-1} e^{\lambda \int_\xi^x \varphi_1^{(i)}(z)\,dz} \left(\gamma_{10m}^{(i)}(x,\xi) + \dfrac{\gamma_{11m}^{(i)}(x,\xi)}{\lambda} + \dfrac{E_{1m}^{(i)}(x,\xi,\lambda)}{\lambda^2} \right) \\ \qquad \text{for } a_i \leqslant \xi \leqslant x \leqslant b_i \\ -\lambda^{m-1} e^{\lambda \int_\xi^x \varphi_2^{(i)}(z)\,dz} \left(\gamma_{20m}^{(i)}(x,\xi) + \dfrac{\gamma_{21m}^{(i)}(x,\xi)}{\lambda} + \dfrac{E_{2m}^{(i)}(x,\xi,\lambda)}{\lambda^2} \right) \\ \qquad \text{for } a_i \leqslant x \leqslant \xi \leqslant b_i \end{cases} \tag{6.2.64}$$

which is valid for suitable numbering of the roots of the characteristic equation (6.2.24). Specifically, we need to have

$$\operatorname{Re} \lambda\varphi_1^{(i)} \leqslant \operatorname{Re} \lambda\varphi_2^{(i)})$$

where

$$\left. \begin{aligned} \gamma_{s0m}^{(i)}(x,\xi) &= \eta_{s0m}^{(i)}(x)\,\zeta_{s0}^{(i)}(\xi) \\ \gamma_{s1m}^{(i)}(x,\xi) &= \eta_{s0m}^{(i)}(x)\,\zeta_{s1}^{(i)}(\xi) + \eta_{s1m}^{(j)}(x)\,\zeta_{s0}^{(i)}(\xi) \end{aligned} \right\} \tag{6.2.64a}$$

both in Π_1 and in Π_2. From these last formulae, it is clear that the tunctions $\gamma_{skm}^{(i)}(x,\xi)$ are $2-k$ times (for $k=0,\ 1$) continuously differentiable with respect to their arguments on the interval $[a_i, b_i]$.

,Thus, with the aid of (6.2.29) and (6.2.60), we obtain from (6.2.63)

$$\begin{aligned} g_{k0}^{(j)}(\xi,\lambda) = {} & -\lambda^{-1} \exp\left[-\lambda \int_{a_j}^{\xi} \varphi_2^{(j)}(z)\,dz \right] \left\{ \zeta_{20}^{(j)}(\xi) \right. \\ & \left. + \frac{\zeta_{21}^{(j)}(\xi)}{\lambda} + \frac{E_2^{(j)}(\xi,\lambda)}{\lambda^2} \right\} [A_{k2}^{(j)}(\lambda)\,\eta_{20}^{(j)}(a_j)] \\ & -\lambda^{-1} \exp\left[\lambda \int_{\xi}^{b_j} \varphi_1^{(j)}(z)\,dz \right] \left\{ \zeta_{10}^{(j)}(\xi) \right. \\ & \left. + \frac{\zeta_{11}^{(j)}(\xi)}{\lambda} + \frac{E_1^{(j)}(\xi,\lambda)}{\lambda^2} \right\} [B_{k1}^{(j)}(\lambda)\,\eta_{10}^{(j)}(b_j)] \\ & (k=1,\ \ldots,\ 2n) \end{aligned} \tag{6.2.65}$$

For suitable numbering of the roots of the characteristic equation (6.2.24), this formula remains valid both in Π_2 and in Π_1.

Since $\operatorname{Re} \lambda\varphi_1^{(i)} \leqslant 0$ and $\operatorname{Re} \lambda\varphi_2^{(i)} \geqslant 0$, the exponents of the exponential functions in the asymptotic representations (6.2.64) and (6.2.65) have non-positive real parts.

Expanding the determinant $\Delta_0^{(i,j)}(x, \xi, \lambda)$ in terms of elements of the first row, we obtain

$$\begin{aligned}\Delta^{(i,j)}(x, \xi, \lambda) = \Delta_0^{(i,j)}(x, \xi, \lambda) = \Delta(\lambda)\, g_0^{(i,j)}(x, \xi, \lambda)\\ + y_1^{(i)}(x, \lambda)\, \Delta_{0,1,2i}^{(i,j)}(x, \xi, \lambda) + y_2^{(i)}(x, \lambda)\, \Delta_{0,1,2i+1}^{(i,j)}(x, \xi, \lambda)\end{aligned} \tag{6.2.66}$$

where $\Delta_{0,1,2i}^{(i,j)}(x, \xi, \lambda)$ and $\Delta_{0,1,2i+1}^{(i,j)}(x, \xi, \lambda)$ are the cofactors of the elements in the corresponding columns (in the first row).

If we substitute the asymptotic representations (6.2.65) into the expressions for the determinants $\Delta_{0,1,2i}^{(i,j)}(x, \xi, \lambda)$ and $\Delta_{0,1,2i+1}^{(i,j)}(x, \xi, \lambda)$, then represent the resulting determinant as the sum of two determinants and take the common factor of all elements of the $(2i-1)$th column outside the determinant we obtain

$$\begin{aligned}\Delta_{0,1,2i}^{(i,j)}(x, \xi, \lambda) = \lambda^{-1} \exp\left(-\lambda \int_{a_j}^{\xi} \varphi_2^{(j)}(z)\, dz\right) \Big\{\zeta_{20}^{(j)}(\xi)\\ + \frac{\zeta_{21}^{(j)}(\xi)}{\lambda} + \frac{E_2^{(j)}(\xi, \lambda)}{\lambda^2}\Big\} D_{11}^{(i,j)}(\lambda) + \lambda^{-1} \exp\left(\lambda \int_{\xi}^{b_j} \varphi_1^{(j)}(z)\, dz\right)\\ \times \Big\{\zeta_{10}^{(j)}(\xi) + \frac{\zeta_{11}^{(j)}(\xi)}{\lambda} + \frac{E_1^{(j)}(\xi, \lambda)}{\lambda^2}\Big\} D_{12}^{(i,j)}(\lambda)\end{aligned} \tag{6.2.67}$$

where

$$D_{11}^{(i,j)}(\lambda) = \begin{vmatrix} u_{11}^{(i)} & u_{12}^{(1)} & \ldots & u_{11}^{(i-1)} & u_{12}^{(i-1)}(\lambda) & [A_{12}^{(j)}\, \eta_{20}^{(j)}(a_j)] & u_{12}^{(i)} & \ldots & u_{11}^{(n)} & u_{12}^{(n)} \\ \cdot & \cdot & \cdot & \cdot & \cdot & \cdot & \cdot & \cdot & \cdot & \cdot \\ u_{2n,1}^{(1)} & u_{2n,2}^{(i)} & \ldots & u_{2n,1}^{(i-1)} & u_{2n,2}^{(i-1)} & [A_{2n,2}^{(j)}\, \eta_{20}^{(j)}(a_j)] & u_{2n,2}^{(i)} & \ldots & u_{2n,1}^{(n)} & u_{2n,2}^{(n)} \end{vmatrix} \tag{6.2.68}$$

$$D_{12}^{(i,j)}(\lambda) = \begin{vmatrix} u_{11}^{(1)} & u_{12}^{(1)} & \ldots & u_{11}^{(i-1)} & u_{12}^{(i-1)} & [B_{11}^{(j)}\eta_{10}^{(j)}(b_j)] & u_{12}^{(i)} & \ldots & u_{11}^{(n)} & u_{12}^{(n)} \\ \cdot & \cdot & \cdot & \cdot & \cdot & \cdot & \cdot & \cdot & \cdot & \cdot \\ u_{2n,1}^{(1)} & u_{2n,2}^{(1)} & \ldots & u_{2n,1}^{(i-1)} & u_{2n,2}^{(i-1)} & [B_{2n,1}^{(j)}\eta_{10}^{(j)}(b_j)] & u_{2n,2}^{(i)} & \ldots & u_{2n,1}^{(n)} & u_{2n,2}^{(n)} \end{vmatrix} \tag{6.2.69}$$

$$\Delta_{0,1,2i+1}^{(i,j)}(x, \xi, \lambda) = \lambda^{-1} \exp\left(-\lambda \int_{a_j}^{\xi} \varphi_2^{(j)}(z)\, dz\right)$$

$$\times \left\{\zeta_{20}^{(j)}(\xi) + \frac{\zeta_{21}^{(j)}(\xi)}{\lambda} + \frac{E_2^{(j)}(\xi, \lambda)}{\lambda^2}\right\} D_{21}^{(i,j)}(\lambda) \tag{6.2.70}$$

$$+ \lambda^{-1} \exp\left(\lambda \int_{\xi}^{b_j} \varphi_1^{(j)}(z)\, dz\right)\left\{\zeta_{10}^{(j)}(\xi) + \frac{\zeta_{11}^{(j)}(\xi)}{\lambda} + \frac{E_1^{(j)}(\xi, \lambda)}{\lambda^2}\right\} \times D_{22}^{(i,j)}(\lambda)$$

$$D_{21}^{(i,j)}(\lambda) = \begin{vmatrix} u_{11}^{(1)} & u_{12}^{(1)} & \dots & u_{11}^{(i-1)} & u_{12}^{(i-1)} & u_{11}^{(i)} & [A_{12}^{(j)}\eta_{20}^{(j)}(a_j)] & u_{11}^{(i+1)} & \dots & u_{11}^{(n)} & u_{12}^{(n)} \\ \dots & \dots & \dots & \dots & \dots & \dots & \dots & \dots & \dots & \dots & \dots \\ u_{2n,1}^{(1)} & u_{2n,2}^{(1)} & \dots & u_{2n,1}^{(i-1)} & u_{2n,2}^{(i-1)} & u_{2n,1}^{(i)} & [A_{2n,2}^{(j)}\eta_{20}^{(j)}(a_j)] & u_{2n,1}^{(i+1)} & \dots & u_{2n,1}^{(n)} & u_{2n,2}^{(n)} \end{vmatrix} \tag{6.2.71}$$

$$D_{22}^{(i,j)}(\lambda) = \begin{vmatrix} u_{11}^{(1)} & u_{12}^{(1)} & \dots & u_{11}^{(i-1)} & u_{12}^{(i-1)} & u_{11}^{(i)} & [B_{11}^{(j)}\eta_{10}^{(j)}(b_j)] & u_{11}^{(i+1)} & \dots & u_{11}^{(n)} & u_{12}^{(n)} \\ \dots & \dots & \dots & \dots & \dots & \dots & \dots & \dots & \dots & \dots & \dots \\ u_{2n,1}^{(1)} & u_{2n,2}^{(1)} & \dots & u_{2n,1}^{(i-1)} & u_{2n,2}^{(i-1)} & u_{2n,1}^{(i)} & [B_{2n,1}^{(j)}\eta_{10}^{(j)}(b_j)] & u_{2n,1}^{(i+1)} & \dots & u_{2n,1}^{(n)} & u_{2n,2}^{(n)} \end{vmatrix} \tag{6.2.72}$$

With the aid of (6.2.29), (6.2.67) and (6.2.70), we obtain from (6.2.66) the following asymptotic representation, which is valid for suitable numbering of the roots of the characteristic equation (6.2.24) both in Π_1 and in Π_2.

$$\frac{\partial^m \Delta^{(i,j)}(x, \xi, \lambda)}{\partial x^m} = \Delta(\lambda) \frac{\partial^m}{\partial x^m} g_0^{(i,j)}(x, \xi, \lambda)$$

$$+ \lambda^{m-1}\left(\eta_{10m}^{(i)}(x) + \frac{1}{\lambda}[\eta_{11m}^{(i)}(x)]\right) \exp\left(\lambda \int_{a_i}^{x} \varphi_1^{(i)}(z)\, dz\right)$$

$$\times \left\{\left(\zeta_{20}^{(j)}(\xi) + \frac{1}{\lambda}[\zeta_{21}^{(j)}(\xi)]\right) \exp\left(-\lambda \int_{a_j}^{\xi} \varphi_2^{(j)}(z)\, dz\right) D_{11}^{(i,j)}(\lambda)\right.$$

$$\left. + \left(\zeta_{10}^{(j)}(\xi) + \frac{1}{\lambda}[\zeta_{11}^{(j)}(\xi)]\right) \exp\left(\lambda \int_{\xi}^{b_j} \varphi_1^{(j)}(z)\, dz\right) D_{12}^{(i,j)}(\lambda)\right\} \tag{6.2.73}$$

$$+ \lambda^{m-1}\left(\eta_{20m}^{(i)}(x) + \frac{1}{\lambda}[\eta_{21m}^{(i)}(x)]\right) \exp\left(-\lambda \int_{x}^{b_i} \varphi_2^{(i)}(z)\, dz\right)$$

$$\times \left\{\left(\zeta_{20}^{(j)}(\xi) + \frac{1}{\lambda}[\zeta_{21}^{(j)}(\xi)]\right) \exp\left(-\lambda \int_{a_j}^{\xi} \varphi_2^{(j)}(z)\, dz\right) D_{21}^{(i,j)}(\lambda)\right.$$

$$\left. + \left(\zeta_{10}^{(j)}(\xi) + \frac{1}{\lambda}[\zeta_{11}^{(j)}(\xi)]\right) \exp\left(\lambda \int_{\xi}^{b_j} \varphi_1^{(j)}(z)\, dz\right) D_{22}^{(i,j)}(\lambda)\right\}$$

On the basis of Theorem 21 and in accordance with Condition B of Section 6.1, if we delete from the λ-plane the interiors of small circles $Q_{\delta k}^{(i)}$ of radius δ with centres at the zeros of $\Delta(\lambda)$, then the inequality

$$\left|\frac{D_{ks}^{(i,j)}(\lambda)}{\Delta(\lambda)}\right| = |\mathscr{E}_{ks}^{(i,j)}(\lambda)| \leqslant C_\delta \qquad (k, s = 1, 2) \qquad (6.2.74)$$

where C_δ is a number depending only on δ, will be satisfied throughout the rest of the λ-plane.

Thus, from (6.2.73) and (6.2.74), we have Theorem 23.

Theorem 23 Under Conditions A and B of Section 6.1, if we delete from the λ-plane the interiors of small circles $Q_{\delta_k}^{(i)}$ of radius δ with centres at the zeros of $\Delta(\lambda)$, then the following asymptotic representation will be valid in the rest of the λ-plane

$$\frac{1}{\Delta(\lambda)}\frac{\partial^m \Delta^{(i,j)}(x,\xi,\lambda)}{\partial x^m} = \frac{\partial^m g_0^{(i,j)}(x,\xi,\lambda)}{\partial x^m}$$

$$+\lambda^{m-1}\exp\left(\lambda\int_{a_i}^{x}\varphi_1^{(i)}(z)\,dz\right)\left(\eta_{10m}^{(i)}(x)+\frac{1}{\lambda}[\eta_{11m}^{(i)}(x)]\right)$$

$$\times\left\{\exp\left(-\lambda\int_{a_j}^{\xi}\varphi_2^{(j)}(z)\,dz\right)\left(\zeta_{20}^{(j)}(\xi)+\frac{1}{\lambda}[\zeta_{21}^{(j)}(\xi)]\right)\mathscr{E}_{11}^{(i,j)}(\lambda)\right.$$

$$\left.+\exp\left(\lambda\int_{\xi}^{b_j}\varphi_1^{(j)}(z)\,dz\right)\left(\zeta_{10}^{(j)}(\xi)+\frac{1}{\lambda}[\zeta_{11}^{(j)}(\xi)]\right)\mathscr{E}_{12}^{(i,j)}(\lambda)\right\} \qquad (6.2.75)$$

$$+\lambda^{m-1}\exp\left(-\lambda\int_{x}^{b_i}\varphi_2^{(i)}(z)\,dz\right)\left(\eta_{20m}^{(i)}(x)+\frac{1}{\lambda}[\eta_{21m}^{(i)}(x)]\right)$$

$$\times\left\{\exp\left(-\lambda\int_{a_j}^{\xi}\varphi_2^{(j)}(z)\,dz\right)\left(\zeta_{20}^{(j)}(\xi)+\frac{1}{\lambda}[\zeta_{21}^{(j)}(\xi)]\right)\mathscr{E}_{21}^{(i,j)}(\lambda)\right.$$

$$\left.+\exp\left(\lambda\int_{\xi}^{b_j}\varphi_1^{(j)}(z)\,dz\right)\left(\zeta_{10}^{(j)}(\xi)+\frac{1}{\lambda}[\zeta_{11}^{(j)}(\xi)]\right)\mathscr{E}_{22}^{(i,j)}(\lambda)\right\}$$

where the symptotic representation

$$\frac{\partial^m g_0^{(i,j)}(x,\xi,\lambda)}{\partial x^m}$$

is given by (6.2.14) and (6.2.64) and the functions

$$E_{km}^{(i)}(x, \xi, \lambda), \quad \mathscr{E}_{ks}^{(i, j)}(\lambda)$$

$$(k, \ s=1, 2; \ m=0, 1, 2)$$

defined in the part of the λ-plane remaining after the interiors of the circles $Q_{\delta k}^{(1)}$ are deleted, are bounded by some number C_δ which depends only on δ.

6.3 SOLUTION OF THE MIXED PROBLEM (6.1.1)–(6.1.3) WITH PARABOLICITY IN THE SENSE OF PETROVSKIY

In this section we shall assume that $\arg c_{02}^{(i)}(x)=\gamma$ (see (6.1.1)) satisfies the inequalities*

$$-\frac{\pi}{2}<\gamma<\frac{\pi}{2} \tag{6.3.1}$$

Let $R(h, \beta)$ denote the set of values of λ which lie outside the strip D_{h1} and satisfy the conditions

$$-\frac{\pi}{2}+\frac{\gamma}{2}+\beta\leqslant\arg\lambda\leqslant\frac{\pi}{2}+\frac{\gamma}{2}-\beta \tag{6.3.2}$$

where the constant β is so chosen that the inequalities

$$-\frac{\pi}{4}\mp\frac{\gamma}{2}<\beta<\frac{\pi}{4}\mp\frac{\gamma}{2} \tag{6.3.3}$$

will be satisfied.

Let M denote a closed contour in the λ-plane (see Fig. 3) which lies in the region $R(h, \beta)$ so that the straight lines defined by the equations

$$\begin{aligned}\arg\lambda&=-\frac{\pi}{2}+\frac{\gamma}{2}+\beta\\ \arg\lambda&=\frac{\pi}{2}+\frac{\gamma}{2}-\beta\end{aligned} \tag{6.3.4}$$

are asymptotes of the curve M.

*It is clear that this condition is equivalent to the condition of parabolicity in the sense of Petrovskiy.

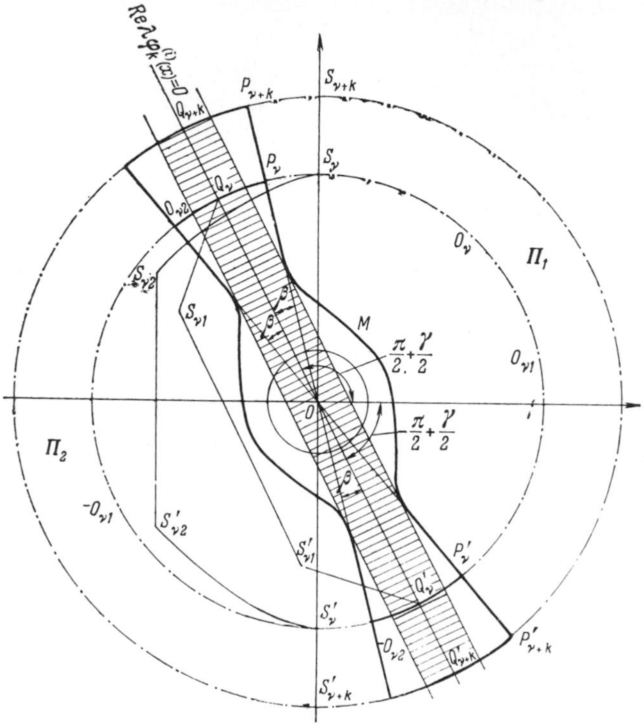

Fig. 3

Let us denote by O_ν a sequence of circles of radius r_ν with centre at the coordinate origin of the λ-plane which do not intersect the circles $Q_{\delta k}^{(i)}$, where $r_\nu \to +\infty$ as $\nu \to +\infty$.

For simplicity, we assume that M is a symmetric curve about the perpendicular to the straight line defined by the equation

$$\mathrm{Re}\,\lambda\varphi_k^{(i)}(x)=0 \qquad (k=1,\ 2) \tag{6.3.5}$$

Suppose that M_ν is that part of the curve M lying inside the circle O_ν and that $M-M_\nu$ coincides with sufficiently distant portions of the straight lines defined by (6.3.4).

Let us denote by $O_{\nu 1}$ the arc of the circle O_ν intercepted by the curve M and situated in the region $R(h, \beta)$. Let us denote by $-O_{\nu 1}$ its mirror image with respect to the straight line defined by (6.3.5). Let $O_{\nu 2}$ and $-O_{\nu 2}$ denote the parts $O_\nu - O_{\nu 1} - (-O_{\nu 1})$. Let $-M_\nu$ denote the mirror image of M_ν with respect to the line defined by (6.3.5). Finally, let us denote by Γ_ν the closed contour consisting of the arcs M_ν, $O_{\nu 2}$, $-M_\nu$, and $-O_{\nu 2}$.

We shall refer to the problem of finding the solutions of the homogeneous equations corresponding to (6.1.1) under boundary conditions (6.2.2) and homogeneous initial conditions as Problem A.

We shall refer to the problem of finding the solutions of (6.1.1) which satisfy the homogeneous boundary conditions (6.1.2) and the initial conditions (6.1.3) as Problem B.

Now, let us prove the Theorem below

Theorem 24 Suppose that Conditions A and B of Section 6.1 are satisfied and that $-\frac{\pi}{2} < \arg c_{02}^{(i)}(x) < \frac{\pi}{2}$. Then, Problem A has a solution $v_1^{(i)}(x, t)$ in the region $a_i < x < b_i$, $0 \leqslant t \leqslant T$ (for $i = 1, \ldots, n$), and this solution is given for $x \in (a_i, b_i)$ by

$$v_1^{(i)}(x, t) = \frac{1}{\pi\sqrt{-1}} \int\limits_M e^{\lambda^2 t} \frac{\Delta^{(i)}(x, \lambda)}{\lambda\Delta(\lambda)}\, d\lambda \tag{6.3.6}$$

It possesses continuous derivatives of all orders with respect to t and first and second derivatives with respect to x for $x \in [a_i, b_i]$ and $t > 0$.

Proof It is easy to show that the integrals

$$J_{m,s}(M) = \frac{1}{\pi\sqrt{-1}} \int\limits_M e^{\lambda^2 t} \frac{\lambda^{2s}}{\lambda\Delta(\lambda)} \frac{d^m}{dx^m} \Delta^{(i)}(x, \lambda)\, d\lambda \tag{6.3.7}$$

converge uniformly with respect to x and t for $t \in (0, T]$ and $x \in [a_i, b_i]$. For this, we need only show that the parts of these integrals over the distant segments $P_\nu P_{\nu+k}$ and $P'_\nu P'_{\nu+k}$ approach zero uniformly for all k with respect to $t \in (0, T)$ and $x \in [a_i, b_i]$ as $\nu \to \infty$. Specifically, on the basis of the choice of the contour M and in accordance with Theorem 22, (6.2.28) holds for $P_\nu P_{\nu+k}$ and $P'_\nu P'_{\nu+k}$ uniformly with respect to ν and k and $t \in (0, T]$, $x \in [a_i, b_i]$. Consequently, we have

$$|J_{m,s}(P_\nu\ P_{\nu+k})| = \left| \int\limits_{P_\nu P_{\nu+k}} e^{\lambda^2 t} \frac{\lambda^{2s}}{\lambda\Delta(\lambda)} \frac{d^m \Delta^{(i)}(x, \lambda)}{dx^m}\, d\lambda \right| \leqslant \tag{6.3.8}$$

$$\leqslant \int_{P_\nu P_{\nu+k}} \exp(t|\lambda|^2 \cos 2 \arg\lambda)\,|\lambda|^{m-1+2s}$$

$$\times \left\{ L_{1\delta} \left| \exp\left(\lambda \int_{a_i}^{x} \varphi_1^{(i)}(\xi)\,d\xi\right)\right| \right. \qquad (6.3.8)\ \text{(cont.)}$$

$$\left. + L_{2\delta} \left| \exp\left(-\lambda \int_{x}^{b_i} \varphi_2^{(i)}(\xi)\,d\xi\right)\right| \right\} |d\lambda|$$

where we set

$$\varphi_1^{(i)}(x) = -\frac{1}{\sqrt{|c_{02}^{(i)}(x)|}} \exp\left(-\sqrt{-1}\,\frac{\gamma}{2}\right)$$

$$\varphi_2^{(i)}(x) = \frac{1}{\sqrt{|c_{02}^{(i)}(x)|}} \exp\left(-\sqrt{-1}\,\frac{\gamma}{2}\right)$$

for the half-plane Π_1. Then

$$\operatorname{Re}\lambda\varphi_1^{(i)}(x) = -\frac{|\lambda|}{\sqrt{|c_{02}^{(i)}(x)|}} \cos\left(-\frac{\gamma}{2} + \arg\lambda\right)$$

$$\operatorname{Re}\lambda\varphi_2^{(i)}(x) = \frac{|\lambda|}{\sqrt{|c_{02}^{(i)}(x)|}} \cos\left(-\frac{\gamma}{2} + \arg\lambda\right)$$

where, in the half-plane Π_1,

$$\cos\left(-\frac{\gamma}{2} + \arg\lambda\right) \geqslant 0$$

It follows from these relations that

$$\operatorname{Re}\left(\lambda \int_{a_i}^{x} \varphi_1^{(i)}(\xi)\,d\xi\right) = -|\lambda| \int_{a_i}^{x} \frac{d\xi}{\sqrt{|c_{02}^{(i)}(\xi)|}}$$

$$\times \cos\left(-\frac{\gamma}{2} + \arg\lambda\right) \leqslant -|\lambda|\,\varkappa^{(i)}(x - a_i) \qquad (6.3.9)$$

$$\operatorname{Re}\left(-\lambda \int_{x}^{b_i} \varphi_2^{(i)}(\xi)\,d\xi\right) = -|\lambda| \int_{x}^{b_i} \frac{d\xi}{\sqrt{|c_{02}^{(i)}(\xi)|}}$$

$$\times \cos\left(-\frac{\gamma}{2} + \arg\lambda\right) \leqslant -|\lambda|\,\varkappa^{(i)}(b_i - x)$$

where

$$\varkappa^{(i)} = \max_{a_i \leqslant x \leqslant b_i} \left(\sqrt{|c_{02}^{(i)}(x)|}\right)^{-1}$$

Let us note also that the following relations hold on the distant part of the contour M which is being moved out:

$$\cos\left(-\frac{\gamma}{2} + \arg\lambda\right) = \cos\left(\frac{\pi}{2} - \beta\right) = \varepsilon_1 > 0$$

$$\cos 2\arg\lambda = \cos(\pi + \gamma - 2\beta) = -\varepsilon_2 \text{ on } P_\nu P_{\nu+k}$$

$$\cos\left(-\frac{\gamma}{2} + \arg\lambda\right) = \cos\left(-\frac{\pi}{2} + \beta\right) = \varepsilon_1$$

$$\cos 2\arg\lambda = \cos(-\pi + \gamma + 2\beta) = -\varepsilon_2 \text{ on } P'_\nu P'_{\nu+k}$$

where $\varepsilon_1 > 0$, $\varepsilon_2 > 0$

Consequently, when we take (6.3.9) into account, we obtain from (6.3.8)

$$\left| \int_{P_\nu P_{\nu+k}} e^{\lambda^2 t}\, d\lambda \frac{\lambda^{2s}}{\lambda\Delta(\lambda)} \frac{d^m\Delta^{(i)}(x, \lambda)}{dx^m} \right| \leqslant \int_{r_\nu}^{r_{\nu+k}} \exp(-\varepsilon_2 \varrho^2 t)\,\{L_{1\delta} e^{-\varkappa^{(i)}\rho(x-a_i)} \tag{6.3.10}$$

$$+ L_{2\delta} \exp(-\varkappa^{(i)}\varrho(b_i - x))\}\, \varrho^{m-1+2s}\, d\varrho$$

$$t > 0, \quad x \in [a_i, b_i]$$

where, in accordance with the choice of β (see (6.3.3)),

$$\frac{\pi}{2} < \pi + \gamma - 2\beta < \frac{3\pi}{2}, \quad -\frac{3\pi}{2} < -\pi + \gamma + 2\beta < -\frac{\pi}{2}$$

from which it follows that $c_{02}^{(i)}(x) > 0$.

Similarly,

$$\left| \int_{P'_\nu P'_{\nu+k}} e^{\lambda^2 t} \frac{\lambda^{2s}}{\lambda\Delta(\lambda)} \frac{d^m\Delta^{(i)}(x, \lambda)}{dx^m}\, d\lambda \right| \leqslant \int_{r_\nu}^{r_{\nu+k}} e^{-\varepsilon_1 \rho^2 t}\,\{L_{1\delta} \exp[-\varkappa^{(i)}\varrho(x - a_i)] \tag{6.3.11}$$

$$+ L_{2\delta} \exp[-\varkappa^{(i)}\varrho(b_i - x)]\}\, \varrho^{2s+m-1}\, d\varrho \quad \text{for } t > 0, \ x \in [a_i, b_i]$$

It is clear from (6.3.10) and (6.3.11) that the integrals (6.3.7) converge uniformly with respect to $x \in [a_i, b_i]$ and $t \in (0, T]$ and that the integral (6.3.6) converges uniformly with respect to t in the region $t \geqslant 0$ for all $x \in (a_i, b_i)$.

Consequently, in (6.3.6), we can differentiate under the integral sign twice with respect to x and infinitely many times with respect to t for $x \in [a_i, b_i]$ and $t > 0$. The functions defined by (6.3.7) are continuous in the region $a_i \leqslant x \leqslant b_i$, $0 < t \leqslant T$ for $m = 0, 1, 2$ and arbitrary s.

Furthermore, we can take the limit under the integral sign in (6.3.7) as $x \to a_i$ and as $x \to b_i$ (for $m = 0, 1$) and we can take the limit under the integral sign in (6.3.6) as $t \to 0$.

Then, if we differentiate (6.3.6) under the integral sign, we obtain

$$c_{02}^{(i)}(x)\frac{\partial^2 v_1^{(i)}}{\partial x^2} + c_{01}^{(i)}(x)\frac{\partial v_1^{(i)}}{\partial x} + c_{00}^{(i)}(x)\, v_1^{(i)} - \frac{\partial v_1^{(i)}}{\partial t}$$

$$\equiv \frac{1}{\pi\sqrt{-1}}\int\limits_M \frac{e^{\lambda^2 t}}{\lambda}\left\{c_{02}^{(i)}(x)\frac{d^2}{dx^2}\frac{\Delta^{(i)}(x, \lambda)}{\Delta(\lambda)}\right.$$

$$+ c_{01}^{(i)}(x)\frac{d}{dx}\frac{\Delta^{(i)}(x, \lambda)}{\Delta(\lambda)} + c_{00}^{(i)}(x)$$

$$\left.\times\frac{\Delta^{(i)}(x, \lambda)}{\Delta(\lambda)} - \lambda^2\frac{\Delta^{(i)}(x, \lambda)}{\Delta(\lambda)}\right\} \equiv 0$$

since the ratios $\frac{\Delta^{(i)}(x, \lambda)}{\Delta(\lambda)}$ are solutions of the corresponding homogeneous equations (6.2.1). Thus, the functions $v_1^{(i)}(x, t)$ defined by (6.3.6) satisfy homogeneous equations corresponding to (6.1.1).

Furthermore, since $\frac{\Delta^{(i)}(x, \lambda)}{\Delta(\lambda)}$ satisfies Conditions (6.2.2) for $t > 0$, we have

$$\sum_{i=1}^{n}\sum_{l,k=0}^{1}\left\{\alpha_{slk}^{(i)}\frac{\partial^{k+l}v_1^{(i)}}{\partial t^k\,\partial x^l}\bigg|_{x=a_i} + \beta_{slk}^{(i)}\frac{\partial^{k+l}v_1^{(i)}}{\partial t^k\,\partial x^l}\bigg|_{x=b_i}\right\}$$

$$\equiv \frac{1}{\pi\sqrt{-1}}\int\limits_M \frac{e^{\lambda^2 t}}{\lambda}\left\{\sum_{i=1}^{n}\sum_{l,k=0}^{1}\left(\alpha_{slk}^{(i)}\lambda^{2k}\frac{d^l}{dx^l}\frac{\Delta^{(i)}(x, \lambda)}{\Delta(\lambda)}\bigg|_{x=a_i}\right.\right.$$

$$\left.\left. + \beta_{slk}^{(i)}\lambda^{2k}\frac{d^l}{dx^l}\frac{\Delta^{(i)}(x, \lambda)}{\Delta(\lambda)}\bigg|_{x=b_i}\right)\right\} d\lambda \tag{6.3.12}$$

$$\equiv \frac{1}{\pi\sqrt{-1}}\int\limits_M \frac{e^{\lambda^2 t}\,d\lambda}{\lambda}\left\{\sum_{i=1}^{n}\sum_{l=0}^{1}\left(\alpha_{sl}^{(i)}(\lambda^2)\frac{d^l}{dx^l}\frac{\Delta^{(i)}(x, \lambda)}{\Delta(\lambda)}\bigg|_{x=a_i}\right.\right.$$

$$\left.\left. + \beta_{sl}^{(i)}(\lambda^2)\frac{d^l}{dx^l}\frac{\Delta^{(i)}(x, \lambda)}{\Delta(\lambda)}\bigg|_{x=b_i}\right)\right\}$$

$$= \frac{\gamma_s}{\pi\sqrt{-1}}\int\limits_M \frac{e^{\lambda^2 t}\,d\lambda}{\lambda}$$

The integrand in the right-hand side of (6.3.12) is an even function of λ. Consequently,

$$\int_{M_\nu} \frac{e^{\lambda^2 t}}{\lambda} d\lambda = \int_{-M_\nu} \frac{e^{\lambda^2 t}}{\lambda} d\lambda \tag{6.3.13}$$

Furthermore, by virtue of the choice of the contour M, we have

$$\lim_{\nu\to\infty} \int_{O_{\nu 2}} \frac{e^{\lambda^2 t}}{\lambda} d\lambda = \lim_{\nu\to\infty} \int_{-O_{\nu 2}} \frac{e^{\lambda^2 t}}{\lambda} d\lambda = 0 \tag{6.3.14}$$

On the basis of (6.3.13) and (6.3.14), we obtain from (6.3.12)

$$\sum_{i=1}^{n} \sum_{l=0}^{1} \left\{ \alpha_{sl}^{(i)} \left(\frac{\partial}{\partial t}\right) \frac{\partial^l v_1^{(i)}}{\partial x^l}\bigg|_{x=a_i} + \beta_{sl}^{(i)} \left(\frac{\partial}{\partial t}\right) \frac{\partial^l v_1^{(i)}}{\partial x^l}\bigg|_{x=b_i} \right\}$$

$$= \frac{\gamma_s}{2\pi\sqrt{-1}} \lim_{\nu\to\infty} \left(\int_{M_\nu} \frac{e^{\lambda^2 t}}{\lambda} d\lambda + \int_{-M_\nu} \frac{e^{\lambda^2 t}}{\lambda} d\lambda \right.$$

$$\left. + \int_{O_{\nu 2}} \frac{e^{\lambda^2 t}}{\lambda} d\lambda + \int_{-O_{\nu 2}} \frac{e^{\lambda^2 t}}{\lambda} d\lambda \right) = \frac{\gamma_s}{2\pi\sqrt{-1}} \lim_{\nu\to\infty} \int_{\Gamma_\nu} \frac{e^{\lambda^2 t}}{\lambda} d\lambda = \gamma_s$$

Thus, the functions (6.3.6) satisfy boundary conditions (6.1.2), i.e. boundary conditions of Problem A.

To complete the proof of Theorem 24, we need to show that the function $v_1^{(i)}(x, t)$ defined by (6.3.6) satisfies the homogeneous bounuary condition. Since the integral (6.3.6) converges uniformly with respect to t on the interval $[0, T]$, we have

$$\lim_{t\to 0} v_1^{(i)}(x, t) = \frac{1}{\pi\sqrt{-1}} \lim_{t\to 0} \int_{M} e^{\lambda^2 t} \frac{\Delta^{(i)}(x, \lambda)}{\lambda\Delta(\lambda)} d\lambda$$

$$= \frac{1}{\pi\sqrt{-1}} \int_{M} \frac{\Delta^{(i)}(x, \lambda)}{\lambda\Delta(\lambda)} d\lambda = \frac{1}{\pi\sqrt{-1}} \lim_{\nu\to\infty} \int_{M_\nu} \frac{\Delta^{(i)}(x, \lambda)}{\lambda\Delta(\lambda)} d\lambda \tag{6.3.15}$$

Since the integrand in the right-hand side of this equation is analytic, we have the following relation between the contours M_ν and $O_{\nu 1}$

$$\lim_{t\to 0} v_1^{(i)}(x, t) = \frac{1}{\pi\sqrt{-1}} \lim_{\nu\to\infty} \int_{O_{\nu 1}} \frac{\Delta^{(i)}(x, \lambda)}{\lambda\Delta(\lambda)} d\lambda \tag{6.3.16}$$

In accordance with Theorem 22 and the choice of circles O_ν, the integrand in the right-hand side of (6.3.16) decreases for $x \in (a_i, b_i)$ on the contours O_ν more rapidly than does any power of λ^{-1}. Consequently, we obtain from (6.3.16)

$$\lim_{t \to 0} v_1^{(i)}(x, t) = v_1^{(i)}(x, 0) = 0$$

which completes the proof.

Thus, by using Theorem 22, we can show that the function $\widetilde{v}_1^{(i)}(x, t)$ defined by

$$\widetilde{v}_1^{(i)}(x, t) = \frac{1}{\pi\sqrt{-1}} \int_{-M} e^{\lambda^2 t} \frac{\Delta^{(i)}(x, \lambda)}{\lambda \Delta(\lambda)} d\lambda \tag{6.3.17}$$

is a solution of Problem A.

It is somewhat more difficult to prove Theorem 25 below.

Theorem 25 Suppose that

$$-\frac{\pi}{2} < \arg c_{02}^{(i)}(x) < \frac{\pi}{2}$$

Suppose also that Conditions A and B of Section 6.1 hold. Let $\Phi^{(i)}(x)$ denote a function with continuous first and second derivatives for $x \in [a_i, b_i]$ and let $f^{(i)}(x, t)$ denote functions with continuous first and second derivatives with respect to x and t for $x \in [a_i, b_i]$, $t \in [0, T]$. Then, Problem B has a solution $v_2^{(i)}(x, t)$ given by

$$v_2^{(i)}(x, t) = \frac{-1}{\pi\sqrt{-1}} \int_M \lambda\, d\lambda \sum_{j=1}^{n} \int_{a_j}^{b_j} G^{(i, j)}(x, \xi, \lambda)$$
$$\times \left\{ e^{\lambda^2 t}\Phi^{(j)}(\xi) + \int_0^t e^{\lambda^2(t-\tau)} f^{(j)}(\xi, \tau)\, d\tau \right\} (c_{02}^{(j)}(\xi))^{-1} d\xi \tag{6.3.18}$$

This solution has continuous first and second derivatives with respect to x and a continuous first derivative with respect to t for $x \in [a_i, b_i]$ and $t \in (0, T]$.

Proof We shall break the proof into two parts. First, we shall show that the function $v_{21}^{(i)}(x, t)$ defined by (6.3.18) for

$f^{(j)}(x, t) \equiv 0$ (where $j = 1, 2, \ldots, n$) satisfies the corresponding homogeneous equation (6.1.1), the corresponding homogeneous boundary conditions (6.1.2) and the initial condition (6.1.3).

In accordance with Theorem 23 and by virtue of the choice of the contour M, the derivatives of the solution of the corresponding spectral problem are bounded uniformly with respect to x on the contour M.

Consequently,

$$\left| \int_{P_\nu P_{\nu+k}} e^{\lambda^2 t} \lambda^{2s+1} \, d\lambda \, \frac{\partial^m}{\partial x^m} \sum_{j=1}^{n} \int_{a_j}^{b_j} G^{(i,j)}(x, \xi, \lambda) \frac{\Phi^{(j)}(\xi)}{c_{02}^{(j)}(\xi)} \, d\xi \right|$$

$$\leqslant \int_{r_\nu}^{r_{\nu+k}} C e^{-\varepsilon_2 \rho^2 t} \rho^{m+2s} \, d\rho$$

$$\leqslant C \exp\left(-\frac{1}{2} \varepsilon_2 r_\nu^2 t\right) \int_0^\infty e^{-\frac{1}{2}\varepsilon_2 \rho^2 t} \rho^{m+2s} \, d\rho$$

$$= \frac{2C}{(\sqrt{\varepsilon_2 t})^{m+1+2s}} \exp\left(-\frac{1}{2} \varepsilon_2 r_\nu^2 t\right) \int_0^\infty e^{-\beta^2} \beta^{m+2s} \, d\beta$$

where C is a constant. This inequality implies the uniform convergence of the integrals

$$\int_M \lambda^{2s+1} e^{\lambda^2 t} \, d\lambda \times \frac{\partial^m}{\partial x^m} \sum_{j=1}^{n} \int_{a_j}^{b_j} G^{(i,j)}(x, \xi, \lambda) \Phi^{(j)}(\xi) (c_{02}^{(j)}(\xi))^{-1} \, d\xi \tag{6.3.19}$$

with respect to $x \in [a_i, b_i]$ and $t \in (0, T]$. This ensures that we may differentiate with respect to x and t under the integral sign in the integral over the contour M. Therefore,

$$c_{02}^{(i)}(x) \frac{\partial^2 v_{21}^{(i)}(x, t)}{\partial x^2} + c_{01}^{(i)}(x) \frac{\partial v_{21}^{(i)}(x, t)}{\partial x} + c_{00}^{(i)}(x) v_{21}^{(i)}(x, t)$$

$$- \frac{\partial v_{21}^{(i)}(x, t)}{\partial t} \equiv \frac{-1}{\pi \sqrt{-1}} \int_M \lambda e^{\lambda^2 t} \, d\lambda \left\{ c_{02}^{(i)}(x) \frac{\partial^2}{\partial x^2} + c_{01}^{(i)}(x) \frac{\partial}{\partial x} \right.$$

$$\left. + c_{00}^{(i)}(x) - \lambda^2 \right\} \sum_{j=1}^{n} \int_{a_j}^{b_j} G^{(i,j)}(x, \xi, \lambda) \Phi^{(j)}(\xi) (c_{02}^{(j)}(\xi))^{-1} \, d\xi$$

$$= \frac{-1}{\pi \sqrt{-1}} \int_M \lambda e^{\lambda^2 t} \, d\lambda \, \Phi^{(i)}(x) = - \frac{\Phi^{(i)}(x)}{2\pi \sqrt{-1}} \lim_{\nu \to \infty} \int_{\Gamma_\nu} \lambda e^{\lambda^2 t} \, d\lambda = 0$$

Thus, the function $v_{21}(x, t)$ given by (6.3.18) for

$$f^{(j)}(x, t) \equiv 0 \quad (j = 1, 2, \ldots, n)$$

satisfies the homogeneous equation corresponding to (6.1.1). Also, the functions defined by the integrals (6.3.19) are continuous on $[a_i, b_i]$ for $t > 0$.

Furthermore, because of the uniform convergence of the integrals (6.3.19) for

$$x \in [a_i, b_i], \ t > 0$$

we have

$$\sum_{i=1}^{n} \sum_{l=0}^{1} \left\{ \alpha_{sl}^{(i)} \left(\frac{\partial}{\partial t} \right) \frac{\partial^l v_{21}^{(i)}}{\partial x^l} \bigg|_{x=a_i} + \beta_{sl}^{(i)} \left(\frac{\partial}{\partial t} \right) \frac{\partial^l v_{21}^{(i)}}{\partial x^l} \bigg|_{x=b_i} \right\}$$

$$= \frac{-1}{\pi \sqrt{-1}} \int_M \lambda e^{\lambda^2 t} \, d\lambda \sum_{i=1}^{n} \sum_{l=0}^{1} \left\{ \alpha_{sl}^{(i)}(\lambda^2) \right.$$

$$\times \frac{\partial^l}{\partial x^l} \sum_{j=1}^{n} \int_{a_j}^{b_j} G^{(i, j)}(x, \xi, \lambda) \, \Phi^{(j)}(\xi) \, (c_{02}^{(j)}(\xi))^{-1} \, d\xi \bigg|_{x=a_i}$$

$$+ \beta_{sl}^{(i)}(\lambda^2) \frac{\partial^l}{\partial x^l} \sum_{j=1}^{n} \int_{a_j}^{b_j} G^{(i, j)}(x, \xi, \lambda)$$

$$\left. \times \Phi^{(j)}(\xi) \, (c_{02}^{(j)}(\xi))^{-1} \, d\xi \bigg|_{x=b_i} \right\} = 0$$

since

$$\sum_{j=1}^{n} \int_{a_j}^{b_j} G^{(i, j)}(x, \xi, \lambda) \, \Phi^{(j)}(\xi) \, (c_{02}^{(j)}(\xi))^{-1} \, d\xi$$

is the solution of the spectral problem (6.2.1)-(6.2.2) with corresponding homogeneous boundary conditions.

Let us now show that $v_{21}^{(i)}(x, t)$ satisfies the initial condition (6.1.3). First show, using the asymptotic representations (6.2.64) and (6.2.75), that, for $x \in (a_i, b_i)$, the integral

$$I(x, t) = \int_M \lambda e^{\lambda^2 t} \left\{ \sum_{j=1}^{n} \int_{a_j}^{b_j} G^{(i, j)}(x, \xi, \lambda) \, \Phi^{(j)}(\xi) \, (c_{02}^{(j)}(\xi))^{-1} \, d\xi \right.$$
$$\left. + \frac{1}{\lambda^2} \left(\frac{F_1^{(i)}(x, x)}{\varphi_1^{(i)}(x)} + \frac{F_2^{(i)}(x, x)}{\varphi_2^{(i)}(x)} \right) \right\} d\lambda \tag{6.3.20}$$

converges uniformly with respect to $t \in [0, T]$, where

$$F_k^{(i)}(x, \xi) = \gamma_{k00}^{(i)}(x, \xi)\, \Phi^{(i)}(\xi)\, (c_{02}^{(i)}(\xi))^{-1} \tag{6.3.21}$$

Then, taking the limit under the integral sign in (6.3.20) as $t \to 0$, we can show that the limit of this integral is equal to zero. Then, to complete the proof of the first part of Theorem 25, we need only note the validity of the equation

$$\frac{1}{\pi\sqrt{-1}} \int_M \frac{e^{\lambda^2 t}}{\lambda} \left(\frac{F_1^{(i)}(x, x)}{\varphi_1^{(i)}(x)} + \frac{F_2^{(i)}(x, x)}{\varphi_2^{(i)}(x)} \right) d\lambda = \Phi^{(i)}(x) \tag{6.3.22}$$

for every $t > 0$.

In accordance with Condition A of Section 6.1, the functions $\gamma_{sk0}^{(i)}(x, \xi)$ in the asymptotic representation (6.2.64) are $2-k$ times continuously differentiable (for $s = 1, 2$ and $k = 0, 1$). Integrating by parts, we obtain

$$\begin{aligned} &\int_{a_i}^{x} \exp\left(\lambda \int_{\xi}^{x} \varphi_1^{(i)}(z)\,dz\right) F_1^{(i)}(x, \xi)\, d\xi \\ &= -\frac{F_1^{(i)}(x, x)}{\lambda \varphi_1^{(i)}(x)} + \frac{\exp\left(\lambda \int_{a_i}^{x} \varphi_1^{(i)}(z)\,dz\right)}{\lambda \varphi_1^{(i)}(a_i)} F_1^{(i)}(x, a_i) \\ &\quad - \frac{1}{\lambda^2} \left\{ \frac{1}{\varphi_1^{(i)}(\xi)} \exp\left(\lambda \int_{\xi}^{x} \varphi_1^{(i)}(z)\,dz\right) \frac{d}{d\xi} \frac{F_1^{(i)}(x, \xi)}{\varphi_1^{(i)}(\xi)} \Bigg|_{a_i}^{x} \right. \\ &\quad \left. + \int_{a_i}^{x} \exp\left(\lambda \int_{\xi}^{x} \varphi_1^{(i)}(z)\,dz\right) \frac{d}{d\xi} \left(\frac{1}{\varphi_1^{(i)}(\xi)} \frac{d}{d\xi} \frac{F_1^{(i)}(x, \xi)}{\varphi_1^{(i)}(\xi)} \right) d\xi \right\} \end{aligned} \tag{6.3.23}$$

$$\begin{aligned} &-\int_{x}^{b_i} \exp\left(-\lambda \int_{x}^{\xi} \varphi_2^{(i)}(z)\,dz\right) F_2^{(i)}(x, \xi)\, d\xi \\ &= \frac{\exp\left(-\lambda \int_{x}^{b_i} \varphi_2^{(i)}(z)\,dz\right)}{\lambda \varphi_2^{(i)}(b_i)} F_2^{(i)}(x, b_i) - \frac{F_2^{(i)}(x, x)}{\lambda \varphi_2^{(i)}(x)} \\ &\quad + \frac{1}{\lambda^2} \left\{ \frac{1}{\varphi_2^{(i)}(\xi)} \exp\left(-\lambda \int_{x}^{\xi} \varphi_2^{(i)}(z)\,dz\right) \frac{d}{d\xi} \frac{F_2^{(i)}(x, \xi)}{\varphi_2^{(i)}(\xi)} \Bigg|_{x}^{b_i} \right. \\ &\quad \left. - \int_{x}^{b_i} \exp\left(-\lambda \int_{x}^{\xi} \varphi_2^{(i)}(z)\,dz\right) \frac{d}{d\xi} \left(\frac{1}{\varphi_2^{(i)}(\xi)} \frac{d}{d\xi} \frac{F_2^{(i)}(x, \xi)}{\varphi_2^{(i)}(\xi)} \right) d\xi \right\} \end{aligned} \tag{6.3.24}$$

Similarly, integrating by parts, we can easily prove the inequalities

$$\left|\int_{a_i}^{x} \exp\left(\lambda \int_{\xi}^{x} \varphi_1^{(i)}(z)\,dz\right) \gamma_{110}^{(i)}(x, \xi)\, \Phi^{(i)}(\xi)\,(c_{02}^{(i)}(\xi))^{-1}\,d\xi\right| < \frac{C_1}{|\lambda|} \tag{6.3.25}$$

$$\left|-\int_{x}^{b_i} \exp\left(-\lambda \int_{x}^{\xi} \varphi_2^{(i)}(z)\,dz\right) \gamma_{210}^{(i)}(x, \xi)\, \Phi^{(i)}(\xi)\,(c_{02}^{(i)})(\xi))^{-1}\,d\xi\right| \leqslant \frac{C_2}{|\lambda|}$$

On the basis of (6.3.23)-(6.3.25), we conclude from the asymptotic formulae (6.2.64) and (6.2.75) that the integrand in (6.3.20) for

$$t \geqslant 0, \qquad x \in (a_i, b_i)$$

decreases on the contour M faster than does λ^{-2}. Consequently, the integral (6.3.20) converges uniformly with respect to $t \in [0, T]$. Then, taking the limit as $t \to 0$, we obtain from (6.3.20)

$$\lim_{t\to 0} I(x, t)$$
$$= \int_M \lambda \left\{ \sum_{j=1}^{n} \int_{a_j}^{b_j} G^{(i,j)}(x, \xi, \lambda)\, \Phi^{(j)}(\xi)\,(c_{02}^{(j)}(\xi))^{-1}\,d\xi \right. \tag{6.3.26}$$
$$\left. + \frac{1}{\lambda^2}\left(\frac{F_1^{(i)}(x, x)}{\varphi_1^{(i)}(x)} + \frac{F_2^{(i)}(x, x)}{\varphi_2^{(i)}(x)}\right)\right\} d\lambda.$$

Since the integrand in (6.3.26) has no singularities between the contours M_ν and $O_{\nu 1}$ and since this function decreases on the contours $O_{\nu 1}$ faster than does λ^{-2}, we have from (6.3.26)

$$\lim_{t\to 0} I(x, t) = 0$$

Thus, the first part of the theorem is proved.

Now, to complete the proof of the theorem, we need to

show that the functions $v_{22}^{(i)}(x, t)$ defined by

$$v_{22}^{(i)}(x, t) = \frac{-1}{\pi\sqrt{-1}} \int_M \lambda\, d\lambda \sum_{j=1}^{n} \int_{a_j}^{b_j} G^{(i, j)}(x, \xi, \lambda) \times \int_0^t e^{\lambda^2 (t-\tau)} f^{(j)}(\xi, \tau)\, d\tau\, (c_{02}^{(j)}(\xi))^{-1}\, d\xi \tag{6.3.27}$$

satisfy the non-homogeneous equations (6.1.1) corresponding to the homogeneous boundary conditions (6.1.2) and the homogeneous initial conditions.

Furthermore, in Problem (6.1.1)-(6.1.3), the derivatives of the functions $v_{22}^{(i)}(x, t)$ are continuous on $[a_i, b_i]$ for $t > 0$.

For this, it will be sufficient to show that it is possible to differentiate the required number of times and take the limit under the integral sign in (6.3.27) for $t > 0$.

Integrating by parts, we obtain

$$\begin{aligned} \int_0^t \exp[\lambda^2(t-\tau)]\, f^{(j)}(\xi, \tau)\, d\tau &= -\frac{1}{\lambda^2} f^{(j)}(\xi, t) + \frac{1}{\lambda^2} e^{\lambda^2 t} f^{(j)}(\xi, 0) \\ &- \frac{1}{\lambda^4} \frac{\partial f^{(j)}(\xi, t)}{\partial t} + \frac{1}{\lambda^4} \frac{\partial f^{(j)}(\xi, t)}{\partial t}\Big|_{t=0} e^{\lambda^2 t} \\ &+ \frac{1}{\lambda^4} \int_0^t \exp[\lambda^2(t-\tau)] \frac{\partial^2 f^{(j)}(\xi, \tau)}{\partial \tau^2}\, d\tau \end{aligned} \tag{6.3.28}$$

Consider the integrals

$$\begin{aligned} &\int_M \lambda\, d\lambda \frac{\partial^{m+s}}{\partial x^m \partial t^s} \sum_{j=1}^{n} \int_{a_j}^{b_j} G^{(i, j)}(x, \xi, \lambda) \times \int_0^t e^{\lambda^2(t-\tau)} f^{(j)}(\xi, \tau)\, d\tau\, (c_{02}^{(j)}(\xi))^{-1}\, d\xi \\ &= \int_M \lambda\, d\lambda \frac{\partial^{m+s}}{\partial x^m \partial t^s} \sum_{j=1}^{n} \int_{a_j}^{b_j} G^{(i, j)}(x, \xi, \lambda) \times \Big\{ -\frac{1}{\lambda^2} f^{(j)}(\xi, t) + \frac{1}{\lambda^2} e^{\lambda^2 t} f^{(j)}(\xi, 0) \\ &- \frac{1}{\lambda^4} \frac{\partial f^{(j)}(\xi, t)}{\partial t} + \frac{e^{\lambda^2 t}}{\lambda^4} \left(\frac{\partial f^{(j)}(\xi, t)}{\partial t} \right)_{t=0} \\ &+ \frac{1}{\lambda^4} \int_0^t \exp[\lambda^2(t-\tau)] \frac{\partial^2 f^{(j)}(\xi, \tau)}{\partial \tau^2}\, d\tau \Big\} (c_{02}^{(j)}(\xi))^{-1}\, d\xi \qquad (m + s \leqslant 2) \end{aligned} \tag{6.3.29}$$

We see from the asymptotic representations (6.2.64) and (6.2.75) and the formula (6.3.28), for large values of λ, the principal part of the integrand in (6.3.29) is

$$\frac{1}{\lambda^2}\frac{\partial^{m+s}}{\partial x^m \partial t^s}\left\{\int_{a_i}^{x} \exp\left(\lambda \int_{\xi}^{x} \varphi_1^{(i)}(z)\,dz\right)\gamma_{100}^{(i)}(x,\xi) \times f^{(i)}(\xi,t)\,(c_{02}^{(i)}(\xi))^{-1}\,d\xi \right.$$

$$\left. -\int_{x}^{b_i} \exp\left[-\lambda \int_{x}^{\xi} \varphi_2^{(i)}(z)\,dz\right]\gamma_{200}^{(i)}(x,\xi)\,f^{(i)}(\xi,t)\,(c_{02}^{(i)}(\xi))^{-1}\,d\xi\right\}$$

$$=\frac{1}{\lambda^2}\frac{\partial^{m}}{\partial x^m}\left\{\int_{a_i}^{x} \exp\left[\lambda \int_{\xi}^{x} \varphi_1^{(i)}(z)\,dz\right]\gamma_{100}^{(i)}(x,\xi) \times \frac{\partial^s f^{(i)}(\xi,t)}{\partial t^s}(c_{02}^{(i)}(\xi))^{-1}\,d\xi \right. \tag{6.3.30}$$

$$\left. -\int_{x}^{b_i} \exp\left(-\lambda \int_{x}^{\xi} \varphi_2^{(i)}(z)\,dz\right)\gamma_{200}^{(i)}(x,\xi) \times \frac{\partial^s f^{(i)}(\xi,t)}{\partial t^s}(c_{02}^{(i)}(\xi))^{-1}\,d\xi\right\}$$

In analogy with (6.3.23) and (6.3.24), we can easily show by integrating by parts that (6.3.30) decreases on the contour M for $m\leqslant 1$ faster than does λ^{-2} and that this decrease is uniform with respect to $t\geqslant 0$ and $x\in[a_i, b_i]$. Consequently, the integrals (6.3.29) for $m\leqslant 1$ and $s\leqslant 2$ converge uniformly with respect to $t\geqslant 0$ and $x\in[a_i, b_i]$. Hence it is permissible to differentiate once with respect to x and twice with respect to t and to take the limit as $t\to 0$, $x\to a_i$ and $x\to b_i$. all under the integral sign in (6.3.27). Then, by taking the limit under the integral sign (6.3.27) as $t\to 0$, we obtain

$$v_{22}^{(i)}(x, 0)=0$$

Furthermore, if we substitute (6.3.27) into the boundary conditions (6.1.2) and keep in mind (6.3.28) and the possibility of differentiating once with respect to x and once with respect to t under the integral sign denoting integrating over the contour M, we obtain

$$\sum_{i=1}^{n}\sum_{l=0}^{1}\left\{\alpha_{sl}^{(i)}\left(\frac{\partial}{\partial t}\right)\frac{\partial^l v_{22}^{(i)}(x,t)}{\partial x^l}\bigg|_{x=a_i}\right. \left. +\beta_{sl}^{(i)}\left(\frac{\partial}{\partial t}\right)\frac{\partial^l v_{22}^{(i)}(x,t)}{\partial x^l}\bigg|_{x=b_i}\right\}$$

$$=\sum_{i=1}^{n}\sum_{l,\,k=0}^{1}\left\{\alpha_{slk}^{(i)}\frac{\partial^{k+l}v_{22}^{(i)}(x,t)}{\partial t^k\,\partial x^l}\bigg|_{x=a_i}+\beta_{slk}^{(i)}\frac{\partial^{k+l}v_{22}^{(i)}(x,t)}{\partial t^k\,\partial x^l}\bigg|_{x=b_i}\right\}$$

$$\equiv\frac{1}{\pi\sqrt{-1}}\int_M\frac{\lambda}{\lambda^2}\left\{\sum_{i=1}^{n}\sum_{l,\,k=0}^{1}\left(\alpha_{slk}^{(i)}\right.\right.$$

$$\times\frac{d^l}{dx^l}\sum_{j=1}^{n}\int_{a_j}^{b_j}G^{(i,\,j)}(x,\xi,\lambda)\frac{\partial^k f^{(j)}(\xi,t)}{\partial t^k}(c_{02}^j(\xi))^{-1}\,d\xi\bigg|_{x=a_i}$$

$$+\beta_{slk}^{(i)}\frac{d^l}{dx^l}\sum_{j=1}^{n}\int_{a_j}^{b_j}G^{(i,\,j)}(x,\xi,\lambda)$$

$$\left.\left.\times\frac{\partial^k f^{(j)}(\xi,t)}{\partial t^k}\,(c_{02}^j(\xi))^{-1}\,d\xi\bigg|_{x=b_i}\right)\right\}d\lambda$$

$$-\frac{1}{\pi\sqrt{-1}}\int_M\frac{\lambda e^{\lambda^2 t}}{\lambda^2}\left\{\sum_{i=1}^{n}\sum_{l,\,k=0}^{1}\left(\alpha_{slk}^{(i)}\lambda^{2k}\right.\right.$$

$$\times\frac{d^l}{dx^l}\sum_{j=1}^{n}\int_{a_j}^{b_j}G^{(i,\,j)}(x,\xi,\lambda)\,f^{(j)}(\xi,0)\,(c_{02}^j(\xi))^{-1}\,d\xi\,|_{x=a_i}$$

$$+\beta_{slk}^{(i)}\lambda^{2k}\frac{d^l}{dx^l}\sum_{j=1}^{n}\int_{a_j}^{b_j}G^{(i,\,j)}(x,\xi,\lambda)$$

$$\left.\left.\times\ f^{(j)}(\xi,0)\,(c_{02}^j(\xi)^{-1}\,d\xi\,|_{x=b_i}\right)\right\}\ d\lambda$$

$$+\frac{1}{\pi\sqrt{-1}}\int_M\frac{\lambda}{\lambda^4}\left\{\sum_{i=1}^{n}\sum_{l,\,k=0}^{1}\left(\alpha_{slk}^{(i)}\right.\right.$$

$$\times\frac{d^l}{dx^l}\sum_{j=1}^{n}\int_{a_j}^{b_j}G^{(i,\,j)}(x,\xi,\lambda)\frac{\partial^{k+1}f^{(j)}(\xi,t)}{\partial t^{k+1}}\,(c_{02}^{(j)}(\xi))^{-1}\,d\xi\bigg|_{x=a_i}+$$

$$+\beta_{slk}^{(i)}\frac{d^l}{dx^l}\sum_{j=1}^{n}\int_{a_j}^{b_j}G^{(i,j)}(x,\xi,\lambda)$$

$$\times\frac{\partial^{k+1}f^{(j)}(\xi,t)}{\partial t^{k+1}}\,(c_{02}^{(j)}(\xi))^{-1}\,d\xi\Big|_{x=b_i}\Big)\Big\}\,d\lambda$$

$$-\frac{1}{\pi\sqrt{-1}}\int_M\frac{\lambda}{\lambda^4}e^{\lambda^2 t}\Big\{\sum_{i=1}^{n}\sum_{l,\,k=0}^{1}\Big(\alpha_{slk}^{(i)}\lambda^{2k}$$

$$\times\frac{d^l}{dx^l}\sum_{j=1}^{n}\int_{a_j}^{b_j}G^{(i,j)}(x,\xi,\lambda)\frac{\partial f^{(j)}(\xi,t)}{\partial t}\Big|_{t=0}(c_{02}^{(j)}(\xi))^{-1}\,d\xi\,|_{x=a_i}$$

$$+\beta_{slk}^{(i)}\lambda^{2k}\frac{d^l}{dx^l}\sum_{j=1}^{n}\int_{a_j}^{b_j}G^{(i,j)}(x,\xi,\lambda)$$

$$\times\frac{\partial f^{(j)}(\xi,t)}{\partial t}\Big|_{t=0}(c_{02}^{(j)}(\xi))^{-1}\,d\xi\,|_{x=b_i}\Big)\Big\}\,d\lambda$$

$$-\frac{1}{\pi\sqrt{-1}}\int_M\frac{\lambda}{\lambda^4}\Big\{\sum_{i=1}^{n}\sum_{l,\,k=0}^{1}\Big(\alpha_{slk}^{(i)}\lambda^{2k}\frac{d^l}{dx^l}\sum_{j=1}^{n}\int_{a_j}^{b_j}G^{(i,j)}(x,\xi,\lambda)$$

$$\times\int_0^t\exp\,[\lambda^2(t-\tau)]\,\frac{\partial^2 f^{(j)}(\xi,\tau)}{\partial\tau^2}\,d\tau\,(c_{02}^{(j)}(\xi))^{-1}\,d\xi\,|_{x=a_i}$$

$$+\beta_{slk}^{(i)}\lambda^{2k}\frac{d^l}{dx^l}\sum_{j=1}^{n}\int_{a_j}^{b_j}G^{(i,j)}(x,\xi,\lambda)$$

$$\times\int_0^t\exp\,(\lambda^2(t-\tau))\,\frac{\partial^2 f^{(j)}(\xi,\tau)}{\partial\tau^2}\,d\tau\,(c_{02}^{(j)}(\xi))^{-1}\,d\xi\,|_{x=b_i}\Big)\Big\}\,d\lambda$$

$$-\frac{1}{\pi\sqrt{-1}}\int_M\frac{\lambda}{\lambda^4}\Big\{\sum_{i=1}^{n}\sum_{l=0}^{1}\Big(\alpha_{sl1}^{(i)}$$

$$\times\frac{d^l}{dx^l}\sum_{j=1}^{n}\int_{a_j}^{b_j}G^{(i,j)}(x,\xi,\lambda)\frac{\partial^2 f^{(j)}(\xi,t)}{\partial t^2}\,(c_{02}^{(j)}(\xi))^{-1}\,d\xi\,|_{x=a_i}$$

$$+\beta_{sl1}^{(i)}\frac{d^l}{dx^l}\sum_{j=1}^{n}\int_{a_j}^{b_j}G^{(i,j)}(x,\xi,\lambda)$$

$$\times\frac{\partial^2 f^{(j)}(\xi,t)}{\partial t^2}(c_{02}^{(j)}(\xi))^{-1}d\xi\,|_{x=b_i}\Big)\Big\}\,d\lambda$$

The first integral over the contour M in the right-hand side of this last equation vanishes because the integrand decreases faster than does λ^{-2}. Consequently, if we represent this integral in the form of the limit of an integral over the contour $O_{\nu 1}$, we see that it is equal to zero. Similarly, we can see that the third and sixth integrals on the right-hand side of this equation are equal to zero. The remaining integrals over the contour M are equal to zero because

$$\sum_{j=1}^{n} \int_{a_j}^{b_j} G^{(i,j)}(x, \xi, \lambda)\, \Phi^{(j)}(\xi, t)\, d\xi$$

is a solution of the spectral problem (6.2.1)-(6.2.2) under corresponding homogeneous boundary conditions.

Thus, the function defined by (6.3.27) satisfies the corresponding homogeneous boundary conditions (6.1.1)-(6.1.3). Therefore, to complete the proof of Theorem 25, we need to show that (6.3.27) satisfies (6.1.1). When we apply the operator

$$L^{(i)}\left(x, \frac{\partial}{\partial x}\right) - \frac{\partial}{\partial t} \equiv c_{02}^{(i)}(x)\frac{\partial^2}{\partial x^2} + c_{01}^{(i)}(x)\frac{\partial}{\partial x} + c_{00}^{(i)}(x) - \frac{\partial}{\partial t} \tag{6.3.31}$$

to the integral (6.3.27), we may not differentiate under the integral sign over the contour M. Therefore, we have to calculate the principal part of this integral separately.

For this, we introduce the notations

$$G_1^{(i)}(x, \xi, \lambda) = \begin{cases} \lambda^{-1}\exp\left(\lambda \int_{\xi}^{x} \varphi_1^{(i)}(z)\,dz\right)\gamma_{100}^{(i)}(x, \xi) \\ \qquad \text{for } a_i \leqslant \xi \leqslant x \leqslant b_i \\ -\lambda^{-1}\exp\left(\lambda \int_{\xi}^{x} \varphi_2^{(i)}(z)\,dz\right)\gamma_{200}^{(i)}(x, \xi) \\ \qquad \text{for } a_i \leqslant x \leqslant \xi \leqslant b_i \end{cases} \tag{6.3.32}$$

$$G_2^{(i,j)}(x, \xi, \lambda) = G^{(i,j)}(x, \xi, \lambda) - G_1^{(i)}(x, \xi, \lambda) \tag{6.3.33}$$

Obviously,

$$-\pi\sqrt{-1}\left(L^{(i)}\left(x, \frac{\partial}{\partial x}\right) v_{22}^{(i)}(x, t) - \frac{\partial v_{22}^{(i)}(x, t)}{\partial t}\right)$$

$$\equiv \left(L^{(i)}\left(x, \frac{\partial}{\partial x}\right) - \frac{\partial}{\partial t}\right) \int_M \lambda\, d\lambda \sum_{j=1}^{n} \int_{a_j}^{b_j} G^{(i,j)}(x, \xi, \lambda)\, d\xi$$

$$\times \int_0^t \exp[\lambda^2 (t-\tau)]\, f^{(j)}(\xi, \tau)\, (c_{02}^{(j)}(\xi))^{-1}\, d\tau$$

$$= \left(L^{(i)}\left(x, \frac{\partial}{\partial x}\right) - \frac{\partial}{\partial t}\right) \int_M \lambda\, d\lambda \int_{a_i}^{b_i} G_1^{(i)}(x, \xi, \lambda)\, (c_{02}^{(i)}(\xi))^{-1}\, d\xi \qquad (6.3.34)$$

$$\times \int_0^t \exp[\lambda^2 (t-\tau)]\, f^{(i)}(\xi, \tau)\, d\tau$$

$$+ \left(L^{(i)}\left(x, \frac{\partial}{\partial x}\right) - \frac{\partial}{\partial t}\right) \int_M \lambda\, d\lambda \sum_{j=1}^{n} \int_{a_j}^{b_j} G_2^{(i,j)}(x, \xi, \lambda)$$

$$\times (c_{02}^{(j)}(\xi))^{-1}\, d\xi \int_0^t \exp[\lambda^2 (t-\tau)]\, f^{(i)}(\xi, \tau)\, d\tau$$

In accordance with Theorem 23 (see (6.2.64) and (6.2.75)) and the identity (6.3.33), the integrand in the second term on the right-hand side of (6.3.34) decreases on the contour M faster than does λ^{-4}. Consequently, this integral can be differentiated twice with respect to x and once with respect to t. Then, obviously, we obtain from (6.3.34)

$$-\pi\sqrt{-1}\left(L^{(i)}\left(x, \frac{\partial}{\partial x}\right) v_{22}^{(i)} - \frac{\partial v_{22}^{(i)}}{\partial t}\right)$$

$$\equiv \left(L^{(i)}\left(x, \frac{\partial}{\partial x}\right) - \frac{\partial}{\partial t}\right) \int_M \lambda\, d\lambda \int_{a_i}^{b_i} G_1^{(i)}(x, \xi, \lambda) \qquad (6.3.35)$$

$$\times (c_{02}^{(i)}(\xi))^{-1}\, d\xi \int_0^t \exp[\lambda^2 (t-\tau)]\, f^{(i)}(\xi, \tau)\, d\tau$$

$$+\int_M \lambda\, d\lambda \left\{ \left(L^{(i)}\left(x, \frac{\partial}{\partial x}\right) - \lambda^2 \right) \sum_{j=1}^{n} \int_{a_j}^{b_j} G_2^{(i,j)}(x, \xi, \lambda) \right.$$

$$\left. \times (c_{02}^{(j)}(\xi))^{-1} d\xi \int_0^t \exp[\lambda^2 (t-\tau)] f^{(j)}(\xi, \tau)\, d\tau \right\}$$

$$- \int_M \left\{ \sum_{j=1}^{n} \int_{a_j}^{b_j} G_2^{(i,j)}(x, \xi, \lambda) (c_{02}^{(j)}(\xi))^{-1} f^{(j)}(\xi, t)\, d\xi \right\} \lambda\, d\lambda \qquad (6.3.35)\ \text{(cont.)}$$

The integrand in the third term decreases on the contour M faster than does λ^{-2}. Therefore, the integral is equal to zero. Then, bearing in mind the identities

$$\left(L^{(i)}\left(x, \frac{\partial}{\partial x}\right) - \lambda^2 \right) \sum_{j=1}^{n} \int_{a_j}^{b_j} G^{(i,j)}(x, \xi, \lambda) (c_{02}^{(j)}(\xi))^{-1} d\xi$$

$$\times \int_0^t \exp[\lambda^2 (t-\tau)] f^{(j)}(\xi, \tau)\, d\tau$$

$$= \int_0^t \exp[\lambda^2 (t-\tau)] f^{(i)}(x, \tau)\, d\tau$$

$$G^{(i,j)}(x, \xi, \lambda) = G_1^{(i)}(x, \xi, \lambda) + G_2^{(i,j)}(x, \xi, \lambda)$$

we obtain from (6.3.35)

$$-\pi \sqrt{-1} \left(L^{(i)}\left(x, \frac{\partial}{\partial x}\right) v_{22}^{(i)} - \frac{\partial v_{22}^{(i)}}{\partial t} \right)$$

$$= \left(L^{(i)}\left(x, \frac{\partial}{\partial x}\right) - \frac{\partial}{\partial t} \right) \int_M \lambda\, d\lambda \int_{a_i}^{b_i} G_1^{(i)}(x, \xi, \lambda) (c_{02}^{(i)}(\xi))^{-1} d\xi$$

$$\times \int_0^t \exp[\lambda^2 (t-\tau)] f^{(i)}(\xi, \tau)\, d\tau$$

$$- \int_M \lambda\, d\lambda \left\{ \left(L^{(i)}\left(x, \frac{\partial}{\partial x}\right) - \lambda^2 \right) \int_{a_i}^{b_i} G_1^{(i)}(x, \xi, \lambda) (c_{02}^{(i)}(\xi))^{-1} d\xi \right.$$

$$\left. \times \int_0^t \exp[\lambda^2 (t-\tau)] f^{(i)}(\xi, \tau)\, d\tau \right\}$$

$$+ \int_M \lambda\, d\lambda \int_0^t \exp[\lambda^2 (t-\tau)] f^{(i)}(x, \tau)\, d\tau \qquad (6.3.36)$$

Since the function

$$\int_{a_i}^{b_i} G_1^{(i)}(x, \xi, \lambda)\,(c_{02}^{(i)}(\xi))^{-1}\,d\xi \int_0^t \exp[\lambda^2(t-\tau)]\,f^{(i)}(\xi, \tau)\,d\tau$$

decreases on the contour M faster than does λ^{-3}, the first-order differential operator in the second term of (6.3.36) can be taken from under the integral sign over the contour M. Then, keeping (6.3.31) in mind, we obtain from (6.3.36)

$$\begin{aligned}
&-\pi\sqrt{-1}\left(L^{(i)}\left(x, \frac{\partial}{\partial x}\right) v_{22}^{(i)} - \frac{\partial v_{22}^{(i)}}{\partial t}\right)\\
&\quad = \left(c_{02}^{(i)}(x)\frac{\partial^2}{\partial x^2} - \frac{\partial}{\partial t}\right)\int_M \lambda\,d\lambda \int_{a_i}^{b_i} G_1^{(i)}(x, \xi, \lambda)\\
&\qquad\times (c_{02}^{(i)}(\xi))^{-1}\,d\xi \int_0^t \exp[\lambda^2(t-\tau)]\,f^{(i)}(\xi, \tau)\,d\tau\\
&\quad -\int_M \lambda\,d\lambda\left\{\left(c_{02}^{(i)}(x)\frac{\partial^2}{\partial x^2} - \lambda^2\right)\int_{a_i}^{b_i} G_1^{(i)}(x, \xi, \lambda)\right.\\
&\qquad\times (c_{02}^{(i)}(\xi))^{-1}\,d\xi \int_0^t \exp[\lambda^2(t-\tau)]\,f^{(i)}(\xi, \tau)\,d\tau\\
&\quad\left. -\int_0^t \exp[\lambda^2(t-\tau)]\,f^{(i)}(x, \tau)\,d\tau\right\}
\end{aligned} \qquad (6.3.37)$$

Let us now evaluate the expressions in the braces in the second integral in (6.3.37). To simplify the writing, we introduce the notation

$$\Phi_s^{(i)}(x, \xi, \tau) = \gamma_{s00}^{(i)}(x, \xi)\,(c_{02}^{(i)}(\xi))^{-1} f^{(i)}(\xi, \tau) \qquad (6.3.38)$$

It follows from (6.2.30), (6.2.60) and (6.2.64) that

$$\Phi_1^{(i)}(x, \xi, \tau) = -\Phi_2^{(i)}(x, \xi, \tau)$$

Keeping (6.3.32) and (6.3.38) in mind, we obtain directly

$$\left(c_{02}^{(i)}(x)\frac{\partial^2}{\partial x^2}-\lambda^2\right)\int\limits_{a_i}^{b_i} G_1^{(i)}(x,\xi,\lambda)$$

$$\times (c_{02}^{(i)}(\xi))^{-1}\,d\xi\int\limits_0^t \exp(\lambda^2(t-\tau))\,f^{(i)}(\xi,\tau)\,d\tau$$

$$=\left(c_{02}^{(i)}(x)\frac{\partial^2}{\partial x^2}-\lambda^2\right)\left\{\frac{1}{\lambda}\int\limits_{a_i}^{x} d\xi\exp\left(\lambda\int\limits_{\xi}^{x}\varphi_1^{(i)}(z)\,dz\right)\right.$$

$$\times \gamma_{100}^{(i)}(x,\xi)\,(c_{02}^{(i)}(\xi))^{-1}\int\limits_0^t e^{\lambda^2(t-\tau)}f^{(i)}(\xi,\tau)\,d\tau$$

$$-\frac{1}{\lambda}\int\limits_{x}^{b_i} d\xi\exp\left(\lambda\int\limits_{\xi}^{x}\varphi_2^{(i)}(z)\,dz\right)\gamma_{200}^{(i)}(x,\xi)$$

$$\left.\times\int\limits_0^t \exp(\lambda^2(t-\tau))\,(c_{02}^{(i)}(\xi))^{-1}f^{(i)}(\xi,\tau)\,d\tau\right\}$$

$$=\int\limits_0^t\frac{e^{\lambda^2(t-\tau)}}{\lambda}\left(c_{02}^{(i)}(x)\frac{\partial^2}{\partial x^2}-\lambda^2\right) \tag{6.3.38a}$$

$$\times\left\{\int\limits_{a_i}^{x} d\xi\exp\left(\lambda\int\limits_{\xi}^{x}\varphi_1^{(i)}(z)\,dz\right)\Phi_1^{(i)}(x,\xi,\tau)\right.$$

$$\left.+\int\limits_{b_i}^{x} d\xi\exp\left(\lambda\int\limits_{\xi}^{x}\varphi_2^{(i)}(z)\,dz\right)\Phi_2^{(i)}(x,\xi,\tau)\right\}d\tau$$

$$=\int\limits_0^t\exp(\lambda^2(t-\tau))\left\{c_{02}^{(i)}(x)\,(\varphi_1^{(i)}(x)\,\Phi_1^{(i)}(x,x,\tau)\right.$$

$$+\varphi_2^{(i)}(x)\,\Phi_2^{(i)}(x,x,\tau))+c_{02}^{(i)}(x)$$

$$\times\left(\frac{d\varphi_1^{(i)}(x)}{dx}\int\limits_{a_i}^{x} d\xi\exp\left(\lambda\int\limits_{\xi}^{x}\varphi_1^{(i)}(z)\,dz\right)\Phi_1^{(i)}(x,\xi,\tau)\right.$$

$$\left.+\frac{d\varphi_2^{(i)}(x)}{dx}\int\limits_{b_i}^{x} d\xi\exp\left(\lambda\int\limits_{\xi}^{x}\varphi_2^{(i)}(z)\,dz\right)\Phi_2^{(i)}(x,\xi,\tau)\right)$$

$$+2c_{02}^{(i)}(x)\left(\varphi_1^{(i)}(x)\int\limits_{a_i}^{x} d\xi\exp\left(\lambda\int\limits_{\xi}^{x}\varphi_1^{(i)}(z)\,dz\right)\frac{\partial\Phi_1^{(i)}(x,\xi,\tau)}{\partial x}+\right.$$

$$+\varphi_2^{(i)}(x)\int_{b_i}^{x} d\xi \exp\left(\lambda\int_{\xi}^{x}\varphi_2^{(i)}(z)\,dz\right)\frac{\partial\Phi_2^{(i)}(x,\xi,\tau)}{\partial x}\Bigg)$$

$$+\frac{c_{02}^{(i)}(x)}{\lambda}\left(\int_{a_i}^{x}\exp\left(\lambda\int_{\xi}^{x}\varphi_1^{(i)}(z)\,dz\right)\frac{\partial^2\Phi_1^{(i)}(x,\xi,\tau)}{\partial x^2}\,d\xi\right. \qquad (6.3.38a)\ (cont.)$$

$$\left.+\int_{b_i}^{x}\exp\left(\lambda\int_{\xi}^{x}\varphi_2^{(i)}(z)\,dz\right)\frac{\partial^2\Phi_2^{(i)}(x,\xi,\tau)}{\partial x^2}\,d\xi\right)\Bigg\}\,d\tau$$

From formulae (6.2.30), (6.2.60a), (6.2.64a) and (6.3.38), we easily see that

$$c_{02}^{(i)}(x)\left(\varphi_1^{(i)}(x)\,\Phi_1^{(i)}(x,x,\tau)+\varphi_2^{(i)}(x)\,\Phi_2^{(i)}(x,x,\tau)\right)=f^{(i)}(x,t)$$

Consequently, if we substitute (6.3.38a) into (6.3.37) and keep (6.3.32) and (6.3.38) in mind, we obtain

$$-\pi\sqrt{-1}\left(L^{(i)}\left(x,\frac{\partial}{\partial x}\right)v_{22}^{(i)}-\frac{\partial v_{22}^{(i)}}{\partial t}\right)$$

$$=\left(c_{02}^{(i)}(x)\frac{\partial^2}{\partial x^2}-\frac{\partial}{\partial t}\right)\int_0^t d\tau\left\{\int_{a_i}^{x}d\xi\,\Phi_1^{(i)}(x,\xi,\tau)\right.$$

$$\times\int_M\exp\left(\lambda^2(t-\tau)+\lambda\int_{\xi}^{x}\varphi_1^{(i)}(z)\,dz\right)d\lambda$$

$$\left.+\int_{b_i}^{x}d\xi\,\Phi_2^{(i)}(x,\xi,\tau)\int_M\exp\left(\lambda^2(t-\tau)+\lambda\int_{\xi}^{x}\varphi_2^{(i)}(z)\,dz\right)d\lambda\right\} \qquad (6.3.39)$$

$$-\int_0^t d\tau\left\{c_{02}^{(i)}(x)\left(\frac{d\varphi_1^{(i)}(x)}{dx}\int_{a_i}^{x}d\xi\,\Phi_1^{(i)}(x,\xi,\tau)\right.\right.$$

$$\times\int_M\lambda\exp\left(\lambda^2(t-\tau)+\lambda\int_{\xi}^{x}\varphi_1^{(i)}(z)\,dz\right)d\lambda$$

$$+\frac{d\varphi_2^{(i)}(x)}{dx}\int_{b_i}^{x}d\xi\,\Phi_2^{(i)}(x,\xi,\tau)\int_M\lambda\exp\left(\lambda^2(t-\tau)\right.$$

$$\left.\left.+\lambda\int_{\xi}^{x}\varphi_2^{(i)}(z)\,dz\right)d\lambda\right)+$$

$$+2c_{02}^{(i)}(x)\Big(\varphi_1^{(i)}(x)\int_{a_i}^{x} d\xi\,\frac{\partial\Phi_1^{(i)}(x,\xi,\tau)}{\partial x}\int_M \lambda\exp\Big(\lambda^2(t-\tau)+\lambda\int_{\xi}^{x}\varphi_1^{(i)}(z)\,dz\Big)\,d\lambda$$

$$+\varphi_2^{(i)}(x)\int_{b_i}^{x} d\xi\,\frac{\partial\Phi_2^{(i)}(x,\xi,\tau)}{\partial x}\int_M \lambda\exp\Big(\lambda^2(t-\tau)+\lambda\int_{\xi}^{x}\varphi_2^{(i)}(z)\,dz\Big)\,d\lambda\Big)$$

$$+c_{02}^{(i)}(x)\Big(\int_{a_i}^{x} d\xi\,\frac{\partial^2\Phi_1^{(i)}(x,\xi,\tau)}{\partial x^2}\int_M \exp\Big(\lambda^2(t-\tau)+\lambda\int_{\xi}^{x}\varphi_1^{(i)}(z)\,dz\Big)d\lambda \qquad \text{(6.5.39) (cont.)}$$

$$+\int_{b_i}^{x} d\xi\,\frac{\partial^2\Phi_2^{(i)}(x,\xi,\tau)}{\partial x^2}\int_M \exp\Big(\lambda^2(t-\tau)+\lambda\int_{\xi}^{x}\varphi_2^{(i)}(z)\,dz\Big)\,d\lambda\Big)\Big\}$$

We note that, in accordance with (6.3.1), in all the integrals over the contour M which appear in (6.3.39), the inequalities

$$\frac{\pi}{2}<\arg\lambda^2<\frac{3\pi}{2}$$

hold on the curve M and on the arcs $P_\nu Q_\nu$ and $P'_\nu Q'_\nu$.

Furthermore, in the half-plane Π_1, we have

$$\operatorname{Re}\lambda\int_{\xi}^{x}\varphi_k^{(i)}(z)\,dz\leqslant 0$$

Consequently, the integrals over the contour M which appear in (6.3.39) converge rapidly. Furthermore, for $t-\tau>0$,

$$\lim_{\nu\to\infty}\int_{\widehat{P_\nu Q_\nu}}\exp\Big(\lambda^2(t-\tau)+\lambda\int_{\xi}^{\tilde{x}}\varphi_s^{(i)}(z)\,dz\Big)\lambda^k\,d\lambda$$

$$=\lim_{\nu\to\infty}\int_{\widehat{P'_\nu Q'_\nu}}\exp\Big(\lambda^2(t-\tau)+\lambda\int_{\xi}^{x}\varphi_s^{(i)}(z)\,dz\Big)\lambda^k\,d\lambda=0$$

$$(s=1,2;\ k=0,1,\ldots)$$

Let us now evaluate the integral

$$I_k = \int_M \lambda^k \exp(\lambda^2 t_1 + \lambda F(x, \xi))\, d\lambda \tag{6.3.40}$$

under the conditions

$$t_1 > 0, \quad \frac{\pi}{2} < \arg \lambda^2 < \frac{3\pi}{2}$$

on the contours

$$M, \ \widehat{P_\nu Q_\nu}, \ \widehat{P'_\nu Q'_\nu} \tag{6.3.41}$$

$\operatorname{Re} \lambda F(x, \xi) \leqslant 0$ (for $F(x, \xi) \neq 0$) in the half-plane Π_1. In accordance with (6.3.41), it is clear that

$$\lim_{\nu\to\infty} \int_{\widehat{P_\nu Q_\nu}} \lambda^k \exp(\lambda^2 t_1 + \lambda F(x, \xi))\, d\lambda$$
$$= \lim_{\nu\to\infty} \int_{\widehat{P'_\nu Q'_\nu}} \lambda^k \exp(\lambda^2 t_1 + \lambda F(x, \xi))\, d\lambda = 0$$

Consequently,

$$\begin{aligned} I_k &= \int_M \lambda^k \exp(\lambda^2 t_1 + \lambda F(x, \xi))\, d\lambda \\ &= \lim_{\nu\to\infty} \int_{M_\nu} \lambda^k \exp(\lambda^2 t_1 + \lambda F(x, \xi))\, d\lambda \\ &= \lim_{\nu\to\infty} \int_{\overline{Q'_\nu Q_\nu}} \lambda^k \exp(\lambda^2 t_1 + \lambda F(x, \xi))\, d\lambda \\ &= e^{-\frac{F^2(x,\xi)}{4t_1}} \lim_{\nu\to\infty} \int_{\overline{Q'_\nu Q_\nu}} \lambda^k \exp\left[\left(\lambda\sqrt{t_1} + \frac{F(x,\xi)}{2\sqrt{t_1}}\right)^2\right] d\lambda \end{aligned} \tag{6.3.42}$$

Making the substitution

$$\lambda\sqrt{t_1} + \frac{F(x, \xi)}{2\sqrt{t_1}} = z \tag{6.3.43}$$

we obtain from (6.3.42)

$$I_k = e^{-\frac{F^2(x,\xi)}{4t_1}} \lim_{\nu\to\infty} \int_{\overline{S'_\nu S_\nu}} \left(z - \frac{F(x, \xi)}{2\sqrt{t_1}}\right)^k t_1^{-\frac{k+1}{2}} e^{z^2}\, dz \tag{6.3.44}$$

where (6.3.43) maps the path of integration in (6.3.42) into the segment $\overline{S'_\nu S_\nu}$ of a straight line parallel to the direction $\overline{Q'_\nu Q_\nu}$.

Let us join the points S_ν and S'_ν to the points Q_ν and Q'_ν, respectively, with straight-line segments. Then, in accordance with (6.3.1), we have

$$\lim_{\nu\to\infty}\int_{\overline{S_\nu Q_\nu}}\left(z-\frac{F(x,\xi)}{2\sqrt{t_1}}\right)^k t_1^{-\frac{k+1}{2}} e^{z^2}\,dz$$
$$=\lim_{\nu\to\infty}\int_{\overline{S'_\nu Q'_\nu}}\left(z-\frac{F(x,\xi)}{2\sqrt{t_1}}\right)^k t_1^{-\frac{k+1}{2}} e^{z^2}\,dz=0$$

Consequently, from (6.3.44), we have

$$I_k=\exp\left(-\frac{F^2(x,\xi)}{4t_1}\right)\lim_{\nu\to\infty}\int_{\overline{Q'_\nu Q_\nu}}\left(z-\frac{F(x,\xi)}{2\sqrt{t_1}}\right)^k t_1^{-\frac{k+1}{2}} e^{z^2}\,dz$$

Finally, after making the substitution

$$z=\alpha\sqrt{-1}\exp\left(\sqrt{-1}\,\frac{\gamma}{2}\right)=\sqrt{-c}\,\alpha$$

we obtain

$$I_k=t_1^{-\frac{k+1}{2}}\exp\left(-\frac{F^2(x,\xi)}{4t_1}\right)\sqrt{-c}$$
$$\times\int_{-\infty}^{\infty}\left(\sqrt{-c}\,\alpha-\frac{F(x,\xi)}{2\sqrt{t_1}}\right)^k e^{-c\alpha^2}\,d\alpha \qquad (6.3.45)$$

where, by assumption, $\operatorname{Re} c=\cos\gamma>0$. The integral (6.3.45) is easily evaluated by integrating by parts,

$$I_k=\int_M \lambda^k\exp\left(\lambda^2 t_1+\lambda F(x,\xi)\right)d\lambda$$
$$=\frac{\sqrt{-1}\sqrt{\pi}}{(\sqrt{t_1})^{k+1}}\exp\left(-\frac{F^2(x,\xi)}{4t_1}\right)P_k\left(-\frac{F(x,\xi)}{2\sqrt{t_1}}\right) \qquad (6.3.46)$$

where

$$P_k(\alpha)=\alpha^k-\frac{k(k-1)}{2!}\frac{1}{2}\alpha^{k-2}+\frac{k(k-1)(k-2)(k-3)}{4!}\frac{1\cdot 3\alpha^{k-4}}{2^2}$$
$$-\frac{k(k-1)(k-2)(k-3)(k-4)(k-5)}{6!}\frac{1\cdot 3\cdot 5}{2^3}\alpha^{k-6}+\dots \qquad (6.3.47)$$

The last term is equal to

$$(-1)^{\frac{k}{2}}\cdot 2^{-\frac{k}{2}}\cdot 1\cdot 3\dots(k-1)$$

if k is even and it is equal to

$$(-1)^{\frac{k-1}{2}}k\cdot 2^{-\frac{k-1}{2}}1\cdot 3\cdot 5\dots(k-2)\alpha$$

if k is odd, $P_0(\alpha)=1$. If we use (6.3.46) to evaluate the integrals over the contour M which appear in (6.3.39), taking into account the relation

$$\varphi_2^{(i)}(x)=-\varphi_1^{(i)}(x),\quad \Phi_2^{(i)}(x,\xi,\tau)=-\Phi_1^{(i)}(x,\xi,\tau)$$

we obtain from (6.3.39)

$$-\pi\sqrt{-1}\left(L^{(i)}\left(x,\frac{\partial}{\partial x}\right)v_{22}^{(i)}-\frac{\partial v_{22}^{(i)}}{\partial t}\right)$$
$$=\sqrt{-1}\sqrt{\pi}\left(c_{02}^{(i)}(x)\frac{\partial^2}{\partial x^2}-\frac{\partial}{\partial t}\right)\int_0^t d\tau\frac{1}{\sqrt{t-\tau}}$$
$$\times\int_{a_i}^{b_i}\exp\left[-\frac{1}{4(t-\tau)}\left(\int_\xi^x\varphi_1^{(i)}(z)\,dz\right)^2\right]\Phi_1^{(i)}(x,\xi,\tau)\,d\xi$$
$$+\frac{\sqrt{-1}\sqrt{\pi}}{2}\int_0^t\frac{d\tau}{(t-\tau)^{3/2}}\left\{\int_{a_i}^{b_i}c_{02}^{(i)}(x)\right.$$
$$\times\left(\frac{d\varphi_1^{(i)}(x)}{dx}\int_\xi^x\varphi_1^{(i)}(z)\,\Phi_1^{(i)}(x,\xi,\tau)\,dz\right. \qquad (6.3.48)$$
$$\left.+2\varphi_1^{(i)}(x)\left(\int_\xi^x\varphi_1^{(i)}(z)\,dz\right)\frac{\partial\Phi_1^{(i)}(x,\xi,\tau)}{\partial x}\right)$$
$$\times\exp\left[-\frac{1}{4(t-\tau)}\left(\int_\xi^x\varphi_1^{(i)}(z)\,dz\right)^2\right]d\xi-2(t-\tau)$$
$$\left.\times\int_{a_i}^{b_i}c_{02}^{(i)}(x)\frac{\partial^2\Phi_1^{(i)}(x,\xi,\tau)}{\partial x^2}\exp\left[-\frac{1}{4(t-\tau)}\left(\int_\xi^x\varphi_1^{(i)}(z)\,dz\right)^2\right]d\xi\right\}$$

Subtracting the operator $\left(c_{02}^{(i)}(x)\frac{\partial^2}{\partial x^2}-\frac{\partial}{\partial t}\right)$ from the first integral on the right-hand side of (6.3.48), we obtain

$$-\pi\sqrt{-1}\left(L^{(i)}\left(x,\frac{\partial}{\partial x}\right)v_{22}^{(i)}-\frac{\partial v_{22}^{(i)}}{\partial t}\right)$$

$$=-\sqrt{-1}\sqrt{\pi}\lim_{\tau\to t}\int_{a_i}^{b_i}\frac{\Phi_1^{(i)}(x,\xi,\tau)}{\sqrt{t-\tau}}$$

$$\times\exp\left[-\frac{1}{4(t-\tau)}\left(\int_{\xi}^{x}\varphi_1^{(i)}(z)\,dz\right)^2\right]d\xi \tag{6.3.49}$$

$$=-\sqrt{-1}\sqrt{\pi}\lim_{t_1\to+0}\int_{a_i}^{b_i}\frac{\Phi_1^{(i)}(x,\xi,t-t_1)}{\sqrt{t_1}}$$

$$\times\exp\left[-\frac{1}{4t_1}\left(\int_{\xi}^{x}\varphi_1^{(i)}(z)\,dz\right)^2\right]d\xi$$

Let us now evaluate the limit of the right-hand side of (6.3.49). Since $\varphi_1^{(i)}(z)$ is a root of the characteristic equation (6.2.24), we have

$$\left(\int_{\xi}^{x}\varphi_1^{(i)}(z)\,dz\right)^2=\left(\int_{x}^{\xi}\frac{dz}{\sqrt{c\,|\,c_{02}^{(i)}(z)\,|}}\right)^2=\frac{1}{c}\left(\int_{x}^{\xi}\varphi^{(i)}(z)\,dz\right)^2$$

where

$$\varphi^{(i)}(z)=\frac{1}{\sqrt{|\,c_{02}^{(i)}(z)\,|}}$$

Then, (6.3.49) can be rewritten in the form

$$\sqrt{\pi}\left(L^{(i)}\left(x,\frac{\partial}{\partial x}\right)v_{22}^{(i)}-\frac{\partial v_{22}^{(i)}}{\partial t}\right)$$

$$=\lim_{t_1\to 0}\int_{a_i}^{b_i}\frac{\Phi_1^{(i)}(x,\xi,t-t_1)}{\sqrt{t_1}}\exp\left[-\frac{1}{4ct_1}\left(\int_{x}^{\xi}\varphi^{(i)}(z)\,dz\right)^2\right]d\xi$$

Furthermore, under the hypotheses of the theorem, we have

$$|\,\Phi_1^{(i)}(x,\xi,t-t_1)-\Phi_1^{(i)}(x,\xi,t)\,|\leqslant Bt_1$$

where B is constant. Consequently, the last equation can be rewritten in the form

$$\sqrt{\pi}\left(L^{(i)}\left(x, \frac{\partial}{\partial x}\right) v_{22}^{(i)} - \frac{\partial v_{22}^{(i)}}{\partial t}\right) = \lim_{t_1\to 0} \int_{a_i}^{b_i} \frac{\Phi_1^{(i)}(x, \xi, t)}{\sqrt{t_1}} \exp\left[-\frac{1}{4ct_1}\left(\int_x^{\xi} \varphi^{(i)}(z)\,dz\right)^2\right] d\xi \tag{6.3.50}$$

To find the limit of the right-hand side of (6.3.50), we can rewrite the integral

$$J^{(i)} = \int_{a_i}^{b_i} \frac{\Phi_1^{(i)}(x, \xi, t)}{\sqrt{t_1}} \exp\left[-\frac{1}{4ct_1}\left(\int_x^{\xi} \varphi^{(i)}(z)\,dz\right)^2\right] d\xi \tag{6.3.51}$$

as the sum of three integrals taken, respectively, over the segments

$$(a_i, x-\sqrt[4]{t_1}), \quad (x-\sqrt[4]{t_1}, x+\sqrt[4]{t_1}), \quad (x+\sqrt[4]{t_1}, b_i)$$

Here, for simplicity of notation, we omit the subscript i

$$\begin{aligned} J &= \int_a^b \frac{\Phi_1(x, \xi, t)}{\sqrt{t_1}} \exp\left(-\frac{1}{4ct_1}\left(\int_x^{\xi} \varphi(z)\,dz\right)^2\right) d\xi \\ &= J_1 + J_2 + J_3 \\ J_1 &= \int_a^{x-\sqrt[4]{t_1}} \frac{\Phi_1(x, \xi, t)}{\sqrt{t_1}} \exp\left[-\frac{1}{4ct_1}\left(\int_x^{\xi} \varphi(z)\,dz\right)^2\right] d\xi \\ J_2 &= \int_{x-\sqrt[4]{t_1}}^{x+\sqrt[4]{t_1}} \frac{\Phi_1(x, \xi, t)}{\sqrt{t_1}} \exp\left(-\frac{1}{4ct_1}\left(\int_x^{\xi} \varphi(z)\,dz\right)^2\right) d\xi \\ J_3 &= \int_{x+\sqrt[4]{t_1}}^{b} \frac{\Phi_1(x, \xi, t)}{\sqrt{t_1}} \exp\left[-\frac{1}{4ct_1}\left(\int_x^{\xi} \varphi(z)\,dz\right)^2\right] d\xi \end{aligned} \tag{6.3.52}$$

The integral J_2 can be represented in the form of a sum

$$J_2 = J_{21} + \frac{\Phi_1(x, x, t)}{\varphi(x)} \int_{x-\sqrt[4]{t_1}}^{x+\sqrt[4]{t_1}} \frac{1}{\sqrt{t_1}} \times \exp\left(-\frac{1}{4ct_1}\left(\int_x^{\xi} \varphi(z)\,dz\right)^2\right) \varphi(\xi)\,d\xi \tag{6.3.53}$$

where

$$J_{21}=\int_{x-\sqrt[4]{t_1}}^{x+\sqrt[4]{t_1}}\left(\frac{\Phi_1(x,\xi,t)}{\varphi(\xi)\sqrt{t_1}}-\frac{\Phi_1(x,x,t)}{\varphi(x)\sqrt{t_1}}\right)$$
$$\times\exp\left(-\frac{1}{4ct_1}\left(\int_x^{\xi}\varphi(z)\,dz\right)^2\right)\varphi(\xi)\,d\xi$$

Making the substitution

$$\int_x^{\xi}\varphi(z)\,dz=2\sqrt{t_1}\,\alpha \tag{6.3.54}$$

we obtain

$$\int_{x-\sqrt[4]{t_1}}^{x+\sqrt[4]{t_1}}\frac{\varphi(\xi)}{\sqrt{t_1}}\exp\left(-\frac{1}{4ct_1}\left(\int_x^{\xi}\varphi(z)\,dz\right)^2\right)d\xi=2\int_{\alpha_1(x,t_1)}^{\alpha_2(x,t_1)}e^{-\frac{\alpha^2}{c}}\,d\alpha \tag{6.3.55}$$

where

$$\alpha_1(x,t_1)=\frac{-1}{2\sqrt{t_1}}\int_{x-\sqrt[4]{t_1}}^{x}\varphi(\xi)\,d\xi\leqslant\frac{-\min\varphi(\xi)}{2\sqrt[4]{t_1}}$$

$$\alpha_2(x,t_1)=\frac{1}{2\sqrt{t_1}}\int_{x}^{x+\sqrt[4]{t_1}}\varphi(\xi)\,d\xi\geqslant\frac{\min\varphi(\xi)}{2\sqrt[4]{t_1}}$$

Then, from (6.3.55), we obtain

$$\lim_{t_1\to 0}\int_{x-\sqrt[4]{t_1}}^{x+\sqrt[4]{t_1}}\frac{\varphi(\xi)}{\sqrt{t_1}}\exp\left[-\frac{1}{4ct_1}\left(\int_x^{\xi}\varphi(z)\,dz\right)^2\right]d\xi$$
$$=2\int_{-\infty}^{\infty}e^{-\frac{\alpha^2}{c}}\,d\alpha=2\sqrt{\pi c} \tag{6.3.56}$$

$$|J_{21}|\leqslant\max_{x-\sqrt[4]{t_1}\leqslant\xi\leqslant x+\sqrt[4]{t_1}}\left|\frac{\Phi_1(x,\xi,t)}{\varphi(\xi)}-\frac{\Phi_1(x,x,t)}{\varphi(x)}\right|$$
$$\times\int_{\alpha_1(x,t)}^{\alpha_2(x,t)}\exp\left\{-\frac{\operatorname{Re}c}{|c|^2}\,\alpha^2\right\}d\alpha$$

From this it follows that

$$\lim_{t_1\to 0}J_{21}=0$$

Consequently, keeping (6.3.56) in mind, we obtain from (6.3.53)

$$\lim_{t_1\to 0} J_2 = \frac{2\sqrt{\pi c}\,\Phi_1(x, x, t)}{\varphi(x)} \tag{6.3.57}$$

Furthermore, with the aid of the substitution (6.3.54), we have

$$|J_1| \leqslant 2 \max_{a\leqslant\xi\leqslant b} \left|\frac{\Phi_1(x, \xi, t)}{\varphi(\xi)}\right| \int_{\beta_1}^{\beta_2} \exp\left[-\frac{\operatorname{Re} c\alpha^2}{|c|^2}\right] d\alpha$$

$$\beta_1 = -\frac{1}{2\sqrt{t_1}} \int_a^x \varphi(z)\,dz \leqslant \frac{-\min\limits_{a\leqslant z\leqslant b} \varphi(z)\,(x-a)}{2\sqrt{t_1}}$$

$$\beta_2 = -\frac{1}{2\sqrt{t_1}} \int_{x-\sqrt[4]{t_1}}^{x} \varphi(z)\,dz \leqslant \frac{-\min\limits_{a\leqslant z\leqslant b} \varphi(z)}{2\sqrt[4]{t_1}}$$

$$|J_3| \leqslant 2 \max_{a\leqslant\xi\leqslant b} \left|\frac{\Phi_1(x, \xi, t)}{\varphi(\xi)}\right| \int_{\gamma_1}^{\gamma_2} \exp\left\{-\frac{\operatorname{Re} c}{|c|^2}\alpha^2\right\} d\alpha$$

$$\gamma_1 = \frac{1}{2\sqrt{t_1}} \int_x^{x+\sqrt[4]{t_1}} \varphi(z)\,dz \geqslant \frac{\min \varphi(z)}{2\sqrt[4]{t_1}}$$

$$\gamma_2 = \frac{1}{2\sqrt{t_1}} \int_x^b \varphi(z)\,dz \geqslant \frac{\min \varphi(z)\,(b-x)}{2\sqrt{t_1}}$$

From these inequalities, we obtain

$$\lim_{t_1\to 0} J_1 = 0; \quad \lim_{t_1\to 0} J_3 = 0.$$

Consequently, keeping (6.3.57), (6.3.52) and (6.3.51) in mind, we obtain

$$\lim_{t_1\to 0} J^{(i)} = \lim_{t_1\to 0} \int_{a_i}^{b_i} \frac{\Phi_1^{(i)}(x, \xi, t)}{\sqrt{t_1}} \tag{6.3.58}$$

$$\times \exp\left[-\frac{1}{4ct_1}\left(\int_x^{\xi} \varphi^{(i)}(z)\,dz\right)^2\right] d\xi = \frac{2\sqrt{\pi}\,\Phi_1^{(i)}(x, x, t)\sqrt{c}}{\varphi^{(i)}(x)}$$

Substituting (6.3.58) into (6.3.50), we have

$$\left(L^{(i)}\left(x, \frac{\partial}{\partial x}\right) v_{22}^{(i)} - \frac{\partial v_{22}^{(i)}}{\partial t}\right)$$

$$= \frac{2\Phi_1^{(i)}(x, x, t)\sqrt{c}}{\varphi^{(i)}(x)} = -2\frac{\Phi_1^{(i)}(x, x, t)}{\varphi_1^{(i)}(x)}$$

$$= -2\frac{\gamma_{100}^{(i)}(x, x)}{\varphi_1^{(i)}(x)}(c_{02}^{(i)}(x))^{-1} f^{(i)}(x, t)$$

$$= -f^{(i)}(x, t)$$

which completes the proof.

Remark In a similar manner, we can prove that the function $\tilde{v}_{2}^{(i)}(x, t)$ defined by

$$\tilde{v}_2^{(i)}(x, t)$$

$$= \frac{-1}{\pi\sqrt{-1}} \int_{-M} \lambda \, d\lambda \sum_{j=1}^{n} \int_{a_j}^{b_j} G^{(i, j)}(x, \xi, \lambda) \left\{ e^{\lambda^2 t} \Phi^{(j)}(\xi) \right. \tag{6.3.59}$$

$$\left. + \int_0^t e^{\lambda^2 (t-\tau)} f^{(j)}(\xi, \tau)\, d\tau \right\} (c_{02}^{(j)}(\xi))^{-1} \, d\xi$$

is a solution of Problem B.

6.4 EXPANSION OF AN ARBITRARY FUNCTION IN A SERIES OF RESIDUES OF THE SPECTRAL PROBLEM: NECESSARY AND SUFFICIENT CONDITIONS FOR THE CORRECT FORMULATION OF PROBLEM (6.1.1)–(6.1.3)

With the aid of Theorem 23, we can prove Theorem 26 below.

Theorem 26 Suppose that Conditions A and B of Section 6.1 are satisfied. Suppose that $\Phi^{(i)}(x)$ has continuous first and second derivatives* for

$$x \in [a_i, b_i] \quad (i = 1, 2, \ldots, n)$$

*If necessary, these smoothness conditions on $\Phi^{(i)}(x)$ can be considerably weakened.

Then,

$$\frac{-1}{2\pi\sqrt{-1}}\sum_{\nu}\int_{c_\nu}\lambda^s\,d\lambda\sum_{j=1}^{n}\int_{a_j}^{b_j}G^{(i,\,j)}(x,\xi,\lambda)(c_{02}^{(j)}(\xi))^{-1}\Phi^{(j)}(\xi)\,d\xi = \begin{cases} 0 & \text{for } s=0 \\ \Phi^{(i)}(x) & \text{for } s=1 \end{cases} \tag{6.4.1}$$

where c_ν is a simple closed contour encircling only one pole λ_ν of the integrand.* Furthermore, the convergence of the series (6.4.1) is uniform with respect to $x\in(a_i, b_i)$.
Proof Let us evaluate the limit of the integrals

$$I_{\nu s}^{(i)}(\Phi)=\frac{-1}{2\pi\sqrt{-1}}\int_{\Gamma_\nu}\lambda^s\,d\lambda \times\sum_{j=1}^{n}\int_{a_j}^{b_j}G^{(i,\,j)}(x,\xi,\lambda)\,(c_{02}^{(j)}(\xi))^{-1}\Phi^{(j)}(\xi)\,d\xi \tag{6.4.2}$$

as $\nu\to\infty$, where Γ_ν is an arbitrary sequence of expanding closed contours in the λ-plane which are located outside a δ-neighbourhood of the spectrum of the Problem (6.2.1)-(6.2.2). This means that the Γ_ν do not intersect the circles $Q_{\delta k}^1$ and that the distance R_ν of the closest point on the contour Γ_ν from the coordinate origin in the λ-plane approaches infinity.

The integral (6.4.2) can be represented in the form of the sum of two integrals over the portions $\Gamma_{\nu 1}$ and $\Gamma_{\nu 2}$ located, respectively, in the half-plane Π_1 and Π_2. Furthermore, if we both add and subtract the expression

$$\frac{1}{\lambda^2}\left(\frac{F_1^{(i)}(x,x)}{\varphi_1^{(i)}(x)}+\frac{F_2^{(i)}(x,x)}{\varphi_2^{(i)}(x)}\right)=\Phi^{(i)}(x)\frac{1}{\lambda^2}$$

*In reference [40n], this theorem is proved for an extremely general spectral problem. However, there the convergence of the series (6.4.1) is understood in the sense of the metric L_2. Also, the restrictions imposed in [40n] on the boundary conditions are more difficult to verify. This formula for equations with continuous coefficients had already been discovered by Tamarkin.

from the integrand, we obtain

$$-2\pi\sqrt{-1}\,I_{\nu s}^{(i)}(\Phi)$$

$$=\int_{\Gamma_{\nu_1}}\lambda^s\,d\lambda\Big\{\sum_{j=1}^{n}\int_{a_j}^{b_j}G^{(i,j)}(x,\xi,\lambda)\,(c_{02}^{(j)}(\xi))^{-1}\Phi^{(j)}(\xi)\,d\xi$$

$$+\frac{1}{\lambda^2}\Big(\frac{F_1^{(i)}(x,x)}{\varphi_1^{(i)}(x)}+\frac{F_2^{(i)}(x,x)}{\varphi_2^{(i)}(x)}\Big)\Big\}$$

$$+\int_{\Gamma_{\nu 2}}\lambda^s\,d\lambda\Big\{\sum_{j=1}^{n}\int_{a_j}^{b_j}G^{(i,j)}(x,\xi,\lambda)\,(c_{02}^{(j)}(\xi))^{-1}\,\Phi^{(j)}(\xi)\,d\xi \tag{6.4.3}$$

$$+\frac{1}{\lambda^2}\Big(\frac{F_1^{(i)}(x,x)}{\varphi_1^{(i)}(x)}+\frac{F_2^{(i)}(x,x)}{\varphi_2^{(i)}(x)}\Big)\Big\}-2\pi\sqrt{-1}\,\Phi^{(i)}(x)\int_{\Gamma_\nu}\frac{\lambda^s}{\lambda^2}\,d\lambda$$

In accordance with Theorem 23, it is clear from (6.3.23)-(6.3.25) that the non-principal part of the integrand in the first two terms on the right-hand side of (6.4.3) decreases on the contours $\Gamma_{\nu 1}$ and $\Gamma_{\nu 2}$ for $x\in(a_i,b_i)$ faster than does λ^{-2}. Using (6.2.75) and integrating by parts, we can easily see that the principal part of this function for $s\leqslant 1$ can be represented in the form

$$\lambda^{s-1}\Big\{\exp\Big(\lambda\int_{a_i}^{x}\varphi_1^{(i)}(z)\,dz\Big)\frac{E_1^{(i)}(x,\lambda)}{\lambda}$$

$$+\exp\Big(-\lambda\int_{x}^{b_i}\varphi_2^{(i)}(z)\,dz\Big)\frac{E_2^{(i)}(x,\lambda)}{\lambda}\Big\}\qquad(s=0,\ 1)$$

where $E_1^{(i)}(x,\lambda)$ and $E_2^{(i)}(x,\lambda)$ are uniformly bounded on the contours $\Gamma_{\nu k}$ (for $k=1,\ 2$). Then, in accordance with Lemma 6 of Section 3.1

$$\lim_{\nu\to\infty}\int_{\Gamma_{\nu k}}\lambda^{s-1}\,d\lambda\Big\{\exp\Big(\lambda\int_{a_i}^{x}\varphi_1^{(i)}(z)\,dz\Big)\frac{E_1^{(i)}(x,\lambda)}{\lambda}$$

$$+\exp\Big(-\lambda\int_{x}^{b_i}\varphi_2^{(i)}(z)\,dz\Big)\frac{E_2^{(i)}(x,\lambda)}{\lambda}\Big\}=0$$

This is uniform with respect to $x \in [a_i+\varepsilon,\ b_i-\varepsilon]$, where $0<\varepsilon<\frac{b_i-a_i}{2}$. Consequently, the limit of the integrals (6.4.3) as $\nu \to \infty$ are equal to zero. Therefore, if we take the limit in (6.4.3) as $\nu \to \infty$, we obtain

$$\lim_{\nu\to\infty} I_{\nu s}^{(i)}(\Phi) = \frac{-1}{2\pi\sqrt{-1}} \lim_{\nu\to\infty} \int_{\Gamma_\nu} \lambda^s \, d\lambda \sum_{j=1}^{n} \int_{a_j}^{b_j} G^{(i,j)}(x,\xi,\lambda)$$

$$\times (c_{02}^{(j)}(\xi))^{-1}\Phi^{(j)}(\xi)\, d\xi = \begin{cases} 0 & \text{for } s=0 \\ \Phi^{(i)}(x) & \text{for } s=1 \end{cases}$$

which completes the proof.

Theorem 27 Suppose that Conditions A and B of Section 6.1 are satisfied and that Problem B for functions $\Phi^{(i)}(x)$ and $f^{(i)}(x,t)$ with continuous first and second derivatives for $x \in [a_i, b_i]$ and $t \in [0, T]$ has a solution $v_2^{(i)}(x,t)$ which is continuous for $x \in (a_i, b_i)$ and $t \in [0, T]$ and which has continuous first and second derivatives for $x \in (a_i, b_i)$, $t>0$. Then, this solution can be represented in the form of a complete integral residue

$$v_2^{(i)}(x,t) = \frac{-1}{2\pi\sqrt{-1}} \sum_{\nu} \int_{c_\nu} \lambda \, d\lambda$$

$$\times \Big\{ \sum_{j=1}^{n} \int_{a_j}^{b_j} G^{(i,j)}(x,\xi,\lambda) \big(\Phi^{(j)}(\xi)\, e^{\lambda^2 t} \tag{6.4.4}$$

$$+ \int_0^t e^{\lambda^2(t-\tau)} f^{(j)}(\xi,\tau)\, d\tau\big) (c_{02}^{(j)}(\xi))^{-1} d\xi \Big\}$$

This theorem is proved on the basis of (6.4.1) in just the same way as the corresponding Theorem 11 of Chapter 3 was proved.

Now, we can easily prove Theorem 28 below.

Theorem 28 Under the hypotheses of Theorem 25, Problem (6.1.1)-(6.1.3) is correctly formulated, and its solution can be represented in the form of a complete integral residue

$$v^{(i)}(x, t) = -\frac{1}{2\pi\sqrt{-1}} \lim_{\nu\to\infty} \int_{\Gamma_\nu} \Big\{ \frac{-e^{\lambda^2 t}\Delta^{(i)}(x, \lambda)}{\lambda\Delta(\lambda)}$$
$$+ \lambda \sum_{j=1}^{n} \int_{a_j}^{b_j} G^{(i,j)}(x, \xi, \lambda) \Big(e^{\lambda^2 t}\Phi^{(j)}(\xi) \qquad (6.4.5)$$
$$+ \int_0^t \exp[\lambda^2 (t-\tau)] f^{(j)}(\xi, \tau)\, d\tau \Big) (c_{02}^{(j)}(\xi))^{-1} d\xi \Big\} d\lambda$$

where Γ_ν is a sequence of closed expanding contours in the λ-plane which are located outside the δ-neighbourhood of the spectrum of Problem (6.2.1)-(6.2.2).

Proof In accordance with Theorems 24 and 25, Problems A and B have sufficiently smooth solutions, and these solutions are unique. To see this, note that the difference of two sufficiently smooth solutions (of either Problem A or Problem B) is also a sufficiently smooth solution of Problem B for homogeneous equations with homogeneous initial conditions. In accordance with Theorem 27, this solution can be represented in the form (6.4.4), where $\Phi^{(i)}(x) \equiv 0$ and $f^{(i)}(x, t) \equiv 0$. Consequently, it is identically zero. Thus, the functions defined by (6.3.6) and (6.3.17) coincide.

Now, taking into account the equations

$$\lim_{\nu\to\infty} \int_{O_{\nu 2}} e^{\lambda^2 t} \frac{\Delta^{(i)}(x, \lambda)}{\lambda\Delta(\lambda)} d\lambda = \lim_{\nu\to\infty} \int_{-O_{\nu 2}} e^{\lambda^2 t} \frac{\Delta^{(i)}(x, \lambda)}{\lambda\Delta(\lambda)} d\lambda \equiv 0$$

and adding (6.3.6) and (6.3.17), we obtain

$$v_1^{(i)}(x, t) = \frac{1}{2\pi\sqrt{-1}} \lim_{\nu\to\infty} \int_{\Gamma_\nu} e^{\lambda^2 t} \frac{\Delta^{(i)}(x, \lambda)}{\lambda\Delta(\lambda)} d\lambda \qquad (6.4.6)$$

Reasoning in the same way, we obtain from (6.3.18) and (6.3.59)

$$v_2^{(i)}(x, t) = \frac{-1}{2\pi\sqrt{-1}} \lim_{\nu\to\infty} \int_{\Gamma_\nu} \lambda\, d\lambda \sum_{j=1}^{n} \int_{a_j}^{b_j} G^{(i,j)}(x, \xi, \lambda)$$
$$\times \Big\{ e^{\lambda^2 t}\Phi^{(j)}(\xi) + \int_0^t \exp[\lambda^2 (t-\tau)] f^{(j)}(\xi, \tau)\, d\tau \Big\} (c_{02}^{(j)}(\xi))^{-1} d\xi \qquad (6.4.7)$$

Thus, we have proved the existence of a unique sufficiently smooth solution of Problem (6.1.1)-(6.1.3) which can be represented in the form (3.4.5). Now, it remains to show that this solution depends continuously on the right-hand sides of (6.1.1), on the right-hand sides of the boundary conditions (6.1.2) and on the initial conditions (6.1.3).

Let us suppose that the closed contours Γ_ν in (6.4.6) are made up either of straight-line segments lying inside the circles O_ν^* but outside and parallel to the strip D_{h1} or of arcs of circles O_ν^* located between these line segments (or a combination of the two).

With such a choice of contours Γ_ν, for the function $v_1^{(i)}(x, t)$, defined by (6.4.6) we have, in accordance with Theorem 22 (see (6.2.58)) the following inequality with $t \geqslant 0$ and $x \in [a_i, b_i]$

$$|v_1^{(i)}(x, t)| \leqslant C_1 \max_{1 \leqslant k \leqslant 2n} |\gamma_k| \tag{6.4.8}$$

where C_1 is a constant.

Furthermore, in accordance with Theorem 23, if the conditions of Theorem 25 are satisfied and if the functions $\Phi^{(i)}(x)$ vanish at the end-points of the segment $[a_i, b_i]$ (for $i=1, 2, \ldots, n$), then, on the basis of (6.3.22)-(6.3.25) and (6.3.28), the integrand on the right-hand side of the equation

$$v_2^{(i)}(x, t) = \frac{-1}{\pi\sqrt{-1}} \int_M \lambda e^{\lambda^2 t} \Big\{ \sum_{j=1}^{n} \int_{a_j}^{b_j} G^{(i, j)}(x, \xi, \lambda) \Big(\Phi^{(j)}(\xi)$$

$$+ \int_0^t e^{-\lambda^2 \tau} f^{(j)}(\xi, \tau)\, d\tau \Big) (c_{02}^{(j)}(\xi))^{-1}\, d\xi$$

$$+ \frac{1}{\lambda^2} \Big(\frac{F_1^{(i)}(x, x)}{\varphi_1^{(i)}(x)} + \frac{F_2^{(i)}(x, x)}{\varphi_2^{(i)}(x)} \Big) \Big\} d\lambda + \Phi^{(i)}(x)$$

decreases on the contour M for $t \geqslant 0$ and $x \in [a_i, b_i]$ faster than does λ^{-2}. Consequently,

$$|v_2^{(i)}(x, t)| \leqslant \sum_{i=1}^{n} \Big\{ \sum_{k=0}^{2} C_{2k} \max \left| \frac{d^k \Phi^{(i)}(x)}{dx^k} \right| + \sum_{k=0}^{1} D_{2k} \max \left| \frac{\partial^k f^{(i)}(x, t)}{\partial t^k} \right| \Big\} \tag{6.4.9}$$

The inequalities (6.4.8) and (6.4.9) imply the continuous

dependence of the solution of Equations (6.1.1)-(6.1.3) on the right-hand sides of (6.1.1), the boundary conditions (6.1.2) and the initial conditions (6.1.3).

Theorem 29 Suppose that Conditions A and B of Section 6.1 are satisfied. If

$$\frac{\pi}{2} < \arg c_{02}^{(i)}(x) < \frac{3\pi}{2}$$

then Problem (6.1.1)-(6.1.3) is independent of the degree of smoothness of the functions $\Phi^{(i)}(x)$ and $f^{(i)}(x, t)$, of which at least one is not identically zero, and has a solution of which the derivatives appearing in (6.1.1)-(6.1.3) are continuous.

Obviously, we can assume without loss of generality that the boundary conditions (6.1.2) are homogeneous (because in the opposite case, Problem (6.1.1)-(6.1.3) can be reduced to the mixed problem with homogeneous boundary conditions). Then, Problem (6.1.1)-(6.1.3) coincides with Problem B. *Proof: by contradiction* Let us suppose that the conditions of the theorem are satisfied and that Problem B has a sufficiently smooth solution $v_2^{(i)}(x, t)$. Then, in accordance with Theorem 27, it can be represented as an integral residue (6.4.7).

Let $\varkappa_\nu$ denote the order of the pole λ_ν lying inside the contour c_ν. If we calculate the residue at the pole λ_ν, we obtain the following representation for the solution (6.4.7)

$$v_2^{(i)}(x, t) = -\sum_{\nu} e^{\lambda_\nu^2 t} \Delta_\nu^{(i)}(x, t, \lambda_\nu) \tag{6.4.10}$$

where

$$e^{\lambda_\nu^2 t}\Delta_\nu^{(i)}(x, t, \lambda_\nu)$$
$$= \frac{1}{(\varkappa_\nu - 1)!} \frac{\partial^{\varkappa_\nu - 1}}{\partial \lambda^{\varkappa_\nu - 1}} \Big\{\Delta^{-1}(\lambda)\Big[\lambda(\lambda - \lambda_\nu)^{\varkappa_\nu}$$
$$\times \sum_{j=1}^{n} \int_{a_j}^{b_j} \Delta^{(i,j)}(x, \xi, \lambda)\Big(\Phi^{(j)}(\xi)\, e^{\lambda^2 t}$$
$$+ \int_0^t \exp[\lambda^2(t-\tau)]\, f^{(j)}(\xi, \tau)\, d\tau\Big)\, d\xi\Big]\Big\}\Big|_{\lambda=\lambda_\nu}$$

As can be seen from the asymptotic formulae (6.2.44), (6.2.45), (6.2.64) and (6.2.75), the ratio

$$\frac{\Delta^{(i)}_{\nu+1}(x, t, \lambda_{\nu+1})}{\Delta^{(i)}_{\nu}(x, t, \lambda_{\nu})}$$

decreases less rapidly than the exponential function for all $x \in (a_i, b_i)$, $t \in (0, T)$.

In accordance with Theorem 21, all the λ_ν are located in a strip D_{h1}. Consequently, on the basis of the hypothesis of the theorem which we have proved, the following inequalities hold for all v

$$\frac{3\pi}{2} < \cos 2 \arg \lambda_\nu < \frac{5\pi}{2}$$

Consequently, we have

$$\operatorname{Re}(\lambda^2_{\nu+1} - \lambda^2_\nu) = |\lambda_{\nu+1}|^2 \cos 2 \arg \lambda_{\nu+1} - |\lambda_\nu|^2 \cos 2 \arg \lambda_\nu$$
$$\geqslant \omega(|\lambda_{\nu+1}|^2 - |\lambda_\nu|^2)$$

where ω is positive.

Furthermore, from (6.2.49), we have $|\lambda_\nu| = p\nu + q_\nu$, where p is constant and q_ν is bounded for large values of ν. Substituting into the last inequality, we have

$$\operatorname{Re}(\lambda^2_{\nu+1} - \lambda^2_\nu) \geqslant \varkappa\nu \qquad (6.4.11)$$

where $\varkappa$ is a positive constant.

It follows from (6.4.11) that, for sufficiently large ν and for certain $x \in (a_i, b_i)$ and $t \in (0, T)$, the ratio

$$\frac{|e^{(\lambda^2_{\nu+1} - \lambda^2_\nu)t} \Delta^{(i)}_{\nu+1}(x, t, \lambda_{\nu+1})|}{\Delta^{(i)}_{\nu}(x, t, \lambda_\nu)}$$

exceeds unity. This means that the series (6.4.10) diverges for these values of x and t, which contradicts the fact that the solution $v^{(i)}_2(x, t)$ of the mixed problem in question can be represented by the series (6.4.10). This contradiction proves the theorem.

6.5 SOLUTION OF MIXED PROBLEMS FOR EQUATIONS CONTAINING FIRST-ORDER TIME DERIVATIVES: NECESSARY AND SUFFICIENT CONDITIONS

Consider the mixed problem of finding the solutions of the equations

$$\frac{\partial^2 v^{(i)}}{\partial t^2} - \sum_{\substack{k+l\leq 2\\ k\leq 1}} c_{kl}^{(i)}(x)\frac{\partial^{k+l}v^{(i)}}{\partial t^k\,\partial x^l} = f^{(i)}(x, t) \tag{6.5.1}$$

for $x\in(a_i, b_i)$ with boundary conditions

$$\sum_{i=1}^{n}\sum_{l=0}^{1}\left\{\alpha_{sl}^{(i)}\left(\frac{\partial}{\partial t}\right)\frac{\partial^l v^{(i)}}{\partial x^l}\bigg|_{x=a_i} + \beta_{sl}^{(i)}\left(\frac{\partial}{\partial t}\right)\frac{\partial^l v^{(i)}}{\partial x^l}\bigg|_{x=b_i}\right\} = 0 \tag{6.5.2}$$

$$(s = 1, 2, \ldots, 2n)$$

and initial conditions

$$v^{(i)}(x, 0) = \Phi_0^{(i)}(x), \qquad \frac{\partial v^{(i)}}{\partial t}\bigg|_{t=0} = \Phi_1^{(i)}(x) \tag{6.5.3}$$

where

$$\alpha_{sl}^{(i)}(z) = \sum_{k=0}^{2}\alpha_{slk}^{(i)}z^k, \qquad \beta_{sl}^{(i)}(z) = \sum_{k=0}^{2}\beta_{slk}^{(i)}z^k$$

and $\alpha_{slk}^{(i)}$ and $\beta_{slk}^{(i)}$ are constants.

By setting up the spectral problem corresponding to Problem (6.5.1)-(6.5.3) according to the procedure laid out in [40d], we arrive at the boundary-value problem

$$\sum_{\substack{k+l\leq 2\\ k\leq 1}} \lambda^k c_{kl}^{(i)}(x)\frac{d^l y^{(i)}}{dx^l} - \lambda^2 y^{(i)} = F_0^{(i)}(x, \Phi, \lambda) \tag{6.5.4}$$

$$\sum_{i=1}^{n}\sum_{l=0}^{1}\left\{\alpha_{sl}^{(i)}(\lambda)\frac{d^l y^{(i)}}{dx^l}\bigg|_{x=a_i} + \beta_{sl}^{(i)}(\lambda)\frac{d^l y^{(i)}}{dx^l}\bigg|_{x=b_i}\right\} = N_s(\Phi, \lambda) \tag{6.5.5}$$

where

$$F_0^{(i)}(x, \Phi, \lambda) = \sum_{k=0}^{1}\lambda^{(1-k)}\Phi_k^{(i)}(x) - \sum_{l=0}^{1}c_{1l}^{(i)}(x)\frac{d^l}{dx^l}\Phi_0^{(i)}(x) \tag{6.5.6}$$

$$N_s(\Phi, \lambda) = -\sum_{i=1}^{n}\sum_{l=0}^{1}\left\{(\alpha_{sl1}^{(i)} + \lambda\alpha_{sl2}^{(i)})\left.\frac{d^l\Phi_0^{(i)}(x)}{dx^l}\right|_{x=a_i} + (\beta_{sl1}^{(i)} + \lambda\beta_{sl2}^{(i)})\left.\frac{d^l\Phi_0^{(i)}(x)}{dx^l}\right|_{x=b_i}\right\} \quad (6.5.7)$$

In this section, Condition A of Section 6.1 is replaced with the more complicated condition

Aa. For $x \in [a_i, b_i]$, the roots $\varphi_k^{(i)}(x)$ (for $k = 1, 2$) of the characteristic equation

$$f^{(i)}(\theta) \equiv c_{02}^{(i)}(x)\,\theta^2 + c_{11}^{(i)}(x)\,\theta - 1 = 0 \quad (i = 1, \ldots, n) \quad (6.5.8)$$

are distinct. Both the arguments of these roots and the arguments of their differences are independent of x and of the index i.

On the interval $[a_i, b_i]$, the coefficients $c_{kl}^{(i)}(x)$ in (6.5.1) are assumed to be sufficiently smooth that the homogeneous equation corresponding to Equation (6.5.4) has a fundamental system of particular solutions $y_s^{(i)}(x, \lambda)$ (for $s = 1, 2$). It is assumed that these particular solutions and their derivatives have asymptotic representations (for large values of λ) of the form

$$\frac{d^m y_s^{(i)}(x, \lambda)}{dx^m} = \lambda^m\left\{\eta_{s0m}^{(i)}(x) + \frac{\eta_{s1m}^{(i)}(x)}{\lambda} + \frac{\eta_{s2m}^{(i)}(x)}{\lambda^2} + \frac{\eta_{s3m}^{(i)}(x)}{\lambda^3} + \frac{E_{s,m}^{(i)}(x, \lambda)}{\lambda^4}\right\} \quad (6.5.9)$$

$$\times \exp\left(\lambda\int_{a_i}^{x}\varphi_s^{(i)}(\xi)\,d\xi\right) \qquad (m = 0, 1, 2)$$

in each of the half-planes Π_j (for $j = 1, 2$), where $\eta_{s0m}^{(i)}(x)$ and $\eta_{s1m}^{(i)}(x)$ are defined as before by (6.2.30) and (6.2.31), where $\eta_{skm}^{(i)}(x)$ (for $k = 0, 1, 2, 3$) have continuous derivatives of the first $3-k$ orders (for $k = 0, 1, 2, 3$) on the interval $[a_i, b_i]$, and where the $E_{s,m}^{(i)}(x, \lambda)$ are continuous with respect to x and bounded for large values of λ. Here, we assume that, for suitable numbering of the roots $\varphi_k^{(i)}(x)$ of the characteristic equation (6.5.8) in each of the half-planes Π_j (for $j = 1, 2$), the inequalities

$$\operatorname{Re}\lambda\varphi_1^{(i)}(x) \leqslant \operatorname{Re}\lambda\varphi_2^{(i)}(x) \quad (6.5.10)$$

are satisfied, where, as before, the boundary of Π_1 and Π_2 is given by

$$\operatorname{Re} \lambda\varphi_1^{(i)}(x) = \operatorname{Re} \lambda\varphi_2^{(i)}(x) \qquad (6.5.11)$$

In accordance with Condition A_1, the roots $\varphi_k^{(i)}(x)$ of the characteristic equation (6.5.8) can be represented either in the form

$$\varphi_k^{(i)}(x) = cP_k^{(i)}(x) \qquad (6.5.12)$$

or in the form

$$\varphi_k^{(i)}(x) = c_k P^{(i)}(x) \qquad (6.5.13)$$

where $P^{(i)}(x) > 0$ for $x \in [a_i, b_i]$ and c_k and c are constants. The following variants are possible for the $P_k^{(i)}(x)$ (for $k = 1, 2$).

1. For $x \in [a_i, b_i]$, the functions $P_1^{(i)}(x)$ and $P_2^{(i)}(x)$ are of opposite sign.
2. For $x \in [a_i, b_i]$, the functions $P_1^{(i)}(x)$ and $P_2^{(i)}(x)$ are of the same sign.

For correctness, let us consider the first possibility: for $x \in [a_i, b_i]$, we have $P_1^{(i)}(x) < 0$ and $P_2^{(i)}(x) > 0$. Then, from (6.5.11), we obtain

$$\begin{aligned} &\operatorname{Re} \lambda\varphi_1^{(i)}(x) - \operatorname{Re} \lambda\varphi_2^{(i)}(x) \\ &\quad = |\lambda|\,|c|\,(P_1^{(i)}(x) - P_2^{(i)}(x)) \\ &\qquad \times \cos[\arg\lambda + \arg c] = 0 \end{aligned}$$

from which we get

$$\arg\lambda = \pm\frac{\pi}{2} - \arg c \qquad (6.5.14)$$

Equations (6.5.14) represent two rays issuing from the coordinate origin in the λ-plane and lying on a single straight line (see Fig. 4). It is clear that these rays coincide with the rays d_j (for $j = 1, 2$) defined by

$$\operatorname{Re} \lambda\varphi_k^{(i)}(x) = 0 \qquad (6.5.15)$$

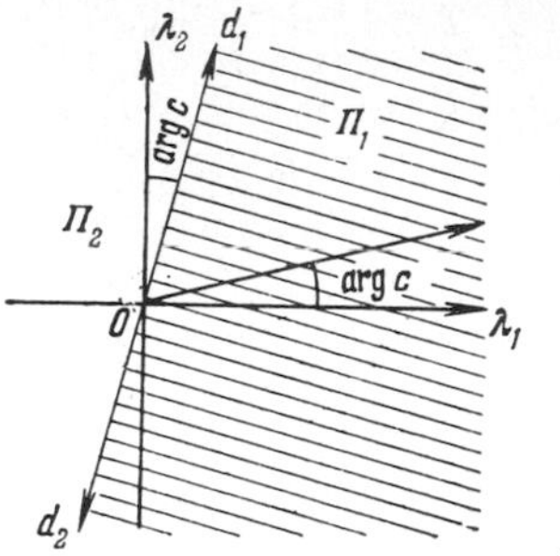

Fig. 4

Condition B of Section 6.1 is satisfied throughout this section except that here, the functions $A_{ks}^{(i)}(\lambda)$ and $B_{ks}^{(i)}(\lambda)$ are defined by

$$A_{ks}^{(i)}(\lambda)=\sum_{l=0}^{1}\alpha_{kl}^{(i)}(\lambda)\,(\lambda\varphi_s^{(i)}(a_i))^l$$
$$B_{ks}^{(i)}(\lambda)=\sum_{l=0}^{1}\beta_{kl}^{(i)}(\lambda)\,(\lambda\varphi_s^{(i)}(b_i))^l$$

where

$$\alpha_{kl}^{(i)}(\lambda)=\sum_{s=0}^{2}\alpha_{kls}^{(i)}\lambda^s,\qquad \beta_{kl}^{(i)}(\lambda)=\sum_{s=0}^{2}\beta_{kls}^{(i)}\lambda^s$$

and $\alpha_{kls}^{(i)}$ and $\beta_{kls}^{(i)}$ are constants.

Obviously, for the spectral problem (6.5.4)-(6.5.5), we have

$$u_{sk}^{(i)}(\lambda)=L_s^{(i)}(y_k^{(i)}(x,\lambda))$$
$$=\sum_{l=0}^{1}\left\{\alpha_{sl}^{(i)}(\lambda)\left.\frac{d^l y_k^{(i)}(x,\lambda)}{dx^l}\right|_{x=a_i}+\beta_{sl}^{(i)}(\lambda)\left.\frac{d^l y_k^{(i)}(x,\lambda)}{dx^l}\right|_{x=b_i}\right\} \tag{6.5.16}$$

Then, it is clear that all the formulae (6.2.4)-(6.2.10) remain in force for the spectral problem (6.5.4)-(6.5.5) except that in (6.2.9) we need to put

$$\gamma_s=N_s(\Phi,\lambda)$$

where $N_s(\Phi,\lambda)$ is given by (6.5.7).

Thus, the solution of the problem (6.5.4)-(6.5.5) is given

by

$$y^{(i)}(x,\lambda)=\frac{\Delta^{(i)}(x,\lambda)}{\Delta(\lambda)}+\sum_{j=1}^{n}\int_{a_j}^{b_j}\frac{\Delta^{(i,j)}(x,\xi,\lambda)}{\Delta(\lambda)}F^{(j)}(\xi,\Phi,\lambda)\,d\xi \tag{6.5.17}$$

where

$$F^{(i)}(x,\Phi,\lambda)=(c_{02}^{(i)}(x))^{-1}F_0^{(i)}(x,\Phi,\lambda)$$

$$\Delta^{(i)}(x,\Phi,\lambda)$$

$$=\begin{vmatrix} 0 & 0 & 0 & \dots & y_1^{(i)}(x,\lambda) & y_2^{(i)}(x,\lambda) & \dots & 0 & 0 \\ -N_1(\Phi,\lambda) & u_{11}^{(1)}(\lambda) & u_{12}^{(1)}(\lambda) & \dots & u_{11}^{(i)}(\lambda) & u_{12}^{(i)}(\lambda) & \dots & u_{11}^{(n)}(\lambda) & u_{12}^{(n)}(\lambda) \\ \cdot & \cdot & \cdot & \cdot & \cdot & \cdot & \cdot & \cdot & \cdot \\ \cdot & \cdot & \cdot & \cdot & \cdot & \cdot & \cdot & \cdot & \cdot \\ -N_{2n}(\Phi,\lambda) & u_{2n,1}^{(1)}(\lambda) & u_{2n,2}^{(1)}(\lambda) & \dots & u_{2n,1}^{(i)}(\lambda) & u_{2n,2}^{(i)}(\lambda) & \dots & u_{2n,1}^{(n)}(\lambda) & u_{2n,2}^{(n)}(\lambda) \end{vmatrix} \tag{6.5.18}$$

$$\Delta^{(i,j)}(x,\xi,\lambda),\quad g^{(i,j)}(x,\xi,\lambda)$$

and $\Delta(\lambda)$ are given by (6.2.13)-(6.2.15). Substituting the asymptotic representations (6.5.9) into (6.2.16), we obtain the following asymptotic formulae, which are valid in the half-plane Π_1,

$$\begin{aligned} u_{k1}^{(i)}(\lambda)&=A_{k1}^{(i)}(\lambda)[\eta_{10}^{(i)}(a_i)]+B_{k1}^{(i)}(\lambda)[\eta_{10}^{(i)}(b_i)]e^{\lambda\omega_1^{(i)}c} \\ u_{k2}^{(i)}(\lambda)&=A_{k2}^{(i)}(\lambda)[\eta_{20}^{(i)}(a_i)]+B_{k2}^{(i)}(\lambda)[\eta_{20}^{(i)}(b_i)]e^{\lambda\omega_2^{(i)}c} \end{aligned} \tag{6.5.19}$$

where

$$\omega_k^{(i)}=\int_{a_i}^{b_i}P_k^{(i)}(x)\,dx \tag{6.5.20}$$

Here, it is clear that $\omega_1^{(i)}<0$ and $\omega_2^{(i)}>0$.

Then, in analogy with what was done in Section 6.2, we obtain the following asymptotic representation, which is valid in the half-plane Π_1, for the characteristic determinant $\Delta(\lambda)$,

$$\Delta(\lambda)=M_1(\lambda)e^{m_1c\lambda}+M_2(\lambda)e^{m_2c\lambda}+\dots+M_\sigma(\lambda)e^{m_\sigma c\lambda} \tag{6.5.21}$$

where

$$\begin{aligned} m_1&=\omega_1^{(1)}+\dots+\omega_1^{(n)}<0 \\ m_\sigma&=\omega_2^{(1)}+\dots+\omega_2^{(n)}>0 \end{aligned}$$

For $M_k(\lambda)$, (6.2.36)-(6.2.43) remain valid.

Consequently, Theorem 21 remains in force for the spectral problem (6.5.4)-(6.5.5) with Conditions Aa and B. In this case, D_{h1} is a strip with centre at the coordinate origin and parallel to the rays d_1 and d_2.

If Condition Aa of this section and Condition B of Section 6.1 are satisfied, Theorem 22 also remains in force for the spectral problem (6.5.4)-(6.5.5).

Furthermore, it is clear that formulae (6.2.13)-(6.2.16), (6.2.30)-(6.2.31), (6.2.36)-(6.2.43), (6.2.59), (6.2.60),(6.2.61)-(6.2.64), (6.2.66), (6.2.68), (6.2.69), (6.2.71) and (6.2.72) remain in force also for the spectral problem (6.5.4)-(6.5.5) when Conditions Aa and B are satisfied. With regard to formulae (6.2.60), (6.2.64), (6.2.65), (6.2.67) and (6.2.70), the presence of more precise asymptotic representations (6.5.9) makes it possible to make the corresponding formulae more precise and to use them to obtain asymptotic formulae in which the coefficients of λ^{-3} are independent of λ and have the required smoothness.

Thus, we have proved the theorem below.

Theorem 30 Suppose that Conditions Aa and B of Section 6.1 are satisfied. If we delete from the λ-plane the interiors of small circles $Q^{(1)}_{\delta k}$ of radius δ with centre at the zeros of $\Delta(\lambda)$, the following asymptotic representation holds in the remainder of the λ-plane for the second term of (6.5.17)

$$\frac{\partial^m}{\partial x^m}\sum_{j=1}^{n}\int_{a_j}^{b_j}\frac{\Delta^{(i,j)}(x,\xi,\lambda)}{\Delta(\lambda)}F^{(j)}(\xi,\Phi,\lambda)\,d\xi$$

$$\varepsilon_m F^{(i)}(x,\Phi,\lambda)-\lambda^{m-1}\Bigg\{\exp\Big(\lambda\int_{a_i}^{x}\varphi_1^{(i)}(z)\,dz\Big)$$
$$\times\Big(\sum_{k=0}^{3}\lambda^{-k}\eta^{(i)}_{1km}(x)+\frac{E^{(i)}_{1m}(x,\lambda)}{\lambda^4}\Big)$$
$$\times\int_{a_i}^{x}\Big(\sum_{k=0}^{3}\lambda^{-k}\zeta^{(i)}_{1k}(\xi)+\frac{E^{(i)}_{1}(\xi,\lambda)}{\lambda^4}\Big) \tag{6.5.22}$$
$$\times\exp\Big(-\lambda\int_{a_i}^{\xi}\varphi_1^{(i)}(z)\,dz\Big)F^{(i)}(\xi,\Phi,\lambda)\,d\xi$$
$$+\exp\Big(\lambda\int_{a_i}^{x}\varphi_2^{(i)}(z)\,dz\Big)\Big(\sum_{k=0}^{3}\lambda^{-k}\eta^{(i)}_{2km}(x)+\frac{E^{(i)}_{2m}(x,\lambda)}{\lambda^4}\Big)\times$$

$$\times \int_{b_i}^{x} \Big(\sum_{k=0}^{3} \lambda^{-k} \zeta_{2k}^{(i)}(\xi) + \frac{E_2^{(i)}(\xi, \lambda)}{\lambda^4} \Big)$$

$$\times \exp\Big(-\lambda \int_{a_i}^{\xi} \varphi_2^{(i)}(z)\,dz \Big) F^{(i)}(\xi, \Phi, \lambda)\,d\xi$$

$$+ \sum_{j=1}^{n} \mathscr{E}_{m1}^{(i,j)}(x, \lambda) \int_{a_j}^{b_j} \Big(\sum_{k=0}^{3} \lambda^{-k} \zeta_{1k}^{(j)}(\xi) + \frac{E_1^{(j)}(\xi, \lambda)}{\lambda^4} \Big) \tag{6.5.22 (cont.)}$$

$$\times \exp\Big(\lambda \int_{\xi}^{b_j} \varphi_1^{(j)}(z)\,dz \Big) F^{(j)}(\xi, \Phi, \lambda)\,d\xi$$

$$+ \sum_{j=1}^{n} \mathscr{E}_{m2}^{(i,j)}(x, \lambda) \int_{a_j}^{b_j} \Big(\sum_{k=0}^{3} \lambda^{-k} \zeta_{2k}^{(j)}(\xi) + \frac{E_2^{(j)}(\xi, \lambda)}{\lambda^4} \Big)$$

$$\times \exp\Big(-\lambda \int_{a_j}^{\xi} \varphi_2^{(j)}(z)\,dz \Big) F^{(j)}(\xi, \Phi, \lambda)\,d\xi \Big\}$$

where the functions

$$\mathscr{E}_{mk}^{(i,j)}(x, \lambda) = [\eta_{10m}^{(i)}(x)] \exp\Big(\lambda \int_{a_i}^{x} \varphi_1^{(i)}(z)\,dz \Big) \mathscr{E}_{1k}^{(i,j)}(\lambda)$$

$$+ [\eta_{20m}^{(i)}(x)] \exp\Big(-\lambda \int_{x}^{b_i} \varphi_2^{(i)}(z)\,dz \Big) \mathscr{E}_{2k}^{(i,j)}(\lambda)$$

$$(k = 1, 2)$$

$$\mathscr{E}_{mk}^{(i,j)}(x, \lambda),\ \mathscr{E}_{sk}^{(i,j)}(\lambda),\ E_k^{(j)}(\xi, \lambda) \quad (s, k = 1, 2;\ m = 0, 1, 2)$$

defined in the portion of the δ-th plane which remains after the interiors of the circles $Q_{\delta h}^{(l)}$ are deleted, are bounded by some number C_δ which depends only on λ and the functions $\mathscr{E}_{sk}^{(i,j)}(\lambda)$ are defined, as before, by (6.2.74),

$$\varepsilon_m = \begin{cases} 0 & \text{for } m = 0, 1 \\ 1 & \text{for } m = 2 \end{cases}$$

In accordance with Theorem 11,* if Problem (6.5.1)-(6.5.3) has a smooth enough solution $v^{(i)}(x, t)$, this solution

* A proof is given in [40f] (see Theorem 5) for equations with continuous coefficients. In a remark in [40d], the corresponding theorem is formulated for equations with discontinuous coefficients.

solution can be represented by

$$v^{(i)}(x, t) = \frac{-1}{2\pi\sqrt{-1}} \sum_{\nu} \int_{c_\nu} e^{\lambda t}\, d\lambda \left\{ \sum_{j=1}^{n} \int_{a_j}^{b_j} \frac{\Delta^{(i,j)}(x, \xi, \lambda)}{\Delta(\lambda)} \right.$$

$$\times \left(F^{(j)}(\xi, \Phi, \lambda) + \int_0^t e^{-\lambda\tau} f^{(j)}(\xi, \tau)\, d\tau\right) (c_{02}^{(j)}(\xi))^{-1}\, d\xi \tag{6.5.23}$$

$$\left. + \frac{\Delta^{(i)}(x, \Phi, \lambda)}{\Delta(\lambda)} \right\}$$

where c_ν is a simple closed contour in the λ-plane which encircles only one pole λ_ν of the function in the integrand and the summation with respect to ν is over all poles of this function.

Let us suppose that the right-hand sides of (6.5.1) and the initial conditions (6.5.3) satisfy Condition C given below.

C. On the interval $[a_i, b_i]$, the functions $\Phi_k^{(i)}(x)$ are $4-k$ times (for $k=0, 1$) continuously differentiable. Also, the first $3-k$ (for $k=0, 1$) derivatives vanish at the end-points of that interval. The functions $\frac{\partial^k f^{(i)}(x, t)}{\partial t^k}$ (for $k=0, 1, 2$) are three times continuously differentiable on the interval $[a_i, b_i]$ and the first-order derivatives of these functions vanish at the end-points of that interval.

As we can see from (6.5.7) and (6.5.18), when Condition C is satisfied, we have

$$\Delta^{(i)}(x, \Phi, \lambda) \equiv 0 \tag{6.5.24}$$

Then, (6.5.23) becomes

$$v^{(i)}(x, t) = \frac{-1}{2\pi\sqrt{-1}} \sum_{\nu} \int_{c_\nu} e^{\lambda t}\, d\lambda \left\{ \sum_{j=1}^{n} \int_{a_j}^{b_j} \frac{\Delta^{(i,j)}(x, \xi, \lambda)}{\Delta(\lambda)} \right.$$

$$\left. \times \left(F^{(j)}(\xi, \Phi, \lambda) + \int_0^t e^{-\lambda\tau} f_1^{(j)}(\xi, \tau)\, d\tau\right) d\xi \right\} \tag{6.5.25}$$

$$f_1^{(j)}(\xi, \tau) = (c_{02}^{(j)}(\xi))\, f_{-1}^{(j)}(\xi, t)$$

Now, we can prove the following theorem.

Theorem 31 Suppose that Condition B of Section 6.1 and Conditions Aa and C of this section are satisfied. Then, if the roots of the characteristic equations (6.5.8) are real the Problem (6.5.1)-(6.5.3) is correctly formulated, i.e. it has a unique solution which depends continuously on the right-hand sides $f^{(i)}(x, t)$ of (6.5.1) and the initial conditions of (6.5.3).

Proof In accordance with Theorem 21, all poles of the integrand in (6.5.25) lie in a strip D_{h1} parallel to the rays d_j (for $j=1, 2$). From the hypothesis of this theorem, the rays d_j defined by (6.5.14) coincide with the imaginary semi-axes of the λ-plane. This means that

$$\arg c = 0 \tag{6.5.26}$$

Consequently, the strip D_{h1} is parallel to the imaginary axis of the λ-plane. Then, it is clear that the boundaries of this strip are given by

$$\operatorname{Re}\lambda = \pm h \quad (h > 0) \tag{6.5.27}$$

Let Γ_ν be a closed curve the interior of which contains N_ν-poles of the integrand in (6.5.25) which is located in that portion of the λ-plane which remains after the interiors of circles $Q_{\delta k}^{(1)}$ of radius δ with centres at the N_ν-poles have been deleted and which consist of arcs of circles O_ν of radius r_ν with centre at the coordinate origin and of line segments (6.5.27) lying within O_ν (see Fig. 4). Thus, we may assume that the boundaries of the contours Γ_ν are located at a distance greater than δ from the poles of the integrand in (6.5.25). Consequently, in accordance with Theorem 30, the asymptotic representations (6.5.22) hold on the boundaries of the contours Γ_ν uniformly with respect to ν.

We introduce the notation

$$v_\nu^{(i)}(x, t) = \frac{-1}{2\pi\sqrt{-1}} \int_{\Gamma_\nu} e^{\lambda t} d\lambda \Big\{ \sum_{j=1}^{n} \int_{a_j}^{b_j} \frac{\Delta^{(i,j)}(x, \xi, \lambda)}{\Delta(\lambda)} \times \Big(F^{(j)}(\xi, \Phi, \lambda) + \int_0^t e^{-\lambda\tau} f_1^{(j)}(\xi, \tau)\, d\tau \Big) d\xi \Big\} \tag{6.5.28}$$

Obviously, from (6.5.25), we have

$$v^{(i)}(x, t) = \lim_{\nu\to\infty} v_\nu^{(i)}(x, t) \tag{6.5.29}$$

We note that to prove the theorem, it will be sufficient to prove that it is permissible to differentiate twice with respect to x and t under the sign indicating passage to the limit (6.5.29). Specifically, by substituting (6.5.29) into the left-hand side of (6.5.1), we obtain

$$\frac{\partial^2 v^{(i)}}{\partial t^2} - \sum_{\substack{k+l\leq 2\\ k\leq 1}} c_{kl}^{(i)}(x) \frac{\partial^{k+l} v^{(i)}}{\partial t^k \, \partial x^l}$$

$$\equiv \lim_{\nu\to\infty} \left\{ \frac{\partial^2 v_\nu^{(i)}(x, t)}{\partial t^2} - \sum_{\substack{k+l\leq 2\\ k\leq 1}} \lambda^k c_{kl}^{(i)}(x) \frac{\partial^{k+l} v_\nu^{(i)}(x, t)}{\partial t^k \, \partial x^l} \right\}$$

$$\equiv \lim_{\nu\to\infty} \left\{ \frac{1}{2\pi\sqrt{-1}} \int_{\Gamma_\nu} e^{\lambda t}\, d\lambda \left(\sum_{\substack{k+l\leq 2\\ k\leq 1}} \lambda^k c_{kl}^{(i)}(x) \frac{d^l}{dx^l} - \lambda^2 \right) \right.$$

$$\times \sum_{j=1}^{n} \int_{a_j}^{b_j} \frac{\Delta^{(i,j)}(x, \xi, \lambda)}{\Delta(\lambda)} \left(F^{(j)}(\xi, \Phi, \lambda) + \int_0^t e^{-\lambda\tau} f_1^{(j)}(\xi, \tau)\, d\tau \right) d\xi \qquad (6.5.30)$$

$$+ \sum_{l\leq 1} c_{1l}^{(i)}(x) \frac{1}{2\pi\sqrt{-1}} \int_{\Gamma_\nu} d\lambda \frac{d^l}{dx^l} \sum_{j=1}^{n} \int_{a_j}^{b_j} \frac{\Delta^{(i,j)}(x, \xi, \lambda)}{\Delta(\lambda)} f_1^{(j)}(\xi, t)$$

$$- \frac{1}{2\pi\sqrt{-1}} \int_{\Gamma_\nu} d\lambda \sum_{j=1}^{n} \int_{a_j}^{b_j} \frac{\Delta^{(i,j)}(x, \xi, \lambda)}{\Delta(\lambda)}$$

$$\left. \times \left(\frac{\partial f_1^{(j)}(\xi, t)}{\partial t} + \lambda f_1^{(j)}(\xi, t) \right) d\xi \right\}$$

It is easy to see that the operator in the parentheses of the integrand of the first integral over Γ_ν is the operator of the spectral problem (6.5.4)-(6.5.5). Consequently, the expression in the integrand of the first integral over Γ_ν is equal to

$$e^{\lambda t} F^{(i)}(x, \Phi, \lambda) + \int_0^t e^{\lambda(t-\tau)} f_1^{(i)}(x, \tau)\, d\tau$$

Since this function is analytic inside the closed contour Γ_ν, the first integral over Γ_ν in the braces in (6.5.30) is identically zero for all x and t.

The limit of the second integral over Γ_ν under the summation with respect to l is, according to Theorem 23, equal to zero for $l=0$. Let us evaluate its limit for $l=1$. First, we note that, under the hypotheses of the theorem, the asymptotic representation holds in each of the half-planes Π_j (for $j=1, 2$):

$$\frac{d}{dx}\sum_{j=1}^{n}\int_{a_j}^{b_j}\frac{\Delta^{(i,j)}(x,\xi,\lambda)}{\Delta(\lambda)}f_1^{(j)}(\xi, t)\,d\xi - \frac{1}{\lambda}\left\{\frac{\eta_{101}^{(i)}(x)\,\zeta_{10}^{(i)}(x)}{\varphi_1^{(i)}(x)}+\frac{\eta_{201}^{(i)}(x)\,\zeta_{20}^{(i)}(x)}{\varphi_2^{(i)}(x)}\right\}f_1^{(i)}(x, t) = \frac{E^{(i)}(x, t, \lambda)}{\lambda^2} \tag{6.5.31}$$

where the function $E^{(i)}(x, t, \lambda)$ is bounded on the circles O_ν by a number which is independent of ν. This is easily seen by integrating by parts the principal terms of the asymptotic representation (6.5.22):

$$\int \exp\left(-\lambda\int_{a_j}^{\xi}\varphi_s^{(j)}(z)\,dz\right)F_{sk}^{(j)}(\xi)\,d\xi = -\frac{F_{sk}^{(j)}(\xi)}{\lambda\varphi_s^{(j)}(\xi)}\exp\left(-\lambda\int_{a_j}^{\xi}\varphi_s^{(j)}(z)\,dz\right) + \frac{1}{\lambda}\int\exp\left(-\lambda\int_{a_j}^{\xi}\varphi_s^{(j)}(z)\,dz\right)\frac{d}{d\xi}\left(\frac{F_{sk}^{(j)}(\xi)}{\varphi_s^{(j)}(\xi)}\right)d\xi \tag{6.5.32}$$

By successive integration by parts, we obtain

$$\int \exp\left(-\lambda\int_{a_j}^{\xi}\varphi_s^{(j)}(z)\,dz\right)F_{sk}^{(j)}(\xi)\,d\xi = -\frac{F_{sk}^{(j)}(\xi)}{\lambda\varphi_s^{(j)}(\xi)}\exp\left(-\lambda\int_{a_j}^{\xi}\varphi_s^{(j)}(z)\,dz\right) - \frac{1}{\lambda^2\varphi_s^{(j)}(\xi)}\frac{d}{d\xi}\left(\frac{F_{sk}^{(j)}(\xi)}{\varphi_s^{(j)}(\xi)}\right)\exp\left(-\lambda\int_{a_j}^{\xi}\varphi_s^{(j)}(z)\,dz\right) + \frac{1}{\lambda^2}\int\exp\left(-\lambda\int_{a_j}^{\xi}\varphi_s^{(j)}(z)\,dz\right) \times\frac{d}{d\xi}\left(\frac{1}{\varphi_s^{(j)}(\xi)}\frac{d}{d\xi}\left(\frac{F_{sk}^{(j)}(\xi)}{\varphi_s^{(j)}(\xi)}\right)\right)d\xi \tag{6.5.33}$$

$$\int \exp\left(-\lambda\int_{a_j}^{\xi}\varphi_s^{(j)}(z)\,dz\right)F_{sk}^{(j)}(\xi)\,d\xi$$

$$=-\frac{F_{sk}^{(j)}(\xi)}{\lambda\varphi_s^{(j)}(\xi)}\exp\left(-\lambda\int_{a_j}^{\xi}\varphi_s^{(j)}(z)\,dz\right)$$

$$-\frac{1}{\lambda^2\varphi_s^{(j)}(\xi)}\frac{d}{d\xi}\left(\frac{F_{sk}^{(j)}(\xi)}{\varphi_s^{(j)}(\xi)}\right)\exp\left(-\lambda\int_{a_j}^{\xi}\varphi_s^{(j)}(z)\,dz\right)$$

$$-\frac{1}{\lambda^3\varphi_s^{(j)}(\xi)}\exp\left(-\lambda\int_{a_j}^{\xi}\varphi_s^{(j)}(z)\,dz\right) \tag{6.5.34}$$

$$\times\frac{d}{d\xi}\left(\frac{1}{\varphi_s^{(j)}(\xi)}\frac{d}{d\xi}\left(\frac{F_{sk}^{(j)}(\xi)}{\varphi_s^{(j)}(\xi)}\right)\right)$$

$$+\frac{1}{\lambda^3}\int\exp\left(-\lambda\int_{a_j}^{\xi}\varphi_s^{(j)}(z)\,dz\right)$$

$$\times\frac{d}{d\xi}\left(\frac{1}{\varphi_s^{(j)}(\xi)}\frac{d}{d\xi}\left(\frac{1}{\varphi_s^{(j)}(\xi)}\frac{d}{d\xi}\left(\frac{F_{sk}^{(j)}(\xi)}{\varphi_s^{(j)}(\xi)}\right)\right)\right)d\xi$$

where

$$F_{sk}^{(j)}(\xi)=\zeta_{sk}^{(j)}(\xi)\,F^{(j)}(\xi) \tag{6.3.35}$$

where $F^{(j)}(\xi)$ is an arbitrary sufficiently smooth function.

As the functions $\lambda^{-2}E^{(i)}(x, t, \lambda)$ are analytic outside the strip D_{h1}, the integral of these functions over the contour Γ_ν is equal to the integral over the circle O_ν. Since $\lambda^{-2}E^{(i)}(x, t, \lambda)$ decreases as λ^{-2} on the circles O_ν, the limit of the integral of $\lambda^{-2}E^{(i)}(x, t, \lambda)$ over the circle O_ν as $\nu\to\infty$ is equal to zero. Consequently, we have from (6.5.31)

$$\frac{1}{2\pi\sqrt{-1}}\lim_{\nu\to\infty}\int_{\Gamma_\nu}d\lambda\frac{d}{dx}\sum_{j=1}^{n}\int_{a_j}^{b_j}\frac{\Delta^{(i,j)}(x,\xi,\lambda)}{\Delta(\lambda)}f_1^{(i)}(\xi, t)\,d\xi$$

$$=\left\{\frac{\eta_{101}^{(i)}(x)\,\zeta_{10}^{(i)}(x)}{\varphi_1^{(i)}(x)}+\frac{\eta_{201}^{(i)}(x)\,\zeta_{20}^{(i)}(x)}{\varphi_2^{(i)}(x)}\right\}f_1^{(i)}(x, t) \tag{6.5.36}$$

Furthermore, on the basis of the first of (6.2.30), we have

$$\frac{\eta^{(i)}_{101}(x)\,\zeta^{(i)}_{10}(x)}{\varphi^{(i)}_1(x)} + \frac{\eta^{(i)}_{201}(x)\,\zeta^{(i)}_{20}(x)}{\varphi^{(i)}_2(x)}$$

$$\qquad (6.5.37)$$

$$= \eta^{(i)}_{10}(x)\,\zeta^{(i)}_{10}(x) + \eta^{(i)}_{20}(x)\,\zeta^{(i)}_{20}(x)$$

It is clear from (6.2.59) that

$$y^{(i)}_1(x,\ \lambda)\,z^{(i)}_1(x,\ \lambda) + y^{(i)}_2(x,\ \lambda)\,z^{(i)}_2(x,\ \lambda) \equiv 0$$

Substituting into this identity the asymptotic representations (6.2.29) and (6.2.60) and equating the coefficients of like powers of λ, it is easily shown that

$$\eta^{(i)}_{10}(x)\,\zeta^{(i)}_{10}(x) + \eta^{(i)}_{20}(x)\,\zeta^{(i)}_{20}(x) \equiv 0$$

Hence we have, from (6.5.36)

$$\lim_{\nu\to\infty} \frac{1}{2\pi\sqrt{-1}} \int_{\Gamma_\nu} d\lambda$$

$$\qquad (6.5.38)$$

$$\times \frac{d}{dx} \sum_{j=1}^n \int_{a_j}^{l_j} \frac{\Delta^{(i,\,j)}(x,\,\xi,\,\lambda)}{\Delta(\lambda)}\, f^{(j)}_1(\xi,\ t)\, d\xi \equiv 0$$

On the basis of this identity and Theorem 26, we obtain from (6.5.30)

$$\lim_{\nu\to\infty} \left\{ \frac{\partial^2 v^{(i)}_\nu(x,\,t)}{\partial t^2} - \sum_{\substack{k+l\le 2 \\ k\le 1}} c^{(i)}_{kl}(x)\, \frac{\partial^{k+l} v^{(i)}_\nu(x,\,t)}{\partial t^k\,\partial k^l} \right\} = f^{(i)}(x,\,t)$$

Thus, we have shown that, if we may differentiate under the limit in (6.5.29) twice with respect to x and t, the limits of the functions (6.5.28) as $\nu \to \infty$ represent the solutions of (6.5.1).

Let us now show that, if it is possible to differentiate under the limit in (6.5.29), the limits of the functions $v^{(i)}_\nu(x,\,t)$ defined by (6.5.28) also satisfy the boundary conditions (6.5.2).

We have

$$\sum_{i=1}^{n}\sum_{l=0}^{1}\left\{\alpha_{sl}^{(i)}\left(\frac{\partial}{\partial t}\right)\frac{\partial^l v^{(i)}}{\partial x^l}\bigg|_{x=a_i}+\beta_{sl}^{(i)}\left(\frac{\partial}{\partial t}\right)\frac{\partial^l v^{(i)}}{\partial x^l}\bigg|_{x=b_i}\right\}$$

$$\equiv \lim_{\nu\to\infty}\sum_{i=1}^{n}\sum_{l=0}^{1}\left\{\alpha_{sl}^{(i)}\left(\frac{\partial}{\partial t}\right)\frac{\partial^l v_\nu^{(i)}}{\partial x^l}\bigg|_{x=a_i}+\beta_{sl}^{(i)}\left(\frac{\partial}{\partial t}\right)\frac{\partial^l v_\nu^{(i)}}{\partial x^l}\bigg|_{x=b_i}\right\}$$

$$=\lim_{\nu\to\infty}\left\{-\frac{1}{2\pi\sqrt{-1}}\int_{\Gamma_\nu}d\lambda e^{\lambda t}\sum_{i=1}^{n}\sum_{l=0}^{1}\left(\alpha_{sl}^{(i)}(\lambda)\frac{\partial^l}{\partial x^l}\right.\right.$$

$$\times\sum_{j=1}^{n}\int_{a_j}^{b_j}\frac{\Delta^{(i,j)}(x,\xi,\lambda)}{\Delta(\lambda)}\left(F^{(j)}(\xi,\Phi,\lambda)\right.$$

$$\left.+\int_0^t e^{-\lambda\tau}f_1^{(j)}(\xi,\tau)\,d\tau\right)d\xi\bigg|_{x=a_i}+\beta_{sl}^{(i)}(\lambda)\frac{\partial^l}{\partial x^l}$$

$$\times\sum_{j=1}^{n}\int_{a_j}^{b_j}\frac{\Delta^{(i,j)}(x,\xi,\lambda)}{\Delta(\lambda)}\left(F^{(j)}(\xi,\Phi,\lambda)+\int_0^t e^{-\lambda\tau}f_1^{(j)}(\xi,\tau)\,d\tau\right)\bigg|_{x=b_i}$$

$$+\sum_{i=1}^{n}\sum_{l=0}^{1}\left(\alpha_{sl1}^{(i)}\left(\frac{-1}{2\pi\sqrt{-1}}\int_{\Gamma_\nu}d\lambda\right.\right. \qquad (6.5.39)$$

$$\times\frac{\partial^l}{\partial x^l}\sum_{j=1}^{n}\int_{a_j}^{b_j}\frac{\Delta^{(i,j)}(x,\xi,\lambda)}{\Delta(\lambda)}f_1^{(j)}(\xi,t)\,d\xi\bigg)_{x=a_i}$$

$$+\beta_{sl1}^{(i)}\left(\frac{-1}{2\pi\sqrt{-1}}\int_{\Gamma_\nu}d\lambda\frac{\partial^l}{\partial x^l}\sum_{j=1}^{n}\int_{a_j}^{b_j}\frac{\Delta^{(i,j)}(x,\xi,\lambda)}{\Delta(\lambda)}\right.$$

$$\left.\left.\times f_1^{(j)}(\xi,t)\,d\xi\right)_{x=b_i}\right)+\sum_{i=1}^{n}\sum_{l=0}^{1}\left(\alpha_{sl2}^{(i)}\left(-\frac{1}{2\pi\sqrt{-1}}\right.\right.$$

$$\times\int_{\Gamma_\nu}d\lambda\frac{\partial^l}{\partial x^l}\sum_{j=1}^{n}\int_{a_j}^{b_j}\frac{\Delta^{(i,j)}(x,\xi,\lambda)}{\Delta(\lambda)}\frac{\partial f_1^{(j)}(\xi,t)}{\partial t}\,d\xi\bigg)_{x=a_i}$$

$$+\beta_{sl2}^{(i)}\left(-\frac{1}{2\pi\sqrt{-1}}\int_{\Gamma_\nu}d\lambda\frac{\partial^l}{\partial x^l}\sum_{j=1}^{n}\int_{a_j}^{b_j}\frac{\Delta^{(i,j)}(x,\xi,\lambda)}{\Delta(\lambda)}\right.$$

$$\left.\left.\times\frac{\partial f_1^{(j)}(\xi,t)}{\partial t}\,d\xi\right)_{x=b_i}\right)+\sum_{i=1}^{n}\sum_{l=0}^{1}\left(\alpha_{sl2}^{(i)}\left(-\frac{1}{2\pi\sqrt{-1}}\times\right.\right.$$

$$\times \int_{\Gamma_\nu} \lambda\, d\lambda \frac{\partial^l}{\partial x^l} \sum_{j=1}^{n} \int_{a_j}^{b_j} \frac{\Delta^{(i,j)}(x, \xi, \lambda)}{\Delta(\lambda)} f_1^{(j)}(\xi, t)\, d\xi \Big)_{x=a} \Big)$$

$$+ \beta_{sl2}^{(i)} \Big(-\frac{1}{2\pi \sqrt{-1}} \int_{\Gamma_\nu} \lambda\, d\lambda \frac{\partial^l}{\partial x^l} \qquad (6.5.39)\ \text{(cont.)}$$

$$\times \sum_{j=1}^{n} \int_{a_j}^{b_j} \frac{\Delta^{(i,j)}(x, \xi, \lambda)}{\Delta(\lambda)} f_1^{(j)}(\xi, t)\, d\xi \Big)_{x=b_i} \Big) \Big\}$$

We note that the functions

$$\sum_{j=1}^{n} \int_{a_j}^{b_j} \frac{\Delta^{(i,j)}(x, \xi, \lambda)}{\Delta(\lambda)} F^{(j)}(\xi, \Phi, \lambda) (c_{02}^{(j)}(\xi))^{-1}\, d\xi$$

are solutions of the equations

$$\sum_{\substack{k+l \leq 2 \\ k \leq 1}} \lambda^k c_{kl}^{(i)}(x) \frac{d^l y^{(i)}}{dx^l} - \lambda^2 y^{(i)} = F^{(i)}(x, \Phi, \lambda)$$

and that they satisfy the homogeneous boundary conditions (6.5.5). Consequently, the expression in (6.5.39) in the integrand of the first integral over Γ_ν is identically zero.

The limits of the second, third, fourth and fifth integrals over Γ_ν are equal to zero for $l = 0$ in accordance with Theorem 26. For $l = 1$, the limits of these integrals are equal to zero by virtue of the identity (6.5.38).

The limits of the last two integrals over Γ_ν can be calculated in a manner similar to that in which the identities (6.5.36) and (6.5.38) were proved.

Thus, it can easily be seen from the asymptotic representation (6.5.22) and the formula (6.5.37) that, under the hypotheses of the theorem,

$$\lim_{\nu\to\infty} \frac{-1}{2\pi \sqrt{-1}} \int_{\Gamma_\nu} \lambda\, d\lambda \frac{d}{dx} \sum_{j=1}^{n} \int_{a_j}^{b_j} \frac{\Delta^{(i,j)}(x, \xi, \lambda)}{\Delta(\lambda)} f_1^{(j)}(\xi, t)\, d\xi$$

$$= \eta_{101}^{(i)}(x) \frac{1}{\varphi_1^{(i)}(x)} \frac{d}{dx} \left(\frac{\zeta_{10}^{(i)}(x) f_1^{(i)}(x, t)}{\varphi_1^{(i)}(x)} \right) \qquad (6.5.40)$$

$$+ \eta_{201}^{(i)}(x) \frac{1}{\varphi_2^{(i)}(x)} \frac{d}{dx} \left(\frac{\zeta_{20}^{(i)}(x) f_1^{(i)}(x, t)}{\varphi_2^{(i)}(x)} \right)$$

It is clear that, in accordance with Theorem 26, when the hypotheses of the theorem are satisfied, the limits of the last two integrals over Γ_ν are, for $l=0$, respectively, equal to

$$f^{(i)}(a_i,\ t),\quad f^{(i)}(b_i,\ t)$$

The limits of these same integrals for $l=1$ are equal respectively to the values of the right-hand side of (6.5.40) at the points $x=a_i$ and $x=b_i$.

Consequently, the right-hand side of (6.5.39) is equal to zero if, for $x\in[a_i,\ b_i]$, the functions $f^{(i)}(x,\ t)$ have continuous first and second derivatives with respect to x and if the first derivatives vanish at the end-points of the intervals $[a_i,\ b_i]$.

Let us now show that if, under the limit in (6.5.29), we may differentiate once with respect to t and may take the limit as $t\to 0$, then the limits of (6.5.28) as $\nu\to\infty$ satisfy the initial conditions (6.5.3). We have

$$\begin{aligned}
v^{(i)}(x,\ 0) &= \lim_{\nu\to\infty} v_\nu^{(i)}(x,\ 0)\\
&= \lim_{\nu\to\infty} \frac{-1}{2\pi\sqrt{-1}} \int_{\Gamma_\nu} d\lambda \sum_{j=1}^{n} \int_{a_j}^{b_j} \frac{\Delta^{(i,\,j)}(x,\ \xi,\ \lambda)}{\Delta(\lambda)} F^{(j)}(\xi,\ \Phi,\ \lambda)\,d\xi\\
&= \lim_{\nu\to\infty} \left\{ \frac{-1}{2\pi\sqrt{-1}} \int_{\Gamma_\nu} \lambda\,d\lambda \sum_{j=1}^{n} \int_{a_j}^{b_j} \frac{\Delta^{(i,\,j)}(x,\ \xi,\ \lambda)}{\Delta(\lambda)} \Phi_0^{(j)}(\xi)\,(c_{02}^{(j)}(\xi))^{-1}d\xi \right.\\
&\quad + \frac{-1}{2\pi\sqrt{-1}} \int_{\Gamma_\nu} d\lambda \sum_{j=1}^{n} \int_{a_j}^{b_j} \frac{\Delta^{(i,\,j)}(x,\ \xi,\ \lambda)}{\Delta(\lambda)} \Big(\Phi_1^{(j)}(\xi)\\
&\quad \left. - \sum_{l=0}^{1} c_{1l}^{(j)}(\xi)\,\frac{d^l\Phi_0^{(j)}(\xi)}{d\xi^l}\Big)(c_{02}^{(j)}(\xi))^{-1}\,d\xi \right\}
\end{aligned} \tag{6.5.41}$$

$$\begin{aligned}
&\left.\frac{\partial v^{(i)}(x,\ t)}{\partial t}\right|_{t=0}\\
&= \lim_{\nu\to\infty} \left\{ \frac{-1}{2\pi\sqrt{-1}} \int_{\Gamma_\nu} \lambda\,d\lambda \sum_{j=1}^{n} \int_{a_j}^{b_j} \frac{\Delta^{(i,\,j)}(x,\ \xi,\ \lambda)}{\Delta(\lambda)} \Phi_1^{(j)}(\xi)\,(c_{02}^{(j)}(\xi))^{-1}\,d\xi \right.\\
&\quad + \frac{-1}{2\pi\sqrt{-1}} \int_{\Gamma_\nu} d\lambda \sum_{j=1}^{n} \int_{a_j}^{b_j} \frac{\Delta^{(i,\,j)}(x,\ \xi,\ \lambda)}{\Delta(\lambda)} \Big(\lambda^2\Phi_0^{(j)}(\xi) -
\end{aligned} \tag{6.5.42}$$

$$- \sum_{l=0}^{1} \lambda c_{1l}^{(j)}(\xi) \frac{d^l \Phi_0^{(j)}(\xi)}{d\xi^l} \Big) (c_{02}^{(j)}(\xi))^{-1} d\xi$$

$$+ \frac{-1}{2\pi\sqrt{-1}} \int_{\Gamma_\nu} d\lambda \sum_{j=1}^{n} \int_{a_j}^{b_j} \frac{\Delta^{(i,j)}(x, \xi, \lambda)}{\Delta(\lambda)} f_1^{(j)}(\xi, 0)\, d\xi \Big\} \tag{6.5.42 (cont.)}$$

If the functions $\sum_{l=0}^{1} c_{0l}^{(i)}(x) \frac{d^l \Phi_0^{(i)}(x)}{dx^l}$, $\Phi_1^{(i)}(x)$ and $f^{(i)}(x, t)$ are twice continuously differentiable on the interval $[a_i, b_i]$, then, in accordance with Theorem 26, the limits of the first and second integrals over Γ_ν in (6.5.41) as $\nu \to \infty$ are equal, respectively, to $\Phi_0^{(i)}(x)$ and 0.

Just as in (6.5.42), the limits of the first and third integrals over Γ_ν as $\nu \to \infty$ are equal, respectively, to $\Phi_1^{(i)}(x)$ and 0. If the function $\sum_{l=0}^{2} c_{0l}^{(i)}(x) \frac{d^l \Phi_0^{(i)}(x)}{dx^l}$ is twice continuously differentiable on the interval $[a_i, b_i]$, then, in accordance with Theorem 26,

$$\frac{-1}{2\pi\sqrt{-1}} \lim_{\nu\to\infty} \int_{\Gamma_\nu} d\lambda \sum_{j=1}^{n} \int_{a_j}^{b_j} \frac{\Delta^{(i,j)}(x, \xi, \lambda)}{\Delta(\lambda)} \sum_{l=0}^{2} c_{0l}^{(j)}(\xi) \frac{d^l \Phi_0^{(j)}(\xi)}{d\xi^l} d\xi = 0$$

Thus, in (6.5.42), the limit of the second integral over Γ_ν as $\nu \to \infty$ is equal to

$$\frac{1}{2\pi\sqrt{-1}} \lim_{\nu\to\infty} \int_{\Gamma_\nu} d\lambda \sum_{j=1}^{n} \int_{a_j}^{b_j} \frac{\Delta^{(i,j)}(x, \xi, \lambda)}{\Delta(\lambda)}$$

$$\times \Big(\sum_{\substack{k+l\leq 2 \\ k\leq 1}} \lambda^k c_{kl}^{(j)}(\xi) \frac{d^l \Phi_0^{(j)}(\xi)}{d\xi^l} - \lambda^2 \Phi_0^{(j)}(\xi) \Big) d\xi = 0$$

which follows from the identity

$$\sum_{j=1}^{n} \int_{a_j}^{b_j} \frac{\Delta^{(i,j)}(x, \xi, \lambda)}{\Delta(\lambda)} \Big(\sum_{\substack{k+l\leq 2 \\ k\leq 1}} \lambda^k c_{kl}^{(j)}(\xi)$$

$$\times \frac{d^l \Phi_0^{(j)}(\xi)}{d\xi^l} - \lambda^2 \Phi_0^{(j)}(\xi) \Big) d\xi \equiv \Phi_0^{(i)}(x)$$

Thus, proof that the limits of the integrals in (6.5.28) as $\nu \to \infty$ constitute a solution of the mixed problem reduces to proving the uniform convergence of the integrals obtained from (6.5.28) by differentiating twice with respect to x and t under the integral sign.

It will be sufficient to prove the uniform convergence of the integrals

$$I_m^{(i)}(\Gamma_\nu) = \frac{-1}{2\pi\sqrt{-1}} \int_{\Gamma_\nu} e^{\lambda t}\, d\lambda \frac{d^m}{dx^m} y^{(i)}(x, t, \Phi, f, \lambda) \qquad (6.5.43)$$

$$J_m^{(i)}(\Gamma_\nu) = \frac{-1}{2\pi\sqrt{-1}} \int_{\Gamma_\nu} d\lambda \frac{d^m}{dt^m} e^{\lambda t} y^{(i)}(x, t, \Phi, f, \lambda) \qquad (6.5.44)$$

with respect to $x \in [a_i, b_i]$ and $t \in [0, T]$, where

$$y^{(i)}(x, t, \Phi, f, \lambda) = \sum_{j=1}^{n} \int_{a_j}^{b_j} \frac{\Delta^{(i,j)}(x, \xi, \lambda)}{\Delta(\lambda)} \left(F^{(j)}(\xi, \Phi, \lambda) + \int_0^t e^{-\lambda\tau} f_1^{(j)}(\xi, \tau)\, d\tau \right) d\xi$$

Let us prove the uniform convergence of the first of the integrals in (6.5.43) and (6.5.44). The uniform convergence of the second is proved in a completely similar fashion.

It is clear (see Fig. 5) that

$$\begin{aligned} \frac{d^m v_{\nu+k}^{(i)}(x, t)}{dx^m} - \frac{d^m v_\nu^{(i)}(x, t)}{dx^m} &= I_m^{(i)}(\Gamma_{\nu+k}) - I_m^{(i)}(\Gamma_\nu) \\ &= I_m^{(i)}(a_\nu a_{\nu+k} b_{\nu+k} b_\nu a_\nu) + I_m^{(i)}(a'_\nu b'_\nu b'_{\nu+k} a'_{\nu+k} a'_\nu) \end{aligned} \qquad (6.5.45)$$

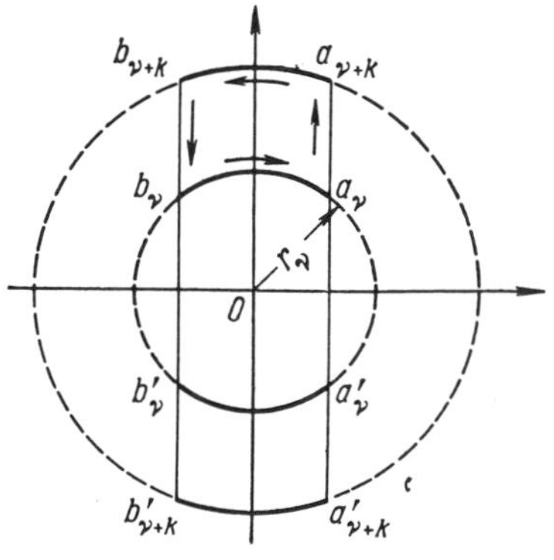

Fig. 5

As can be seen from (6.5.43), when we integrate the principal terms by parts and take Condition C into consideration, we obtain from (6.5.22)

$$\frac{d^m y^{(i)}(x, t, f, \Phi, \lambda)}{dx^m} = \varepsilon_m\left(F^{(i)}(x, \Phi, \lambda) + \int_0^t e^{-\lambda\tau} f^{(i)}(x, \tau)\, d\tau\right)$$

$$+ \sum_{k=0}^{1} \lambda^{-3} P_k^{(i)}(x, t) + \frac{E^{(i)}(x, t, \lambda)}{\lambda^2} \qquad (6.5.46)$$

where $E^{(i)}(x, t, \lambda)$ is bounded on the contours $a_\nu a_{\nu+k} b_{\nu+k} b_\nu a_\nu$ and $a'_\nu a'_{\nu+k} b'_{\nu+k} b'_\nu a'_\nu$ by a number C_δ which is independent of ν and k and the $P_k^{(i)}(x, t)$ are continuous functions for $x \in [a_i, b_i]$, $t \in [0, T]$. If we substitute (6.5.46) into (6.5.45) and remember that the first two terms in the right-hand side of (6.5.46) are analytic within the closed contours

$$a_\nu a_{\nu+k} b_{\nu+k} b_\nu a_\nu$$

$$a'_\nu a'_{\nu+k} b'_{\nu+k} b'_\nu a'_\nu$$

we obtain from (6.5.45)

$$\left|\frac{d^m v_{\nu+k}^{(i)}(x, t)}{dx^m} - \frac{d^m v_\nu^{(i)}(x, t)}{dx^m}\right|$$

$$\leqslant C_\delta\Big\{\int_{\overline{a_\nu a_{\nu+k}}} |\lambda|^{-2}|d\lambda| + \int_{\widehat{a_{\nu+k} b_{\nu+k}}} |\lambda|^{-2}|d\lambda| \qquad (6.5.47)$$

$$+ \int_{\overline{b_{\nu+k} b_\nu}} |\lambda|^{-2}|d\lambda| + \int_{\widehat{b_\nu a_\nu}} |\lambda|^{-2}|d\lambda| + \int_{\overline{b'_\nu b'_{\nu+k}}} |\lambda|^{-2}|d\lambda|$$

$$+ \int_{\widehat{b'_{\nu+k} a'_{\nu+k}}} |\lambda|^{-2}|d\lambda| + \int_{\overline{a'_{\nu+k} a'_\nu}} |\lambda|^{-2}|d\lambda| + \int_{\widehat{a'_\nu b'_\nu}} |\lambda|^{-2}|d\lambda|\Big\}$$

Suppose that

$$\lambda = |\lambda| e^{i\theta} = re^{i\theta}$$

Obviously,

$$\int_{a_{\nu+k}b_{\nu+k}} |\lambda|^{-2}|d\lambda| \leqslant \int_0^{\pi} \frac{d\theta}{r_{\nu+k}} = \frac{\pi}{r_{\nu+k}} \longrightarrow 0 \quad \text{as} \quad \nu \longrightarrow \infty$$

$$\int_{\overline{a_\nu a_{\nu+k}}} |\lambda|^{-2}|d\lambda| \leqslant \int_{\overline{a_\nu a_{\nu+k}}} r^{-2}\{dr + r\,d\theta\}$$

$$\leqslant \int_r^{\infty} \frac{dr}{r^2} + \frac{1}{r_\nu}\int_0^{\frac{\pi}{2}} d\theta = \frac{1}{r_\nu} + \frac{\pi}{2r_\nu} \longrightarrow 0 \quad \text{as} \quad \nu \longrightarrow \infty$$

In the same way, we can prove that all the integrals on the right-hand side of (6.5.47) approach zero as $\nu \longrightarrow \infty$.

Thus, we have proved the uniform convergence of the sequences

$$\frac{d^m v_\nu^{(i)}(x, t)}{dx^m} \qquad (i = 1, 2, \ldots, n;\ \nu = 1, 2, \ldots)$$

with respect to $x \in [a_i, b_i]$ and $t \in [0, T]$. This ensures that we may differentiate under the limit in (6.5.29) and take the limit as $t \longrightarrow 0$, $x \longrightarrow a_i$ and $x \longrightarrow b_i$. Hence the first part of Theorem 31 is proved.

To prove the second part, we note that, under Condition C, if we twice integrate by parts the terms containing λ^0 in the asymptotic representation of the function $y^{(i)}(x, t, f, \Phi, \lambda)$ and if we integrate the terms containing λ^{-1} by parts once, we obtain the following inequality because of the uniform and absolute convergence of (6.5.28) as $\nu \longrightarrow \infty$.

$$\begin{aligned} |v^{(i)}(x, t)| \leqslant & \sum_{k=0}^{1}\sum_{j=1}^{n} L_{1k}^{(j)} \left|\frac{\partial^k \Phi_0^{(j)}}{\partial x^k}\right| + \sum_{k=0}^{1}\sum_{j=1}^{n} L_{2k}^{(j)} \left|\frac{\partial \Phi_1^{(j)}(x)}{\partial x}\right| \\ & + \sum_{k=0}^{1}\sum_{j=1}^{n} L_{3k}^{(j)} \max\left|\frac{\partial^k f^{(i)}(x, t)}{\partial x^k}\right| + \sum_{k=0}^{1}\sum_{j=1}^{n} L_{4k}^{(j)} \left|\frac{\partial^{k+1} f^{(j)}(x, t)}{\partial t\, \partial x^k}\right| \end{aligned} \tag{6.5.48}$$

where the $L_{sk}^{(j)}$ (for $s = 1, 2, 3, 4$ and $j = 1, \ldots, n$) are constants.

This inequality implies the continuous dependence of the solution (6.5.29) of Problem (6.5.1)-(6.5.3) on the right-hand sides of the equations and the initial conditions of the problem.

The following theorem is a corollary of the theorem of the representability of a sufficiently smooth solution of mixed problems of the type (6.5.1)-(6.5.3) in the form of a complete integral residue (6.5.23) (see Theorem 11, Section 3.1).

Theorem 32 Under Conditions Aa, B and C, for the mixed problem (6.5.1)-(6.5.3) to be correctly formulated, it is necessary that the roots of the characteristic equations (6.5.8) be real.

Proof If the roots of the characteristic equations (6.5.8) are non-real, then arg $c \neq 0$ and the strip D_{h1} in which all the poles of the integrand occur will not be parallel to the imaginary axis. Thus the real parts of the poles lying in the right-hand half of the λ-plane will increase without bound. Then, for some $f^{(i)}(x, t)$ and $\Phi^{(i)}(x)$ and some $t \in [0, T]$ and $x \in [a_i, b_i]$, the series (6.5.23) will diverge, which contradicts the assumption of representability of a sufficiently smooth solution of the problem in the form (6.5.23).

CHAPTER 7

Solution of one-dimensional mixed problems for linear differential equations with discontinuous coefficients and time-dependent boundary conditions

7.1 ASYMPTOTIC REPRESENTATION OF THE SOLUTION OF A SPECTRAL PROBLEM OUTSIDE A δ-NEIGHBOURHOOD

Let us find the solutions of the equations

$$\sum_{k=0}^{q-1}\sum_{l=0}^{m} A^{(i)}_{q-1-k,\, mk+l}(x)\,\lambda^{m(q-1-k)}\frac{d^{mk+l}y^{(i)}}{dx^{mk+l}}-\lambda^{p}y^{(i)} = F^{(i)}_{0}(x,\Phi,\lambda^{m}),\ x\in(a_i,\ b_i)\quad (i=1,\ldots,n) \tag{7.1.1}$$

with boundary conditions $(s=1,\ \ldots,\ np)$

$$\sum_{i=1}^{n}\ \sum_{\substack{k\leqslant q\\ l\leqslant p-1}}\lambda^{mk}\left\{\alpha^{(i)}_{skl}\left.\frac{d^{l}y^{(i)}}{dx^{l}}\right|_{x=a_i}+\beta^{(i)}_{skl}\left.\frac{d^{l}y^{(i)}}{dx^{l}}\right|_{x=b_i}\right\}=N_{s0}(\Phi,\lambda^{m}) \tag{7.1.2}$$

where m and q are natural numbers, $p=mq$, the $(a_i,\ b_i)$ are non-overlapping intervals with common end-points,

$$F^{(i)}_{0}(x,\Phi,\lambda^{m})=\sum_{s=0}^{q-1}\lambda^{m(q-1-s)}\Phi^{(i)}_{s}(x)$$
$$\sum_{\substack{1\leqslant k\leqslant q-1\\ mk+l\leqslant p}} A^{(i)}_{kl}(x)\frac{d^{l}}{dx^{l}}\left(\lambda^{m(k-1)}\Phi^{(i)}_{0}(x)+\ldots+\Phi^{(i)}_{k-1}(x)\right) \tag{7.1.3}$$

$$N_{s0}(\Phi, \lambda^m) = -\sum_{i=1}^{n} \sum_{\substack{0<k<q-2 \\ l\leq p-1}} \left\{ \alpha_{skl}^{(i)} \frac{d^l}{dx^l} (\lambda^{m(k-1)}\Phi_0^{(i)}(x) + \dots \right.$$

$$\left. \dots + \Phi_{k-1}^{(i)}(x)) \right|_{x=a_i}$$

$$\left. + \beta_{skl}^{(i)} \frac{d^l}{dx^l} (\lambda^{m(k-1)}\Phi_0^{(i)}(x) + \dots + \Phi_{k-1}^{(i)}(x)) \right|_{x=b_i} \Big\}$$

$$-\sum_{i=1}^{n} \sum_{l=0}^{p-1} \Big\{ (\alpha_{sq-1l}^{(i)} + \lambda^m \alpha_{sql}^{(i)}) \tag{7.1.4}$$

$$\times \left. \frac{d^l}{dx^l} (\lambda^{m(q-2)}\Phi_0^{(i)}(x) + \dots + \Phi_{q-1}^{(i)}(x)) \right|_{x=a_i}$$

$$+ (\beta_{sq-1l}^{(i)} + \lambda^m \beta_{sql}^{(i)})$$

$$\times \left. \frac{d^l}{dx^l} (\lambda^{m(q-2)}\Phi_0^{(i)}(x) + \dots + \Phi_{q-2}^{(i)}(x)) \right|_{x=b_i} \Big\}$$

the $\alpha_{skl}^{(i)}$ and $\beta_{skl}^{(i)}$ are constants and the $A_{kl}^{(i)}(x)$ and $\Phi_k^{(i)}(x)$ are complex functions of a real argument x which are defined on the interval (a_i, b_i). We note that, in this section, $F_0^{(i)}(x, \Phi, \lambda^m)$ and $N_{s0}(\Phi, \lambda^m)$ can be arbitrary polynomials in λ^m, but their choice in accordance with (7.1.3) and (7.1.4) is connected with the problems of the following sections.

As we know from the theory of ordinary linear differential equations, if the coefficients $A_{kl}^{(i)}(x)$ are continuous on an interval (a_i, b_i) and $A_{0p}^{(i)}(x) \neq 0$ on that interval, then the homogeneous equation corresponding to (7.1.1) has a fundamental system of particular solutions

$$y_1^{(i)}(x, \lambda), \quad y_2^{(i)}(x, \lambda), \quad \dots, \quad y_p^{(i)}(x, \lambda) \tag{7.1.5}$$

which are entire functions of λ (see Poincaré's theorem and the remark on page 28 of [12a])

By applying the method of variation of parameters, we obtain for the general solution of (7.1.1) the following representation:

$$y^{(i)} = \sum_{k=1}^{p} c_k^{(i)} y_k^{(i)}(x, \lambda)$$

$$+ \int_{x_0^{(i)}}^{x} \frac{\sum_{k=1}^{p} y_k^{(i)}(x, \lambda) W_{pk}^{(i)}(\xi, \lambda)}{W^{(i)}(\xi, \lambda) A_{0p}^{(i)}(\xi)} F_0^{(i)}(\xi, \Phi, \lambda^m)\, d\xi \tag{7.1.6}$$

where $W^{(i)}(\xi, \lambda)$ is the Wronskian determinant of the functions $y_k^{(i)}(x, \lambda)$ of System (7.1.5), $W_{pk}^{(i)}(\xi, \lambda)$ is the cofactor of the corresponding element of the p-th row in that determinant, $x_0^{(i)}$ is an arbitrary value in the interval $[a_i, b_i]$ and the $c_k^{(i)}$ are arbitrary constants.

In (7.1.6) let us take for $x_0^{(i)}$ first the value $x = a_i$, then the value $x = b_i$, add the formulae obtained and divide the result by 2. Then, for the general solution of (7.1.1), we obtain the following representation, which will be more convenient for our later calculations:

$$y^{(i)}(x, \lambda) = \sum_{s=1}^{p} c_s^{(i)} y_s^{(i)}(x, \lambda) + \int_{a_i}^{b_i} g^{(i)}(x, \xi, \lambda) F^{(i)}(\xi, \Phi, \lambda^m)\, d\xi \quad (7.1.7)$$

where

$$g^{(i)}(x, \xi, \lambda) = \begin{cases} +\frac{1}{2} \sum_{s=1}^{p} y_s^{(i)}(x, \lambda) z_s^{(i)}(\xi, \lambda) \\ \quad \text{for } a_i \leqslant \xi \leqslant x \leqslant b_i \\ -\frac{1}{2} \sum_{s=1}^{p} y_s^{(i)}(x, \lambda) z_s^{(i)}(\xi, \lambda) \\ \quad \text{for } a_i \leqslant x \leqslant \xi \leqslant b_i \end{cases} \quad (7.1.8)$$

$$z_s^{(i)}(\xi, \lambda) = \frac{W_{ps}^{(i)}(\xi, \lambda)}{W^{(i)}(\xi, \lambda)} \quad (s = 1, \ldots, p) \quad (7.1.9)$$

$$F^{(i)}(\xi, \Phi, \lambda^m) = (A_{0p}^{(i)}(\xi))^{-1} F_0^{(i)}(\xi, \Phi, \lambda^m)$$

It follows from the notations (7.1.9) that

$$\frac{d^k y_1^{(i)}(x, \lambda)}{dx^k} z_1^{(i)}(x, \lambda) + \ldots + \frac{d^k y_p^{(i)}(x, \lambda)}{dx^k} z_p^{(i)}(x, \lambda) = \begin{cases} 0 & \text{for } k = 0, 1, \ldots, p-2 \\ 1 & \text{for } k = p-1 \end{cases} \quad (7.1.10)$$

Obviously, (7.1.7) represents solutions of (7.1.1) which satisfy the boundary conditions (7.1.2) if the constants $c_s^{(i)}$ satisfy the algebraic system

$$u_{k1}^{(1)}(\lambda) c_1^{(1)} + \ldots + u_{kp}^{(1)}(\lambda) c_p^{(1)} + \ldots + u_{k1}^{(n)}(\lambda) c_1^{(n)} + \ldots + u_{kp}^{(n)}(\lambda) c_p^{(n)}$$
$$= N_{k0}(\Phi, \lambda^m) - \sum_{j=1}^{n} \int_{a_j}^{b_j} L_k^{(j)}(g^{(j)}(x, \xi, \lambda))_x \quad (7.1.11)$$
$$\times (A_{0p}^{(j)}(\xi))^{-1} F_0^{(j)}(\xi, \Phi, \lambda^m)\, d\xi$$

where

$$u_{ks}^{(i)}(\lambda) = L_k^{(i)}(y_s^{(i)}(x,\lambda))$$
$$= \sum_{l=0}^{p-1} \left\{ d_{kl}^{(i)}(\lambda) \frac{d^l y_s^{(i)}(x,\lambda)}{dx^l}\bigg|_{x=a_i} + \beta_{kl}^{(i)}(\lambda) \frac{d^l y_s^{(i)}(x,\lambda)}{dx^l}\bigg|_{x=b_i} \right\} \qquad (7.1.12)$$

$$L_k^{(j)}(g^{(j)}(x,\xi,\lambda))_x$$
$$= \sum_{l=0}^{p-1} \left\{ \alpha_{kl}^{(j)}(\lambda) \frac{d^l g^{(j)}(x,\xi,\lambda)}{dx^l}\bigg|_{x=a_j} + \beta_{kl}^{(j)}(\lambda) \frac{d^l g^{(j)}(x,\xi,\lambda)}{dx^l}\bigg|_{x=b_j} \right\}$$
$$= -\frac{1}{2}\sum_{s=1}^{p} z_s^{(j)}(\xi,\lambda) \sum_{l=0}^{p-1} \alpha_{kl}^{(j)}(\lambda) \frac{d^l y_s^{(j)}(x,\lambda)}{dx^l}\bigg|_{x=a_j} \qquad (7.1.13)$$
$$+\frac{1}{2}\sum_{s=1}^{p} z_s^{(j)}(\xi,\lambda) \sum_{l=0}^{p-1} \beta_{kl}^{(j)}(\lambda) \frac{d^l y_s^{(j)}(x,\lambda)}{dx^l}\bigg|_{x=b_j}$$
$$(k = 1, 2, \ldots, np)$$

$$\alpha_{kl}^{(j)}(\lambda) = \sum_{s=0}^{q} \alpha_{ksl}^{(j)} \lambda^{ms}, \quad \beta_{kl}^{(j)}(\lambda) = \sum_{s=0}^{q} \beta_{ksl}^{(j)} \lambda^{ms} \qquad (7.1.14)$$

Let $\Delta(\lambda)$ denote the determinant of System (7.1.11),

$$\Delta(\lambda) = \begin{vmatrix} u_{11}^{(1)}(\lambda) \ldots u_{1p}^{(1)}(\lambda) \ldots u_{11}^{(n)}(\lambda) \ldots u_{1p}^{(n)}(\lambda) \\ \cdots\cdots\cdots\cdots\cdots\cdots \\ u_{np,1}^{(1)}(\lambda) \ldots u_{np,p}^{(1)}(\lambda) \ldots u_{np,1}^{(n)}(\lambda) \ldots u_{np,p}^{(n)}(\lambda) \end{vmatrix} \qquad (7.1.15)$$

Obviously, if $\Delta(\lambda) \neq 0$, (7.1.11) has a unique solution, which is given by Cramer's rule.

Thus, when we find all the $c_k^{(i)}$ in (7.1.11) and substitute them into (7.1.7), we obtain the following representation for the solution of the spectral problem (7.1.1)-(7.1.2):

$$y^{(i)}(x,\lambda) = \frac{1}{\Delta(\lambda)} \left\{ \sum_{j=1}^{n} \int_{a_j}^{b_j} \Delta^{(i,j)}(x,\xi,\lambda) F^{(j)}(\xi,\Phi,\lambda^m) d\xi \right. \qquad (7.1.16)$$
$$\left. + \Delta^{(i)}(x,\Phi,\lambda^m) \right\}$$

$$\Delta^{(i,j)}(x,\xi,\lambda) = \begin{vmatrix} g^{(i,j)} & 0 & \dots & 0 & \dots & 0 & \dots & 0 & y_1^{(i)} & \dots & y_p^{(i)} & 0 & \dots & 0 & \dots & 0 & \dots & 0 \\ L_{1,x}^{(j)} & u_{11}^{(1)} & \dots & u_{1p}^{(1)} & \dots & u_{11}^{(i-1)} & \dots & u_{1p}^{(i-1)} & u_{11}^{(i)} & \dots & u_{1p}^{(i)} & u_{11}^{(i+1)} & \dots & u_{1p}^{(i+1)} & \dots & u_{11}^{(n)} & \dots & u_{1p}^{(n)} \\ \dots & \dots & \dots & \dots & \dots & \dots & \dots & \dots & \dots & \dots & \dots & \dots & \dots & \dots & \dots & \dots & \dots & \dots \\ L_{np,x}^{(j)} & u_{np,1}^{(1)} & \dots & u_{np,p}^{(1)} & \dots & u_{np,1}^{(i-1)} & \dots & u_{np,p}^{(i-1)} & u_{np,1}^{(i)} & \dots & u_{np,p}^{(i)} & u_{np,1}^{(i+1)} & \dots & u_{np,p}^{(i+1)} & \dots & u_{np,1}^{(n)} & \dots & u_{np,p}^{(n)} \end{vmatrix} \quad (7.1.17)$$

where $g^{(i,j)} = g^{i,j}(x, \xi, \lambda)$, $L^j_{k,x} = L^j_k(g^{(j)}(x, \xi, \lambda))_x$ (for $k = 1, 2, \dots, np$) and $\Delta^{(i)}(x, \Phi, \lambda^m)$ is obtained from the determinant (7.1.17) if the elements of the first column are replaced with the numbers

$$0, \; -N_{10}(\Phi, \lambda^m), \; \dots, \; -N_{np,0}(\Phi, \lambda^m)$$

$$g^{(i,j)}(x, \xi, \lambda) = \begin{cases} 0 & \text{for } i \neq j \\ g^{(i)}(x, \xi, \lambda) & \text{for } i = j \end{cases} \quad (7.1.18)$$

for $x \in (a_i, b_i)$ and $\xi \in (a_j, b_j)$.

Suppose that the following conditions are satisfied.

1. The θ-roots $\varphi_1^{(i)}(x), \dots, \varphi_p^{(i)}(x)$ of the characteristic equations

$$f^{(i)}(\theta) \equiv \theta^p A_{0p}^{(i)}(x) + \theta^{p-m} A_{1,(q-1)m}^{(i)}(x) + \dots \\ \dots + \theta^m A_{q-1,m}^{(i)}(x) - 1 = 0 \quad (7.1.19)$$

   for $x \in [a_i, b_i]$ (where $i = 1, \dots, n$) are distinct and non-zero and their arguments and the arguments of their differences are independent of x (and also of the index i).*

2. On the interval $[a_i, b_i]$, the functions $A_{kl}^{(i)}(x)$ are $p-s$ times continuously differentiable for $mk + l = p-s$ (where $s = 0, 1, \dots, p$).

Consider the set of complex values λ which satisfy the equation

$$\operatorname{Re} \lambda\varphi_k^{(i)}(x) = \operatorname{Re} \lambda\varphi_s^{(i)}(x) \quad \text{for} \quad k \neq s \quad (7.1.20)$$

*The case in which the arguments depend on the index i can be studied in a similar manner.

Obviously, we have

$$\operatorname{Re}\lambda\varphi_k^{(i)}(x)-\operatorname{Re}\lambda\varphi_s^{(i)}(x) = |\lambda|\,|\varphi_k^{(i)}(x)-\varphi_s^{(i)}(x)|\cos(\arg\lambda+\psi_{ks}^{(i)}) \qquad (7.1.21)$$

where

$$\psi_{ks}^{(i)}=\arg(\varphi_k^{(i)}(x)-\varphi_s^{(i)}(x))$$

On the basis of Condition 1, we find $|\varphi_k^{(i)}(x)-\varphi_s^{(i)}(x)|\neq 0$ for $x\in[a_i,\ b_i]$ and the $\psi_{ks}^{(i)}$ are independent of x and the index i. From now on, we shall drop the index i in the expression $\psi_{ks}^{(i)}$.

Consequently, on the basis of (7.1.21), (7.1.20) is equivalent to the equation

$$\cos(\arg\lambda+\psi_{ks})=0$$

From this we obtain

$$\arg\lambda=\pm\frac{\pi}{2}-\psi_{ks}$$

Thus, under Condition 1, (7.1.20) determines, for fixed values of k and s, a straight line passing through the coordinate origin in the λ-plane.

If we let k and s range over the values 1, 2, ..., p, we obtain a finite set of straight lines passing through the coordinate origin of the λ-plane. These straight lines divide the λ-plane into a finite number of sectors Σ_j, in each of which, for suitable numbering of the roots $\varphi_k^{(i)}(x)$ of the characteristic equations (7.1.19), the inequalities

$$\operatorname{Re}\lambda\varphi_1^{(i)}(x)\leqslant\operatorname{Re}\lambda\varphi_2^{(i)}(x)\leqslant\ldots\leqslant\operatorname{Re}\lambda\varphi_p^{(i)}(x) \qquad (7.1.22)$$

are satisfied for all $x\in[a_i,\ b_i]$ and $i=1,\ 2,\ \ldots,\ n$.

It is clear that, when Conditions 1 and 2 of this section are satisfied, we can apply Theorem 6 (Tamarkin's theorem) to the corresponding homogeneous equations (7.1.1). In this case, the number p, which appeared in the formulation of Theorem 6, is equal to unity. Then, $r=0$. Consequently, in accordance with Theorem 6, if the functions $A_k^{(i)}(x)$ are $s+2-r$ times continuously differentiable on the interval

$[a_i, b_i]$ for $mr+l=p-r$ (where $r=0, 1, \ldots, s+2$), the corresponding homogeneous differential equation (7.1.1) has a fundamental system of particular solutions $y_j^{(i)}(x, \lambda)$ (for $j=1, \ldots, p$ and $i=1, 2, \ldots, n$) which have the asymptotic representations

$$\frac{d^\nu y_j^{(i)}(x, \lambda)}{dx^\nu} = \lambda^\nu \exp\left(\lambda \int_{a_i}^{x} \varphi_j^{(i)}(\xi)\, d\xi\right) \times \left\{\eta_{j\nu 0}^{(i)}(x) + \frac{\eta_{j\nu 1}^{(i)}(x)}{\lambda} + \ldots + \frac{\eta_{j\nu s}^{(i)}(x)}{\lambda^s} + \frac{E_{s\nu}^{(i)}(x, \lambda)}{\lambda^{s+1}}\right\} \tag{7.1.23}$$

$$(s=0, 1, \ldots;\ j=1, \ldots, p;\ \nu=0, \ldots, p-1)$$

in the sector Σ_k. Also, in the sector Σ_k, the functions $E_{s\nu}^{(i)}$ are continuous with respect to $x \in [a_i, b_i]$ and bounded with respect to λ,

$$\eta_{j\nu 0}^{(i)}(x) = (\varphi_j^{(i)}(x))^\nu \left(\sqrt{\left.\frac{df^{(i)}(\theta)}{d\theta}\right|_{\theta=\varphi_j^{(i)}(x)}}\right)^{-1} \times \exp\left(-\int_{a_i}^{x} \left.\frac{f_1^{(i)}(\theta)}{\frac{df^{(i)}(\theta)}{d\theta}}\right|_{\theta=\varphi_j^{(i)}(\xi)}\right) d\xi = (\varphi_j^{(i)}(x))^\nu \eta_{j00}^{(i)}(x) \tag{7.1.24}$$

$$f_1^{(i)}(\theta) = A_{0,p-1}^{(i)}(x)\,\theta^{p-1} + A_{1,p-m-1}^{(i)}(x)\,\theta^{p-m-1} + A_{2,p-2m-1}^{(i)}(x)\,\theta^{p-2m-1} + \ldots + A_{q-1,m-1}^{(i)}(x)\,\theta^{m-1}$$

In the sector Σ_k, (7.1.22) are satisfied for the roots $\varphi_j^{(i)}(x)$ of the characteristic equations (7.1.19).

Now, in addition to Conditions 1 and 2, suppose that the following condition is satisfied.

3. The coefficients $A_{kl}^{(i)}(x)$ of (7.1.1) are assumed to be sufficiently smooth on $[a_i, b_i]$ that the functions $\eta_{j\nu r}^{(i)}(x)$ in the asymptotic representations (7.1.23) are $s-r$ times continuously differentiable (for $r=0, 1, \ldots, s$) on that interval.

Let us now derive asymptotic formulae for the derivatives of the solution of Problem (7.1.1)-(7.1.2) outside a δ-neighbourhood of the spectrum. To do this, we first need to find an asymptotic representation of the characteristic determinant $\Delta(\lambda)$ in the sector Σ_j.

We note that the asymptotic representation of the element

$u_{ks}^{(i)}(\lambda)$ of the determinant $\Delta(\lambda)$ in the sector Σ_j can be obtained from (7.1.12) by using the asymptotic formulae (7.1.23). Since only the principal terms play a part in the derivation of such formulae, we shall, for brevity, follow Birkhoff and denote by $[\eta_{j\nu 0}^{(i)}(x)]$ the expressions contained in the braces in (7.1.23). Then, if we substitute (7.1.23) into (7.1.12), we obtain

$$u_{ks}^{(i)}(\lambda) = [A_{ks}^{(i)}(\lambda)\,\eta_{s00}^{(i)}(a_i)] + [B_{ks}^{(i)}(\lambda)\,\eta_{s00}^{(i)}(b_i)]\,e^{\lambda W_s^{(i)}} \tag{7.1.25}$$

$$\left.\begin{aligned} A_{ks}^{(i)}(\lambda) &= \sum_{l=0}^{p-1} \alpha_{kl}^{(i)}(\lambda)\,\lambda^l\,(\varphi_s^{(i)}(a_i))^l \\ B_{ks}^{(i)}(\lambda) &= \sum_{l=0}^{p-1} \beta_{kl}^{(i)}(\lambda)\,\lambda^l\,(\varphi_s^{(i)}(b_i))^l \end{aligned}\right\} \tag{7.1.26}$$

$$W_s^{(i)} = \int_{a_s}^{b_s} \varphi_s^{(i)}(\xi)\,d\xi \tag{7.1.27}$$

In accordance with Condition 1, the equations

$$\operatorname{Re}\lambda W_s^{(i)} = 0 \tag{7.1.28}$$

for $s = 1, 2, \ldots, p$ define $2\mu (\leqslant 2p)$ distinct rays passing through the coordinate origin of the λ-plane. To see this, note that, under Condition 1, (7.1.28) are equivalent to the equations

$$\cos(\arg\lambda + \arg W_s^{(i)}) = 0$$

Therefore,

$$\arg\lambda = \pm\frac{\pi}{2} - \arg W_s^{(i)} \tag{7.1.29}$$

According to Condition 1, $\arg W_s^{(i)}$ is independent of the index i. Then, on the basis of (7.1.29), (7.1.28) determines, for fixed s, a single straight line which the coordinate origin divides into two rays. For $s = 1, 2, \ldots, p$, we obtain 2μ (where $2\mu \leqslant 2p$) distinct rays d_j (for $j = 1, 2, 3, \ldots, 2\mu$). Let $\frac{\pi}{2} - \alpha_j$ (for $j = 1, \ldots, 2\mu$) denote the argument of the ray d_j and let us assume that the rays d_j are so numbered that

$$0 \leqslant \alpha_1 < \alpha_2 < \ldots < \alpha_{2\mu} < 2\pi$$

Consider a second set of rays d_j' (for $j = 1, 2, \ldots, 2\mu$) which are distinct from the rays d_j and which, as viewed in a counterclockwise order, are arranged

$$d_1',\ d_1,\ d_2',\ d_2,\ \ldots,\ d_{2\mu}',\ d_{2\mu},\ d_1'$$

The complex λ-plane is divided by the rays d_j' into 2μ sectors T_s.

Furthermore, let us denote by

$$W_{1j}^{(i)},\ W_{2j}^{(i)},\ \ldots,\ W_{\nu_j j}^{(i)}$$

those of the numbers $W_1^{(i)}, W_2^{(i)}, \ldots, W_p^{(i)}$ lying on the straight line which makes an angle α_j with the positive real axis. According to Condition 1, the arguments of the numbers $W_{kj}^{(i)}$ are independent of the index i. Obviously, $\arg W_{kj}^{(i)}$ is equal either to α_j or to $\alpha_j+\pi$. In the first case, we have

$$W_{kj}^{(i)}=|W_{kj}^{(i)}|\exp(\sqrt{-1}\alpha_j)$$

In the second case

$$W_{kj}^{(i)}=-|W_{kj}^{(i)}|\exp(\sqrt{-1}\alpha_j)$$

Then, these numbers have the following representation

$$W_{kj}^{(i)}=\mu_{kj}^{(i)}\exp(\sqrt{-1}\alpha_j)\quad (k=1,\ 2,\ \ldots,\ \nu_j)$$

where the $\mu_{kj}^{(i)}$ are real numbers indexed in increasing order of size

$$\mu_{1j}^{(i)}<\mu_{2j}^{(i)}<\ldots<\mu_{s_j j}^{(i)}<0<\mu_{s_j+1 j}^{(i)}<\ldots<\mu_{\nu_j j}^{(i)} \qquad (7.1.30)$$

Here, if all the numbers $\mu_{kj}^{(i)}$ are positive, we put $s_j=0$; if they are all negative, we put $s_j=\nu_j$.

We delete from the set of numbers

$$W_1^{(1)},\ \ldots,\ W_p^{(1)},\ \ldots,\ W_1^{(n)},\ \ldots,\ W_p^{(n)}$$

all the numbers $W_{kj}^{(i)}$ and divide the remaining set into two subsets $(W_k^{(i,1)})$ and $(W_k^{(i,2)})$, giving to the set $(W_k^{(i,1)})$ those of the numbers $W_k^{(i)}$ such that, in the sector T_j,

$$\operatorname{Re}\lambda W_k^{(i)}\to-\infty \quad \text{as} \quad |\lambda|\to\infty$$

and giving to the second set $(W_k^{(i,2)})$ those numbers $W_k^{(i)}$

such that, in the sector T_j,

$$\operatorname{Re} \lambda W_k^{(i)} \to +\infty \quad \text{as} \quad |\lambda| \to +\infty$$

Thus, in the sector T_j, we have

$$\operatorname{Re} \lambda W_k^{(i,1)} \to -\infty \quad (k = 1, 2, \ldots, \varkappa_j)$$

$$\operatorname{Re} \lambda W_k^{(i,2)} \to +\infty \quad (k = \varkappa_j + \nu_j + 1, \ldots, p) \quad \text{as} \quad |\lambda| \to \infty$$

Obviously, when we make the substitution

$$z = \exp(\sqrt{-1}\alpha_j)\lambda$$

the ray d_j in the λ-plane is mapped into the positive half of the imaginary axis of the z-plane and the sector T_j is mapped into a sector T of the z-plane which contains the positive half of the imaginary axis.

The numbers $W_k^{(i)}$ can be so numbered that the following inequalities hold in the sector T_j:

$$\begin{aligned} \operatorname{Re} \lambda W_1^{(i,1)} \leqslant \operatorname{Re} \lambda W_2^{(i,1)} \leqslant \ldots \leqslant \operatorname{Re} \lambda W_{\varkappa_j}^{(i,1)} \\ \leqslant \operatorname{Re} \lambda W_{\varkappa_j+1j}^{(i)} \leqslant \ldots \leqslant \operatorname{Re} \lambda W_{\varkappa_j+s_jj}^{(i)} \leqslant 0 \\ \leqslant \operatorname{Re} \lambda W_{\varkappa_j+s_j+1,\, j}^{(i)} \leqslant \ldots \leqslant \operatorname{Re} \lambda W_{\varkappa_j+\nu_j+j}^{(i)} \\ \leqslant \operatorname{Re} \lambda W_{\varkappa_j+\nu_j+1}^{(i,2)} \leqslant \ldots \leqslant \operatorname{Re} \lambda W_p^{(i,2)} \end{aligned}$$

It is easy to see that if we take $\exp\left(\lambda \sum_{i,k} W_k^{(i,2)}\right)$ outside the determinant $\Delta(\lambda)$, where the summation with respect to i and k is taken over all numbers $W_k^{(i)}$ of the second set $(W_k^{(i,2)})$, then the real parts of the exponentials which remain in the determinant cannot approach $+\infty$ everywhere in the sector T_j as $|\lambda| \to +\infty$. Let

$$\Delta(\lambda) = \exp\left(\lambda \sum_{i,k} W_k^{(i,2)}\right) \Delta_0(\lambda) \tag{7.1.31}$$

Obviously, the ith group of columns in the determinant $\Delta_0(\lambda)$ is distributed into the following three categories.

A. The columns of the first category consist of elements $u_{ks}^{(i)}(\lambda)$ with the asymptotic representations

$$u_{ks}^{(i)}(\lambda) = [A_{ks}^{(i)}(\lambda)\, \eta_{s00}^{(i)}(a_i)] \quad (s = 1, 2, \ldots, \varkappa_j) \tag{7.1.32}$$

in the sector T_j.

B. The columns of the second category consist of elements with the asymptotic representations

$$u_{ks}^{(i)}(\lambda) = [A_{ks}^{(i)}(\lambda)\,\eta_{s00}^{(i)}(a_i)] + [B_{ks}^{(i)}(\lambda)\,\eta_{s00}^{(i)}(b_i)]\exp(\lambda W_{s-\varkappa_j, j}^{(i)}) \tag{7.1.33}$$

$$(s = \varkappa_j + 1, \ldots, \varkappa_j + \nu_j)$$

in the sector T_j.

C. The columns of the third category are made up of the elements

$$e^{-\lambda W_s^{(i,2)}} u_{ks}^{(i)}(\lambda) \quad (s = \varkappa_j + \nu_j + 1, \ldots, p)$$

which possess the asymptotic representations

$$\exp(-\lambda W_s^{(i,2)})\,u_{ks}^{(i)}(\lambda) = [B_{ks}^{(i)}(\lambda)\,\eta_{s00}^{(i)}(b_i)] \quad (s = \varkappa_j + \nu_j + 1, \ldots, p) \tag{7.1.34}$$

in T_j.

From the structure of the asymptotic representations (7.1.32)-(7.1.34) of the elements of the determinant $\Delta_0(\lambda)$, it is easy to see that when we expand this determinant into a sum of determinants out of which we can take all the exponential functions $\exp(\lambda W_{s-\varkappa_j j}^{(i)})$, we obtain

$$\exp\Big(-\lambda \sum_{i,k} W_k^{(i,2)}\Big)\Delta(\lambda) = \Delta_0(\lambda)$$

$$= \pm\Big\{[\det M_{1j}(\lambda)]\,N_{1j}\exp\Big(\lambda\sum_{i=1}^{n}\sum_{k=1}^{s_j} W_{kj}^{(i)}\Big) + \ldots \tag{7.1.35}$$

$$\ldots + [\det M_{\sigma_j j}(\lambda)]\,N_{\sigma_j j}\exp\Big(\lambda\sum_{i=1}^{n}\sum_{k=s_j+1}^{\nu_j} W_{kj}^{(i)}\Big)\Big\}$$

Here, the matrices $M_{1j}(\lambda)$ and $M_{\sigma_j j}(\lambda)$ are composed, respectively, of the matrix cells $M_{1j}^{(i)}(\lambda)$ and $M_{\sigma_j j}^{(i)}(\lambda)$

$$M_{1j}(\lambda) = (M_{1j}^{(1)}(\lambda), \ldots, M_{1j}^{(n)}(\lambda))$$

$$M_{\sigma_j j}(\lambda) = (M_{\sigma_j j}^{(1)}(\lambda), \ldots, M_{\sigma_j j}^{(n)}(\lambda))$$

$$M_{1j}^{(i)}(\lambda) = (A_{\varkappa_j}^{(i)}\,B_{\varkappa_j+s_j}^{(i)}\,A_{\varkappa_j+\nu_j}^{(i)}\,B_p^{(i)}),$$

where

$$A_{\varkappa_j}^{(i)} = \begin{pmatrix} A_{11}^{(i)} & \dots & A_{1\varkappa_j}^{(i)} \\ \dots & \dots & \dots \\ A_{np,1}^{(i)} & \dots & A_{np,\varkappa_j}^{(i)} \end{pmatrix}, \quad B_{\varkappa_j+s_j}^{(i)} = \begin{pmatrix} B_{1\varkappa_j+1}^{(i)} & \dots & B_{1,\varkappa_j+s_j}^{(i)} \\ \dots & \dots & \dots \\ B_{np,\varkappa_j+1}^{(i)} & \dots & B_{np,\varkappa_j+s_j}^{(i)} \end{pmatrix}$$

$$A_{\varkappa_j+\nu_j}^{(i)} = \begin{pmatrix} A_{1,\varkappa_j+s_j+1}^{(i)} & \dots & A_{1,\varkappa_j+\nu_j}^{(i)} \\ \dots & \dots & \dots \\ A_{np,\varkappa_j+s_j+1}^{(i)} & \dots & A_{np,\varkappa_j+\nu_j}^{(i)} \end{pmatrix}$$

$$B_p^{(i)} = \begin{pmatrix} B_{1,\varkappa_j+\nu_j+1}^{(i)} & \dots & B_{1p}^{(i)} \\ \dots & \dots & \dots \\ B_{np,\varkappa_j+\nu_j+1}^{(i)} & \dots & B_{np,p}^{(i)} \end{pmatrix}$$

$$M_{\sigma_j j}^{(i)}(\lambda) = \begin{pmatrix} A_{11}^{(i)}(\lambda) & \dots & A_{1\varkappa_j+s_j}^{(i)}(\lambda) & B_{1\varkappa_j+s_j+1}^{(i)}(\lambda) & \dots & B_{1p}^{(i)}(\lambda) \\ \dots & \dots & \dots & \dots & \dots & \dots \\ A_{np,1}^{(i)}(\lambda) & \dots & A_{np,\varkappa_j+s_j}^{(i)}(\lambda) & B_{np,\varkappa_j+s_j+1}^{(i)}(\lambda) & \dots & B_{np,p}^{(i)}(\lambda) \end{pmatrix}$$

$$\begin{aligned} N_{1j} = \prod_{i=1}^{n} \{ & \eta_{100}^{(i)}(a_i) \dots \eta_{\varkappa_j 00}^{(i)}(a_i)\, \eta_{\varkappa_j+100}^{(i)}(b_i) \dots \\ & \dots \eta_{\varkappa_j+s_j 00}^{(i)}(b_i)\, \eta_{\varkappa_j+s_j+100}^{(i)}(a_i) \dots \\ & \dots \eta_{\varkappa_j+\nu_j 00}^{(i)}(a_i)\, \eta_{\varkappa_j+\nu_j+100}^{(i)}(b_i) \dots \eta_{p00}^{(i)}(b_i)\} \end{aligned} \tag{7.1.36}$$

$$N_{\sigma_j j} = \prod_{i=1}^{n} \{\eta_{100}^{(i)}(a_i) \dots \eta_{\varkappa_j+s_j 00}^{(i)}(a_i)\, \eta_{\varkappa_j+s_j+100}^{(i)}(b_i) \dots \eta_{p00}^{(i)}(b_i)\} \tag{7.1.37}$$

The principal parts of the coefficients of the intermediary terms of the exponential polynomial (7.1.35) are determinants of order np which are composed of other combinations of the columns of the matrices

$$A(\lambda) = \begin{pmatrix} A_{11}^{(1)}(\lambda) & \dots & A_{1p}^{(1)}(\lambda) & \dots & A_{11}^{(n)}(\lambda) & \dots & A_{1p}^{(n)}(\lambda) \\ \dots & \dots & \dots & \dots & \dots & \dots & \dots \\ A_{np,1}^{(1)}(\lambda) & \dots & A_{np,p}^{(1)}(\lambda) & \dots & A_{np,1}^{(n)}(\lambda) & \dots & A_{np,p}^{(n)}(\lambda) \end{pmatrix}$$

$$B(\lambda) = \begin{pmatrix} B_{11}^{(1)}(\lambda) & \dots & B_{1p}^{(1)}(\lambda) & \dots & B_{11}^{(n)}(\lambda) & \dots & B_{1p}^{(n)}(\lambda) \\ \dots & \dots & \dots & \dots & \dots & \dots & \dots \\ B_{np,1}^{(1)}(\lambda) & \dots & B_{np,p}^{(1)}(\lambda) & \dots & B_{np,1}^{(n)}(\lambda) & \dots & B_{np,p}^{(n)}(\lambda) \end{pmatrix}$$

Finally, let us suppose that, in addition to Conditions 1 - 3, the following conditions are satisfied.

4. The determinants of the matrices $M_{1j}(\lambda)$ and $M_{\sigma_j j}(\lambda)$ for all $j=1, \ldots, 2\mu$ are non-zero polynomials in λ of the same degree d. Let M_{1j} and $M_{\sigma_j j}$ denote, respectively, the coefficients of the highest power of λ in these polynomials.
5. All the determinants of order np composed of all possible combinations of columns of the matrices $A(\lambda)$ and $B(\lambda)$ are polynomials of degrees not exceeding d.

As can be seen from (7.1.31), (7.1.35), (7.1.36) and (7.1.37), when Conditions 1 - 5 are satisfied, the characteristic determinant $\Delta(\lambda)$ of the Green's function of the spectral problem (7.1.1)-(7.1.2) in the sector T_j admits the following asymptotic representation:

$$\Delta(\lambda) = \lambda^d e^{\lambda \sum\limits_{i=1}^{n} \sum\limits_{k=\varkappa_j+\nu_j+1}^{p} w_k^{(i,2)}} \times \{[N_{1j} M_{1j}] e^{m_{1j} z} + \ldots + [N_{\sigma_j j} M_{\sigma_j j}] e^{m_{\sigma_j j} z}\} \tag{7.1.38}$$

where

$$z = \lambda e^{\sqrt{-1}\alpha_j}, \quad m_{1j} < m_{2j} < \ldots < m_{\sigma_j j}$$

$$m_{1j} = \begin{cases} \sum\limits_{i=1}^{n} \sum\limits_{k=1}^{s_j} \mu_{kj}^{(i)}, & \text{for} \quad s_j > 0 \\ 0 & \text{for} \quad s_j = 0 \end{cases} \tag{7.1.39}$$

$$m_{\sigma_j j} = \begin{cases} \sum\limits_{i=1}^{n} \sum\limits_{k=s_j+1}^{\nu_j} \mu_{kj}^{(i)}, & \text{for} \quad s_j < \nu_j \\ 0 & \text{for} \quad s_j = \nu_j \end{cases} \tag{7.1.40}$$

$$N_{1j} M_{1j} \neq 0, \qquad N_{\sigma_j j} M_{\sigma_j j} \neq 0 \tag{7.1.41}$$

Now, we can easily prove Theorem 33 below.

Theorem 33 Suppose that Conditions 1 - 5 of the present section are satisfied. Suppose that the characteristic determinant $\Delta(\lambda)$ of the Green's function

$$G^{(i,j)}(x, \xi, \lambda) = \frac{\Delta^{(i,j)}(x, \xi, \lambda)}{\Delta(\lambda)}$$

of Problem (7.1.1)-(7.1.2) has an infinite set of zeros $\lambda_k^{(j)}$, which are poles of the solution of (7.1.1)-(7.1.2). Let this set of zeros be divided into 2μ subsets in such a way that the j th subset contains those zeros which lie in a strip (D_{hj}) of finite width h parallel to the ray d_j and containing that ray.

Then, if the interiors of small circles of radius δ with centres at the zeros $\lambda_k^{(j)}$ are deleted from the sector T_j, the following inequality will hold in the remaining part of the sector T_j:

$$\lambda^{-d} e^{-\lambda W} \Delta(\lambda) | \geqslant K_\delta \tag{7.1.42}$$

where K_δ is a positive number depending only on δ and W is the sum of all $W_h^{(i)}$ which satisfy

$$\operatorname{Re} \lambda W_k^{(i)} \geqslant 0$$

in the sector T_j. Let N be the number of zeros of $\Delta(\lambda)$ lying within the rectangle $(\Pi_h^{(j)})$, which is cut from the strip (D_{hj}) by straight lines perpendicular to the ray d_j which lie at distances r_{1j} and r_{2j} from the coordinate origin in the λ-plane.

The number N satisfies the inequality

$$\begin{aligned} \frac{1}{2\pi}(m_{\sigma_j j} - m_{1j})(r_{2j} - r_{1j}) - \sigma_j \leqslant N \\ \leqslant \frac{1}{2\pi}(m_{\sigma_j j} - m_{1j})(r_{2j} - r_{1j}) + \sigma_j \end{aligned} \tag{7.1.43}$$

For $\lambda_k^{(j)}$, we have the asymptotic representation

$$|\lambda_k^{(j)}| = \frac{2\pi k}{m_{\sigma_j j} - m_{1j}}\left(1 + O\left(\frac{1}{k}\right)\right)$$

Proof The proof of this theorem follows from Lemma 1 of Section 3.1 since we note that, in accordance with (7.1.38)-(7.1.41), when Conditions 1 - 5 are satisfied, the exponential polynomial

$$\lambda^{-d} e^{-\lambda W} \Delta(\lambda)$$

with asymptotically constant coefficients satisfies all the conditions of that lemma (see Section 3.1).

The boundaries of the sectors Σ_s and T_j divide the λ-plane into sectors R_j, each of which lies simultaneously in one of the sectors Σ_s and in one of the sectors T_j. Consequently, the numbers $W_k^{(i)}$ can be so numbered that the following inequalities* will hold in the sector R_j:

$$
\begin{aligned}
\operatorname{Re}\lambda W_1^{(i,1)} &\leqslant \operatorname{Re}\lambda W_2^{(i,1)} \leqslant \ldots \leqslant \operatorname{Re}\lambda W_{\varkappa_j}^{(i,1)} \\
&\leqslant \operatorname{Re}\lambda W_{1j}^{(i)} \leqslant \operatorname{Re}\lambda W_{2j}^{(i)} \leqslant \ldots \leqslant \operatorname{Re}\lambda W_{s_j j}^{(i)} \leqslant 0 \\
&\leqslant \operatorname{Re}\lambda W_{s_j+1 j}^{(i)} \leqslant \operatorname{Re}\lambda W_{s_j+2 j}^{(i)} \leqslant \ldots \leqslant \operatorname{Re}\lambda W_{\nu_j j}^{(i)} \\
&\leqslant \operatorname{Re}\lambda W_{\varkappa_j+\nu_j+1}^{(i,2)} \leqslant \ldots \leqslant \operatorname{Re}\lambda W_{p}^{(i,2)}
\end{aligned} \tag{7.1.44}
$$

Let us now derive an asymptotic representation of the determinant $\Delta^{(i,j)}(x, \xi, \lambda)$ which appears in (7.1.16) and (7.1.17) in the sector R_j.

First of all, we need to get the asymptotic representations of $z_s^{(i)}(x, \lambda)$ in the sector R_j.†

When we substitute the asymptotic representations (7.1.23) into the expressions for the determinants

$$W_{pk}^{(i)}(x, \lambda), \qquad W^{(i)}(x, \lambda)$$

take the common factors of the elements in the rows and columns outside these determinants and divide by them, we obtain from (7.1.9)

$$z_k^{(i)}(x, \lambda) = \frac{\delta_{pk}^{(i)}(x, \lambda)}{\delta^{(i)}(x, \lambda)} \lambda^{-(p-1)} \exp\left(-\lambda \int_{a_i}^{x} \varphi_k^{(i)}(t)\, dt\right) \tag{7.1.45}$$

where $\delta^{(i)}(x, \lambda)$ is the p-th order determinant composed of the elements $m_{\nu j}^{(i)}(x, \lambda)$ (for $\nu = 1, \ldots, p; j = 1, \ldots, p$) of the form

$$\sum_{r=0}^{s} \eta_{j\nu-1r}^{(i)}(x)\, \lambda^{-r} + \frac{E_{j\nu-1}^{(i)}(x, \lambda)}{\lambda^{s+1}} \tag{7.1.46}$$

and $\delta_{pk}^{(i)}(x, \lambda)$ is the cofactor of the element $m_{pk}^{(i)}(x, \lambda)$ in the determinant $\delta^{(i)}(x, \lambda)$.

The determinants $\delta_{pk}^{(i)}(x, \lambda)$ and $\delta^{(i)}(x, \lambda)$ can be expanded as the sum of determinants, out of which we may take the powers of λ^{-1} as the common factors of the elements of the

*In practice, it is convenient to arrange the numbers $W_k^{(i)}$ in order of size of their arguments and then construct the rays d_j and the boundaries of the sector Σ_s. Then, the numbers $W_k^{(i)}$ should be so numbered that the inequalities (7.1.44) are satisfied.

†Here, the sectors R_j which do not contain rays d_j are not considered since the asymptotics of the Green's function do not require them.

columns. Then, we obtain

$$\delta^{(i)}(x, \lambda) = D_0^{(i)}(x) + \frac{D_1^{(i)}(x)}{\lambda} + \dots + \frac{D_s^{(i)}(x)}{\lambda^s} + \frac{\mathscr{E}_{s+1}^{(i)}(x, \lambda)}{\lambda^{s+1}}$$

$$\delta_{pk}^{(i)}(x, \lambda) = D_{k0}^{(i)}(x) + \frac{D_{k1}^{(i)}(x)}{\lambda} + \dots + \frac{D_{ks}^{(i)}(x)}{\lambda^s} + \frac{\mathscr{E}_{ks+1}^{(i)}(x, \lambda)}{\lambda^{s+1}} \qquad (7.1.47)$$

where the $D_k^{(i)}(x)$ are p-th order determinants composed of the elements $\eta_{jv-1r}^{(i)}(x)$. Also,

$$D_0^{(i)}(x) = \begin{vmatrix} \eta_{100}^{(i)}(x) & \eta_{200}^{(i)}(x) & \dots & \eta_{p00}^{(i)}(x) \\ \eta_{110}^{(i)}(x) & \eta_{210}^{(i)}(x) & \dots & \eta_{p10}^{(i)}(x) \\ \dots & \dots & \dots & \dots \\ \eta_{1,p-1,0}^{(i)}(x) & \eta_{2,p-1,0}^{(i)}(x) & \dots & \eta_{p,p-1,0}^{(i)}(x) \end{vmatrix} \qquad (7.1.48)$$

The $D_\nu^{(i)}(x)$ and $D_{k\nu}^{(i)}(x)$ have continuous derivatives of the first $s-\nu$ orders on the interval $[a_i, b_i]$. The $\mathscr{E}_{s+1}^{(i)}(x, \lambda)$ and $\mathscr{E}_{ks+1}^{(i)}(x, \lambda)$ are continuous with respect to x on that interval and are bounded with respect to λ in the sector R_j.

With the aid of (7.1.24), we obtain from (7.1.48)

$$D_0^{(i)}(x) = \eta_{100}^{(i)}(x) \dots \eta_{p00}^{(i)}(x) \times \begin{vmatrix} 1 & 1 & \dots & 1 \\ \varphi_1^{(i)}(x) & \varphi_2^{(i)}(x) & \dots & \varphi_p^{(i)}(x) \\ \dots & \dots & \dots & \dots \\ (\varphi_1^{(i)}(x))^{p-1} & (\varphi_2^{(i)}x))^{p-1} & \dots & (\varphi_p^{(i)}(x))^{p-1} \end{vmatrix} \qquad (7.1.49)$$

As can be seen from (7.1.49), by virtue of Condition 1, the function $D_0^{(i)}(x) \neq 0$ for $x \in [a_i, b_i]$. Furthermore from (7.1.47), we have

$$\frac{1}{\delta^{(i)}(x, \lambda)} = \frac{1}{D_0^{(i)}(x)} \, \frac{1}{1 + \frac{P^{(i)}(x, \lambda)}{\lambda}}$$

where

$$P^{(i)}(x, \lambda) = \frac{1}{D_0^{(i)}(x)} \left(D_1^{(i)}(x) + \frac{D_2^{(i)}(x)}{\lambda} + \dots + \frac{D_s^{(i)}(x)}{\lambda^{s-1}} + \frac{\mathscr{E}_{s+1}^{(i)}(x, \lambda)}{\lambda^s} \right)$$

Expanding the fraction

$$\frac{1}{1+\lambda^{-1}P^{(i)}(x, \lambda)}$$

in powers of $\lambda^{-1}P^{(i)}(x, \lambda)$, we obtain

$$\begin{aligned}\frac{1}{\delta^{(i)}(x, \lambda)} = \frac{1}{D_0^{(i)}(x)} - \frac{1}{\lambda}\frac{D_1^{(i)}(x)}{(D_0^{(i)}(x))^2} \\ + \frac{1}{\lambda^2}\left(\frac{D_2^{(i)}(x)}{(D_0^{(i)}(x))^2} + \frac{D_1^{(i)}(x)}{D_0^{(i)}(x)}\right) + \dots\end{aligned} \tag{7.1.50}$$

Substituting the expansions for $\delta_{pk}^{(i)}(x, \lambda)$ and $(\delta^{(i)}(x, \lambda))^{-1}$ given by (7.1.47) and (7.1.50) into (7.1.45), we obtain the following asymptotic representations for $z_k^{(i)}(x, \lambda)$:

$$\begin{aligned}z_k^{(i)}(x, \lambda) = \lambda^{-(p-1)} \exp\left(-\lambda \int_{a_i}^{x} \varphi_k^{(i)}(t)\, dt\right) \\ \times \left\{\zeta_{k0}^{(i)}(x) + \frac{\zeta_{k1}^{(i)}(x)}{\lambda} + \dots + \frac{\zeta_{ks}^{(i)}(x)}{\lambda^s} + \frac{\mathscr{E}_k^{(i)}(x, \lambda)}{\lambda^{s+1}}\right\}\end{aligned} \tag{7.1.51}$$

where the $\zeta_{kj}^{(i)}(x)$ are $s-j$ times continuously differentiable on $[a_i, b_i]$ and the $\mathscr{E}_k^{(i)}(x, \lambda)$ are continuous functions with respect to x on $[a_i, b_i]$ and are bounded for $\lambda \in R_j$.

If we substitute the asymptotic formulae (7.1.23) and (7.1.51) into the identity (7.1.10) and equate the coefficients of like powers of λ, we obtain the identity

$$\sum_{k=1}^{p} \eta_{kp-10}^{(i)}(x)\, \zeta_{k0}^{(i)}(x) \equiv 1 \tag{7.1.52}$$

Now, to obtain a suitable asymptotic representation for the determinant $\Delta^{(i, r)}(x, \xi, \lambda)$, let us first transform it in such a way that the elements of the first column of the transformed determinant will not contain exponential functions, the real parts of the argument of which increase in R_j. To do this, we multiply the columns with elements $u_{k1}^{(r)}(\lambda), u_{k2}^{(r)}(\lambda), \dots, u_{k\tau_j}^{r}(\lambda)$ (for $k = 1, \dots, np$) in the determinant $\Delta^{(i, r)}(x, \xi, \lambda)$, respectively, by $\frac{1}{2} z_1^{(r)}(\xi, \lambda), \dots, \frac{1}{2} z_{\tau_j}^{(r)}(\xi, \lambda)$ and the columns with elements $u_{k\tau_j+1}^{(r)}(\lambda), \dots, u_{kp}^{(r)}(\lambda)$ (for $k = 1, \dots, np$) by

$$-\frac{1}{2} z_{\tau_j+1}^{(r)}(\xi, \lambda), \dots, -\frac{1}{2} z_p^{(r)}(\xi, \lambda)$$

and add the result to the first column, where $\tau_j = \varkappa_j + s_j$ is the number defined in the inequalities (7.1.44).

Let us denote the determinant obtained in this manner by $\Delta_0^{(i,r)}(x, \xi, \lambda)$ and the elements of its first column by

$$g_0^{(i,r)}(x, \xi, \lambda),\ g_1^{(r)}(\xi, \lambda),\ \ldots,\ g_{np}^{(r)}(\xi, \lambda)$$

As we see from (7.1.8), (7.1.17) and (7.1.18), we have

$$g_0^{(i,r)}(x, \xi, \lambda) = g^{(i,r)}(x, \xi, \lambda) = 0 \quad \text{for } i \neq r \tag{7.1.53}$$

$$g_0^{(i,i)}(x, \xi, \lambda) = \begin{cases} \displaystyle\sum_{k=1}^{\tau_j} y_k^{(i)}(x, \lambda)\, z_k^{(i)}(\xi, \lambda) & \text{for } a_i \leqslant \xi \leqslant x \leqslant b_i \\ \displaystyle -\sum_{k=\tau_j+1}^{p} y_k^{(i)}(x, \lambda)\, z_k^{(i)}(\xi, \lambda) & \text{for } a_i \leqslant x \leqslant \xi \leqslant b_i \end{cases} \tag{7.1.54}$$

Furthermore, using (7.1.12) and (7.1.13), we obtain

$$\begin{aligned} g_k^{(r)}(\xi, \lambda) &= L_k^{(r)}(g^{(r)}(x, \xi, \lambda))_x \\ &+ \frac{1}{2}\sum_{q=1}^{\tau_j} u_{kq}^{(r)}(\lambda)\, z_q^{(r)}(\xi, \lambda) - \frac{1}{2}\sum_{q=\tau_j+1}^{p} u_{kq}^{(r)}(\lambda)\, z_q^{(r)}(\xi, \lambda) \\ &= -\sum_{q=\tau_j+1}^{p} z_q^{(r)}(\xi, \lambda) \sum_{l=0}^{p-1} \alpha_{kl}^{(r)}(\lambda) \left.\frac{d^l y_q^{(r)}(x, \lambda)}{dx^l}\right|_{x=a_r} \\ &+ \sum_{q=1}^{\tau_j} z_q^{(r)}(\xi, \lambda) \sum_{l=0}^{p-1} \beta_{kl}^{(r)}(\lambda) \left.\frac{d^l y_q^{(r)}(x, \lambda)}{dx^l}\right|_{x=b_r} \qquad (k = 1, \ldots, np) \end{aligned} \tag{7.1.55}$$

Expanding the determinant $\Delta_0^{(i,r)}(x, \xi, \lambda)$ in terms of elements of the first row, we have

$$\begin{aligned} \Delta^{(i,r)}(x, \xi, \lambda) = \Delta_0^{(i,r)}(x, \xi, \lambda) &= \Delta(\lambda)\, g_0^{(i,r)}(x, \xi, \lambda) \\ &+ \sum_{k=1}^{p} y_k^{(i)}(x, \lambda)\, \Delta_{0,\,1,\,(i-1)p+k+1}^{(i,r)}(x, \xi, \lambda) \end{aligned} \tag{7.1.56}$$

where

$$\Delta_{0,\,1,\,(i-1)p+k+1}^{(i,r)}(x, \xi, \lambda)$$

is the cofactor of the element $(1, (i-1)p+k+1)$ in the determinant $\Delta_0^{(i,r)}(x, \xi, \lambda)$ which is obtained from $\Delta(\lambda)$ by replacing the $[(i-1)p+k]$th column with the column

$$-\begin{pmatrix} g_1^{(r)}(\xi, \lambda) \\ g_2^{(r)}(\xi, \lambda) \\ \vdots \\ g_{np}^{(r)}(\xi, \lambda) \end{pmatrix}$$

Furthermore, if we substitute the expression for $g_k^{(r)}(\xi, \lambda)$ given by (7.1.55) into the expression for the determinant $\Delta_{0,1,(i-1)p+k+1}^{(i,r)}(x, \xi, \lambda)$ and expand the resulting determinant as a sum of determinants outside each of which we can take $z_q^{(r)}(\xi, \lambda)$, since it is a common factor of all the elements of the $[(i-1)p+k]$th column, we obtain

$$\Delta_{0,1,(i-1)p+k+1}^{(i,r)}(x, \xi, \lambda) = \sum_{q=\tau_j+1}^{p} z_q^{(r)}(\xi, \lambda) A_{k,q}^{(i,r)}(\lambda) - \sum_{q=1}^{\tau_j} z_q^{(r)}(\xi, \lambda) B_{k,q}^{(i,r)}(\lambda) \tag{7.1.57}$$

where the $A_{kq}^{(i,r)}(\lambda)$ and $B_{kq}^{(i,r)}(\lambda)$ are the determinants obtained from $\Delta(\lambda)$ by eliminating the $[(i-1)p+k]$th column and replacing it, respectively, with the columns consisting of the elements

$$\sum_{l=0}^{p-1} \alpha_{kl}^{(r)}(\lambda) \left.\frac{d^l y_q^{(r)}(x, \lambda)}{dx^l}\right|_{x=a_r} \qquad (k=1, 2, \ldots, np)$$

$$\sum_{l=0}^{p-1} \beta_{kl}^{(r)}(\lambda) \left.\frac{d^l y_q^{(r)}(x, \lambda)}{dx^l}\right|_{x=b_r} \qquad (k=1, 2, \ldots, np)$$

Thus, $A_{kq}^{(i,r)}(\lambda)$ and $B_{kq}^{(i,r)}(\lambda)$ denote the following determinants:

$$A_{kq}^{(i,r)}(\lambda) = \begin{vmatrix} u_{11}^{(1)} \ldots u_{1,k-1}^{(i)} & \sum_{l=0}^{p-1} \alpha_{1l}^{(r)} \left.\frac{d^l y_q^{(r)}(x, \lambda)}{dx^l}\right|_{x=a_r} & u_{1,k+1}^{(i)} \ldots u_{1p}^{(n)} \\ \ldots & \ldots & \ldots \\ u_{np,1}^{(1)} \ldots u_{np,k-1}^{(i)} & \sum_{l=0}^{p-1} \alpha_{np,l}^{(r)} \left.\frac{d^l y_q^{(r)}(x, \lambda)}{dx^l}\right|_{x=a_r} & u_{np,k+1}^{(i)} \ldots u_{np,p}^{(n)} \end{vmatrix} \tag{7.1.58}$$

$$B_{kq}^{(i,r)}(\lambda)=$$

$$=\begin{vmatrix} u_{11}^{(1)}\dots u_{1,k-1}^{(i)} & \sum_{l=0}^{p-1}\beta_{1l}^{(r)}\frac{d^l y_q^{(r)}(x,\lambda)}{dx^l}\Big|_{x=b_r} & u_{1,k+1}^{(i)}\dots u_{1p}^{(n)} \\ \dots & \dots & \dots \\ u_{np,1}^{(1)}\dots u_{np,k-1}^{(i)} & \sum_{l=0}^{p-1}\beta_{np,l}^{(r)}\frac{d^l y_q^{(r)}(x,\lambda)}{dx^l}\Big|_{x=b_r} & u_{np,k+1}^{(i)}\dots u_{np,p}^{(n)} \end{vmatrix} \tag{7.1.59}$$

Noting (7.1.53), (7.1.54), (7.1.56) and (7.1.57), we obtain for the first term of (7.1.16)

$$y^{(i)}(x,\lambda)=\sum_{r=1}^{n}\int_{a_r}^{b_r}\frac{\Delta^{(i,r)}(x,\xi,\lambda)}{\Delta(\lambda)}F^{(r)}(\xi,\Phi,\lambda^m)\,d\xi$$

$$=\sum_{r=1}^{n}\int_{a_r}^{b_r}\frac{\Delta_0^{(i,r)}(x,\xi,\lambda)}{\Delta(\lambda)}F^{(r)}(\xi,\Phi,\lambda^m)\,d\xi$$

$$=\int_{a_i}^{x}\sum_{k=1}^{\tau_j}y_k^{(i)}(x,\lambda)\,z_k^{(i)}(\xi,\lambda)\,F^{(i)}(\xi,\Phi,\lambda^m)\,d\xi$$

$$-\int_{x}^{b_i}\sum_{k=\tau_j+1}^{p}y_k^{(i)}(x,\lambda)\,z_k^{(i)}(\xi,\lambda)\,F^{(i)}(\xi,\Phi,\lambda^m)\,d\xi$$

$$+\sum_{r=1}^{n}\int_{a_r}^{b_r}\sum_{k=1}^{p}y_k^{(i)}(x,\lambda)\left\{\sum_{q=\tau_j+1}^{p}\frac{A_{kq}^{(i,r)}(\lambda)}{\Delta(\lambda)}z_q^{(r)}(\xi,\lambda)\right.$$

$$\left.-\sum_{q=1}^{\tau_j}\frac{B_{kq}^{(i,r)}(\lambda)}{\Delta(\lambda)}z_q^{(r)}(\xi,\lambda)\right\}F^{(r)}(\xi,\Phi,\lambda^m)\,d\xi$$

If we differentiate the last equation with respect to x and keep the identities (7.1.10) in mind, we have

$$\frac{d^\nu y^{(i)}(x,\lambda)}{dx^\nu}=\varepsilon_\nu^{(i)}F^{(i)}(x,\Phi,\lambda^m)$$

$$+\int_{a_i}^{x}\sum_{k=1}^{\tau_j}\frac{d^\nu y_k^{(i)}(x,\lambda)}{dx^\nu}z_k^{(i)}(\xi,\lambda)\,F^{(i)}(\xi,\Phi,\lambda^m)\,d\xi- \tag{7.1.60}$$

$$-\int_{x}^{b_i} \sum_{k=\tau_j+1}^{p} \frac{d^\nu y_k^{(i)}(x, \lambda)}{dx^\nu} z_k^{(i)}(\xi, \lambda) F^{(i)}(\xi, \Phi, \lambda^m)\, d\xi$$

$$+\sum_{r=1}^{n} \int_{a_r}^{b_r} \Big\{ \sum_{k=1}^{\tau_j} \sum_{q=\tau_j+1}^{p} \frac{d^\nu y_k^{(i)}(x, \lambda)}{dx^\nu} \frac{A_{kq}^{(i,r)}(\lambda)}{\Delta(\lambda)} z_q^{(r)}(\xi, \lambda)$$

$$+\sum_{k=\tau_j+1}^{p} \sum_{q=\tau_j+1}^{p} \frac{d^\nu y_k^{(i)}(x, \lambda)}{dx^\nu} \cdot \frac{A_{kq}^{(i,r)}(\lambda)}{\Delta(\lambda)} z_q^{(r)}(\xi, \lambda) \qquad (7.1.60)$$
(cont.)

$$-\sum_{k=1}^{\tau_j} \sum_{q=1}^{\tau_j} \frac{d^\nu y_k^{(i)}(x, \lambda)}{dx^\nu} \cdot \frac{B_{kq}^{(i,r)}(\lambda)}{\Delta(\lambda)} z_q^{(r)}(\xi, \lambda)$$

$$-\sum_{k=\tau_j+1}^{p} \sum_{q=1}^{\tau_j} \frac{d^\nu y_k^{(i)}(x, \lambda)}{dx^\nu} \cdot \frac{B_{kq}^{(i,r)}(\lambda)}{\Delta(\lambda)} z_q^{(r)}(\xi, \lambda) \Big\} F^{(r)}(\xi, \Phi, \lambda^m)\, d\xi$$

where

$$\varepsilon_\nu^{(i)} = \begin{cases} 0 & \text{for} \quad \nu = 0, 1, \ldots, p-1 \\ 1 & \text{for} \quad \nu = p \end{cases}$$

Consider the increase in the integrands on the right-hand side of (7.1.60) in the sector R_j outside a δ-neighbourhood of the spectrum.

In accordance with the asymptotic formulae (7.1.23) and (7.1.51) and the inequalities (7.1.44), the products

$$\frac{d^\nu y_k^{(i)}(x, \lambda)}{dx^\nu} z_k^{(i)}(\xi, \lambda) \qquad (7.1.61)$$

are bounded in the sector R_j since the real parts of the exponential functions in both integrals are non-positive in the asymptotic representation of these products. The product (7.1.61) under the first double-summation sign in the braces in (7.1.60) has the same property.

The ratio

$$\frac{A_{kq}^{(i,r)}(\lambda)}{\Delta(\lambda)}$$

can obviously be represented in the form

$$\frac{A_{kq}^{(i,r)}(\lambda)}{\Delta(\lambda)} = \frac{e^{-\lambda W} A_{kq}^{(i,r)}(\lambda)}{e^{-\lambda W} \Delta(\lambda)} \qquad (7.1.62)$$

where W denotes the sum of all the $W_k^{(i)}$ such that

$$\operatorname{Re} \lambda W_k^{(i)} \geqslant 0 \quad (i = 1, 2, \ldots, n)$$

in the sector R_j. Bearing in mind (7.1.58), we see from the asymptotic formulae (7.1.25) and (7.1.26) that the numerator of the fraction in the right-hand side of (7.1.62) is bounded in the sector R_j and that the denominator of that fraction is, in accordance with Theorem 32, bounded below by a positive number in the sector R_j. Therefore, the right-hand side of (7.1.62) is, in accordance with Conditions 4 and 5, bounded in the sector R_j outside a δ-neighbourhood of the spectrum.

Consequently, for $k \leqslant \tau_j$ and $q \geqslant \tau_j + 1$, we have

$$\frac{d^\nu y_k^{(i)}(x, \lambda)}{dx^\nu} \frac{A_{kq}^{(i, r)}(\lambda)}{\Delta(\lambda)} z_q^{(r)}(\xi, \lambda) = \frac{d^\nu y_k^{(i)}(x, \lambda)}{dx^\nu} z_q^{(r)}(\xi, \lambda)\, \mathscr{E}_{kq}^{(i, r)}(\lambda) \tag{7.1.63}$$

where

$$\mathscr{E}_{kq}^{(i, r)}(\lambda) = \frac{A_{kq}^{(i, r)}(\lambda)}{\Delta(\lambda)} \qquad (k \leqslant \tau_j;\ q \geqslant \tau_j + 1) \tag{7.1.64}$$

is bounded in the sector R_j outside a δ-neighbourhood of the spectrum.

For $k \geqslant \tau_j + 1$, we see from (7.1.30) and the asymptotic representation (7.1.23) in the sector R_j that the first factor in the product (7.1.61) can increase as $|\lambda| \to \infty$. Therefore, since the factor $e^{W_k^{(i)}}$ does not appear in the asymptotic representation of the determinant (7.1.58), the left-hand side of (7.1.63) for $k \geqslant \tau_j + 1$ can be represented in the form

$$\frac{d^\nu y_k^{(i)}(x, \lambda)}{dx^\nu} \cdot \frac{A_{kq}^{(i, r)}(\lambda)}{\Delta(\lambda)} z_q^{(r)}(\xi, \lambda) = \frac{d^\nu y_k^{(i)}(x, \lambda)}{dx^\nu} \cdot e^{-\lambda W_k^{(i)}} z_q^{(r)}(\xi, \lambda)\, \mathscr{E}_{kq}^{(i, r)}(\lambda) \tag{7.1.65}$$

where

$$\mathscr{E}_{kq}^{(i, r)}(\lambda) = \frac{e^{\lambda W_k^{(i)}} A_{kq}^{(i)}(\lambda)}{\Delta(\lambda)} = \frac{e^{-\lambda\left(W - W_k^{(i)}\right)} A_{kq}^{(i, r)}(\lambda)}{e^{-\lambda W}\Delta(\lambda)} \tag{7.1.66}$$

$$(k \geqslant \tau_j + 1;\ q \geqslant \tau_j + 1)$$

is, in accordance with Conditions 4 and 5 and Theorem 32, bounded in the sector R_j outside a δ-neighbourhood of the spectrum.

Similarly, in accordance with Theorem 32 and Conditions 4 and 5, we have, for $k \leqslant \tau_j$ and $q \leqslant \tau_j$,

$$\frac{d^\nu y_k^{(i)}(x, \lambda)}{dx^\nu} \frac{B_{kq}^{(i, r)}(\lambda)}{\Delta(\lambda)} z_q^{(r)}(\xi, \lambda) = \frac{d^\nu y_k^{(i)}(x, \lambda)}{dx^\nu} z_q^{(r)}(\xi, \lambda) e^{\lambda W_q^{(r)}} \mathscr{E}_{kq}^{(i, r)}(\lambda) \tag{7.1.67}$$

where

$$\mathscr{E}_{kq}^{(i, r)}(\lambda) = \frac{\exp\left(-\lambda W_q^{(r)}\right) B_{kq}^{(i, r)}(\lambda)}{\Delta(\lambda)} \quad (k \leqslant \tau_j;\ q \leqslant \tau_j) \tag{7.1.68}$$

is bounded in the sector R_j outside a δ-neighbourhood of the spectrum.

Finally, for $k \geqslant \tau_j + 1$ and $q \leqslant \tau_j$, we have

$$\frac{d^\nu y_k^{(i)}(x, \lambda)}{dx^\nu} \frac{B_{kq}^{(i, r)}(\lambda)}{\Delta(\lambda)} z_q^{(r)}(\xi, \lambda) = \frac{d^\nu y_k^{(i)}(x, \lambda)}{dx^\nu} e^{-\lambda W_k^{(i)}} z_q^{(r)}(\xi, \lambda) \exp\left(\lambda W_q^{(i)}\right) \mathscr{E}_{kq}^{(i, r)}(\lambda) \tag{7.1.69}$$

where

$$\mathscr{E}_{kq}^{(i, r)}(\lambda) = \frac{\exp\left(\lambda W_k^{(i)} - \lambda W_q^{(i)}\right) B_{kq}^{(i, r)}(\lambda)}{\Delta(\lambda)} \quad (k \geqslant \tau_j + 1;\ q \leqslant \tau_j) \tag{7.1.70}$$

is bounded in the sector R_j outside a δ-neighbourhood of the spectrum.

Thus, noting (7.1.63)-(7.1.70), we can write (7.1.60) in the form

$$\frac{d^\nu y^{(i)}(x, \lambda)}{dx^\nu} = \varepsilon_\nu F^{(i)}(x, \Phi, \lambda^m) + \sum_{k=1}^{\tau_j} \frac{d^\nu y_k^{(i)}(x, \lambda)}{dx^\nu} \int_{a_i}^{x} z_k^{(i)}(\xi, \lambda) F^{(i)}(\xi, \Phi, \lambda^m) \partial\xi + \sum_{k=\tau_j+1}^{p} \frac{d^\nu y_k^{(i)}(x, \lambda)}{dx^\nu} \int_{b_i}^{x} z_k^{(i)}(\xi, \lambda) F^{(i)}(\xi, \Phi, \lambda^m) d\xi + \tag{7.1.71}$$

$$+\sum_{r=1}^{n}\sum_{k=1}^{\tau_j}\sum_{q=\tau_j+1}^{p}\frac{d^\nu y_k^{(i)}(x,\lambda)}{dx^\nu}\mathscr{E}_{kq}^{(ir)}(\lambda)$$

$$\times\int_{a_r}^{b_r} z_q^{(r)}(\xi,\lambda)\,F^{(r)}(\xi,\Phi,\lambda^m)\,d\xi$$

$$+\sum_{r=1}^{n}\sum_{k=\tau_j+1}^{p}\sum_{q=\tau_j+1}^{p}\frac{d^\nu y_k^{(i)}(x,\lambda)}{dx^\nu}e^{-\lambda W_k^{(i)}}\mathscr{E}_{kq}^{(i,r)}(\lambda)$$

$$\times\int_{a_r}^{b_r} z_q^{(r)}(\xi,\lambda)\,F^{(r)}(\xi,\Phi,\lambda^m)\,d\xi$$

$$-\sum_{r=1}^{n}\sum_{k=1}^{\tau_j}\sum_{q=1}^{\tau_j}\frac{d^\nu y_k^{(i)}(x,\lambda)}{dx^\nu}e^{\lambda W_q^{(r)}}\mathscr{E}_{kq}^{(i,r)}(\lambda) \qquad (7.1.71)\ (\text{cont.})$$

$$\times\int_{a_r}^{b_r} z_q^{(r)}(\xi,\lambda)\,F^{(r)}(\xi,\Phi,\lambda^m)\,d\xi$$

$$-\sum_{r=1}^{n}\sum_{k=\tau_j+1}^{p}\sum_{q=1}^{\tau_j}\frac{d^\nu y_k^{(i)}(x,\lambda)}{dx^\nu}e^{-\lambda W_k^{(i)}+\lambda W_q^{(i)}}\mathscr{E}_{kq}^{(i,r)}(\lambda)$$

$$\times\int_{a_r}^{b_r} z_q^{(r)}(\xi,\lambda)\,F^{(r)}(\xi,\Phi,\lambda^m)\,d\xi$$

Substituting the asymptotic representations (7.1.23) and (7.1.51) into (7.1.71), we obtain the following asymptotic representation for the derivatives of the solution of the spectral problem (7.1.1)-(7.1.2) with homogeneous boundary conditions in the sector R_j outside a δ-neighbourhood of the spectrum :

$$\frac{d^\nu y^{(i)}(x,\lambda)}{dx^\nu}=\varepsilon_\nu\,F^{(i)}(x,\Phi,\lambda^m)$$

$$+\sum_{k=1}^{\tau_j}[\eta_{k\nu0}^{(i)}(x)]\,\lambda^{\nu-p+1}\int_{a_i}^{x}\left\{\zeta_{k0}^{(i)}(\xi)+\ldots+\frac{\zeta_{ks}^{(i)}(\xi)}{\lambda^s}+\frac{E_{ks}^{(i)}(\xi,\lambda)}{\lambda^{s+1}}\right\} \qquad (7.1.72)$$

$$\times\exp\left(\lambda\int_{\xi}^{x}\varphi_k^{(i)}(t)\,dt\right)F^{(i)}(\xi,\Phi,\lambda^m)\,d\xi+$$

$$+\lambda^{\nu-p+1}\sum_{k=\tau_j+1}^{p}[\eta_{k\nu 0}^{(i)}(x)]$$

$$\times\int_{b_i}^{x}\left\{\zeta_{k0}^{(i)}(\xi)+\ldots+\frac{\zeta_{ks}^{(i)}(\xi)}{\lambda^s}+\frac{E_{ks}^{(i)}(\xi,\lambda)}{\lambda^{s+1}}\right\}$$

$$\times\exp\left(\lambda\int_{\xi}^{x}\varphi_k^{(i)}(t)\,dt\right)F^{(i)}(\xi,\Phi,\lambda^m)\,d\xi$$

$$+\sum_{r=1}^{n}\sum_{k=1}^{\tau_j}\sum_{q=\tau_j+1}^{p}[\eta_{k\nu 0}^{(i)}(x)]\,\lambda^{\nu-p+1}\mathscr{E}_{kq}^{(i,r)}(\lambda)$$

$$\times\exp\left(\lambda\int_{a_i}^{x}\varphi_k^{(i)}(t)\,dt\right)\times\int_{a_r}^{b_r}\left\{\zeta_{q0}^{(r)}(\xi)+\ldots+\frac{\zeta_{qs}^{(r)}(\xi)}{\lambda^s}\right.$$

$$\left.+\frac{E_{qs}^{(r)}(\xi,\lambda)}{\lambda^{s+1}}\right\}\exp\left(-\lambda\int_{a_r}^{\xi}\varphi_q^{(r)}(t)\,dt\right)F^{(r)}(\xi,\Phi,\lambda^m)\,d\xi$$

$$+\sum_{r=1}^{n}\sum_{k=\tau_j+1}^{p}\sum_{q=\tau_j+1}^{p}[\eta_{k\nu 0}^{(i)}(x)]\,\lambda^{\nu-p+1}\mathscr{E}_{kq}^{(i,r)}(\lambda) \qquad (7.1.72)\ (\text{cont.})$$

$$\times\exp\left(-\lambda\int_{x}^{b_i}\varphi_k^{(i)}(t)\,dt\right)\int_{a_r}^{b_r}\left\{\zeta_{q0}^{(r)}(\xi)+\ldots+\frac{\zeta_{qs}^{(r)}(\xi)}{\lambda^s}\right.$$

$$\left.+\frac{E_{qs}^{(r)}(\xi,\lambda)}{\lambda^{s+1}}\right\}\exp\left(-\lambda\int_{a_r}^{\xi}\varphi_q^{(r)}(t)\,dt\right)F^{(r)}(\xi,\Phi,\lambda^m)\,d\xi\ -$$

$$-\sum_{r=1}^{n}\sum_{k=1}^{\tau_j}\sum_{q=1}^{\tau_j}[\eta_{k\nu 0}^{(i)}(x)]\,\lambda^{\nu-p+1}$$

$$\times\exp\left(\lambda\int_{a_i}^{x}\varphi_k^{(i)}(t)\,dt+\lambda W_q^{(r)}\right)\mathscr{E}_{kq}^{(i,r)}(\lambda)\int_{a_r}^{b_r}\left\{\zeta_{q0}^{(r)}(\xi)+\ldots\right.$$

$$\left.\ldots+\frac{\zeta_{qs}^{(r)}(\xi)}{\lambda^s}+\frac{E_{qs}^{(r)}(\xi,\lambda)}{\lambda^{s+1}}\right\}$$

$$\times\exp\left(-\lambda\int_{a_r}^{\xi}\varphi_q^{(r)}(t)\,dt\right)F^{(r)}(\xi,\Phi,\lambda^m)\,d\xi\ -$$

$$-\sum_{r=1}^{n}\sum_{k=\tau_j+1}^{p}\sum_{q=1}^{\tau_j}[\eta_{k\nu 0}^{(i)}(x)]\,\lambda^{\nu-p+1}$$

$$\times\exp(-\lambda W_k^{(i)})\,\mathscr{E}_{kq}^{(i,r)}(\lambda)\int_{a_r}^{b_r}\left\{\zeta_{q0}^{(r)}(\xi)+\ldots+\frac{\zeta_{qs}^{(r)}(\xi)}{\lambda^s}\right. \quad (7.1.72)\ \text{(cont.)}$$

$$\left.+\frac{E_{qs}^{(r)}(\xi,\lambda)}{\lambda^{s+1}}\right\}\exp\left(-\lambda\int_{a_r}^{\xi}\varphi_q^{(r)}(t)\,dt\right)F^{(r)}(\xi,\Phi,\lambda^m)\,d\xi$$

This proves the following theorem.

Theorem 34 When Conditions 1 - 5 of this section are satisfied, the derivatives of the solution of the spectral problem (7.1.1)-(7.1.2) with homogeneous boundary conditions admit an asymptotic representation (7.1.72) where the functions $\mathscr{E}_{kq}^{(i,r)}(\lambda)$ are bounded in the sector R_j outside a δ-neighbourhood of the spectrum.

7.2 SOLUTION OF MIXED PROBLEMS FOR EQUATIONS CONTAINING ONLY FIRST-ORDER TIME DERIVATIVES

Consider the mixed problem

$$\frac{\partial v^{(i)}}{\partial t}=\sum_{l=0}^{p}A_{0l}^{(i)}(x)\frac{\partial^l v^{(i)}}{\partial x^l}+f^{(i)}(x,t)\quad \text{for } x\in(a_i,b_i) \quad (7.2.1)$$

$$\sum_{i=1}^{n}\sum_{\substack{k\leq 1\\ l\leq p-1}}\left\{\alpha_{skl}^{(i)}\frac{\partial^{k+l}v^{(i)}}{\partial t^k\partial x^l}\bigg|_{x=a_i}+\beta_{skl}^{(i)}\frac{\partial^{k+l}v^{(i)}}{\partial t^k\partial x^l}\bigg|_{x=b_i}\right\}=0 \quad (7.2.2)$$

$$(s=1,2,\ldots,np;\ p>2)$$

$$v^{(i)}(x,0)=\Phi_0^{(i)}(x) \quad (7.2.3)$$

where, as before, the intervals (a_i, b_i) for $(i=1,\ldots,n)$ are non-overlapping intervals with common end-points and $\alpha_{skl}^{(i)}$ and $\beta_{skl}^{(i)}$ are constants.

Suppose that Conditions 1 - 5 of Section 7.1 are satisfied for the corresponding spectral problem obtained from (7.1.1) and (7.1.2) for $m=p, q=1$, $F_0^{(i)}(x,\Phi,\lambda^m)=\Phi_0^{(i)}(x)$ and $N_{s_0}(\Phi,\lambda^m)=0$ (for $s=1,2,\ldots,np$).

As before, we denote by R_j the sector representing the intersection of any one of the sectors Σ_s and any one of the sectors T_k containing the ray d_j (for $j = 1, 2, \ldots, 2\mu$). Suppose that O_ν is a sequence of circles with centre at the coordinate origin which do not intersect small circles $Q^{(1)}_{\delta k}$ of radius δ with centres at the poles λ_k (these poles being numbered in increasing order of their moduli), and suppose that the radius of these circles $r_\nu \to \infty$ as $\nu \to \infty$. Let h denote a sufficiently large positive number that all the poles $\lambda^{(j)}_k$ of the spectral problem are located within the strip D_{hj} with centre at the coordinate origin and sides parallel to the ray d_j. Suppose that there is no pole in one of the strips D_{hj}. Let ε represent a sufficiently small positive number. From the coordinate origin, we draw two rays defined by

$$\arg\lambda = \arg d_j \pm \varepsilon \tag{7.2.4}$$

Let a_j^- and a_j^+ denote the points of intersection of the boundaries of the strip D_{hj} with the rays (7.2.4) and $q_{j\nu}^-$ and $q_{j\nu}^+$ the points of intersection of the rays (7.2.4) with the circle O_ν (where $r_\nu > |a_j^-|$ for $j = 1, \ldots, 2\mu$). Let us denote by Γ_ν the closed contour (see Fig. 6) consisting of arcs joining a_{j-1}^- and a_j^+ (for $j = 1, \ldots, 2\mu$), of the segments $a_{j-1}^- q_{j-1\nu}^-$ and $a_j^+ q_{j\nu}^+$ (for $j = 1, \ldots, 2\mu$), of the rays (7.2.4), and of the arcs $q_{j\nu}^- q_{j\nu}^+$ (for $j = 1, \ldots, 2\mu$) of the circles O_ν. Thus, the contours are drawn in such a way that the following hold.

1. Each pole of the spectral problem is within some Γ_ν.
2. For every ν, the contour Γ_ν lies outside a δ-neighbourhood of the spectrum corresponding to the spectral problem.
3. The mapping

$$\lambda^m = z \tag{7.2.5}$$

maps all the rays d_j (for $j = 1, \ldots, 2\mu$) of the λ-plane into rays lying in the left half of the z-plane and not coinciding with the imaginary semi-axes of that plane. Then, for sufficiently small ε and for a sufficiently distant part of the contour Γ_ν, we have the inequality

$$\operatorname{Re}\lambda^m \leqslant -\eta(\varepsilon)|\lambda|^m \tag{7.2.6}$$

where $\eta(\varepsilon) > 0$.

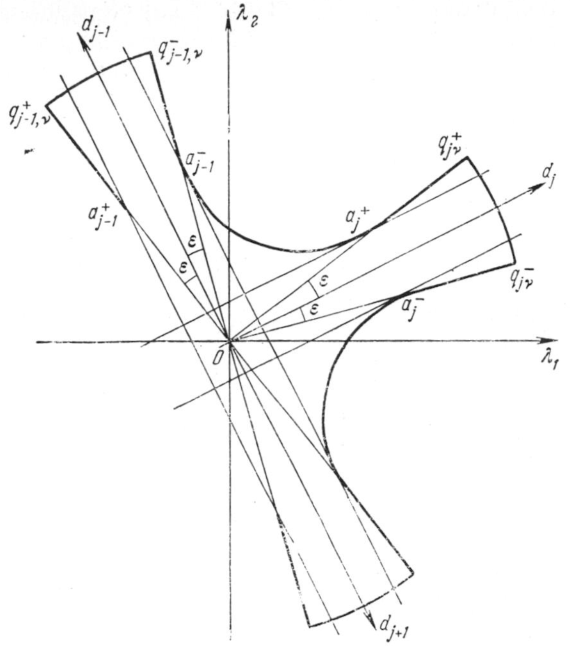

Fig. 6

Let us denote by $S_{\nu j}$ (for $j = 1, 2, \ldots, 2\mu$) that part of the contour Γ_ν consisting of the arc connecting the points a_{j-1}^- and a_j^+ and of the segments $a_{j-1}^- q_{j-1\nu}^-$ and $a_j^+ q_{j\nu}^+$,

$$\Gamma_\nu = \sum_{j=1}^{2\mu} (S_{\nu j} + \widehat{q_{j\nu}^- q_{j\nu}^+}) \tag{7.2.7}$$

Finally, let us denote by S_j the limiting contour

$$S_j = \lim_{\nu \to \infty} S_{\nu j} \tag{7.2.8}$$

Now, we can prove Theorem 35.

Theorem 35 Suppose that (7.2.5) maps all the rays d_j (for $j = 1, \ldots, 2\mu$) of the λ-plane into rays lying in the left half-plane which do not coincide with the imaginary semi-axes of the z-plane.

Suppose also that Conditions 1, 2, 4 and 5 of Section 7.1 are satisfied, that Condition 3 of that section is also satisfied for

$s=1$, and that the functions $\Phi_0^{(i)}(x)$ have continuous first and second derivatives for $x \in [a_i, b_i]$. Then, Problem (7.2.1)-(7.2.3) for $f^{(i)}(x, t) \equiv 0$ (for $i = 1, \ldots, n$) has a solution $v_1^{(i)}(x, t)$ given by

$$v_1^{(i)}(x, t) = -\frac{1}{2\pi\sqrt{-1}} \sum_{j=1}^{2\mu} \int_{S_j} \lambda^{p-1} e^{\lambda^p t} \, d\lambda \sum_{m=1}^{n} \int_{a_m}^{b} G^{(i, m)}(x, \xi, \lambda) \times (A_{0p}^{(m)}(\xi))^{-1} \Phi_0^{(m)}(\xi) \, d\xi \tag{7.2.9}$$

$$v_1^{(i)}(x, t) = \frac{-1}{2\pi\sqrt{-1}} \lim_{\nu\to\infty} \int_{\Gamma_\nu} \lambda^{p-1} e^{\lambda^p t} \, d\lambda \times \sum_{m=1}^{n} \int_{am}^{b} G^{(i, m)}(x, \xi, \lambda) (A_{0p}^{(m)}(\xi))^{-1} \Phi_0^{(m)}(\xi) \, d\xi \tag{7.2.10}$$

which has continuous derivatives of the first p orders with respect to x and a continuous first derivative with respect to t for $x \in [a_i, b_i]$ and $t \in [0, T]$, where $G^{(i, m)}(x, \xi, \lambda)$ is the Green's function of the corresponding spectral problem.

Proof In accordance with Theorem 33 of Section 7.1 and the choice of the contours S_j, we have

$$\left| \int_{q_{j\nu} q_{j\nu+k}} e^{\lambda^p t} \lambda^{p(s+1)-1} d\lambda \times \frac{\partial^\nu}{\partial x^\nu} \sum_{m=1}^{n} \int_{a_m}^{b_m} G^{(i, m)}(x, \xi, \lambda) \frac{\Phi_0^{(m)}(\xi)}{A_{0p}^{(m)}(\xi)} d\xi \right| \leqslant \int_{r_\nu}^{r_{\nu+k}} C \exp(-2\varrho^p t) \varrho^{\nu+ps} d\varrho \tag{7.2.11}$$

where C is a constant. It follows from (7.2.11) that the integrals

$$\int_{S_j} \lambda^{p(s+1)-1} e^{\lambda^p t} d\lambda \times \frac{\partial^\nu}{\partial x^\nu} \sum_{m=1}^{n} \int_{a_m}^{b_m} G^{(i, m)}(x, \xi, \lambda) \Phi_0^{(m)}(\xi) (A_{0p}^{(m)}(\xi))^{-1} d\xi \tag{7.2.12}$$

$$(s = 0, 1; \quad \nu = 0, 1, \ldots, p)$$

converge uniformly with respect to $x \in [a_i, b_i]$ and $t \in (0, T)$. This ensures the permissibility of differentiating with respect to x and t under the integral sign denoting the integral over the contour S_j (for $j = 1, \ldots, 2\mu$). Consequently, we have

$$\sum_{l=0}^{p} A_{0l}^{(i)}(x) \frac{\partial^l v_1^{(i)}(x, t)}{\partial x^l} - \frac{\partial v_1^{(i)}(x, t)}{\partial t}$$

$$\equiv \frac{-1}{2\pi \sqrt{-1}} \sum_{j=1}^{2\mu} \int_{S_j} \lambda^{p-1} d\lambda e^{\lambda^p t}$$

$$\times \left\{ \left(\sum_{l=0}^{p} A_{0l}^{(i)}(x) \frac{\partial^l}{\partial x^l} - \lambda^p \right) \sum_{m=1}^{n} \int_{a_m}^{b} G^{(i,m)}(x, \xi, \lambda) \right.$$

$$\left. \times \Phi_0^{(m)}(\xi) (A_{0p}^{(m)}(\xi))^{-1} d\xi \right\}$$

$$\equiv \frac{-1}{2\pi \sqrt{-1}} \sum_{j=1}^{2\mu} \int_{S_j} \lambda^{p-1} e^{\lambda^p t} d\lambda \Phi_0^{(i)}(x) \equiv 0$$

Thus, the functions $v_1^{(i)}(x, t)$ defined by (7.2.9) satisfy the homogeneous equations corresponding to (7.2.1). Also, these functions $v_1^{(i)}(x, t)$ are continuous and have continuous derivatives of the first p orders with respect to x and of all orders with respect to t for $x \in [a_i, b_i]$ and $t > 0$.

Furthermore, on the basis of the uniform convergence of the integrals (7.2.12) for $x \in [a_i, b_i]$ and $t > 0$, it can be directly verified that

$$\sum_{i=1}^{n} \sum_{\substack{k \leq 1 \\ l \leq p-1}} \left\{ \alpha_{skl}^{(i)} \frac{\partial^{k+l} v_1^{(i)}}{\partial t^k \partial x^l} \bigg|_{x=a_i} + \beta_{skl}^{(i)} \frac{\partial^{k+l} v_1^{(i)}}{\partial t^k \partial x^l} \bigg|_{x=b_i} \right\} = 0$$

Let us now show that $v_1^{(i)}(x, t)$ satisfies the initial condition (7.2.3). First, we show that, for $x \in (a_i, b_i)$, the integral

$$I(x, t) = \int_{S_j} \lambda^{p-1} e^{\lambda^p t} \left\{ \sum_{m=1}^{n} \int_{a_m}^{b_m} G^{(i, m)}(x, \xi, \lambda) \right.$$

$$\times (A_{0p}^{(m)}(\xi))^{-1} \Phi_0^{(m)}(\xi) d\xi \quad (7.2.13)$$

$$\left. + \frac{1}{\lambda^p} \sum_{k=1}^{p} \frac{\eta_{k00}^{(i)}(x) \zeta_{k0}^{(i)}(x)}{\varphi_k^{(i)}(x)} (A_{0p}^{(i)}(x))^{-1} \Phi_0^{(i)}(x) \right\} d\lambda$$

converges uniformly with respect to $t \in [0, T]$. Then, by taking the limit under the integral sign in (7.2.13) as $t \to 0$, we can show that its limit is equal to zero. Then, to complete the proof of the first part of Theorem 34, we need only note that

$$\frac{1}{2\pi\sqrt{-1}} \sum_{j=1}^{2\mu} \int_{S_j} \frac{e^{\lambda^p t}}{\lambda} d\lambda \times \sum_{k=1}^{p} \frac{\eta_{k00}^{(i)}(x)\, \zeta_{k0}^{(i)}(x)}{\varphi_k^{(i)}(x)} (A_{0p}^{(i)}(x)^{-1} \Phi_0^{(i)}(x)$$

$$= \frac{1}{2\pi\sqrt{-1}} \lim_{\nu\to\infty} \int_{\Gamma_\nu} \frac{e^{\lambda^p t}}{\lambda} d\lambda \sum_{k=1}^{p} \frac{\eta_{k00}^{(i)}(x)\, \zeta_{k0}^{(i)}(x)}{\varphi_k^{(i)}(x)} (A_{0p}^{(i)}(x))^{-1} \Phi_0^{(i)}(x) \quad (7.2.14)$$

$$= \sum_{k=1}^{p} \frac{\eta_{k00}^{(i)}(x)\, \zeta_{k0}^{(i)}(x)}{\varphi_k^{(i)}(x)} (A_{0p}^{(i)}(x))^{-1} \Phi_0^{(i)}(x)$$

for every $t > 0$.

Since $\varphi_k^{(i)}(x)$ is a solution of the characteristic equation (7.1.19), the right-hand side of (7.2.14) is equal to

$$\sum_{k=1}^{p} \eta_{k00}^{(i)}(x)\, \zeta_{k0}^{(i)}(x)\, (\varphi_k^{(i)}(x))^{p-1} \Phi_0^{(i)}(x) = \sum_{k=1}^{p} \eta_{kp-10}^{(i)}(x)\, \zeta_{k0}^{(i)}(x)\, \Phi_0^{(i)}(x)$$

which in turn is equal to $\Phi_0^{(i)}(x)$ by virtue of (7.1.52).

In accordance with the conditions of the theorem, the principal terms in the asymptotic representation (7.1.71) admit integration by parts

$$\int_{a_i}^{x} \zeta_{k0}^{(i)}(\xi) F^{(i)}(\xi) \exp\left(\lambda \int_{\xi}^{x} \varphi_k^{(i)}(t)\,dt\right) d\xi$$

$$= -\frac{\zeta_{k0}^{(i)}(x) F^{(i)}(x)}{\lambda \varphi_k^{(i)}(x)} + \frac{\zeta_{k0}^{(i)}(a_i) F^{(i)}(a_i)}{\lambda \varphi_k^{(i)}(a_i)} \exp\left(\lambda \int_{a_i}^{x} \varphi_k^{(i)}(t)\,dt\right) \quad (7.2.15)$$

$$- \frac{1}{\lambda^2} \left\{ \frac{\exp\left(\lambda \int_{\xi}^{x} \varphi_k^{(i)}(t)\,dt\right)}{\varphi_k^{(i)}(\xi)} \frac{d}{d\xi}\left(\frac{\zeta_{k0}^{(i)}(\xi) F^{(i)}(\xi)}{\varphi_k^{(i)}(\xi)}\right)\Bigg|_{a_i}^{x} \right.$$

$$\left. - \int_{a_i}^{x} \exp\left(\lambda \int_{\xi}^{x} \varphi_k^{(i)}(t)\,dt\right) \frac{d}{d\xi}\left(\frac{1}{\varphi_k^{(i)}(\xi)} \frac{d}{d\xi}\left(\frac{\zeta_{k0}^{(i)}(\xi) F^{(i)}(\xi)}{\varphi_k^{(i)}(\xi)}\right)\right) d\xi \right\}$$

$$\int_{b_i}^{x} \zeta_{k0}^{(i)}(\xi) F^{(i)}(\xi) \exp\left(\lambda \int_{\xi}^{x} \varphi_k^{(i)}(t)\, dt\right) d\xi$$

$$= -\frac{\zeta_{k0}^{(i)}(x) F^{(i)}(x)}{\lambda \varphi_k^{(i)}(x)} + \frac{\zeta_{k0}^{(i)}(b_i) F^{(i)}(b_i)}{\lambda \varphi_k^{(i)}(b_i)} \exp\left(\lambda \int_{b_i}^{x} \varphi_k^{(i)}(t)\, dt\right)$$

$$-\frac{1}{\lambda^2}\left\{\frac{\exp\left(\lambda \int_{\xi}^{x} \varphi_k^{(i)}(t)\, dt\right)}{\varphi_k^{(i)}(\xi)} \frac{d}{d\xi}\left(\frac{\zeta_{k0}^{(i)}(\xi) F^{(i)}(\xi)}{\varphi_k^{(i)}(\xi)}\right)\Bigg|_{b_i}^{x} \right. \tag{7.2.16}$$

$$-\int_{b_i}^{x} \exp\left(\lambda \int_{\xi}^{x} \varphi_k^{(i)}(t)\, dt\right) \frac{d}{d\xi}\left(\frac{1}{\varphi_k^{(i)}(\xi)}\right.$$

$$\left.\times \frac{d}{d\xi}\left(\frac{\zeta_{k0}^{(i)}(\xi) F^{(i)}(\xi)}{\varphi_k^{(i)}(\xi)}\right)\right) d\xi\Bigg\}$$

where

$$F^{(i)}(\xi) = (A_{0p}^{(i)}(\xi))^{-1} \Phi_0^{(i)}(\xi) \tag{7.2.17}$$

Similarly, we can easily show by integrating by parts that

$$\left|\int_{a_i}^{x} \exp\left(\lambda \int_{\xi}^{x} \varphi_k^{(i)}(t)\, dt\right) \zeta_{k1}^{(i)}(\xi) F^{(i)}(\xi)\, d\xi\right| < \frac{C_1}{|\lambda|}$$

$$\left|\int_{b_i}^{x} \exp\left(\lambda \int_{\xi}^{x} \varphi_k^{(i)}(t)\, dt\right) \zeta_{k1}^{(i)}(\xi) F^{(i)}(\xi)\, d\xi\right| < \frac{C_2}{|\lambda|}, \tag{7.2.18}$$

where C_1 and C_2 are constants.

From the asymptotic formula (7.1.72) for $s=1$, we conclude on the basis of the choice of the contours S_j and (7.2.15), (7.2.16) and (7.2.18) that the integrand in (7.2.13) decreases faster than does λ^{-2}. Consequently, the integral (7.2.13) converges uniformly with respect to $t \in [0, T]$. If we take the limit in (7.2.13) as $t \to 0$, we obtain

$$\lim_{t\to 0} I(x, t) = \int_{S_j} \lambda^{p-1} \left\{\sum_{m=1}^{n} \int_{a_m}^{b_m} G^{(i,m)}(x, \xi, \lambda)\right.$$

$$\times (A_{0p}^{(i)}(\xi))^{-1} \Phi_0^{(m)}(\xi)\, d\xi + \frac{1}{\lambda^p} \sum_{k=1}^{p} \frac{\eta_{k00}^{(i)}(x) \zeta_{k0}^{(i)}(x)}{\varphi_k^{(i)}(x)} \tag{7.2.19}$$

$$\left.\times (A_{0p}^{(i)}(x))^{-1} \Phi_0^{(i)}(x)\right\} d\lambda$$

Since the integrand in (7.2.19) has no singularities between the contours $S_{j\nu}$ and the arcs $O_{\nu j}$ of the circles O_ν and since this function decreases on $O_{\nu j}$ faster than does λ^{-2}, we have, from (7.2.19)

$$\lim_{t\to 0} I(x, t) = 0$$

as we wished to show.

Finally, to obtain (7.2.10), we need only note that, for $t > 0$ the limits of the integral (7.2.10) over the arcs $\widehat{q_{j\nu}^{-} q_{j\nu}^{+}}$ as $\nu \to \infty$ are equal to zero.

Theorem 36 Suppose that (7.2.5) maps all the rays d_j (for $j = 1, 2, \ldots, 2\mu$) of the λ-plane into rays lying in the left half of the z-plane which do not coincide with the imaginary semi-axes of the z-plane. Suppose also that Conditions 1, 2, 4 and 5 of Section 7.1 are satisfied, that Condition 3 of Section 7.1 is satisfied for $s = p - 1$, the functions $f^{(i)}(x, t)$ have continuous derivatives of the first p orders with respect to x and continuous first and second derivatives with respect to t for $x \in [a_i, b_i]$ and $t \in (0, T)$ and the derivatives of the first $p-2$ orders with respect to x vanish at the end-points of the interval $[a_i\ b_i]$. Then, for $\Phi_0^{(i)}(x) \equiv 0$ (where $i = 1, \ldots, n$), Problem (7.2.1)-(7.2.3) has a solution $v_2^{(i)}(x, t)$ given by

$$v_2^{(i)}(x, t) = -\frac{1}{2\pi\sqrt{-1}} \sum_{j=1}^{2\mu} \int_{S_j} \lambda^{p-1}\, d\lambda \times \sum_{m=1}^{n} \int_{a_m}^{b_m} d\xi\, G^{(i, m)}(x, \xi, \lambda) \times \int_0^t d\tau e^{\lambda^p (t-\tau)} f^{(m)}(\xi, \tau) (A_{0p}^{(m)}(\xi))^{-1} \quad (7.2.20)$$

$$v_2^{(i)}(x, t) = -\frac{1}{2\pi\sqrt{-1}} \lim_{\nu\to\infty} \int_{\Gamma_\nu} \lambda^{p-1}\, d\lambda \times \sum_{m=1}^{n} \int_{a_m}^{b_m} G^{(i, m)}(x, \xi, \lambda) (A_{0p}^{(m)}(\xi))^{-1} \times \int_0^t d\tau \exp(\lambda^p (t-\tau)) f^{(m)}(\xi, \tau)\, d\xi \quad (7.2.21)$$

Theorem 36 can be directly proved with the aid of Theorem 33. When the hypotheses of Theorems 34 and 35 are satisfied, it is possible to show that Problem (7.2.1)-(7.2.3) is correctly formulated.

Following the procedure used in proving Theorem 29, one can also prove the following theorem.

Theorem 37 Suppose that the (7.2.5) maps one of the rays d_j of the λ-plane into a ray lying in the right half of the z-plane but not along the imaginary axis. Then, independently of the degree of smoothness of the given functions $\Phi^{(i)}(x)$ and $f^{(i)}(x, t)$, at least one of which is assumed not to be identically zero, Problem (7.2.1)-(7.2.3) does not have a sufficiently smooth solution.

The basic restriction was the assumption that the roots of the characteristic equations of the spectral problems considered in Chapters 1 - 7 are distinct. A study of certain particular cases shows that the methods developed in Chapters 1 - 7 can be extended to problems with multiple or zero roots of the characteristic equations.

In 1953, Aliyev studied an example of such a problem (encountered in elasticity theory). He considered the problem

$$\frac{\partial^2 u}{\partial t^2} = \alpha \frac{\partial^4 u}{\partial x^4} + \beta \frac{\partial^4 u}{\partial t^2 \, \partial x^2} \tag{7.2.22}$$

$$\sum_{j=1}^{4} \left\{ \alpha_{ij} \left. \frac{\partial^{j-1} u}{\partial x^{j-1}} \right|_{x=0} + \beta_{ij} \left. \frac{\partial^{j-1} u}{\partial x^{j-1}} \right|_{x=1} \right\} = 0 \quad (i = 1, 2, 3, 4) \tag{7.2.23}$$

$$\left. \frac{\partial^k u}{\partial t^k} \right|_{t=0} = \Phi_k(x) \tag{7.2.24}$$

where α, β, α_{ij} and β_{ij} are constants.

The corresponding spectral problem is of the form

$$\alpha y'''' + \beta \lambda^2 y'' - \lambda^2 y = \lambda \Phi_0(x) + \Phi_1(x) \tag{7.2.25}$$

$$L_i(y) \equiv \sum_{j=1}^{n} \{\alpha_{ij} y^{(j-1)}(0) + \beta_{ij} y^{(j-1)}(1)\} = 0 \quad (i = 1, 2, 3, 4) \tag{7.2.26}$$

Clearly the characteristic equation in the sense of Birkhoff

$$\alpha\theta^4 + \beta\theta^2 = 0$$

has multiple and zero roots. Therefore, Problem (7.2.22)-(7.2.24) is not included in the theories developed in Chapters 1 - 5 or 6 and 7.

Since the coefficients in (7.2.25) are constants, it is easy to obtain the following asymptotic representations of the fundamental system of particular solutions $y_s(x, \lambda)$ of the corresponding homogeneous equation

$$\frac{d^\nu y_s}{dx^\nu} = \lambda^{\nu p} e^{\lambda^p \theta_s x} \left\{ \sum_{k=0}^{3} \eta_{sk\nu}(x) \lambda^{-k} + \frac{E_{sk}(x, \lambda)}{\lambda^4} \right\} \tag{7.2.27}$$

where

$$p = \begin{cases} 0 & \text{for} \quad s = 1, 3 \\ 1 & \text{for} \quad s = 2, 4 \end{cases}$$

$$\eta_{i0\nu}(x) = \eta_{i00}(x)\,\theta_i^\nu, \quad \eta_{ik0}(x) = \eta_{ik}(x), \quad \eta_{i0}(x) = 1$$

$$(i = 1, 2, 3, 4; \quad \nu, k = 0, 1, 2, 3)$$

$$\theta_1 = -\theta_3 = \beta^{-\frac{1}{2}}, \quad \theta_2 = -\theta_4 = \sqrt{-1}\ \ \beta^{\frac{1}{2}} \alpha^{-\frac{1}{2}}$$

and $E_{sk}(x, \lambda)$ are continuous with respect to x and are bounded for large values of λ.

Suppose that the non-zero coefficients of the highest derivatives of orders $\nu_{1i} - 1$ and $\nu_{2i} - 1$ which appear in the boundary conditions (7.2.26) assume the values $\alpha_{i\nu_{1i}}$ and $\beta_{i\nu_{2i}}$ at the left and right end-points of the interval $[0, 1]$ respectively. Let us number these conditions in such a way that the orders of the derivatives at one of the end-points of the interval $[0, 1]$ will not increase with increasing number of the boundary condition. To be more definite, let us look at the left end-point of the interval and assume that the following conditions are satisfied.

1. $\nu_{i1} = \nu_{2i} = \nu_i \quad (i = 1, 2, 3, 4), \quad \nu_2 < \nu_3$

2. $$M = \begin{vmatrix} \sum_{j=1}^{\nu_1} (\alpha_{1j} + \beta_{1j} e^{\theta_1}) \theta_1^{j-1} & \sum_{j=1}^{\nu_1} (\alpha_{1j} + \beta_{1j} e^{\theta_3}) \theta_3^{j-1} \\ \sum_{j=1}^{\nu_2} (\alpha_{2j} + \beta_{2j} e^{\theta_1}) \theta_1^{j-1} & \sum_{j=1}^{\nu_2} (\alpha_{2j} + \beta_{2j} e^{\theta_3}) \theta_3^{j-1} \end{vmatrix} \neq 0$$

$$N = \begin{vmatrix} \alpha_{3\nu_3}(-1)^{\nu_3 - 1} & \beta_{3\nu_3} \\ \alpha_{4\nu_4}(-1)^{\nu_4 - 1} & \beta_{4\nu_4} \end{vmatrix} \neq 0$$

3. The functions $\Phi_k(x)$ have continuous derivatives of the first $8 - k$ orders; the first $6 - k$ of these derivatives

vanish at the end-point of the interval [0, 1].

Aliyev showed by methods developed in Chapters 1 - 7 that the following assertions hold under Conditions 1 - 3.

1. If we delete from the λ-plane the interiors of small circles of radius δ with centres at the zeros of the characteristic determinant $\Delta(\lambda)$ of the Green's function of the problem, then, in the remaining part of the λ-plane, the solution of Problem (7.2.25)-(7.2.26) has the asymptotic representation

$$\frac{d^\nu y(x,\lambda)}{dx^\nu} = \frac{\Phi_0^{(\nu)}(x)}{\lambda} + \frac{\Phi_1^{(\nu)}(x)}{\lambda^2} + \frac{\gamma_{1\nu}(x)}{\lambda^3} + \frac{\gamma_{2\nu}(x)}{\lambda^4} + \frac{E_\nu(x,\lambda)}{\lambda^5}$$

where the $E_\nu(x, \lambda)$ are bounded for large values of λ outside a δ-neighbourhood of the spectrum.

2. If $\arg\alpha - \arg\beta = \pm\pi$, Problem (7.2.22)-(7.2.24) has a solution given by

$$u(x,t) = \frac{1}{2\pi\sqrt{-1}} \lim_{\nu\to\infty} \int_{\Gamma_\nu} e^{\lambda t}\, d\lambda$$

$$\times \int_0^1 G(x,\xi,\lambda) \frac{\lambda(\beta\Phi_0''(\xi) - \Phi_0(\xi)) + (\beta\Phi_1''(\xi) - \Phi_1(\xi))}{\alpha}\, d\xi$$

where $G(x, \xi, \lambda)$ is the Green's function of the Problem (7.2.25) and (7.2.26) and the Γ_ν are closed curves situated outside a δ-neighbourhood of the spectrum, these curves being chosen in a similar manner to that in Fig. 5.

3. The following expansion formula is valid

$$\frac{1}{2\pi\sqrt{-1}} \sum_\nu \int_{c_\nu} \lambda\, d\lambda \int_0^1 G(x,\xi,\lambda) \frac{\beta\Phi''(\xi) - \Phi(\xi)}{\alpha}\, d\xi = \Phi(x)$$

where c_ν is a simple closed curve encircling only one pole λ_ν of the function in the inner integrand and where the summation with respect to ν is over all the poles of that function

4. Under the conditions of assertion 3, every sufficiently smooth solution of Problem (7.2.22)-(7.2.24) is represented by

$$u(x,t) = \frac{1}{2\pi\sqrt{-1}} \sum_\nu \int_{c_\nu} e^{\lambda t}\, d\lambda \int_0^1 G(x,\xi,\lambda)$$

$$\times \frac{\lambda(\beta\Phi_0''(\xi) - \Phi_0(\xi)) + (\beta\Phi_1''(\xi) - \Phi_1(\xi))}{\alpha}\, d\xi$$

5. Under the conditions of assertion 2, Problem (7.2.22)-(7.2.24) is correctly formulated.

Gadzhibekov applied the contour-integral method of this chapter to prove (4.3.20) for the case of the operators $M_1\left(t, \frac{\partial}{\partial t}\right)$ and $M_2\left(t, \frac{\partial}{\partial t}\right)$ of the form

$$M_1\left(t, \frac{\partial}{\partial t}\right) = (\alpha t+\beta)^2 \frac{\partial^2}{\partial t^2} + (\alpha t+\beta)\frac{\partial}{\partial t} + \gamma_1$$

$$M_2\left(t, \frac{\partial}{\partial t}\right) = (\alpha t+\beta)\frac{\partial}{\partial t} + \gamma_2$$

$$L\left(x, \frac{\partial}{\partial x}\right) y \equiv \sum_{k=0}^{2} c_k(x) \frac{d^k y}{dx^k}$$

where α, β and γ_k are constants. Under certain restrictions imposed on its given conditions, a mixed problem of the form (4.3.19), (4.3.1) and (4.3.3) is correctly formulated.

CHAPTER 8

Solution of a multi-dimensional spectral problem for a single elliptic equation with a large complex parameter

8.1 FUNDAMENTAL SOLUTION AND ITS BOUNDS

The fundamental solution of a single elliptic equation applying to a bounded region and containing a real parameter was constructed by Carleman [17].

For our purposes, we need to construct a fundamental solution for a complex parameter in a region R_δ and to obtain suitable bounds for it. To do this, we use the method of Levi [25]. This method was successfully adapted by Carleman [17] to the construction of a fundamental solution of an equation with a real parameter.

Assume that the following condition is satisfied regarding the coefficients in (8.1.1).

1. In the region $D+\Gamma$, the function $c(x)$ is once continuously differentiable and the coefficients $a_i(x)$ and $a(x)$ are continuous. If D is an unbounded region, all these functions are assumed to be bounded in $D+\Gamma$. The function $c(x)$ is positive in the region $D+\Gamma$ and there exists a constant $\varkappa > 0$ such that $\sqrt{c(x)} \geqslant \varkappa$ for all $x \in D+\Gamma$.

Consider the following homogeneous equation in some region D with boundary Γ:

$$L_1\left(x, \frac{\partial}{\partial x}, \lambda\right) u \equiv L\left(x, \frac{\partial}{\partial x}\right) u - \lambda^2 c(x) u = 0 \quad (8.1.1)$$

where

$$L\left(x, \frac{\partial}{\partial x}\right) \equiv \sum_{i=1}^{3} \left(\frac{\partial^2}{\partial x_i^2} + a_i(x) \frac{\partial}{\partial x_i}\right) + a(x)$$

It can be directly verified that the function

$$P_0(x-\xi, \xi, \lambda) = \frac{\exp\left(-\lambda \sqrt{c(\xi)}\, |x-\xi|\right)}{4\pi |x-\xi|} \quad (8.1.2)$$

is a fundamental solution with respect to the point $x = (x_1, x_2, x_3)$ with a singularity at the point $\xi = (\xi_1, \xi_2, \xi_3)$ of the equation

$$\sum_{i=1}^{3} \frac{\partial^2 u}{\partial x^2} - \lambda^2 c(\xi) u = 0 \quad (8.1.3)$$

where $|x-\xi|$ denotes the length of the vector $x-\xi$.

Following the Levi-Carleman method, let us seek a fundamental solution of (8.1.1) with singularity at a point $\xi \in D$ in the form

$$P(x, \xi, \lambda) = P_0(x-\xi, \xi, \lambda) + \int_D P_0(x-\eta, \eta, \lambda) h(\eta, \xi, \lambda)\, d_\eta D \quad (8.1.4)$$

where $h(\eta, \xi, \lambda)$ is so determined that (8.1.4) will satisfy (8.1.1) when $x \neq \xi$.

If we substitute (8.1.4) into (8.1.1) and use the familiar device for differentiating the integral function in the right-hand side of (8.1.4), we obtain the Fredholm integral equation

$$h(x, \xi, \lambda) = K(x, \xi, \lambda) + \int_D K(x, \eta, \lambda) h(\eta, \xi, \lambda)\, d_\eta D, \quad (8.1.5)$$

where

$$K(x, \xi, \lambda) = \Big\{\sum_{i=1}^{3} a_i(x) \frac{\partial}{\partial x_i} + a(x) - \lambda^2 (c(x) - c(\xi))\Big\} P_0(x - \xi, \xi, \lambda) \tag{8.1.6}$$

Let R and δ denote positive numbers and suppose that δ is a sufficiently small positive number, for example, $\delta < \frac{1}{2}$ Let us denote by R_δ the set of values of λ which satisfy the inequalities

$$|\lambda| > R, \ \cos\arg\lambda \geqslant \delta$$

We shall now show that, for sufficiently large R, the integral equation (8.1.5) has a unique solution for all $\lambda \in R_\delta$ and that the solution can be constructed by successive approximations. Obviously, it will be sufficient for us to show that the series

$$h(x, \xi, \lambda) = K(x, \xi, \lambda) + \sum_{\nu=2}^{\infty} K_\nu(x, \xi, \lambda) \tag{8.1.7}$$

is convergent with respect to ξ in the region D for all values of $\lambda \in R_\delta$ and that the identity

$$\begin{aligned}\int_D K(x, \eta, \lambda) \Big\{K(\eta, \xi, \lambda) + \sum_{\nu=2}^{\infty} K_\nu(\eta, \xi, \lambda)\Big\} d_\eta D \\ = \int_D K(x, \eta, \lambda) K(\eta, \xi, \lambda) d_\eta D \\ + \sum_{\nu=2}^{\infty} \int_D K(x, \eta, \lambda) K_\nu(\eta, \xi, \lambda) d_\eta D\end{aligned} \tag{8.1.8}$$

holds, where $K_\nu(x, \xi, \lambda)$ is the νth iteration of the kernel $K(x, \xi, \lambda)$.

When Condition 1 is satisfied, noting (8.1.2), we obtain from (8.1.6) the following inequality for all $\lambda \in R_\delta$:

$$|K(x, \xi, \lambda)| < C \frac{\exp(-2\varepsilon |\lambda| |x-\xi|)}{|x-\xi|^2} \tag{8.1.9}$$

where C is a constant independent of λ and $3\varepsilon = \varkappa\delta$.

In accordance with (8.1.9) we have for the second iteration of the kernel $K(x, \xi, \lambda)$

$$|K_2(x, \xi, \lambda)| = \left| \int_D K(x, \eta, \lambda) K(\eta, \xi, \lambda)\, d_\eta D \right|$$

$$\leqslant \int_D \frac{C^2 \exp[-2|\lambda| \varepsilon (|x-\eta| + |\eta-\xi|)]}{|x-\eta|^2 |\eta-\xi|^2} d_\eta D \tag{8.1.10}$$

$$\leqslant C^2 \exp(-\varepsilon |\lambda| |x-\xi|) \int_D \frac{\exp(-\varepsilon |\lambda| |x-\eta|)}{|x-\eta|^2 |\eta-\xi|^2} d_\eta D$$

In order to find a bound for the integral in the right-hand side of this inequality, let us shift to polar coordinates, taking the origin at the point x and directing the third axis

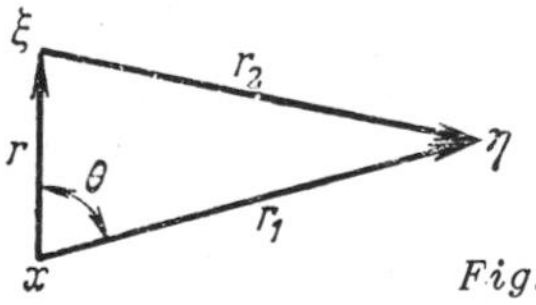

Fig. 7

along the vector $\xi - x$ (see Fig. 7). If we denote $|x-\eta|$, $|\eta-\xi|$ and $|x-\xi|$ by r_1, r_2 and r, respectively, we have

$$\int_D \frac{\exp(-\varepsilon |\lambda| |x-\eta|)}{|x-\eta|^2 |\eta-\xi|^2} d_\eta D$$

$$\leqslant \int_0^\infty dr_1 \int_0^{2\pi} d\varphi \int_0^\pi \frac{\exp(-\varepsilon |\lambda| r_1)}{r_1^2 r_2^2} r_1^2 \sin\theta\, d\theta =$$

$$= 2\pi \int_0^\infty dr_1 \int_0^\pi \frac{\exp(-\varepsilon |\lambda| r_1) \sin\theta\, d\theta}{r_1^2 + r^2 - 2rr_1 \cos\theta}$$

$$= \frac{2\pi}{r} \int_0^\infty \exp(-\varepsilon |\lambda| rt)\, dt \int_0^\pi \frac{\sin\theta\, d\theta}{1 + t^2 - 2t\cos\theta} \tag{8.1.11}$$

$$= \frac{2\pi}{r} \int_0^\infty \exp(-\varepsilon |\lambda| rt) \frac{1}{2t} \ln \frac{1+t^2+2t}{1+t^2-2t} dt$$

$$= \frac{\pi}{r} \int_0^\infty \exp(-\varepsilon |\lambda| rt) \frac{1}{t} \ln \left| \frac{1+t}{1-t} \right| dt.$$

For the integral in the right-hand side of (8.1.11), it is easy to show that

$$\int_0^{\infty} \frac{\exp(-\varepsilon|\lambda|rt)}{t} \ln\left|\frac{1+t}{1-t}\right| dt \leqslant \frac{C_\varepsilon}{|\lambda| r}$$

where C_ε is a constant depending only on ε. Bearing in mind this last inequality, we obtain from (8.1.11)

$$\int_D \frac{\exp(-\varepsilon|\lambda||x-\eta|)}{|x-\eta|^2|\eta-\xi|^2} d_\eta D \leqslant \frac{\pi C_\varepsilon}{|\lambda||x-\xi|^2} \tag{8.1.12}$$

From (8.1.12) and (8.1.10) it follows that

$$|K_2(x, \xi, \lambda)| \leqslant \frac{\pi C^2 C_\varepsilon}{|\lambda||x-\xi|^2} \exp(-\varepsilon|\lambda||x-\xi|) \tag{8.1.13}$$

Thus, with the aid of (8.1.9) and (8.1.12), it is easy to show by induction that the inequality

$$|K_n(x, \xi, \lambda)| \leqslant \left(\frac{\pi C C_\varepsilon}{|\lambda|}\right)^{n-1} \frac{C}{|x-\xi|^2} \exp(-\varepsilon|\lambda||x-\xi|) \tag{8.1.14}$$

is valid for all $\lambda \in R_\delta$ and $n \geqslant 2$.

Inequality (8.1.14) implies the uniform convergence of the series (8.1.7) and the validity of the identity (8.1.8) for all $\lambda \in R_\delta$ for sufficiently large R. Also, for the limit $h(x, \xi, \lambda)$ of the series (8.1.7), we have the bound

$$|h(x, \xi, \lambda)| \leqslant \frac{C}{|x-\xi|^2} \exp(-\varepsilon|\lambda||x-\xi|) \tag{8.1.15}$$

where C is positive. This assertion is clear if D is a bounded region. In the case of an unbounded region D, the identity (8.1.8) is not so clear. In this connection, let us show that, if Q is a sufficiently large positive number, the absolute value of the integral

$$\int_{|x-\eta| \geqslant Q} K(x, \eta, \lambda) \sum_{\nu=2}^{\infty} K_\nu(\eta, \xi, \lambda) d_\eta D$$

can be made arbitrarily small. By virtue of (8.1.9) and

(8.1.14), we have

$$\left| \int_{|x-\eta|\geq Q} K(x, \eta, \lambda) \sum_{\nu=2}^{\infty} K_\nu(\eta, \xi, \lambda)\, d_\eta D \right|$$

$$\leqslant \int_{|x-\eta|\geq Q} |K(x, \eta, \lambda)| \sum_{\nu=2}^{\infty} |K_\nu(\eta, \xi, \lambda)|\, d_\eta D$$

$$\leqslant \int_{|x-\eta|\geq Q} C\frac{\exp(-2\varepsilon|\lambda||x-\eta|)}{|x-\eta|^2} \sum_{\nu=2}^{\infty} \frac{C}{|\eta-\xi|^2}\left(\frac{\pi CC_\varepsilon}{|\lambda|}\right)^{\nu-1}$$

$$\times \exp(-\varepsilon|\lambda||\eta-\xi|)\, d_\eta D$$

$$\leqslant \int_{|x-\eta|\geq Q} \frac{\exp(-\varepsilon|\lambda||x-\eta|)}{|x-\eta|^2|\eta-\xi|^2} \frac{\pi C^3 C_\varepsilon}{|\lambda|\left(1-\frac{\pi CC_\varepsilon}{|\lambda|}\right)} d_\eta D$$

$$\leqslant \frac{1}{Q^2} \frac{\pi C^3 C_\varepsilon}{|\lambda|\left(1-\frac{\pi CC_\varepsilon}{|\lambda|}\right)} \int_{|x-\eta|\geq Q} \frac{\exp(-\varepsilon|\lambda||x-\eta|)}{|\eta-\xi|^2} d_\eta D.$$

To obtain a suitable bound for the fundamental solution, we need to get a bound for the integral function in (8.1.4). In accordance with Condition 1, we obtain from (8.1.2)

$$\left|\frac{\partial^k P_0(x-\xi, \xi, \lambda)}{\partial x_i^k}\right| \leqslant \frac{C_1 \exp(-2\varepsilon|\lambda||x-\xi|)}{|x-\xi|^{1+k}} \qquad (k=0, 1, 2), \tag{8.1.16}$$

where C_1 is a constant. Keeping (8.1.16) and (8.1.15) in mind, we have

$$|P_1(x, \xi, \lambda)| = \left| \int_D P_0(x-\eta, \eta, \lambda)\, h(\eta, \xi, \lambda)\, d_\eta D \right|$$

$$\leqslant CC_1 \int_D \frac{\exp[-\varepsilon|\lambda|(2|x-\eta|+|\eta-\xi|)]}{|x-\eta||\eta-\xi|^2} d_\eta D \tag{8.1.17}$$

$$\leqslant CC_1 \exp\left(-\frac{\varepsilon}{2}|\lambda||x-\xi|\right) \int_D \frac{\exp\left(-\frac{\varepsilon}{2}|\lambda||\eta-\xi|\right)}{|x-\eta||\eta-\xi|^2} d_\eta D$$

Changing to polar coordinates with origin at the point ξ, we obtain*

$$\int_D \frac{\exp\left(-\frac{\varepsilon}{2}|\lambda|\,|\eta-\xi|\right)}{|x-\eta|\,|\eta-\xi|^2}\,d_\eta D \leqslant$$

$$\leqslant \int_0^\infty dr_1 \int_0^{2\pi} d\varphi \int_0^\pi \frac{\exp\left(-\frac{\varepsilon}{2}|\lambda|\,r_1\right)}{r_1^2 r_2}\,r_1^2 \sin\theta\, d\theta \qquad (8.1.18)$$

$$= 2\pi \int_0^\infty \exp\left(-\frac{\varepsilon}{2}|\lambda|\,rt\right)\frac{|t+1|-|t-1|}{t}\,dt = \frac{4\pi}{\varepsilon|\lambda|\,r}$$

Substituting this into (1.1.17) we obtain the following estimate for the integral function of the fundamental solution

$$\left|\int_D P_0(x-\eta,\ \eta,\ \lambda)\,h(\eta,\ \xi,\ \lambda)\,d_\eta D\right| \leqslant \frac{C_2}{|\lambda|\,|x-\xi|}\exp\left(-\frac{\varepsilon}{2}|\lambda|\,|x-\xi|\right) \qquad (8.1.19)$$

where $C_2 = \frac{4\pi CC_1}{\varepsilon}$. Furthermore, keeping (8.1.2) in mind, we get from (8.1.4)

$$\frac{\partial P(x,\ \xi,\ \lambda)}{\partial x_i} + \frac{\partial P_0(x-\xi,\ \xi,\ \lambda)}{\partial \xi_i} = -\frac{\lambda}{4\pi}\exp\left(-\lambda\sqrt{c(\xi)}\,|x-\xi|\right)\frac{\partial}{\partial \xi_i}\sqrt{c(\xi)} + \int_D \frac{\partial P_0(x-\eta,\ \eta,\ \lambda)}{\partial x_i}\,h(\eta,\ \xi,\ \lambda)\,d_\eta D \qquad (8.1.19a)$$

With the aid of (8.1.15) and (8.1.16), we have

$$\left|\int_D \frac{\partial P_0(x-\eta,\ \eta,\ \lambda)}{\partial x_i}\,h(\eta,\ \xi,\ \lambda)\,d_\eta D\right| \leqslant CC_1\exp\left(-\varepsilon|\lambda|\,|x-\xi|\right)\int_D \frac{\exp\left(-\varepsilon|\lambda|\,|x-\eta|\right)}{|x-\eta|^2\,|\eta-\xi|^2}\,d_\eta D \qquad (8.1.20)$$

Shifting to polar coordinates with origin at the point x,

* The third axis is along the direction of the vector $x - \xi$.

we obtain

$$\int_D \frac{\exp(-\varepsilon|\lambda||x-\eta|)}{|x-\eta|^2|\eta-\xi|^2}\, d_\eta D$$

$$\leqslant 2\pi \int_0^\infty \exp(-\varepsilon|\lambda|r_1|)\, dr_1 \int_0^\pi \frac{\sin\theta\, d\theta}{r_1^2+r^2-2rr_1\cos\theta}$$

$$\leqslant 2\pi \int_0^\infty dr_1 \int_0^\pi \frac{\sin\theta\, d\theta}{r_1^2+r^2-2rr_1\cos\theta}$$

$$=\frac{2\pi}{r}\int_0^\infty dt \int_0^\pi \frac{\sin\theta\, d\theta}{t^2+1-2t\cos\theta}=\frac{2\pi}{r}\int_0^\infty \frac{1}{t}\ln\left|\frac{t+1}{t-1}\right| dt \leqslant \frac{C_2}{r}$$

where C_2 is an arbitrary constant.

If we substitute this into (8.1.20), we obtain for the integral in the right-hand side of (8.1.19a)

$$\left|\int_D \frac{\partial P_0(x-\eta,\eta,\lambda)}{\partial x_i} h(\eta,\xi,\lambda)\, d_\eta D\right| \leqslant \frac{C_3}{|x-\xi|}\exp(-\varepsilon|\lambda||x-\xi|) \tag{8.1.21}$$

Consequently, on the basis of Condition 1, we have the following inequalities from (8.1.19)

$$\left|\frac{\partial P(x,\xi,\lambda)}{\partial x_i}+\frac{\partial P_0(x-\xi,\xi,\lambda)}{\partial \xi_i}\right| \leqslant \frac{C_4}{|x-\xi|}\exp(-\varepsilon|\lambda||x-\xi|) \tag{8.1.22}$$

$$\left|\frac{\partial^k P(x,\xi,\lambda)}{\partial x_i^k}\right| \leqslant \frac{C_5}{|x-\xi|^{1+k}}\exp(-\varepsilon|\lambda||x-\xi|) \quad (k=0,\ 1) \tag{8.1.23}$$

where C_4 and C_5 are positive constants.

With the aid of these two inequalities, it is easy to show that, if $F(x)$ is continuously differentiable in the region D and if it and its first derivatives are bounded in that region, then the function

$$u(x,\lambda)=-\int_D P(x,\xi,\lambda)F(\xi)\, d_\xi D \tag{8.1.24}$$

is a solution of the non-homogeneous equation

$$L_1\left(x, \frac{\partial}{\partial x}, \lambda\right) u = F(x)$$

corresponding to the homogeneous equation (8.1.1) for all $\lambda \in R_\delta$ and sufficiently large R.

In Section 8.3, in order to obtain a bound for a solution of the spectral problem, we shall need to have a bound for the second derivatives of the fundamental solution.

The first factor of the integral function of the fundamental solution (8.1.4) has a first-order pole. Consequently, this integral can be differentiated once under the integral sign

$$\frac{\partial^2 P(x, \xi, \lambda)}{\partial x_i^2} = \frac{\partial^2 P_0(x-\xi, \xi, \lambda)}{\partial x_i^2} + \frac{\partial}{\partial x_i} \int\limits_D \frac{\partial P_0(x-\eta, \eta, \lambda)}{\partial x_i} h(\eta, \xi, \lambda)\, d_\eta D. \tag{8.1.25}$$

The second term in the right-hand side of (8.1.25) cannot be differentiated immediately under the integral sign. Therefore, to calculate the second derivatives of the fundamental solution, let us represent the integral in the right-hand side of (8.1.25) in the form of a sum of two integrals, one over the sphere* $Ш_\sigma(x)$ of radius σ with centre at the point x, the other over $D-Ш_\sigma(x)$, where 2σ denotes the length of the vector $x-\xi$. Then, obviously, if we denote by J the integral in the right-hand side of (8.1.25), we have

$$\begin{aligned} \frac{\partial J}{\partial x_i} &= \frac{\partial J_1}{\partial x_i} + \frac{\partial J_2}{\partial x_i} \\ J_1 &= \int\limits_{Ш_\sigma(x)} \frac{\partial P_0(x-\eta, \eta, \lambda)}{\partial x_i} h(\eta, \xi, \lambda)\, d_\eta D \\ J_2 &= \int\limits_{D-Ш_\sigma(x)} \frac{\partial P_0(x-\eta, \eta, \lambda)}{\partial x_i} h(\eta, \xi, \lambda)\, d_\eta D \\ \frac{\partial J_2}{\partial x_i} &= \int\limits_{D-Ш_\sigma(x)} \frac{\partial^2 P_0(x-\eta, \eta, \lambda)}{\partial x_i^2} h(\eta, \xi, \lambda)\, d_\eta D. \end{aligned} \tag{8.1.26}$$

It is easy to find a bound for the integral $\frac{\partial J_2}{\partial x_i}$ since we have bounds for the integrand. As regards $\frac{\partial J_1}{\partial x_i}$, we note that J_1 can be differentiated directly under the integral sign. Therefore, assuming the validity of differentiating h with respect to the coordinates of the point η, let us begin by transforming the integral J_1.

*The symbol $Ш$ is the initial letter, pronounced 'shah', of the Russian word shar, meaning 'sphere'.

Obviously,

$$J_1=\int\limits_{Ш_\sigma(x)}\left(\frac{\partial P_0(x-\eta,\eta,\lambda)}{\partial x_i}+\frac{\partial P_0(x-\eta,\eta,\lambda)}{\partial\eta_i}\right)h(\eta,\xi,\lambda)d_\eta D$$
$$-\int\limits_{Ш_\sigma(x)}\frac{\partial P_0(x-\eta,\eta,\lambda)}{\partial\eta_i}h(\eta,\xi,\lambda)\,d_\eta D \qquad (8.1.27)$$

The first term in the right-hand side of (8.1.27) can be differentiated under the integral sign. We can transform the second term by integrating by parts

$$J_1=\int\limits_{Ш_\sigma(x)}\left(\frac{\partial P_0(x-\eta,\eta,\lambda)}{\partial x_i}+\frac{\partial P_0(x-\eta,\eta,\lambda)}{\partial\eta_i}\right)h(\eta,\xi,\lambda)\,d_\eta D$$
$$-\int\limits_{\Gamma_\sigma(x)}P_0(x-\eta,\eta,\lambda)\,h(\eta,\xi,\lambda)\cos(n,\eta_i)\,d_\eta\Gamma \qquad (8.1.28)$$
$$+\int\limits_{Ш_\sigma(x)}P_0(x-\eta,\eta,\lambda)\frac{\partial h(\eta,\xi,\lambda)}{\partial\eta_i}\,d_\eta D$$

where $\Gamma_\sigma(x)$ is the sphere of radius σ with centre at the point x and n denotes the direction of the outer normal to the sphere at the point η.

Obviously, all the terms in the right-hand side of (8.1.28) can be differentiated under the integral signs. Therefore, from our last formula, we obtain

$$\frac{\partial J_1}{\partial x_i}=\int\limits_{Ш_\sigma(x)}\frac{\partial}{\partial x_i}\left(\frac{\partial P_0(x-\eta,\eta,\lambda)}{\partial x_i}+\frac{\partial P_0(x-\eta,\eta,\lambda)}{\partial\eta_i}\right)$$
$$\times h(\eta,\xi,\lambda)\,d_\eta D-\int\limits_{\Gamma_\sigma(x)}\frac{\partial P_0(x-\eta,\eta,\lambda)}{\partial x_i}h(\eta,\xi,\lambda)\cos(n,\eta_i)d_\eta\Gamma$$
$$+\int\limits_{Ш_\sigma(x)}\frac{\partial P_0(x-\eta,\eta,\lambda)}{\partial x_i}\frac{\partial h(\eta,\xi,\lambda)}{\partial\eta_i}\,d_\eta D \qquad (8.1.29)$$

As can be seen from (8.1.29), to obtain a bound for $\frac{\partial J_1}{\partial x_i}$ for large $\lambda\in R_\delta$, we need a bound for $\frac{\partial h(\eta,\xi,\lambda)}{\partial\eta_i}$, when $|\xi-\eta|>\sigma$.

Obviously, if the series

$$\frac{\partial K(x,\xi,\lambda)}{\partial x_i}+\sum_{\nu=2}^{\infty}\frac{\partial K_\nu(x,\xi,\lambda)}{\partial x_i} \qquad (8.1.30)$$

converges uniformly, its limit is equal to $\frac{\partial h(x, \xi, \lambda)}{\partial x_i}$.

Let us now show that the series (8.1.30) converges uniformly when $|x-\xi| \geqslant 2\sigma > 0$ and obtain a bound for this limit for large values of λ in R_δ. Since $K(x, \eta, \lambda)$ has a second-order pole, the function

$$K_{n+1}(x, \xi, \lambda) = \int_D K(x, \eta, \lambda) K_n(\eta, \xi, \lambda)\, d_\eta D \quad (n = 1,2,3,\ldots)$$

cannot be differentiated immediately under the integral sign. Therefore, we must first transform the above integral. Bearing in mind (8.1.6), we represent this integral as the sum of two integrals and then integrate by parts. We then obtain

$$\begin{aligned} &K_{n+1}(x, \xi, \lambda) \\ &= \int_{Ш_\sigma(x)} \left\{\sum_{j=1}^{3} a_j(x) \left(\frac{\partial}{\partial x_j} P_0(x-\eta, \eta, \lambda) + \frac{\partial P_0(x-\eta, \eta, \lambda)}{\partial \eta_j}\right)\right. \\ &\left. + [a(x) - \lambda^2 (c(x) - c(\eta))] P_0(x-\eta, \eta, \lambda)\right\} K_n(\eta, \xi, \lambda) d_\eta D \\ &- \int_{\Gamma_\sigma(x)} \sum_{j=1}^{3} a_j(x) P_0(x-\eta, \eta, \lambda) \cos(n, \eta_j) K_n(\eta, \xi, \lambda)\, d_\eta \Gamma \\ &+ \int_{Ш_\sigma(x)} \sum_{j=1}^{3} a_j(x) P_0(x-\eta, \eta, \lambda) \frac{\partial K_n(\eta, \xi, \lambda)}{\partial \eta_i} d_\eta D \\ &+ \int_{D-Ш_\sigma(x)} K(x, \eta, \lambda) K_n(\eta, \xi, \lambda)\, d_\eta D \end{aligned}$$

All the terms in the right-hand side of the last equation can be differentiated once under the integral signs. We obtain

$$\begin{aligned} \frac{\partial K_{n+1}(x, \xi, \lambda)}{\partial x_i} &= \int_{Ш_\sigma(x)} \frac{\partial}{\partial x_i} \left\{\sum_{j=1}^{3} a_j(x)\right. \\ &\times \left(\frac{\partial}{\partial x_j} P_0(x-\eta, \eta, \lambda) + \frac{\partial}{\partial \eta_j} P_0(x-\eta, \eta, \lambda)\right) \\ &\left. + [a(x) - \lambda^2 (c(x) - c(\eta))] P_0(x-\eta, \eta, \lambda)\right\} \times K_n(\eta, \xi, \lambda)\, d_\eta D \\ &- \int_{\Gamma_\sigma(x)} \frac{\partial}{\partial x_i} \sum_{j=1}^{3} a_j(x) P_0(x-\eta, \eta, \lambda) \times \cos(n, \eta_j) K_n(\eta, \xi, \lambda)\, d_\eta \Gamma + \end{aligned} \tag{8.1.31}$$

$$+\int\limits_{Ш_\sigma(x)} \frac{\partial}{\partial x_i} \sum_{j=1}^{3} a_j(x) P_0(x-\eta, \eta, \lambda) \frac{\partial K_n(\eta, \xi, \lambda)}{\partial \eta_j} d_\eta D$$

$$+\int\limits_{D-Ш_\sigma(x)} \frac{\partial K(x, \eta, \lambda)}{\partial x_i} K_n(\eta, \xi, \lambda) d_\eta D \qquad (8.1.31) \text{ (cont.)}$$

It is easy to show the validity of the inequalities

$$\left| \frac{\partial}{\partial x_i} \left\{ \sum_{j=1}^{3} a_j(x) \left(\frac{\partial}{\partial x_j} P_0(x-\xi, \xi, \lambda) + \frac{\partial P_0(x-\xi, \xi, \lambda)}{\partial \xi_j} \right) + [a(x) - \lambda^2 (c(x) - c(\xi))] \times P_0(x-\xi, \xi, \lambda) \right\} \right| \leqslant \frac{L_1 \exp(-\varepsilon |\lambda| |x-\xi|)}{|x-\xi|^2}$$

$$|K_n(x, \xi, \lambda)| \leqslant \left(\frac{L_1}{|\lambda|} \right)^{n-1} \frac{1}{|x-\xi|^2} \times \exp(-\varepsilon |\lambda| |x-\xi|)$$

$$\left| \frac{\partial K(x, \xi, \lambda)}{\partial x_i} \right| \leqslant \frac{L_1}{|x-\xi|^3} \exp(-\varepsilon |\lambda| |x-\xi|) \qquad (8.1.32)$$

$$\left| \frac{\partial}{\partial x_i} \sum_{j=1}^{3} a_j(x) P_0(x-\xi, \xi, \lambda) \cos(n, \xi_j) \right| \leqslant \frac{L_1 \exp(-\varepsilon |\lambda| |x-\xi|)}{|x-\xi|^2}$$

$$\left| \frac{\partial}{\partial x_i} \sum_{j=1}^{3} a_j(x) P_0(x-\xi, \xi, \lambda) \right| \leqslant \frac{L_1}{|x-\xi|^2} \exp(-\varepsilon |\lambda| |x-\xi|)$$

where L_1 is some positive constant. The second of the inequalities (8.1.32) follows directly from (8.1.14) if we put

$$L_1 \geqslant \pi C C_\varepsilon \sqrt[n-1]{C} \quad (n = 2, 3, \ldots)$$

In accordance with (8.1.9) and (8.1.32), from (8.1.31) we obtain for $n=1$ and $|x-\xi| = 2\sigma$

$$\left|\frac{\partial K_2(x,\xi,\lambda)}{\partial x_i}\right| \leqslant \int\limits_{Ш_\sigma(x)} \frac{L_1 C \exp[-\varepsilon|\lambda|(|x-\eta|+|\eta-\xi|)]}{|x-\eta|^2|\eta-\xi|^2}\,d_\eta D$$

$$+\int\limits_{\Gamma_\sigma(x)} \frac{L_1 C \exp[-\varepsilon|\lambda|(|x-\eta|+|\eta-\xi|)]}{|x-\eta|^2|\eta-\xi|^2}\,d_\eta \Gamma$$

$$+\int\limits_{Ш_\sigma(x)} \frac{L_1^2 \exp[-\varepsilon|\lambda|(|x-\eta|+|\eta-\xi|)]}{|x-\eta|^2|\eta-\xi|^3}\,d_\eta D$$

$$+\int\limits_{D-Ш_\sigma(x)} \frac{L_1 C \exp[-\varepsilon|\lambda|(|x-\eta|+|\eta-\xi|)]}{|x-\eta|^3|\eta-\xi|^2}\,d_\eta D$$

$$\leqslant\left\{\frac{L_1^2}{\sigma^2}\int\limits_{Ш_\sigma(x)} \frac{\exp\left(-\frac{\varepsilon}{2}|\lambda||x-\eta|\right)}{|x-\eta|^2}\,d_\eta D\right.$$

$$+\frac{4\pi L_1 e^{-\varepsilon|\lambda|\sigma}}{\sigma^2}+\frac{L_1^2}{\sigma^3}\int\limits_{Ш_\sigma(x)} \frac{\exp\left(-\frac{\varepsilon}{2}|\lambda||x-\eta|\right)}{|x-\eta|^2}\,d_\eta D$$

$$\left.+\frac{L_1^2}{\sigma^3}\int\limits_{D-Ш_\sigma(x)} \frac{\exp\left(-\frac{\varepsilon}{2}|\lambda||\eta-\xi|\right)}{|\eta-\xi|^2}\,d_\eta D\right\}\times\exp\left(-\frac{\varepsilon}{2}|\lambda||x-\xi|\right)$$

Here, it is assumed that $C\leqslant L_1$.

Shifting to polar coordinates, we easily obtain the inequalities

$$\int\limits_{Ш_\sigma(x)} \frac{\exp\left(-\frac{\varepsilon}{2}|\lambda||x-\eta|\right)}{|x-\eta|^2}\,d_\eta D\leqslant\frac{8\pi}{\varepsilon|\lambda|}$$

$$\int\limits_{D-Ш_\sigma(x)} \frac{\exp\left(-\frac{\varepsilon}{2}|\lambda||x-\eta|\right)}{|x-\eta|^2}\,d_\eta D\leqslant\frac{8\pi}{\varepsilon|\lambda|}$$

Consequently, from the preceding inequality, we have

$$\left|\frac{\partial K_2(x,\xi,\lambda)}{\partial x_i}\right|\leqslant\frac{8\pi L_2}{\sigma^3}\exp\left(-\frac{\varepsilon}{2}|\lambda||x-\xi|\right) \qquad (8.1.33)$$

where

$$L_2=L_1\left\{\frac{L_1(\sigma+2)}{\varepsilon|\lambda|}+L_1\sigma\right\}$$

Thus, with the aid of (8.1.9), (8.1.32) and (8.1.33), we obtain from (8.1.31) for $n=2$

$$\left|\frac{\partial K_3(x,\xi,\lambda)}{\partial x_i}\right|\leqslant\frac{8\pi}{\sigma^3}\,\frac{L_1}{|\lambda|}\,L_3\exp\left(-\frac{\varepsilon}{2}|\lambda||x-\xi|\right)$$

where

$$L_3 = \frac{L_1(\sigma+1)}{\varepsilon|\lambda|} + L_1\sigma + \frac{8\pi}{\varepsilon} L_2.$$

Let us suppose that, for natural numbers $n \geqslant 3$,

$$\left|\frac{\partial K_n(x, \xi, \lambda)}{\partial x_i}\right| \leqslant \frac{8\pi}{\sigma^3}\left(\frac{L_1}{|\lambda|}\right)^{n-2} L_n \exp\left(-\frac{\varepsilon}{2}|\lambda||x-\xi|\right) \quad (8.1.34)$$

where

$$L_n = \frac{L_1(\sigma+1)}{\varepsilon|\lambda|} + L_1\sigma + \frac{8\pi}{\varepsilon} L_{n-1} \quad (8.1.35)$$

Let us show that the inequality (8.1.34) also holds for $n+1$. Using (8.2.32) and (8.1.34), we obtain from (8.1.31)

$$\left|\frac{\partial K_{n+1}(x, \xi, \lambda)}{\partial x_i}\right|$$

$$\leqslant \int\limits_{III_\sigma(x)} \frac{L_1 \exp(-\varepsilon|\lambda||x-\eta|)}{|x-\eta|^2}\left(\frac{L_1}{|\lambda|}\right)^{n-1}\frac{1}{|\eta-\xi|^2}$$

$$\times \exp(-\varepsilon|\lambda||\eta-\xi|)\, d_\eta D$$

$$+ \int\limits_{\Gamma_\sigma(x)} \frac{L_1 \exp(-\varepsilon|\lambda||x-\eta|)}{|x-\eta|^2}\left(\frac{L_1}{|\lambda|}\right)^{n-1}\frac{1}{|\eta-\xi|^2}$$

$$\times \exp(-\varepsilon|\lambda||\eta-\xi|)\, d_\eta\Gamma + \int\limits_{III_\sigma(x)} \frac{L_1 \exp(-\varepsilon|\lambda||x-\eta|)}{|x-\eta|^2}$$

$$\times \frac{8\pi}{\sigma^3}\left(\frac{L_1}{|\lambda|}\right)^{n-2} L_n \exp\left(-\frac{\varepsilon}{2}|\lambda||\eta-\xi|\right) d_\eta D$$

$$+ \int\limits_{D-III_\sigma(x)} \frac{L_1 \exp(-\varepsilon|\lambda||x-\eta|)}{|x-\eta|^3}\left(\frac{L_1}{|\lambda|}\right)^{n-1}$$

$$\times \frac{\exp(-\varepsilon|\lambda||\eta-\xi|)}{|\eta-\xi|^2}\, d_\eta D \leqslant \left\{\frac{L_1}{\sigma^2}\left(\frac{L_1}{|\lambda|}\right)^{n-1}\right.$$

$$\times \int\limits_{III_\sigma(x)} \frac{\exp\left(-\frac{\varepsilon}{2}|\lambda||x-\eta|\right)}{|x-\eta|^2}\, d_\eta D + \frac{L_1}{\sigma^2}\left(\frac{L_1}{|\lambda|}\right)^{n-1} 4\pi$$

$$+ \frac{8\pi L_1}{\sigma^3}\left(\frac{L_1}{|\lambda|}\right)^{n-2} L_n \int\limits_{III_\sigma(x)} \frac{\exp\left(-\frac{\varepsilon}{2}|\lambda||x-\eta|\right)}{|x-\eta|^2}\, d_\eta D$$

$$\left. + \frac{L_1}{\sigma^3}\left(\frac{L_1}{|\lambda|}\right)^{n-1} \int\limits_{D-III_\sigma(x)} \frac{\exp\left(-\frac{\varepsilon}{2}|\lambda||\eta-\xi|\right)}{|\eta-\xi|^2}\, d_\eta D \right\}$$

$$\times \exp\left(-\frac{\varepsilon}{2}|\lambda||x-\xi|\right) < \left\{\frac{L_1\sigma}{\varepsilon|\lambda|} + L_1\sigma + \frac{8\pi}{\varepsilon} L_n\right.$$

$$+\frac{L_1}{\varepsilon|\lambda|}\Big\}\left(\frac{L_1}{|\lambda|}\right)^{n-1}\frac{8\pi}{\sigma^3}\exp\left(-\frac{\varepsilon}{2}|\lambda||x-\xi|\right)$$

$$=\frac{8\pi}{\sigma^3}L_{n+1}\left(\frac{L_1}{|\lambda|}\right)^{n-1}\exp\left(-\frac{\varepsilon}{2}|\lambda||x-\xi|\right)$$

where

$$L_{n+1}=\frac{L_1(\sigma+1)}{\varepsilon|\lambda|}+L_1\sigma+\frac{8\pi}{\varepsilon}L_n$$

Thus, (8.1.34) holds for all natural numbers from 3 on.

It follows from (8.1.34) that the series (8.1.30) converges uniformly. Consequently, its limit is equal to $\frac{\partial h(x, \xi, \lambda)}{\partial x_i}$. In accordance with (8.1.34), we have the following bound for this derivative:

$$\left|\frac{\partial h(x, \xi, \lambda)}{\partial x_i}\right|\leqslant\frac{C_6}{|x-\xi|^3}\exp\left(-\frac{\varepsilon}{2}|\lambda||x-\xi|\right) \quad (8.1.36)$$

where C_6 is a positive constant.*

Furthermore, in accordance with (8.1.15), we get from (8.1.26)

$$\left|\frac{\partial J_2}{\partial x_i}\right|\leqslant\frac{C\exp\left(-\frac{\varepsilon}{2}|\lambda||x-\xi|\right)}{\sigma^3}\times\int\limits_{D-III_\sigma(x)}\frac{\exp\left(-\frac{\varepsilon}{2}|\lambda||\eta-\xi|\right)}{|\eta-\xi|^2}d_\eta D \quad (8.1.37)$$

$$\leqslant\frac{C_7}{|x-\xi|^3}\exp\left(-\frac{\varepsilon}{2}|\lambda||x-\xi|\right)$$

On the basis of (8.1.15) and (8.1.36), we obtain from (8.1.29)

$$\left|\frac{\partial J_1}{\partial x_i}\right|\leqslant\frac{C_8}{|x-\xi|^3}\exp\left(-\frac{\varepsilon}{2}|\lambda||x-\xi|\right) \quad (8.1.38)$$

Bearing in mind (8.1.38), (8.1.37) and (8.1.26), we obtain from (8.1.25)

$$\left|\frac{\partial^2 P(x, \xi, \lambda)}{\partial x_i^2}\right|\leqslant\frac{C_9}{|x-\xi|^3}\exp(-\varepsilon|\lambda||x-\xi|) \quad (8.1.39)$$

where ε is a small positive number.

*In what follows, C with a subscript denotes a positive constant.

Finally, with the aid of (8.1.36), we can obtain a bound for the derivatives in the left-hand side of (8.1.22). To do this, we need to get a bound for the second derivative of the integral function

$$P_1(x, \xi, \lambda) = \int_D P_0(x-\eta, \eta, \lambda)\, h(\eta, \xi, \lambda)\, d_\eta D \tag{8.1.40}$$

of the fundamental solution (8.1.4).

For the first derivative, we have

$$\frac{\partial P_1(x, \xi, \lambda)}{\partial x_i} = \int_D \frac{\partial P_0(x-\eta, \eta, \lambda)}{\partial x_i} h(\eta, \xi, \lambda)\, d_\eta D \tag{8.1.41}$$

Since each of the factors in the integrand of (8.1.41) has a weak (second-order) singularity, to get an expression for the second derivative of (8.1.40) and a bound for its absolute value, we first need to transform the integral (8.1.41).

From (8.1.41), we have

$$\frac{\partial P_1(x, \xi, \lambda)}{\partial x_i} = \int_D \left\{\frac{\partial P_0(x-\eta, \eta, \lambda)}{\partial x_i} + \frac{\partial P_0(x-\eta, \eta, \lambda)}{\partial \eta_i}\right\} h(\eta, \xi, \lambda)\, d_\eta D - \int_D \frac{\partial P_0(x-\eta, \eta, \lambda)}{\partial \eta_i} h(\eta, \xi, \lambda)\, d_\eta D \tag{8.1.42}$$

The first factor in the first integrand in this expression has a singularity of order not exceeding unity. Consequently, it can be differentiated once under the integral sign. The first factor in the second integrand has a second-order singularity. Therefore, an evaluation of its derivatives can be made after an appropriate transformation of this integral. Let $|x-\xi| = 2\sigma$. Let us represent the second integral (8.1.42) as the sum of two integrals, one over the sphere $Ш_\sigma(x)$ of radius σ with centre at the point x, the other over the complement of this sphere with respect to the region D.

Then, from (8.1.42), we have

$$\frac{\partial^2 P_1(x, \xi, \lambda)}{\partial x_i^2} = \int_D \frac{\partial}{\partial x_i} \left\{ \frac{\partial P_0(x-\eta, \eta, \lambda)}{\partial x_i} + \frac{\partial P_0(x-\eta, \eta, \lambda)}{\partial \eta_i} \right\} h(\eta, \xi, \lambda)\, d_\eta D$$
$$- \frac{\partial}{\partial x_i} \int_{III_\sigma(x)} \frac{\partial P_0(x-\eta, \eta, \lambda)}{\partial \eta_i} h(\eta, \xi, \lambda)\, d_\eta D \tag{8.1.43}$$
$$- \int_{D-III_\sigma(x)} \frac{\partial^2 P_0(x-\eta, \eta, \lambda)}{\partial x_i \partial \eta_i} h(\eta, \xi, \lambda)\, d_\eta D.$$

We integrate the second integral on the right-hand side of this equation by parts, remembering that the point ξ is outside the sphere $III_\sigma(x)$, within which $h(\eta, \xi, \lambda)$ has no singularity. Thus, when we have performed this integration by parts, (8.1.43) becomes

$$\frac{\partial^2 P_1(x, \xi, \lambda)}{\partial x_i^2} = \int_D \frac{\partial}{\partial x_i} \left\{ \frac{\partial P_0(x-\eta, \eta, \lambda)}{\partial x_i} + \frac{\partial P_0(x-\eta, \eta, \lambda)}{\partial \eta_i} \right\} h(\eta, \xi, \lambda)\, d_\eta D$$
$$- \int_{S_\sigma(x)} \frac{\partial P_0(x-\eta, \eta, \lambda)}{\partial x_i} \cos(n, \eta_i)\, h(\eta, \xi, \lambda)\, d_\eta S \tag{8.1.44}$$
$$+ \int_{III_\sigma(x)} \frac{\partial P_0(x-\eta, \eta, \lambda)}{\partial x_i} \frac{\partial h(\eta, \xi, \lambda)}{\partial \eta_i}\, d_\eta D$$
$$- \int_{D-III_\sigma(x)} \frac{\partial^2 P_0(x-\eta, \eta, \lambda)}{\partial x_i \partial \eta_i} h(\eta, \xi, \lambda)\, d_\eta D,$$

where $S_\sigma(x)$ denotes the sphere of radius σ with centre at the point x and n denotes the direction of the outer normal to the sphere.

We now find a bound for the left-hand side of (8.1.44). The closest point in the sphere $III_\sigma(x)$ to the point ξ is at a distance σ. Consequently, in accordance with (8.1.2) and

(8.1.36), we have

$$\left| \int_{III_\sigma(x)} \frac{\partial P_0(x-\eta,\eta,\lambda)}{\partial x_i} \frac{\partial h(\eta,\xi,\lambda)}{\partial \eta_i} d_\eta D \right|$$

$$\leqslant \int_{III_\sigma(x)} \frac{C_{10}\exp(-\varepsilon|\lambda||x-\eta|)\, C_6 \exp\left(-\frac{\varepsilon}{2}|\lambda||\eta-\xi|\right)}{|x-\eta|^2|\eta-\xi|^3} d_\eta D$$

$$\leqslant \frac{C_6C_{10}}{|x-\xi|} \exp\left(-\frac{\varepsilon}{2}|\lambda||x-\xi|\right) \times \int_{III_\sigma(x)} \frac{\exp\left(-\frac{\varepsilon}{2}|\lambda||x-\eta|\right)}{|x-\eta|^2|\eta-\xi|^2} d_\eta D \qquad (8.1.45)$$

The integral on the right-hand side of this inequality appeared in (8.1.20), and it does not exceed $\frac{C_2}{|x-\xi|}$. Therefore, substituting into (8.1.75), we obtain

$$\left| \int_{III_\sigma(x)} \frac{\partial P_0(x-\eta,\eta,\lambda)}{\partial x_i} \frac{\partial h(\eta,\xi,\lambda)}{\partial \eta_i} d_\eta D \right| \leqslant \frac{C_2C_6C_{10}}{|x-\xi|^2} \exp\left(-\frac{\varepsilon}{2}|\lambda||x-\xi|\right) \qquad (8.1.46)$$

In the same manner, we can use (8.1.2) and (8.1.15) to get a similar bound for the last term in the right-hand side of (8.1.44). Similarly, it is easy to obtain inequalities of the form (8.1.46) for the first and second terms also. Consequently, from (8.1.44), we have

$$\left| \frac{\partial^2 P_1(x,\xi,\lambda)}{\partial x_i^2} \right| \leqslant \frac{C_{11}\exp\left(-\frac{\varepsilon}{2}|\lambda||x-\xi|\right)}{|x-\xi|^2} \qquad (8.1.47)$$

On the basis of (8.1.22) and (8.1.47), it is easy to show that

$$\left| \frac{\partial^k}{\partial x_i^k} \left\{ \frac{\partial P(x,\xi,\lambda)}{\partial x_i} + \frac{\partial P_0(x-\xi,\xi,\lambda)}{\partial \xi_i} \right\} \right| \leqslant \frac{C_{12}\exp(-\varepsilon|\lambda||x-\xi|)}{|x-\xi|^{1+k}} \quad (k=0,\ 1) \qquad (8.1.48)$$

Thus, we have proved the following lemma.

Lemma 1 For sufficiently large R, (8.1.1) has a fundamental solution $P(x, \xi, \lambda)$ of the form (8.1.4), where (8.1.19), (8.1.21) and (8.1.47) hold for the integral function, which is analytic with respect to λ for all $\lambda \in R_\delta$. The inequalities (8.1.23), (8.1.39) and (8.1.48) hold for this fundamental solution when $\lambda \in R_\delta$. If $F(x)$ is continuously differentiable in the region D and if $F(x)$ and its first derivatives are bounded in that region, then the function (8.1.24) is a solution of the equation

$$L_1\left(x, \frac{\partial}{\partial x}, \lambda\right) u = F(x)$$

for all $\lambda \in R_\delta$.

Remark Suppose that x is an interior point of the region D. Let us draw through x a normal to the boundary Γ of the region D. Let y be the point of intersection of this normal with the boundary Γ and let n_y denote the direction of the inner normal passing through the point x. Denote by n_z the direction of the inner normal to Γ at a point $z \in \Gamma$. Then, by using (8.1.2) and (8.1.21), it is easy to show the validity of the representations

$$\frac{dP(x, z, \lambda)}{dn_y} = \exp\left(-\lambda\sqrt{c(z)}\,|x-z|\right)\frac{d}{dn_y}\cdot\frac{1}{4\pi|x-z} + \frac{E_1(x, z, \lambda)}{|x-z|}\exp(-\varepsilon|\lambda||x-z\,) \tag{8.1.49}$$

$$\frac{dP(x, z, \lambda)}{dn_z} = \exp\left(-\lambda\sqrt{c(z)}\,|x-z|\right)\frac{d}{dn_z}\cdot\frac{1}{4\pi(x-z)} + \frac{E_2(x, z, \lambda)}{|x-z|}\exp(-\varepsilon|\lambda||x-z|) \tag{8.1.50}$$

where $E_i(x, z, \lambda)$ are continuous functions of the points x, $z \in D+\Gamma$ which are bounded for all $\lambda \in R_\delta$.

8.2 FORMULAE FOR THE SALTUS IN THE POTENTIALS OF A SINGLE AND A DOUBLE LAYER

Let us suppose that Condition 1 of Section 8.1 is satisfied and that the boundary Γ of the region D is a Lyapunov surface. Suppose that $\mu(z)$ is a continuous function of $z \in \Gamma$.

We shall call the function $V(x, \lambda)$ defined by

$$V(x, \lambda) = \int_\Gamma P(x, z, \lambda)\, \mu(z)\, d_z\Gamma \tag{8.2.1}$$

the potential of a single layer for (8.1.1) for $\lambda \in R_\delta$ (provided R is sufficiently great), where $P(x, z, \lambda)$ is the fundamental solution, constructed in Section 8.1, (8.1.1) with a singularity at $x = z$.

Similarly, we shall call the function

$$W(x, \lambda) = \int_\Gamma \mu(z) \frac{d}{dn_z} P(x, z, \lambda)\, d_z\Gamma \tag{8.2.2}$$

which is defined for all $\lambda \in R_\delta$, the potential of a double layer for (8.1.1).

Obviously, for every interior point x of the region D, we have

$$\frac{dV(x, \lambda)}{dn_y} = \int_\Gamma \frac{dP(x, z, \lambda)}{dn_y} \mu(z)\, d_z\Gamma \tag{8.2.3}$$

where n_y is the direction of the inner normal to Γ which passes through the point x and where y is the point of intersection of this normal with Γ.

From the representations (8.1.49) and (8.1.50), we have

$$\frac{dP(x, z, \lambda)}{dn_y} = \frac{d}{dn_y} \cdot \frac{1}{4\pi |x-z|} + \frac{\varepsilon_1(x, z, y, \lambda)}{|x-z|} \tag{8.2.4}$$

$$\frac{dP(x, z, \lambda)}{dn_z} = \frac{d}{dn_z} \cdot \frac{1}{4\pi |x-z|} + \frac{\varepsilon_2(x, z, \lambda)}{|x-z|} \tag{8.2.5}$$

where $\varepsilon_1(x, z, y, \lambda)$ and $\varepsilon_2(x, z, \lambda)$ are, for $\lambda \in R_\delta$, continuous functions of the points $x \in D + \Gamma$ and z; $y \in \Gamma$ for all possible relative positions of x.

In accordance with the representation (8.2.5), by letting x approach the boundary point z, we find from (8.2.2)

$$(W(y, \lambda))_i = \frac{\mu(y)}{2} + \int_\Gamma \mu(z) \frac{d}{dn_z} P(y, z, \lambda)\, d_z\Gamma \tag{8.2.6}$$

if D is the region lying inside the closed surface Γ. On the other hand, if D is the region lying outside the closed surface Γ, then, as we let $x \to y$, we obtain from (8.2.2)

$$(W(y, \lambda))_e = -\frac{\mu(y)}{2} + \int_\Gamma \mu(z) \frac{d}{dn_z} P(y, z, \lambda)\, d_z\Gamma \quad (8.2.7)$$

Similarly, if we let the point x in (8.2.3) approach the boundary point y along the normal n_y, then, in accordance with the representation (8.2.4), we obtain the following formulae for the saltus in the normal derivative of the potential of a single layer:

$$\left(\frac{dV(y, \lambda)}{dn_y}\right)_i = \frac{\mu(y)}{2} + \int_\Gamma \mu(z) \frac{dP(y, z, \lambda)}{dn_y}\, d_z\Gamma \quad (8.2.8)$$

if the region D is the portion of three-dimensional space lying inside the closed surface Γ and

$$\left(\frac{dV(y, \lambda)}{dn_y}\right)_e = -\frac{\mu(y)}{2} + \int_\Gamma \mu(z) \frac{d}{dn_y} P(y, z, \lambda)\, d_z\Gamma \quad (8.2.9)$$

if the region D is that portion of space lying outside the surface Γ.

8.3 SOLUTION OF THE SPECTRAL PROBLEM FOR A HOMOGENEOUS EQUATION AND BOUNDS FOR IT

We shall use the term 'spectral problem' to apply to the problem of finding the solution $u_1(x, \lambda)$ of the equation

$$L_1\left(x, \frac{\partial}{\partial x}, \lambda\right) u = \sum_{i=1}^{3} \left(\frac{\partial^2}{\partial x_i^2} + a_i(x) \frac{\partial}{\partial x_i}\right) u + (a(x) - \lambda^2 c(x))\, u = 0 \quad (8.3.1)$$

in a region D with boundary condition

$$\lim_{x \to y} B\left(y, \frac{d}{dn_y}, \lambda^2\right) u(x, \lambda) = \psi(y), \qquad y \in \Gamma \quad (8.3.2)$$

where Γ is the boundary of D. This problem will come up in

Section 9.1. Here,

$$B\left(y, \frac{d}{dn_y}, \lambda^2\right) = \alpha_1(y)\frac{d}{dn_y} + \alpha_2(y)\lambda^2\left(\frac{d}{dn_y} + \alpha_3(y)\right) + \alpha_4(y)$$

In addition to Condition 1 of Section 8.1, suppose that the following conditions are also satisfied.

2. On the surface Γ, the coefficients $\alpha_i(y)$ and $\psi(y)$ in the boundary condition (8.3.2) are continuous and one of the functions $\alpha_1(y)$, $\alpha_2(y)$ does not vanish.
3. Γ is a Lyapunov surface.

Let us show that the solution $u_1(x, \lambda)$ of Problem (8.3.1)-(8.3.2) exists for all $\lambda \in R_\delta$ (where R is sufficiently large) and can be represented as the potential of a single layer

$$u_1(x, \lambda) = \int_\Gamma P(x, z, \lambda)\, \mu(z)\, d_z\Gamma \tag{8.3.3}$$

where $\mu(z)$ is the density of this potential, to be determined. Then, let us find suitable bounds for this solution.

If we substitute (8.3.3) into the boundary condition (8.3.2) and keep in mind the saltus formulae (8.2.8) and (8.2.9), for the normal derivative of the potential (8.3.3), we obtain the integral equation

$$\mu(y, \lambda) = \psi_1(y, \lambda) + \int_\Gamma K(y, \xi, \lambda)\, \mu(\xi, \lambda)\, d_\xi\Gamma \tag{8.3.4}$$

where

$$\psi_1(y, \lambda) = \frac{2\psi(y)}{\alpha_1(y) + \lambda^2\alpha_2(y)}$$

$$K(y, \xi, \lambda) = -2\left\{\frac{d}{dn_y}P(y, \xi, \lambda) + \frac{\alpha_4(y) + \lambda^2\alpha_2(y)\alpha_3(y)}{\alpha_1(y) + \lambda^2\alpha_2(y)}P(y, \xi, \lambda)\right\} \tag{8.3.5}$$

if the region D is the portion of space within the closed surface Γ. If D is the region outside the closed surface Γ, we have

$$\psi_1(y, \lambda) = -\frac{2\psi(y)}{\alpha_1(y) + \lambda^2\alpha_2(y)}$$

$$K(y, \xi, \lambda) = 2\left\{\frac{d}{dn_y}P(y, \xi, \lambda) + \frac{\alpha_4(y) + \lambda^2\alpha_2(y)\alpha_3(y)}{\alpha_1(y) + \lambda^2\alpha_2(y)}P(y, \xi, \lambda)\right\} \tag{8.3.6}$$

Obviously, if the series

$$K(y, \xi, \lambda) + K_2(y, \xi, \lambda) + \ldots + K_n(y, \xi, \lambda) + \ldots \quad (8.3.7)$$

of iterations of the kernel $K(y, \xi, \lambda)$ converges uniformly with respect to the point $\xi \in \Gamma$, its limit $R(y, \xi, \lambda)$ will be the resolvent of the integral equation (8.3.4). Consequently,

$$\mu(y, \lambda) = \psi_1(y, \lambda) + \int_\Gamma R(y, \xi, \lambda)\, \psi_1(\xi, \lambda)\, d_\xi\Gamma \quad (8.3.8)$$

Thus, proof that Problem (8.3.1)-(8.3.2) has a solution reduces to proving the uniform convergence of the series (8.3.7) with respect to the point $\xi \in \Gamma$.

By virtue of the remark made at the end of Section 8.1, we can use the representation (8.1.49) to obtain easily the inequality

$$\begin{aligned}&\left|\frac{dP(x, z, \lambda)}{dn_y}\right| \\ &\leqslant \left\{B_1 \frac{|\cos(n_y, z-x)|}{|z-x|^2} + \frac{B_2}{|z-x|}\right\} \exp(-\varepsilon|\lambda||z-x|)\end{aligned} \quad (8.3.9)$$

where B_1 and B_2 are constants and n_y is the direction of the inner normal to Γ at the point y.

The following inequality for the kernel $K(y, \xi, \lambda)$ of the integral equation (8.3.4) follows from (8.1.23) and (8.3.9):

$$\begin{aligned}&|K(y, \xi, \lambda)| \\ &\leqslant \left\{C_1 \frac{|\cos(n_y, \xi-y)|}{|\xi-y|^2} + \frac{C_2}{|\xi-y|}\right\} \exp(-\varepsilon|\lambda||\xi-y|)\end{aligned} \quad (8.3.10)$$

where, as before, the C_k (for $k = 1, 2, \ldots$) denote sufficiently large positive numbers.

In accordance with (8.3.10), for the second iteration of the kernel $K(y, \xi, \lambda)$, we have

$$\begin{aligned}|K_2(y, \xi, \lambda)| &= \left|\int_\Gamma K(y, \zeta, \lambda)\, K(\zeta, \xi, \lambda)\, d_\zeta\Gamma\right| \\ &\leqslant \left\{C_1^2 \int_\Gamma \frac{|\cos(n_y, \zeta-y)|\,|\cos(n_\zeta, \xi-\zeta)|}{|\zeta-y|^2\,|\xi-\zeta|^2}\, d_\zeta\Gamma\right.\end{aligned} \quad (8.3.11)$$

$$+C_1C_2\int_\Gamma \frac{|\cos(n_y,\zeta-y)|}{|\zeta-y|^2(\xi-\zeta|}d\Gamma+C_2C_1\int_\Gamma\frac{|\cos(n_\zeta,\xi-\zeta)|}{|\zeta-y||\xi-\zeta|^2}d_\zeta\Gamma$$

$$+C_2^2\int_\Gamma\frac{d_\zeta\Gamma}{|\zeta-y||\xi-\zeta|}\Big\}\exp(-\varepsilon|\lambda||y-\xi|) \qquad \begin{matrix}(8.3.11)\\ (\text{cont.})\end{matrix}$$

We denote the integrals in the right-hand side of (8.3.11) by I_1, I_2, I_3 and I_4, respectively. Suppose also that $\Gamma_d(y)$ is a Lyapunov d-neighbourhood of the point $y\in\Gamma$. We know that the inequalities

$$\frac{|\cos(n_y,\zeta-y)|}{|\zeta-y|^2}\leqslant\frac{C_3}{|\zeta-y|^{2-\alpha}}$$
$$\frac{|\cos(n_\zeta,\xi-\zeta)|}{|\xi-\zeta|^2}\leqslant\frac{C_3}{|\zeta-\xi|^{2-\alpha}} \qquad (8.3.12)$$

where C_3 is a constant and α is a Lyapunov number, are satisfied for all points ζ in a Lyapunov neighbourhood of the point $y\in\Gamma$.

From these inequalities, it follows that, at the point $y=\xi$, the integral I_1 has a pole of order $2-2\alpha$, the integrals I_2 and I_3 have a logarithmic singularity and the integral I_4 does not have a singularity. Consequently, from (8.3.11), we obtain

$$|K_2(y,\xi,\lambda)|\leqslant\frac{C_4}{|\zeta-\xi|^{2-2\alpha}}\exp(-\varepsilon|\lambda||y-\xi|)\,(\alpha<1) \qquad (8.3.13)$$

Bearing in mind (8.3.10), (8.3.12) and (8.3.13), we can show by mathematical induction that

$$|K_m(y,\xi,\lambda)|\leqslant\frac{C_5}{|y-\xi|^{2-m\alpha}}\exp(-\varepsilon|\lambda||y-\xi|) \quad \text{for } m\geqslant 2$$

Obviously, for sufficiently large m, $K_m(y,\xi,\lambda)$ does not have a singularity. Consequently,

$$|K_m(y,\xi,\lambda)|\leqslant C_6\exp(-\varepsilon|\lambda||y-\xi|),\quad m\alpha>2 \qquad (8.3.14)$$

Now, let us find a bound for the $(m+1)$ th iteration of the kernel $K(y,\xi,\lambda)$. Let us denote by r the length of the vector $y-\xi$, by $\Gamma_\sigma(z)$ that part of the surface Γ inside the sphere of radius σ with centre at the point y and by $\Sigma_\sigma(z)$ the projection of $\Gamma_\sigma(z)$ on to the tangent plane $T(y)$ to Γ at the point $y \in \Gamma$. Then, for $\sigma < d$, we shall have the inequalities

$$\frac{1}{2} r \leqslant \varrho \leqslant r, \quad \cos\gamma \geqslant \frac{1}{2} \tag{8.3.15}$$

where γ is the angle between the directions of n_y and n_ζ and ϱ is the length of the projection of the vector $y-\xi$ on to the plane $T(y)$.

In accordance with (8.3.10) and (8.3.14), we have*

$$|K_{m+1}(y, \xi, \lambda)| \leqslant \int_\Gamma |K(y, \zeta, y)|\,|K_m(\zeta, \xi, \lambda)|\, d_\zeta\Gamma$$

$$\leqslant C_6 \left\{ C_1 \int_\Gamma \frac{|\cos(n_y, \zeta - y)|}{|\zeta - y|^2} \exp(-\varepsilon|\lambda|\,|\zeta - y|)\, d_\zeta\Gamma \right.$$

$$\left. + C_2 \int_\Gamma \frac{1}{|\zeta - y|} \exp(-\varepsilon|\lambda|\,|\zeta - y|)\, d_\zeta\Gamma \right\} \exp(-\varepsilon|\lambda|\,|y - \xi|) \tag{8.3.16}$$

Let us denote the integrals in the right-hand side of (8.3.16) by $J_1(\Gamma)$ and $J_2(\Gamma)$, respectively, and let us find bounds for them.

Obviously,

$$\begin{aligned} J_1(\Gamma - \Gamma_\sigma(z)) &\leqslant \frac{\operatorname{mes}\Gamma}{\sigma^2} e^{-\varepsilon\sigma|\lambda|} \\ J_2(\Gamma - \Gamma_\sigma(z)) &\leqslant \frac{\operatorname{mes}\Gamma}{\sigma^2} e^{-\varepsilon\sigma|\lambda|} \end{aligned} \tag{8.3.17}$$

Furthermore, in accordance with (8.3.12),

$$J_1(\Gamma_\sigma(y)) \leqslant C_3 \int_{\Gamma_\sigma(y)} \frac{1}{|\zeta - y|^{2-\alpha}} \exp(-\varepsilon|\lambda|\,|\zeta - y|)\, d_\zeta\Gamma \tag{8.3.18}$$

We can find a bound for the integral in the right-hand side of (8.3.18) by projecting the region of integration $\Gamma_\sigma(y)$ on to the plane $T(y)$ and shifting to a polar system of coordinates:**

* For convenience in writing, ϵ is replaced by 2ϵ in (8.3.10) and (8.3.14).

** When we change over to an integral over a plane region $\Sigma_\sigma(y)$, it is convenient to denote the integral with a double integral sign.

Then, in view of (8.3.15), we have

$$\begin{aligned}
&\int\limits_{\Gamma_\sigma(y)} \frac{1}{|\zeta-y|^{2-\alpha}} \exp(-\varepsilon|\lambda||\zeta-y|)\, d_\zeta\Gamma \\
&\leqslant \int\int\limits_{\Sigma_\sigma} \frac{1}{|\zeta-y|^{2-\alpha}} \exp(-\varepsilon|\lambda||\zeta-y|)\, \frac{d\zeta_1\, d\zeta_2}{\cos\gamma} \\
&\leqslant 2\int\limits_0^{2\pi} d\varphi \int\limits_0^{\sigma} \frac{1}{\varrho^{1-\alpha}} e^{-\varepsilon|\lambda|\rho} d\varrho = \frac{4\pi}{|\lambda|^\alpha} \int\limits_0^{|\lambda|\sigma} \beta^{\alpha-1} e^{-\varepsilon\beta}\, d\beta \\
&\leqslant \frac{4\pi}{|\lambda|^\alpha} \int\limits_0^{\infty} \beta^{\alpha-1} e^{-\varepsilon\beta}\, d\beta \leqslant \frac{C_1(\varepsilon, \alpha)}{|\lambda|^\alpha}
\end{aligned} \tag{8.3.19}$$

where $C_1(\varepsilon, \alpha)$ is a positive number depending only on ε and α.

For $\alpha = 1$, we obtain from (8.3.19)

$$J_2(\Gamma_\sigma(z)) = \int\limits_{\Gamma_\sigma(y)} \frac{1}{|\zeta-y|} \exp(-\varepsilon|\lambda||\zeta-y|) d_\zeta\Gamma \leqslant \frac{4\pi}{\varepsilon|\lambda|} \tag{8.3.20}$$

From (8.3.17)-(8.3.20), we get the inequalities

$$J_1(\Gamma) \leqslant \frac{C(\varepsilon, \alpha)}{|\lambda|^\alpha}, \quad J_2(\Gamma) \leqslant \frac{C(\varepsilon)}{|\lambda|}$$

where $C(\varepsilon, \alpha)$ and $C(\varepsilon)$ are positive numbers depending only on ε and α in the first case and only on ε in the second. From these two inequalities, we conclude that

$$\begin{aligned}
&C_1 \int\limits_\Gamma \frac{|\cos(n_y, \zeta-y)|}{|\zeta-y|^2} \exp(-\varepsilon|\lambda||\zeta-y|)\, d_\zeta\Gamma \\
&+ C_2 \int\limits_\Gamma \frac{1}{|\zeta-y|^2} \exp(-\varepsilon|\lambda||\zeta-y|)\, d_\zeta\Gamma \leqslant \frac{C_7}{|\lambda|^\alpha}
\end{aligned} \tag{8.3.21}$$

Consequently, we obtain from (8.3.16)

$$|K_{m+1}(y, \xi, \lambda)| \leqslant \frac{C_6 C_7}{|\lambda|^\alpha} \exp(-\varepsilon|\lambda||y-\xi|) \tag{8.3.22}$$

Keeping in mind (8.3.10), (8.3.21) and (8.3.22), we can easily show by induction that, for $n \geqslant 1$,

$$|K_{m+n}(y, \xi, \lambda)| \leqslant C_6 \left(\frac{C_7}{|\lambda|^\alpha}\right)^n \exp(-\varepsilon|\lambda||y-\xi|) \tag{8.3.23}$$

It follows from (8.3.23) that the series (8.3.7) converges uniformly for all $\lambda \in R_\delta$ if R is sufficiently great. Then, if we note (8.3.10) and (8.3.12)-(8.3.14), we have the following bound for the limit $R(y, \xi, \lambda)$ of that series:

$$|R(y, \xi, \lambda)| \leqslant \frac{C_8}{|y-\xi|^{2-\alpha}} \exp(-\varepsilon|\lambda||y-\xi|) \qquad (8.3.24)$$

(for $y, \xi \in \Gamma$). Here, $R(y, \xi, \lambda)$ is an analytic function with respect to λ in the region R_δ.

Then, in accordance with (8.3.24), we conclude from (8.3.8) that $\mu(y, \lambda)$ is an analytic function with respect to λ in the region R_δ and that

$$|\mu(y, \lambda)| \leqslant C_9 \quad \text{for } \lambda \in R_\delta \qquad (8.3.25)$$

It follows from these assertions that, when Conditions 1-3 are satisfied, Problem (8.3.1)-(8.3.2) has a solution $u_1(x, \lambda)$, given by (8.3.3), which is analytic with respect to λ in the region R_δ. Here, in accordance with (8.3.23), (8.1.39) and (8.3.25), the inequality

$$\left|\frac{\partial^k u_1(x, \lambda)}{\partial x_i^k}\right| \leqslant \frac{Ce^{-\varepsilon|\lambda|\sigma}}{\sigma^{k+1}} \quad (k=0,\ 1,\ 2) \qquad (8.3.26)$$

holds for this solution uniformly throughout every region D_1 the closure of which is contained in the region D. Here, σ denotes the minimum distance between points of the boundaries of the regions D_1 and D, and C is a sufficiently large positive constant. Furthermore, in accordance with (8.1.22) and (8.3.25), we obtain from (8.3.3) and (8.2.6)

$$\left|\frac{d^k u_1(x, \lambda)}{dn_y^k}\right| \leqslant C \qquad (k=0,\ 1) \qquad (8.3.27)$$

which is valid for $x \in D+\Gamma$, where n_y is the direction of the inner normal to Γ at the point $y \in \Gamma$ on which x lies.

Thus, we have proved the following lemma.

Lemma 2 Suppose that Conditions 1-3 of Sections 8.1 and 8.3 are satisfied. Suppose that for sufficiently large R and all $\lambda \in R_\delta$ there exists a solution to Problem (8.3.1)-(8.3.2) which is analytic with respect to λ and which can be represented in the form (8.3.3), where $P(x, z, \lambda)$ is a fundamental solution of (8.3.1) with a singularity at the point z. The integral equation (8.3.4) for the density $\mu(y, \lambda)$ of the potential (8.3.3) has a resolvent $R(y, \xi, \lambda)$ which satisfies (8.3.24). The inequalities (8.3.26) and (8.3.27) hold for the solution $u_1(x, \lambda)$ of Problem (8.3.1)-(8.3.2).

8.4 BOUND FOR THE REGULAR PART OF THE GREEN'S FUNCTION OF THE SPECTRAL PROBLEM

We shall refer to the boundary-value problem with parameter λ for the equation

$$L_1\left(x, \frac{\partial}{\partial x}, \lambda\right) u \equiv L\left(x, \frac{\partial}{\partial x}\right) u - \lambda^2 c(x) u$$
$$\equiv \sum_{i=1}^{3} \left(\frac{\partial^2 u}{\partial x_i^2} + a_i(x) \frac{\partial u}{\partial x_i}\right) + a(x) u - \lambda^2 c(x) u = c(x) \varphi(x) \tag{8.4.1}$$

in the region D with boundary condition

$$\lim_{x \to y} B\left(y, \frac{\partial}{\partial n_y}, \lambda^2\right) u(x, \lambda) = \lim_{x \to y} \left\{\alpha_1(y) \frac{du(x, \lambda)}{dn_y}\right. \tag{8.4.2}$$
$$\left. + \lambda^2 \alpha_2(y) \left(\frac{du(x, \lambda)}{dn_y} + \alpha_3(y) u(x, \lambda)\right) + \alpha_4(y) u(x, \lambda)\right\} = 0$$
$$y \in \Gamma$$

where Γ is the boundary of D, as the spectral problem. We shall encounter it in Section 9.2. Here, n_y denotes the direction of the inner normal to Γ at the point y.

Under the conditions of Lemma 1, Problem (8.4.1)-(8.4.2) has a Green's function $G(x, \xi, \lambda)$, with the aid of which the solution $u_2(x, \lambda)$ of (8.4.1)-(8.4.2) can be represented as follows:

$$u_2(x, \lambda) = -\int_D G(x, \xi, \lambda) c(\xi) \varphi(\xi) d_\xi D \tag{8.4.3}$$

Specifically, we put

$$G(x, \xi, \lambda) = P(x, \xi \lambda) - Q(x, \xi, \lambda) \tag{8.4.4}$$

where $Q(x, \xi, \lambda)$ is a regular solution of the homogeneous equation corresponding to (8.4.1). Then, obviously, if (8.4.4) satisfies the boundary condition (8.4.2), the function (8.4.3) is a solution of (8.4.1)-(8.4.2). Thus, Problem (8.4.1)-(8.4.2) has a Green's function if a solution $Q(x, \xi, \lambda)$ exists for the homogeneous equation

$$L_1\left(x, \frac{\partial}{\partial x}, \lambda\right) u = 0 \tag{8.4.5}$$

satisfying the boundary condition

$$\lim_{x \to y} \left\{ \frac{dQ(x, \xi, \lambda)}{dn_y} + \frac{\lambda^2 \alpha_2(y) \alpha_3(y) + \alpha_4(y)}{\alpha_1(y) + \lambda^2 \alpha_2(y)} Q(x, \xi, \lambda) \right\} = f(y, \xi, \lambda), \quad y \in \Gamma \tag{8.4.6}$$

where x is an interior point of the region D which approaches the point y along the normal n_y to Γ at the point y and

$$f(y, \xi, \lambda) = \frac{dP(y, \xi, \lambda)}{dn_y} + \frac{\lambda^2 \alpha_2(y) \alpha_3(y) + \alpha_4(y)}{\alpha_1(y) + \lambda^2 \alpha_2(y)} P(y, \xi, \lambda). \tag{8.4.7}$$

If ξ is an interior point of the region D, the function $f(y, \xi, \lambda)$ is obviously a continuously differentiable function with respect to y. Consequently, in accordance with Lemma 2, Problem (8.4.5)-(8.4.6) has, for $\lambda \in R_\delta$, a solution which is analytic with respect to λ in the region R_δ and which can be represented as the potential of a single layer

$$Q(x, \xi, \lambda) = \int_\Gamma P(x, z, \lambda) \mu(z, \xi, \lambda) \, d_z \Gamma \tag{8.4.8}$$

Here, $\mu(y, \xi, \lambda)$ is given by

$$\mu(y, \xi, \lambda) = 2f(y, \xi, \lambda) + 2\int_\Gamma R(y, z, \lambda) f(z, \xi, \lambda) \, d_z \Gamma \tag{8.4.9}$$

where $R(y, z, \lambda)$ is the resolvent of the integral equation (8.3.4). With the aid of (8.1.23), we obtain from (8.4.7) the inequality

$$|f(y, \xi, \lambda)| \leqslant \frac{C_1 \exp(-\varepsilon |\lambda| |y - \xi|)}{|y - \xi|^2} \tag{8.4.10}$$

where, as before, the C_k (for $k = 1, 2, \ldots$) denote sufficiently large positive numbers and where $\varepsilon > 0$.

Then, it follows from (8.4.9) on the basis of (8.3.24) and (8.4.10) that

$$|\mu(y,\ \xi,\ \lambda)| \leqslant \frac{C_2 \exp(-\varepsilon|\lambda||y-\xi|)}{|y-\xi|^2} \tag{8.4.11}$$

Also, (8.4.11) is satisfied uniformly for $\xi \in D_1$, where D_1 is a region whose closure is contained in D.

In view of (8.1.23), (8.1.39) and (8.4.11), we obtain from (8.4.8) the following inequality for $x, \xi \in D_1$:

$$\left|\frac{\partial^k Q(x,\ \xi,\ \lambda)}{\partial x_i^k}\right| \leqslant \frac{C_3 \exp(-\varepsilon|\lambda||x-\xi|)}{\sigma^{k+3}} \quad (k=0,\ 1,\ 2) \tag{8.4.12}$$

where σ denotes the minimum distance between points of the boundaries of the regions D and D_1.

Similarly, on the basis of (8.1.23), (8.2.3), (8.2.8) and (8.2.9), we obtain from (8.4.8) the inequality

$$\left|\frac{dQ(x,\ \xi,\ \lambda)}{dn_z}\right| \leqslant \frac{C_4}{\sigma^2}, \qquad z \in \Gamma \tag{8.4.13}$$

which is satisfied uniformly with respect to x (on n_z) $\in D+\Gamma$ and for $\xi \in D_1$.

Thus, we have proved the following lemma.

Lemma 3 Suppose that the conditions of Lemma 2 are satisfied. Then, for all $\lambda \in R_\delta$, Problem (8.4.1)-(8.4.2) has a solution $u_2(x,\ \lambda)$, given by (8.4.3), which is analytic with respect to λ in the region R_δ. The regular part $Q(x,\ \xi,\ \lambda)$ of the Green's function $G(x,\ \xi,\ \lambda)$ given by (8.4.4) can be represented in the form of the potential of a single layer (8.4.8). Every pair of points $(x,\ \xi)$ in a region D_1 whose closure is contained in the region D satisfies (8.4.12). If $x \in D+\Gamma$ and lies on the normal n_z (for $z \in \Gamma$) and if $\xi \in D_1$, then (8.4.13) holds.

CHAPTER 9

Multi-dimensional mixed problem for a parabolic equation with time-dependent boundary conditions

9.1 MIXED PROBLEM FOR A HOMOGENEOUS EQUATION WITH HOMOGENEOUS INITIAL CONDITION

In this section, we shall solve the mixed problem

$$c(x)\, M\left(t, \frac{\partial}{\partial t}\right) v = L\left(x, \frac{\partial}{\partial x}\right) v \tag{9.1.1}$$

$$\lim_{x \to y} B\left(y, \frac{d}{dn_y}, M\right) v(x, t) = \psi(y) \exp\left(-\int_0^t b_0^{-1}(\tau)\, b_1^{v}(\tau)\, d\tau\right), \qquad y \in \Gamma \tag{9.1.2}$$

$$v(x, 0) = 0 \tag{9.1.3}$$

where

$$L\left(x, \frac{\partial}{\partial x}\right)=\sum_{i=1}^{3}\left(\frac{\partial^2}{\partial x_i^2}+a_i(x)\frac{\partial}{\partial x_i}\right)+a(x)$$

$$B\left(y, \frac{\partial}{\partial y}, M\right)=\alpha_1(y)\frac{d}{dn_y}+\alpha_2(y)M\left(\frac{d}{dn_y}+\alpha_3(y)\right)+\alpha_4(y)$$

$$M=b_0(t)\frac{\partial}{\partial t}+b_1(t)$$

We shall call the Problem (9.1.1)-(9.1.3) 'Problem A'. The Problem (8.3.1)-(8.3.2) is the spectral problem corresponding to it.

Suppose that S is an infinite curve lying in a region R_δ of the complex λ-plane and that it approaches the straight lines

$$\cos\arg\lambda=\delta \tag{9.1.4}$$

asymptotically (see Fig. 8).*

Let $-S$ denote the curve which is symmetric to S about the imaginary axis of the λ-plane, d denote the distance from the imaginary axis to the closest point of the curve S and S_n denote that portion of the curve S which lies to the left of the straight line**

$$\operatorname{Re}\lambda=nd \tag{9.1.5}$$

where n is a natural number.

Suppose also that a_n and c_n are, respectively, the points of intersection of the curves S and $-S$ with the straight lines (9.1.5) and let a_n' and c_n' denote the points that are symmetric to them about the real axis of the λ-plane. Denote by r_n the distance from the point a_n to the coordinate origin in the λ-plane.

Let us describe a circle of radius r_n with centre at the origin. Let b_n and b_n' denote, respectively, the points of intersection of this circle with the imaginary axis of the λ-plane.

* For simplicity, we assume that the portions of the curve S lying outside a circle of sufficiently large radius with centre at the coordinate origin of the λ-plane coincide with the rays (2.1.4) produced.

** When displaced along the straight line (2.1.5) from the lower to the upper half of the λ-plane.

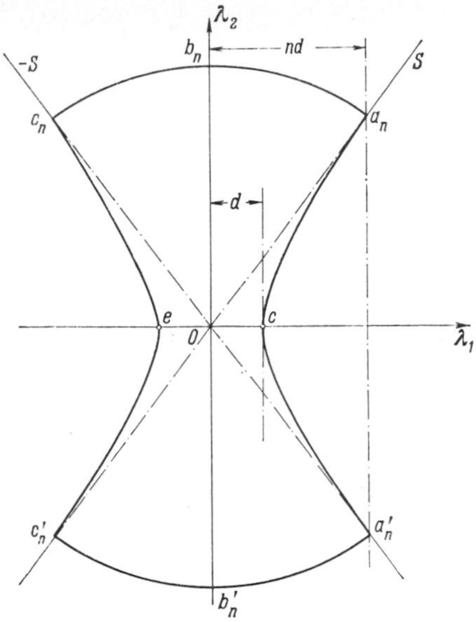

Fig. 8

Finally, let c and e denote respectively the closest points of the curves S and $-S$ to the coordinate origin. For brevity of writing, we denote the closed curve $a_nb_nc_nec'_nb'_na'_nca_n$ by Γ_n.

Theorem 38 Suppose that Conditions 1-3 of Sections 8.1 and 8.3 are satisfied. Then, if the functions $b_0(t)$ and $b_1(t)$ are continuous on the interval $[0, T]$ and if $b_0(t) > 0$ for $t > 0$, Problem A has a solution given by

$$v_1(x, t) = \frac{1}{\pi\sqrt{-1}} \int\limits_S \frac{e^{\lambda^2 t_1 - t_2}}{\lambda} u_1(x, \lambda)\, d\lambda \qquad (9.1.6)$$

where

$$t_1 = \int\limits_0^t b_0^{-1}(\tau)\, d\tau, \quad t_2 = \int\limits_0^t b_0^{-1}(\tau)\, b_1(\tau)\, d\tau$$

and $u_1(x, \lambda)$ is the solution of the spectral problem (8.3.1)-(8.3.2) corresponding to Problem A.

Proof For simplicity, let us assume that, for sufficiently large natural n, the portion of the contour S lying in the region

$$|\lambda| \geqslant r_n \tag{9.1.7}$$

coincides with the continuations of the rays (9.1.4). Then, it is clear that, on the portion of the contour S lying in the region (9.1.7),

$$\cos\arg\lambda = \delta$$

$$\begin{aligned}\left|\frac{d^k}{dt^k} e^{\lambda^2 t_1 - t_2}\right| \\ &= (|\lambda|^2 b_0^{-1}(t)\,|1-\lambda^{-2} b_1(t)|)^k \exp(-t_2 + t_1 \operatorname{Re}\lambda^2) \\ &\leqslant C(|\lambda|^2 b_0^{-1}(t)\,|1-\lambda^{-2} b_1(t)|)^k \exp(t_1|\lambda|^2(2\delta^2-1))\end{aligned} \tag{9.1.8}$$

$$(k = 0, 1)$$

As is clear from (9.1.8), the function $e^{\lambda^2 t_1 - t_2}$, for $t > 0$ and $2\delta^2 < 1$, decreases on the contour S more rapidly than does an arbitrary power of λ^{-1}.

If x is an interior point of the region D, then, in accordance with Lemma 2 on the solution $u_1(x, \lambda)$ of the spectral problem corresponding to Problem A, inequality (8.3.26) is satisfied for $\lambda \in R_\delta$. Consequently, in accordance with (9.1.8) and (8.3.26), the integral (9.1.6) can be differentiated the necessary number of times with respect to t and x under the integral sign representing the integral around the contour S. Therefore,

$$\left\{L\left(x, \frac{\partial}{\partial x}\right) - c(x) M\left(t, \frac{\partial}{\partial t}\right)\right\} v_1(x, t)$$

$$\equiv \frac{1}{\pi\sqrt{-1}} \int_S \frac{e^{\lambda^2 t_1 - t_2}}{\lambda} \left\{L\left(x, \frac{\partial}{\partial x}\right) u_1(x, \lambda) - \lambda^2 c(x) u_1(x, \lambda)\right\} d\lambda$$

Since $u_1(x, \lambda)$ is a solution of (8.3.1), we conclude from the above equation that the function $v_1(x, t)$ defined by (9.1.6) satisfies the homogeneous equation (9.1.1).

Similarly, in accordance with (9.1.8) and (8.3.27) (see Lemma 2), the operator in the boundary condition (9.1.2) can, for $t > 0$, be put under the integral sign for the integral around S. Therefore,

$$\lim_{x \to y} B\left(y, \frac{d}{dn_y}, M\right) v_1(x, t)$$

$$= \frac{1}{\pi \sqrt{-1}} \int_S \frac{\exp(\lambda^2 t_1 - t_2)}{\lambda} \lim_{x \to y} B\left(y, \frac{d}{dn_y}, \lambda^2\right) u_1(x, \lambda)\, d\lambda$$

$$= \frac{1}{\pi \sqrt{-1}} \int_S \frac{\exp(\lambda^2 t_1 - t_2)}{\lambda} \psi(y)\, d\lambda.$$

since $u_1(x, \lambda)$ satisfies the boundary condition (8.3.2). Because the integrand is an odd function, we have, from the last equation,

$$\lim_{x \to y} B\left(y, \frac{d}{dn_y}, M\right) v_1(x, t) \tag{9.1.9}$$

$$= \frac{\psi(y)}{2\pi \sqrt{-1}} e^{-t_2} \left\{ \int_S \frac{e^{\lambda^2 t_1}}{\lambda} d\lambda + \int_{-S} \frac{e^{\lambda^2 t_1}}{\lambda} d\lambda \right\}$$

Obviously, in the region $\cos \arg \lambda \leqslant \delta$

$$\left| e^{\lambda^2 t_1} \right| \leqslant e^{t_1 |\lambda|^2 (2\delta^2 - 1)}$$

Consequently, for $2\delta^2 < 1$, the integrand in (9.1.9) decreases on the arcs $a_n b_n c_n$ and $a'_n b'_n c'_n$ more rapidly than does an arbitrary power of λ^{-1}. Therefore,

$$\lim_{n \to \infty} \int_{\widehat{a_n b_n c_n}} \frac{e^{\lambda^2 t_1}}{\lambda} d\lambda = \lim_{n \to \infty} \int_{\widehat{a'_n b'_n c'_n}} \frac{e^{\lambda^2 t_1}}{\lambda} d\lambda = 0$$

On the basis of these two equations, we obtain from (9.1.9)

$$\lim_{x \to y} B\left(y, \frac{d}{dn_y}, M\right) v_1(x, t) = \frac{\psi(y)}{2\pi \sqrt{-1}} e^{-t_2} \lim_{n \to \infty} \int_{\Gamma_n} \frac{e^{\lambda^2 t_1}}{\lambda} d\lambda$$

Inside the closed contour Γ_n, the function $\lambda^{-1} e^{\lambda^2 t_1}$ has a single pole $\lambda = 0$. Therefore, we conclude from the last equation that $v_1(x, t)$ satisfies the boundary-condition (9.1.2).

In accordance with the inequality (8.3.26) of Lemma 2 and the inequality (9.1.8), the integral (9.1.6) converges uniformly on the interval $[0, T]$. Consequently, if we take the limit under the integral sign in (9.1.6) as $t \to 0$, we obtain

$$v_1(x, 0) = \frac{1}{\pi\sqrt{-1}} \int_S \frac{u_1(x, \lambda)}{\lambda} d\lambda \tag{9.1.10}$$

Here, in accordance with the assertion of Lemma 2, the integrand is an analytic function in the region R_δ, and it decreases on the arcs O_ν faster than does an arbitrary power of λ^{-1}. Therefore, from (9.1.10), we obtain

$$\begin{aligned} v_1(x, 0) &= \frac{1}{\pi\sqrt{-1}} \lim_{n\to\infty} \int_{S_n} \frac{u_1(x, \lambda)}{\lambda} d\lambda \\ &= \frac{1}{\pi\sqrt{-1}} \lim_{n\to\infty} \int_{Q_n} \frac{u_1(x, \lambda)}{\lambda} d\lambda = 0 \end{aligned}$$

which completes the proof.

9.2 MIXED PROBLEM FOR A NON-HOMOGENEOUS EQUATION WITH HOMOGENEOUS BOUNDARY BUT NON-HOMOGENEOUS INITIAL CONDITIONS

We shall call the following problem 'Problem B'

$$c(x) M\left(t, \frac{\partial}{\partial t}\right) v = L\left(x, \frac{\partial}{\partial x}\right) v + f(x, t) \tag{9.2.1}$$

$$\lim_{x\to y} B\left(y, \frac{d}{dn_y}, M\right) v(x, t) = 0, \quad y \in \Gamma \tag{9.2.2}$$

$$v(x, 0) = \varphi(x) \tag{9.2.3}$$

where

$$L\left(x, \frac{\partial}{\partial x}\right) = \sum_{i=1}^{3} \left(\frac{\partial}{\partial x_i^2} + a_i(x) \frac{\partial}{\partial x_i}\right) + a(x)$$

$$M\left(t, \frac{\partial}{\partial t}\right) = b_0(t) \frac{\partial}{\partial t} + b_1(t)$$

$$\begin{aligned} B&\left(y, \frac{d}{dn_y}, M\right) \\ &= \alpha_1(y) \frac{d}{dn_y} + \alpha_2(y) M\left(\frac{d}{dn_y} + \alpha_3(y)\right) + \alpha_4(y) \end{aligned}$$

The corresponding spectral problem is of the form (8.4.1)-(8.4.2).

Now, with the aid of Lemmas 1-3, we can prove Theorem 39 below.

Theorem 39 Under the conditions of Theorem 38, if two functions $\varphi(x)$ and $f(x, t)$ are continuously differentiable with respect to all their arguments for $x \in \bar{D}$, $t \in [0, T]$ and if they vanish in some boundary strip of the region D, then Problem B has a solution $v_2(x, t)$ given by

$$v_2(x, t) = \frac{1}{\pi\sqrt{-1}} \int_S \lambda \, d\lambda \int_D G(x, \xi, \lambda)\, y(t, \xi, \lambda)\, d_\xi D \quad (9.2.4)$$

where $G(x, \xi, \lambda)$ is the Green's function of the spectral problem (8.4.1)-(8.4.2) corresponding to the Problem B and $y(t, \xi, \lambda)$ is a solution of the Cauchy problem

$$M\left(t, \frac{\partial}{\partial t}\right) y - \lambda^2 y = f(\xi, t); \quad y(0) = c(\xi)\,\varphi(\xi)$$

Furthermore, if D is an unbounded region, the functions $c(x)$, $\varphi(x)$ and $f(x, t)$, where $t \in [0, T]$, are assumed to be bounded and absolutely integrable in the region D.

Proof First, let us note that the solution of the Cauchy Problem in the formulation of the theorem is given by

$$\begin{aligned} y(t, \xi, \lambda) &= c(\xi)\,\varphi(\xi) \exp(\lambda^2 t_1 - t_2) \\ &+ \int_0^t b_0^{-1}(\tau)\, f(\xi, \tau) \exp(\lambda^2 t_1(\tau) - t_2(\tau))\, d\tau \end{aligned} \quad (9.2.5)$$

where

$$\begin{aligned} t_1(\tau) &= \int_\tau^t b_0^{-1}(\tau_1)\, d\tau_1 \\ t_2(\tau) &= \int_\tau^t b_0^{-1}(\tau_1)\, b_1(\tau)\, d\tau_1 \\ t_1 = t_1&(0), \quad t_2 = t_2(0) \end{aligned} \quad (9.2.6)$$

For convenience, we shall carry out the proof of this theorem in two stages. First, let us show that the function

$v_2^{(1)}(x, t)$ defined by

$$v_2^{(1)}(x, t) = \frac{1}{\pi\sqrt{-1}} \int_S \lambda e^{\lambda^2 t_1 - t_2} d\lambda \int_D G(x, \xi, \lambda) c(\xi) \varphi(\xi) d_\xi D \quad (9.2.7)$$

satisfies the homogeneous equation corresponding to (9.2.1), the boundary condition (9.2.2) and the initial one (9.2.3). Then, we shall show that the function

$$v_2^{(2)}(x, t) = \frac{1}{\pi\sqrt{-1}} \int_S \lambda \, d\lambda \int_D G(x, \xi, \lambda) \, d_\xi D \times \int_0^t b_0^{-1}(\tau) f(\xi, \tau) \exp(\lambda^2 t_1(\tau) - t_2(\tau)) \, d\tau \quad (9.2.8)$$

satisfies the non-homogeneous equation (9.2.1), the boundary condition (9.2.2) and the homogeneous initial condition

$$v_2^{(2)}(x, 0) = 0 \quad (9.2.9)$$

Both assertions will be directly verified. Therefore, we first need to show that the necessary number of differentiations and passages to the limit under the integral sign in the contour integrals (9.2.7) and (9.2.8) are permissible. For this, we need to find a bound for the solution $u_2(x, \lambda)$, defined by (8.4.3) of Problem (8.4.1)-(8.4.2). Obviously,

$$u_2(x, \lambda) = u_{21}(x, \lambda) + u_{22}(x, \lambda) + u_{23}(x, \lambda) \quad (9.2.10)$$

where

$$u_{21}(x, \lambda) = -\int_D P_0(x - \xi, \xi, \lambda) c(\xi) \varphi(\xi) d_\xi D \quad (9.2.11)$$

$$u_{22}(x, \lambda) = -\int_D P_1(x, \xi, \lambda) c(\xi) \varphi(\xi) d_\xi D \quad (9.2.12)$$

$$u_{23}(x, \lambda) = \int_D Q(x, \xi, \lambda) c(\xi) \varphi(\xi) d_\xi D \quad (9.2.13)$$

$P_0(x - \xi, \xi, \lambda)$ is the function (8.1.2), $P_1(x, \xi, \lambda)$ is the integral function of the fundamental solution (8.1.4) and $Q(x, \xi, \lambda)$

is the regular part of the Green's function of Problem (8.4.1)-(8.4.2).

For $\lambda \in R_\delta$ and $k=0, 1$, when we shift to polar coordinates with origin at the point x, we obtain from (9.2.11) in accordance with (8.1.2)

$$\left|\frac{\partial^k u_{21}(x, \lambda)}{\partial x_i^k}\right| \leqslant \int_D \frac{C_1 \exp(-\varepsilon |\lambda| \, |x-\xi|) F}{|x-\xi|^{1+k}} d_\xi D \leqslant \frac{4\pi C_1 F}{(\varepsilon |\lambda|)^{2-k}} \quad (k=0, 1) \tag{9.2.14}$$

where F denotes the least upper bound of the right-hand side of (8.4.1) in the region D, i.e. $\sup |c(\xi)\varphi(\xi)|$ in $D+\Gamma$.

The integral (9.2.11) cannot be differentiated twice under the integral sign directly.

Obviously, we have

$$\frac{\partial u_{21}(x, \lambda)}{\partial x_i} = -\int_D \left\{\frac{\partial P_0(x-\xi, \xi, \lambda)}{\partial x_i} + \frac{\partial P_0(x-\xi, \xi, \lambda)}{\partial \xi_i}\right\} c(\xi)\varphi(\xi)\, d_\xi D + \int_D \frac{\partial P_0(x-\xi, \xi, \lambda)}{\partial \xi_i} c(\xi)\varphi(\xi)\, d_\xi D$$

Then, because of the restriction imposed on $\varphi(\xi)$, integration by parts yields

$$\frac{\partial u_{21}(x, \lambda)}{\partial x_i} = -\int_D \left\{\frac{\partial P_0(x-\xi, \xi, \lambda)}{\partial x_i} + \frac{\partial P_0(x-\xi, \xi, \lambda)}{\partial \xi_i}\right\} c(\xi)\varphi(\xi)\, d_\xi D - \int_D P_0(x-\xi, \xi, \lambda) \frac{\partial}{\partial \xi_i}(c(\xi)\varphi(\xi))\, d_\xi D$$

Each of the integrals in the right-hand side of this equation can be differentiated once under the integral sign.

Consequently,

$$\frac{\partial^2 u_{22}(x, \lambda)}{\partial x_i^2} = -\int_D \frac{\partial}{\partial x_i}\left\{\frac{\partial P_0(x-\xi, \xi, \lambda)}{\partial x_i} + \frac{\partial P_0(x-\xi, \xi, \lambda)}{\partial \xi_i}\right\} c(\xi)\varphi(\xi)\, d_\xi D - \int_D \frac{\partial P_0(x-\xi, \xi, \lambda)}{\partial x_i} \frac{\partial(c(\xi)\varphi(\xi))}{\partial \xi_i}\, d_\xi D \tag{9.2.15}$$

From (9.2.15), we obtain the inequality

$$\left| \frac{\partial^2 u_{21}(x, \lambda)}{\partial x_i^2} \right| \leqslant \frac{C_2 F}{\varepsilon |\lambda|} \tag{9.2.16}$$

which is valid for sufficiently large R and all $\lambda \in R_\delta$ and $x \in D + \Gamma$.

Similarly, with the aid of inequalities (8.1.19), (8.1.21) and (8.1.47), by shifting to polar coordinates with origin at the point x, we obtain from (9.2.12) the inequality

$$\left| \frac{\partial^k u_{22}(x,\lambda)}{\partial x_i^k} \right| \leqslant \frac{C_3 F}{|\lambda|^{3-k}} \quad (k=0, 1, 2) \tag{9.2.17}$$

which is valid for all $x \in D + \Gamma$.

Furthermore, for every interior point x of the region D, there exists a region D_1 which contains the point x and whose closure lies in D. By the hypothesis of the theorem, the functions $\varphi(\xi)$ and $f(x, t)$ vanish in some boundary strip of the region D. Without loss of generality, we may assume that functions $\varphi(x)$ and $f(x, t)$ vanish outside the region D_1.

Then, in accordance with (8.4.12) of Lemma 3 and on the basis of the boundedness of $c(\xi)\varphi(\xi)$ in the region D, we obtain from (9.2.13) the following inequality when $\lambda \in R_\delta$:

$$\begin{aligned} \left| \frac{\partial^k u_{23}(x, \lambda)}{\partial x_i^k} \right| &= \left| \int_D \frac{\partial^k Q(x, \xi, \lambda)}{\partial x_i^k} c(\xi)\varphi(\xi) d_\xi D \right| \\ &= \left| \int_D \frac{\partial^k Q(x, \xi, \lambda)}{\partial x_i^k} c(\xi)\varphi(\xi) d_\xi D \right| \\ &\leqslant \int_{D_1} \frac{C_3 \exp(-\varepsilon|\lambda|\,|x-\xi|)}{\sigma^{3+k}} |c(\xi)\varphi(\xi)| d_\xi D \\ &\leqslant \frac{C_3 F}{\sigma^{k+3}} \int_D \exp(-\varepsilon|\lambda|\,|x-\xi|)\, d_\xi D \end{aligned} \tag{9.2.18}$$

where σ denotes the minimum distance between points of the boundaries of the regions D and D_1.

By shifting to polar coordinates with origin at the point x, we obtain from (9.2.18) the inequality

$$\left| \frac{\partial^k u_{23}(x,\lambda)}{\partial x_i^k} \right| \leqslant \frac{C_4 F}{\sigma^{k+3} |\lambda|^3} \quad (k=0, 1, 2) \tag{9.2.19}$$

which is valid for all $\lambda \in R_\delta$ whenever R is sufficiently large.

With the aid of (8.4.13) of Lemma 3, remembering the absolute integrability of $c(x)\varphi(x)$ in the region D, we obtain from (9.2.13) the inequality

$$\left|\frac{du_{23}(x, \lambda)}{dn_z}\right| \leqslant C_5 F_1, \quad z \in \Gamma \tag{9.2.20}$$

which is valid for all $x \in D+\Gamma$, where the point x lies on the normal n_z to Γ at the point z, where

$$F_1 = \int_D |c(\xi)\varphi(\xi)|\, d_\xi D$$

From (9.2.16), (9.2.17) and (9.2.20) we immediately get the inequality

$$\left|\frac{d^k u_2(x, \lambda)}{dn_y^k}\right| \leqslant F_1 C_6, \quad y \in \Gamma \;\; (k=0, 1) \tag{9.2.21}$$

which is satisfied uniformly for all $x \in D+\Gamma$ lying on n_y.

In accordance with the choice of contour S and inequalities (9.1.8), (9.2.16), (9.2.17) and (9.2.19), both the integral (9.2.7) and the integrals obtained from it by differentiating with respect to t and x under the integral sign the necessary number of times (for $2\delta^2 < 1$) converge uniformly with respect to $x \in D$ and $t \in (0, T)$. Consequently, if we substitute (9.2.7) into (9.1.1), we obtain

$$\begin{aligned}
&\left\{L\left(x, \frac{\partial}{\partial x}\right) - c(x) M\right\} v_2^{(1)}(x, t) \\
&\quad = \frac{-1}{\pi\sqrt{1}} \int_S \lambda e^{\lambda^2 t_1 - t_2}\, d\lambda \left\{L\left(x, \frac{\partial}{\partial x}\right) - \lambda^2 c(x)\right\} u_2(x, \lambda) \\
&\quad = \frac{-1}{\pi\sqrt{-1}} \int_S \lambda e^{\lambda^2 t_1 - t_2}\, c(x)\varphi(x)\, d\lambda \equiv 0
\end{aligned}$$

Similarly, in accordance with (9.1.8) and (9.2.21), we obtain for $t > 0$

$$\begin{aligned}
&\lim_{x \to y} B\left(y, \frac{d}{dn_y}, M\right) v_2^{(1)}(x, t) \\
&\quad = \frac{-1}{\pi\sqrt{-1}} \int_S \lambda e^{\lambda^2 t_1 - t_2}\, d\lambda \lim_{x \to y} B\left(y, \frac{d}{dn_y}, \lambda^2\right) u_2(x, \lambda) = 0
\end{aligned}$$

It remains for us to verify the initial condition. To do this, we represent the integral (9.2.7) as the sum of two integrals

$$v_2^{(1)}(x, t) = \frac{-1}{\pi\sqrt{-1}} \int_S \lambda u_{21}(x, \lambda)\, e^{\lambda^2 t_1 - t_2}\, d\lambda$$
$$+ \frac{-1}{\pi\sqrt{-1}} \int_S \lambda e^{\lambda^2 t_1 - t_2} (u_{22}(x, \lambda) + u_{23}(x, \lambda))\, d\lambda \tag{9.2.22}$$

Inequalities (9.2.17) and (9.2.19) imply the uniform convergence of the second of the integrals in the right-hand side of (9.2.22) for $t \in [0, T]$. Consequently,

$$\frac{1}{\pi\sqrt{-1}} \lim_{t\to 0} \int_S \lambda e^{\lambda^2 t_1 - t_2} (u_{22}(x, \lambda) + u_{23}(x, \lambda))\, d\lambda$$
$$= \frac{1}{\pi\sqrt{-1}} \int_S \lambda (u_{22}(x, \lambda) + u_{23}(x, \lambda))\, d\lambda \tag{9.2.23}$$
$$= \frac{1}{\pi\sqrt{-1}} \lim_{n\to\infty} \int_{S_n} \lambda (u_{22}(x, \lambda) + u_{23}(x, \lambda))\, d\lambda$$

Remembering that the integrand in (9.2.23) has no singularities between the contour S_n and the arc O_ν of the circle of radius r_ν with centre at the coordinate origin in the λ-plane (see Fig. 3), we obtain from (9.2.23) by use of Cauchy's theorem

$$\frac{1}{\pi\sqrt{-1}} \lim_{t\to 0} \int_S \lambda e^{\lambda^2 t_1 - t_2} (u_{22}(x, \lambda) + u_{23}(x, \lambda))\, d\lambda$$
$$= \frac{1}{\pi\sqrt{-1}} \lim_{t\to 0} \int_{Q_n} \lambda (u_{22}(x, \lambda) + u_{23}(x, \lambda))\, d\lambda = 0 \tag{9.2.24}$$

since, in accordance with inequalities (9.2.17) and (9.2.19), the integrand in the right-hand side of (9.2.24) decreases faster than does λ^{-2} on the arc Q_n.

On the basis of (9.2.24), we obtain from (9.2.22), keeping

(8.1.2) and (9.2.11) in mind,

$$v_2^{(1)}(x, 0) = \lim_{t\to 0} \frac{1}{\pi\sqrt{-1}} \int_S \lambda e^{\lambda^2 t_1} d\lambda \times \int_D \frac{\exp(-\lambda\sqrt{c(\xi)}\,|x-\xi|)}{4\pi|x-\xi|} c(\xi)\varphi(\xi)\, d_\xi D$$

$$= \lim_{t_1\to 0} \int_D \frac{1}{4\pi^2\sqrt{-1}\,|x-\xi|} \exp\left(\frac{c(\xi)\,|x-\xi|^2}{-4t_1}\right) c(\xi)\varphi(\xi)\, d_\xi D \times \int_S \exp\left(\lambda\sqrt{t_1} - \frac{\sqrt{c(\xi)}\,|x-\xi|}{2\sqrt{t_1}}\right)^2 \lambda\, d\lambda \qquad (9.2.25)$$

From (6.3.46), we have

$$\int_S \exp\left(\lambda\sqrt{t_1} - \frac{\sqrt{c(\xi)}\,|x-\xi|}{2\sqrt{t_1}}\right)^2 \lambda\, d\lambda = \frac{\sqrt{\pi}\sqrt{-1}\sqrt{c(\xi)}\,|x-\xi|}{2t_1^{\frac{3}{2}}} \qquad (9.2.26)$$

Substituting this into (9.2.25), we obtain

$$v_2^{(1)}(x, 0) = \lim_{t_1\to 0} \int_D \frac{\exp\left(-\frac{c(\xi)\,|x-\xi|^2}{4t_1}\right)}{8\pi^{\frac{3}{2}} t_1^{\frac{3}{2}}} c^{\frac{3}{2}}(\xi)\varphi(\xi)\, d_\xi D \qquad (9.2.27)$$

To evaluate the limit in the right-hand side of (9.2.27), we represent the integral over region D as the sum of two integrals, one over the sphere $Ш_{\sqrt[4]{t_1}}(x)$ of radius $\sqrt[4]{t_1}$ with centre at the point x, the other over its complement with respect to the region D.

$$(2\sqrt{\pi t_1})^{-3} \int_D \exp\left(-\frac{c(\xi)\,|x-\xi|^2}{4t_1}\right) c^{\frac{3}{2}}(\xi)\varphi(\xi)\, d_\xi D$$

$$= (2\sqrt{\pi t_1})^{-3} \int_{D-Ш_{\sqrt[4]{t_1}}(x)} \exp\left(-\frac{c(\xi)\,|x-\xi|^2}{4t_1}\right) c^{\frac{3}{2}}(\xi)\varphi(\xi)\, d_\xi D \qquad (9.2.28)$$

$$+ (2\sqrt{\pi t_1})^{-3} \int_{Ш_{\sqrt[4]{t_1}}(x)} \exp\left(-\frac{c(\xi)\,|x-\xi|^2}{4t_1}\right) c^{\frac{3}{2}}(\xi)\varphi(\xi)\, d_\xi D$$

Let us denote the terms in the right-hand side of (9.2.28) by $J_1(x, t)$ and $J_2(x, t)$, respectively, and evaluate their limits as $t_1 \to 0$.

Since $c^{\frac{3}{2}}(\xi)\varphi(\xi)$ is bounded in the region D, we have

$$|J_1(x, t_1)| \leqslant C_8 \int\limits_{|x-\xi| \geqslant \sqrt[4]{t_1}} (2\sqrt{\pi t_1})^{-3} \exp\left(-\frac{c|x-\xi|^2}{4t_1}\right) d_\xi D$$

where c is the smallest value of $c(x)$ in the region D.

Shifting to polar coordinates with origin at the point x, we obtain from the last inequality

$$|J_1(x, t_1)| \leqslant (2\sqrt{\pi})^{-1} C_8 \int\limits_{\sqrt[4]{t_1}}^{\infty} t_1^{-\frac{3}{2}} \exp\left(-\frac{cr^2}{4t_1}\right) r^2\, dr$$

$$= (\sqrt{\pi})^{-1} C_8 c^{-\frac{3}{2}} \int\limits_{\sqrt{c}\,(2\sqrt[4]{t_1})^{-1}}^{\infty} 4\varrho^2 e^{-\varrho^2}\, d\varrho \to 0 \qquad (9.2.29)$$

as $t_1 \to 0$.

Obviously,

$$J_2(x, t_1) = \int\limits_{Ш_{\sqrt[4]{t_1}}(x)} (2\sqrt{\pi t_1})^{-3} \left(c^{\frac{3}{2}}(\xi)\varphi(\xi)\right.$$

$$\left. - c^{\frac{3}{2}}(x)\varphi(x)\right) \exp\left(-\frac{c(\xi)|x-\xi|^2}{4t_1}\right) d_\xi D \qquad (9.2.30)$$

$$+ c^{\frac{3}{2}}(x)\varphi(x) \int\limits_{Ш_{\sqrt[4]{t_1}}(x)} (2\sqrt{\pi t_1})^{-3} \exp\left(-\frac{c(\xi)|x-\xi|^2}{4t_1}\right) d_\xi D$$

Suppose that $J_{21}(x, t)$ and $J_{22}(x, t)$ denote, respectively, the terms in the right-hand side of (9.2.30). Since $c^{\frac{3}{2}}(x)\varphi(x)$ is continuous, we have

$$|J_{21}(x, t)| \leqslant \varepsilon(t_1) \int\limits_{Ш_{\sqrt[4]{t_1}}(x)}$$

$$\times (2\sqrt{\pi t_1})^{-3} \exp\left(-\frac{c(\xi)|x-\xi|^2}{4t_1}\right) d_\xi D \qquad (9.2.31)$$

where

$$\lim_{t \to 0} \varepsilon(t_1) = 0 \tag{9.2.32}$$

Let us denote by $c_1(x, t)$ and $c_2(x, t)$ the smallest and greatest values of $c(\xi)$ in the sphere $Ш_{\sqrt[4]{t_1}}(x)$, respectively. Obviously,

$$\int_{Ш_{\sqrt[4]{t_1}}(x)} (2\sqrt{\pi t_1})^{-3} \exp\left(-\frac{c_2(x, t)\,|x-\xi|^2}{4t_1}\right) d_\xi D$$
$$< \int_{Ш_{\sqrt[4]{t_1}}(x)} (2\sqrt{\pi t_1})^{-3} \exp\left(-\frac{c(\xi)\,|x-\xi|^2}{4t_1}\right) d_\xi D \tag{9.2.33}$$
$$< \int_{Ш_{\sqrt[4]{t_1}}(x)} (2\sqrt{\pi t_1})^{-3} \exp\left(-\frac{c_1(x, t)\,|x-\xi|^2}{4t_1}\right) d_\xi D$$

Shifting to polar coordinates with origin at the point x we find by performing a simple calculation,

$$\int_{Ш_{\sqrt[4]{t_1}}(x)} (2\sqrt{\pi t_1})^{-3} \exp\left(-\frac{c_k(x, t)\,|x-\xi|^2}{4t_1}\right) d_\xi D$$
$$= 4(\sqrt{\pi})^{-1} c_k^{-\frac{3}{2}}(x, t) \int_0^{\sqrt{c_k(x, t)}\,(2\sqrt[4]{t_1})^{-1}} e^{-\rho^2}\rho^2\, d\rho$$

If we take the limit as $t \to 0$, we obtain

$$\lim_{t \to 0} \int_{Ш_{\sqrt[4]{t_1}}(x)} (2\sqrt{\pi t_1})^{-3} \exp\left(-\frac{c_k(x, t)\,|x-\xi|^2}{4t_1}\right) d_\xi D = c^{-\frac{3}{2}}(x)$$

With the aid of this equation, we find by taking the limit as $t \to 0$ in (9.2.33)

$$\lim_{t \to 0} \int_{Ш_{\sqrt[4]{t_1}}(x)} (2\sqrt{\pi t_1})^{-3} \exp\left(-\frac{c(\xi)\,|x-\xi|^2}{4t_1}\right) d_\xi D = c^{-\frac{3}{2}}(x) \tag{9.2.34}$$

On the basis of (9.2.34) and (9.2.32), we obtain from (9.2.31)

$$\lim_{t \to 0} J_{21}(x, t) = 0$$

Therefore, remembering (9.2.34), we have from (9.2.30)

$$\lim_{t\to 0} J_2(x, t) = \varphi(x) \tag{9.2.35}$$

Finally, keeping (9.2.27)-(9.2.29) and (9.2.35) in mind, we obtain

$$v_2^{(1)}(x, 0) = \varphi(x) \tag{9.2.36}$$

Thus, the first part of the theorem is proved.

Let us now prove the second assertion. Suppose that

$$G(x, \xi, \lambda) = P_0(x-\xi, \xi, \lambda) + G_1(x, \xi, \lambda) \tag{9.2.37}$$

From (9.2.8), we have

$$v_2^{(2)}(x, t) = v_{21}^{(2)}(x, t) + v_{22}^{(2)}(x, t) \tag{9.2.38}$$

where

$$\begin{aligned} v_{21}^{(2)}(x, t) = &\frac{1}{\pi\sqrt{-1}} \int_S \lambda\, d\lambda \int_D P_0(x-\xi, \xi, \lambda)\, d_\xi D \\ &\times \int_0^t b_0^{-1}(\tau) f(\xi, \tau) \exp(\lambda^2 t_1(\tau) - t_2(\tau))\, d\tau \end{aligned} \tag{9.2.39}$$

$$\begin{aligned} v_{22}^{(2)}(x, t) = &\frac{1}{\pi\sqrt{-1}} \int_S \lambda\, d\lambda \int_D G_1(x, \xi, \lambda)\, d_\xi D \\ &\times \int_0^t b_0^{-1}(\tau) f(\xi, \tau) \exp(\lambda^2 t_1(\tau) - t_2(\tau))\, d\tau \end{aligned} \tag{9.2.40}$$

Obviously, we then have

$$\begin{aligned} &\left(L\left(x, \frac{\partial}{\partial x}\right) - c(x) M\right) v_2^{(2)} \\ &\quad = \left(\sum_{i=1}^{3} \frac{\partial^2}{\partial x_i^2} - c(x) M\right) v_{21}^{(2)}(x, t) \\ &\qquad + \left(\sum_{i=1}^{3} a_i(x) \frac{\partial}{\partial x_i} + a(x)\right) v_{21}^{(2)}(x, t) \\ &\qquad + \left(L\left(x, \frac{\partial}{\partial x}\right) - c(x) M\right) v_{22}^{(2)}(x, t) \end{aligned} \tag{9.2.41}$$

Integrating by parts, we obtain

$$
\begin{aligned}
&\int_0^t b_0^{-1}(\tau) f(\xi, \tau) \exp(\lambda^2 t_1(\tau) - t_2(\tau))\, d\tau \\
&\quad = -\frac{f(\xi, t)}{\lambda^2} + \frac{1}{\lambda^2} \exp(\lambda^2 t_1(\tau) - t_2(\tau)) f(\xi, 0) \\
&\quad - \frac{1}{\lambda^4}\left(b_1(t) f(\xi, t) + b_0(t) \frac{\partial f(\xi, t)}{\partial t}\right) \qquad (9.2.42) \\
&\quad + \frac{b_1(0) f(\xi, 0) + b_0(0) \dfrac{\partial f(\xi, 0)}{\partial t}}{\lambda^4} \exp(\lambda^2 t_1(\tau) - t_2(\tau)) \\
&\quad + \frac{1}{\lambda^4} \int_0^t e^{\lambda^2 t_1(\tau)} \frac{\partial}{\partial \tau}\left(b_0(\tau) \frac{\partial}{\partial \tau}(e^{-t_2(\tau)} f(\xi, \tau))\right) d\tau
\end{aligned}
$$

$$
\begin{aligned}
&\frac{\partial}{\partial t} \int_0^t b_0^{-1}(\tau) f(\xi, \tau) \exp(\lambda^2 t_1(\tau) - t_2(\tau))\, d\tau \\
&\quad = -\frac{\dfrac{\partial f(\xi, t)}{\partial t}}{\lambda^2} + \frac{b_0^{-1}(t)(\lambda^2 - b_1(t))}{\lambda^2} \exp(\lambda^2 t_1(0) \\
&- t_2(0)) f(\xi, 0) - \frac{1}{\lambda^4} \frac{\partial}{\partial t}\left(b_1(t) f(\xi, t) + b_0(t) \frac{\partial f(\xi, t)}{\partial t}\right) \\
&\quad + \frac{1}{\lambda^4} b_0^{-1}(t)(\lambda^2 - b_1(t))(b_1(0) f(\xi, 0) \\
&\quad + b_0(0) f_t'(\xi, 0)) \exp(\lambda^2 t_1(0) - t_2(0)) \qquad (9.2.43) \\
&\quad + \frac{b_0^{-1}(t)}{\lambda^2} \int_0^t e^{\lambda^2 t_1(\tau)} \frac{\partial}{\partial \tau}\left(b_0(\tau) \frac{\partial}{\partial \tau}(e^{-t_2(\tau)} f(\xi, \tau))\right) d\tau \\
&\quad + \frac{1}{\lambda^4} \frac{\partial}{\partial t}\left(b_0(t) \frac{\partial f(\xi, t)}{\partial t}\right) + \frac{1}{\lambda^4} \int_0^t e^{\lambda^2 t_1(\tau)} \frac{\partial}{\partial \tau}(b_0(\tau) \\
&\quad \times \frac{\partial}{\partial \tau}(b_0^{-1}(t) b_1(t) e^{t_2(\tau)} f(\xi, \tau)))\, d\tau
\end{aligned}
$$

On the basis of Equations (9.2.42) and (9.2.43) and the inequalities (9.2.17) and (9.2.19),* the expression on the right-hand side of (9.2.40) can be differentiated twice with respect to x and once with respect to t under the integral

*In the present case, the quantity F in the inequalities corresponding to (9.2.17) and (9.2.19) does not exceed the least upper bound of the absolute values of the right-hand sides of (9.2.42) and (9.2.43).

sign. Therefore, in view of (9.2.37), we obtain

$$\left\{L\left(x, \frac{\partial}{\partial x}\right) - c(x) M\right\} v_{22}^{(2)}(x, t)$$
$$= \frac{1}{\pi\sqrt{-1}} \int_S \lambda \, d\lambda \left\{\left[L\left(x, \frac{\partial}{\partial x}\right) - \lambda^2 c(x)\right]\right.$$
$$\times \int_D G_1(x, \xi, \lambda) \, d_\xi D \int_0^t b_0^{-1}(\tau) f(\xi, \tau) \exp(\lambda^2 t_1(\tau)$$
$$\left. - t_2(\tau)) \, d\tau - \int_D G_1(x, \xi, \lambda) \, d_\xi D f(\xi, t)\right\}$$

In accordance with (9.2.17) and (9.2.19), the integral $\int_D G_1(x, \xi, \lambda) f(\xi, t) \, d_\xi D$ decreases in the region R_δ for $t \in [0, T]$ faster than does λ^{-2}. Consequently, keeping (8.4.3) in mind, we obtain from the last equation

$$\left\{L\left(x, \frac{\partial}{\partial x}\right) - c(x) M\right\} v_{22}^{(2)}(x, t)$$
$$\equiv \frac{1}{\pi\sqrt{-1}} \int_S \lambda \, d\lambda \left\{-\left(L\left(x, \frac{\partial}{\partial x}\right)\right.\right.$$
$$\left. - c(x)\lambda^2\right) \int_D P_0(x-\xi, \xi, \lambda) \, d_\xi D \int_0^t b_0^{-1}(\tau) f(\xi, \tau)$$
$$\times \exp(\lambda^2 t_1(\tau) - t_2(\tau)) \, d\tau$$
$$\left. - \int_0^t b_0^{-1}(\tau) f(x, \tau) \exp(\lambda^2 t_1(\tau) - t_2(\tau) \, d\tau)\right\}$$
$$= \frac{-1}{\pi\sqrt{-1}} \int_S \lambda \, d\lambda \left\{\left(\sum_{i=1}^{3} \frac{\partial^2}{\partial x_i^2} - c(x)\lambda^2\right)\right.$$
$$\times \int_D P_0(x-\xi, \xi, \lambda) \, d_\xi D \int_0^t b_0^{-1}(\tau)$$
$$\times f(\xi, \tau) \exp(\lambda^2 t_1(\tau) - t_2(\tau)) \, d\tau$$
$$\left. + \int_0^t b_0^{-1}(\tau) f(x, \tau) \exp(\lambda^2 t_1(\tau) - t_2(\tau)) \, d\tau\right\}$$
$$+ \frac{-1}{\pi\sqrt{-1}} \int_S \lambda \, d\lambda \left(\sum_{i=1}^{3} a_i(x) \frac{\partial}{\partial x_i} + a(x)\right)$$
$$\times \int_D P_0(x-\xi, \xi, \lambda) \, d_\xi D \int_0^t b_0^{-1}(\tau) f(\xi, \tau)$$
$$\times \exp(\lambda^2 t_1(\tau) - t_2(\tau)) \, d\tau \tag{9.2.44}$$

On the basis of (9.2.42) and (9.2.43), the second contour integral in the right-hand side of (9.2.44) converges uniformly with respect to $x \in D$ as $t \to 0$ (since the integrand decreases on S faster than does λ^{-3}). Therefore, the operator in the large parentheses can be taken from under the contour-integral sign. On the other hand, it is easy to see that the following identity holds:

$$\left[\sum_{i=1}^{3} \frac{\partial^2}{\partial x_i^2} - c(x)\lambda^2\right] \int_D P_0(x-\xi, \xi, \lambda)\, d_\xi D \times \int_0^t b_0^{-1}(\tau) f(\xi, \tau) \exp(\lambda^2 t_1(\tau) - t_2(\tau))\, d\tau$$

$$= -\int_0^t b_0^{-1}(\tau) f(x, \tau) \exp(\lambda^2 t_1(\tau) - t_2(\tau))\, d\tau$$

$$-\lambda^2 \int_D (c(x) - c(\xi)) P_0(x-\xi, \xi, \lambda)\, d_\xi D \int_0^t b_0^{-1}(\tau) f(\xi, \tau) \times \exp(\lambda^2 t_1(\tau) - t_2(\tau))\, d\tau$$

Therefore, we obtain from (9.2.44)

$$\left\{L\left(x, \frac{\partial}{\partial x}\right) - c(x) M\right\} v_{22}^{(2)}(x, t)$$

$$= \frac{1}{\pi\sqrt{-1}} \int_S \lambda^3\, d\lambda \int_D (c(x) - c(\xi)) P_0(x-\xi, \xi, \lambda)\, d_\xi D \times \int_0^t b_0^{-1}(\tau) f(\xi, \tau) \exp(\lambda^2 t_1(\tau) - t_2(\tau))\, d\tau$$

$$-\left(\sum_{i=1}^{3} a_i(x) \frac{\partial}{\partial x_i} + a(x)\right) v_{21}^{(2)}(x, t)$$

Substituting this into (9.2.41), we have

$$\left\{L\left(x, \frac{\partial}{\partial x}\right) - c(x) M\right\} v_2^{(2)}(x, t)$$

$$= \left\{\sum_{i=1}^{3} \frac{\partial^2}{\partial x_i^2} - c(x) M\right\} v_{21}^{(2)}(x, t)$$

$$+ \frac{1}{\pi\sqrt{-1}} \int_S \lambda^3\, d\lambda \int_D (c(x) - c(\xi)) P_0(x-\xi, \xi, \lambda)\, d_\xi D \times \int_0^t b_0^{-1}(\tau) f(\xi, \tau) \exp(\lambda^2 t_1(\tau) - t_2(\tau))\, d\tau =$$

$$= \left\{ \sum_{i=1}^{3} \frac{\partial^2}{\partial x_i^2} - c(x) M \right\} v_{21}^{(2)}(x, t)$$

$$+ \frac{1}{\pi \sqrt{-1}} \int_S \lambda \, d\lambda \left\{ \lambda^2 \int_D (c(x) - c(\xi)) P_0(x-\xi, \xi, \lambda) \, d_\xi D \right.$$

$$\times \int_0^t b_0^{-1}(\tau) f(\xi, \tau) \exp(\lambda^2 t_1(\tau) - t_2(\tau)) \, d\tau$$

$$\left. + \int_D (c(x) - c(\xi)) P_0(x-\xi, \xi, \lambda) f(\xi, t) \, d_\xi D \right\}$$

$$= \left\{ \sum_{i=1}^{3} \frac{\partial^2}{\partial x_i^2} - c(x) M \right\} v_{21}^{(2)}(x, t)$$

$$+ \frac{1}{\pi \sqrt{-1}} M \int_S \lambda \, d\lambda \, (c(x) - c(\xi)) P_0(x-\xi, \xi, \lambda)$$

$$\times \int_0^t b_0^{-1}(\tau) f(\xi, \tau) \exp(\lambda^2 t_1(\tau) - t_2(\tau)) \, d\tau$$

Keeping (9.2.39) and (8.1.2) in mind, we can write the last equation in the form

$$\left\{ L\left(x, \frac{\partial}{\partial x}\right) - c(x) M \right\} v_2^{(2)}(x, t)$$

$$= \frac{1}{\pi \sqrt{-1}} \left\{ \sum_{i=1}^{3} \frac{\partial^2}{\partial x_i^2} \int_S \lambda \, d\lambda \int_D \frac{\exp(-\lambda \sqrt{c(\xi)} \, |x-\xi|)}{4\pi |x-\xi|} \, d_\xi D \right.$$

$$\times \int_0^t b_0^{-1}(\tau) f(\xi, \tau) \exp(\lambda^2 t_1(\tau) - t_2(\tau)) \, d\tau$$

$$- M \int_S \lambda \, d\lambda \int_D c(\xi) \frac{\exp(-\lambda \sqrt{c(\xi)} \, |x-\xi|)}{4\pi |x-\xi|} \, d_\xi D \qquad (9.2.45)$$

$$\left. \times \int_0^t b_0^{-1}(\tau) f(\xi, \tau) \exp(\lambda^2 t_1(\tau) - t_2(\tau)) \, d\tau \right\}$$

$$= \frac{1}{4\pi \sqrt{-1}} \left\{ \sum_{i=1}^{3} \frac{\partial^2}{\partial x_i^2} \int_D \frac{d_\xi D}{|x-\xi|} \right.$$

$$\times \int_0^t b_0^{-1}(\tau) f(\xi, \tau) e^{-t_2(\tau)} \, d\tau \exp\left(-\frac{c(\xi) \, |x-\xi|^2}{4 t_1(\tau)} \right)$$

$$\times \int_S \lambda \exp\left(\lambda^2 t_1(\tau) - \lambda \sqrt{c(\xi)} \, |x-\xi| + \frac{c(\xi) \, |x-\xi|^2}{4 t_1(\tau)} \right) d\lambda \, -$$

$$-M\int_D \frac{c(\xi)}{|x-\xi|}\,d_\xi D\int_0^t b_0^{-1}(\tau)f(\xi,\tau)\,e^{-t_2(\tau)}\,d\tau$$

$$\times\exp\left(-\frac{c(\xi)\,|x-\xi|^2}{4t_1(\tau)}\right)\int_S \lambda\exp\left(\lambda^2 t_1(\tau)\right. \qquad (9.2.45)\ \text{(cont.)}$$

$$\left.-\lambda\sqrt{c(\xi)}\,|x-\xi|+\frac{c(\xi)\,|x-\xi|^2}{4t_1(\tau)}\right)d\lambda\Bigg\}$$

If we substitute into this equation the value of the contour integral given by (9.2.26), we obtain

$$\left\{L\left(x,\frac{\partial}{\partial x}\right)-c(x)\,M\right\}v_2^{(2)}(x,t)$$

$$=\Bigg\{\sum_{i=1}^{3}\frac{\partial^2}{\partial x_i^2}\int_D\sqrt{c(\xi)}\,d_\xi D$$

$$\times\int_0^t\frac{b_0^{-1}(\tau)f(\xi,\tau)\exp\left(-t_2(\tau)-\dfrac{c(\xi)\,|x-\xi|^2}{4t_1(\tau)}\right)}{(2\sqrt{\pi t_1(\tau)})^3}\,d\tau$$

$$-M\int_D c^{\frac{3}{2}}(\xi)\,d_\xi D \qquad (9.2.46)$$

$$\times\int_0^t b_0^{-1}(\tau)\,\frac{f(\xi,\tau)\exp\left(-t_2(\tau)-\dfrac{c(\xi)\,|x-\xi|^2}{4t_1(\tau)}\right)}{(2\sqrt{\pi t_1(\tau)})^3}\,d\tau\Bigg\}$$

$$=\Bigg\{\int_D\sqrt{c(\xi)}\,d_\xi D\int_0^t b_0^{-1}(\tau)f(\xi,\tau)\left(\sum_{i=1}^{3}\frac{\partial^2}{\partial x_i^2}-c(\xi)\,M\right)$$

$$\times\frac{\exp\left(-t_2(\tau)-\dfrac{c(\xi)\,|x-\xi|^2}{4t_1(\tau)}\right)}{(2\sqrt{\pi t_1(\tau)})^3}\,d\tau-b_0(t)\lim_{\tau\to t}\int_D c^{\frac{3}{2}}(\xi)\,b_0^{-1}(\tau)$$

$$\times\frac{f(\xi,\tau)\exp\left(-t_2(\tau)-\dfrac{c(\xi)\,|x-\xi|^2}{4t_1(\tau)}\right)}{(2\sqrt{\pi t_1(\tau)})^3}\,d_\xi D\Bigg\}$$

Bearing in mind the identity

$$\left[\sum_{i=1}^{3}\frac{\partial^2}{\partial x_i^2}-c(\xi)\,M\right]\frac{\exp\left[-t_2(\tau)-\dfrac{c(\xi)\,|x-\xi|^2}{4t_1(\tau)}\right]}{(2\sqrt{\pi t_1(\tau)})^3}\equiv 0$$

and (9.2.27) and (9.2.36), we obtain from (9.2.46)

$$\left\{L\left(x, \frac{\partial}{\partial x}\right) - c(x) M\right\} v_2^{(2)}(x, t) = -f(x, t)$$

As can be seen from (9.2.14), (9.2.17), (9.2.19) and (9.2.42), the integral (9.2.8) converges uniformly for $x \in D_1$ with respect to t for $t \geqslant 0$. Consequently, we may take the limit under the integral sign in (9.2.8) as $t \to 0$. Then, we obtain

$$v_2^{(2)}(x, 0) = 0$$

Finally, in accordance with (9.2.21), (9.2.42) and (9.2.43), the integrals

$$\int_S \lambda\, d\lambda \frac{\partial}{\partial x_i} \int_D G(x, \xi, \lambda)\, d_\xi D \times \int_0^t b_0^{-1}(\tau) f(\xi, \tau) \exp[\lambda^2 t_1(\tau) - t_2(\tau)]\, d\tau$$

$$\int_S \lambda\, d\lambda \frac{\partial^2}{\partial t\, \partial x_i} \int_D G(x, \xi, \lambda)\, d_\xi D \times \int_0^t b_0^{-1}(\tau) f(\xi, \tau) \exp[\lambda^2 t_1(\tau) - t_2(\tau)]\, d\tau$$

converge uniformly w.r.t. $x \in D + \Gamma$ as $t \to 0$, and so

$$\lim_{x \to y} B\left(y, \frac{d}{dn_y}, M\right) v_2^{(2)}(x, t)$$

$$= \frac{1}{\pi \sqrt{-1}} \int_S \lambda\, d\lambda \lim_{x \to y} B\left(y, \frac{d}{dn_y}, M\right)$$

$$\times \int_D G(x, \xi, \lambda)\, d_\xi D \int_0^t b_0^{-1}(\tau) f(\xi, \tau) \exp[\lambda^2 t_1(\tau) - t_2(\tau)]\, d\tau$$

$$= \frac{1}{\pi \sqrt{-1}} \int_S \lambda\, d\lambda \lim_{x \to y} B\left(y, \frac{d}{dn_y}, \lambda^2\right) \int_D G(x, \xi, \lambda)\, d_\xi D$$

$$\times \int_0^t b_0^{-1}(\tau) f(\xi, \tau) \exp(\lambda^2 t_1(\tau) - t_2(\tau))\, d\tau$$

$$+ \frac{1}{\pi \sqrt{-1}} \int_S \lambda\, d\lambda \int_D \alpha_2(y) \left(\frac{d}{dn_y} + \alpha_3(y)\right) \qquad (9.2.47)$$

$$\times G(y, \xi, \lambda) f(\xi, t)\, d_\xi D$$

$$= \frac{1}{\pi \sqrt{-1}} \int_S \lambda\, d\lambda \int_D \alpha_2(y) \left(\frac{d}{dn_y} + \alpha_3(y)\right)$$

$$\times G(y, \xi, \lambda) f(\xi, t)\, d_\xi D$$

From a property of a Green's function,

$$\alpha_2(y)\left(\frac{d}{dn_y}+\alpha_3(y)\right)G(y,\xi,\lambda)$$
$$=-\lambda^2\left(\alpha_1(y)\frac{d}{dn_y}+\alpha_4(y)\right)G(y,\xi,\lambda)$$

Thus, the integrand in the right-hand side of (9.2.47) decreases in the region R_δ faster than does λ^{-2}. Therefore, we obtain from (9.2.47)

$$\lim_{x\to y} B\left(y,\frac{d}{dn_y},M\right)v_2^{(2)}(x,t)=0$$

Thus, with the aid of the potential of a double layer, we solve the mixed problem with Dirichlet's boundary condition.

9.3 ACTUAL SOLUTION OF MIXED PROBLEMS

In the article [40i], the contour-integral method which has been expounded in this book is applied to the actual solution of Problem (9.2.1)-(9.2.3) with

$$\alpha_2(y)=0$$

By 'actual solution', we mean that the contour integral with respect to λ in (9.2.4) is actually evaluated.

Here, we shall, for simplicity, construct such a solution of the simpler mixed problem

$$M\left(t,\frac{\partial}{\partial t}\right)v=\sum_{i=1}^{3}\frac{\partial^2 v}{\partial x_i^2}+f(x,t) \tag{9.3.1}$$

$$\lim_{x\to y}\left(\frac{d}{dn_y}+\alpha(y)\right)v(x,t)=0,\quad y\in\Gamma \tag{9.3.2}$$

$$v(x,0)=\varphi(x) \tag{9.3.3}$$

To be more definite, we assume that D is a region bounded by a closed Lyapunov surface Γ.

The spectral problem corresponding to Problem (9.3.1)-(9.3.3) is of the form

$$\sum_{i=1}^{3}\frac{\partial^2 u}{\partial x_i^2}-\lambda^2 u=\Phi(x) \tag{9.3.4}$$

$$\lim_{x \to y} \left(\frac{d}{dn_y} + \alpha(y) \right) u(x, \lambda) = 0, \quad y \in \Gamma \tag{9.3.5}$$

The fundamental solution of the homogeneous equation corresponding to (9.3.4) is given by (8.1.2), where, for (9.3.4), we have

$$c(x) \equiv 1$$

We seek the Green's function $G(x, \xi, \lambda)$ of Problem (9.3.4)-(9.3.5) in the form

$$G(x, \xi, \lambda) = \frac{e^{-\lambda|x-\xi|}}{4\pi|x-\xi|} - Q(x, \xi, \lambda) \tag{9.3.6}$$

where $Q(x, \xi, \lambda)$ is the regular part (of the Green's function) which is sought for Problem (9.3.4)-(9.3.5) in the form of the potential of a single layer

$$Q(x, \xi, \lambda) = \int_{\Gamma} \frac{e^{-\lambda|x-z|}}{4\pi|x-z|} \mu(z, \xi, \lambda) \, d_z\Gamma \tag{9.3.7}$$

Substituting (9.3.6) into the boundary condition (9.3.5), we obtain, in accordance with (8.2.8) and (9.3.7), the following integral equation for finding the density $\mu(y, \xi, \lambda)$:

$$\mu(y, \xi, \lambda) = 2f(y, \xi, \lambda) - \int_{\Gamma} 2f(y, z, \lambda) \mu(z, \xi, \lambda) \, d_z\Gamma \tag{9.3.8}$$

where

$$f(y, \xi, \lambda) = \left(\frac{d}{dn_y} + \alpha(y) \right) \frac{\exp(-\lambda|y-\xi|)}{4\pi|y-\xi|} \tag{9.3.9}$$

As can be seen from the procedure used in proving Lemma 2, the integral equation (9.3.8) has, for all $\lambda \in R_\delta$, a solution, which can be found by successive approximations

$$\mu(y, \xi, \lambda) = 2f(y, \xi, \lambda) - \sum_{n=2}^{\infty} (-1)^{n-1} 2^n f_n(y, \xi, \lambda) \tag{9.3.10}$$

where $f_n(y, \xi, \lambda)$ is the nth interation of $f(y, \xi, \lambda)$

$$f_n(y, \xi, \lambda) = \int_{\Gamma} f(y, z_{n-1}, \lambda) f_{n-1}(z_{n-1}, \xi, \lambda) \, d_{z_{n-1}}\Gamma \quad (n = 2, 3, \ldots; f_1 = f) \tag{9.3.11}$$

Substituting (9.3.10) into (9.3.7), we obtain

$$Q(x, \xi, \lambda) = \int_{\Gamma} \frac{e^{-\lambda|x-z|}}{4\pi|x-z|} \sum_{n=1}^{\infty} (-1)^{n-1} 2^n f_n(z, \xi, \lambda)\, d_z\Gamma \quad (9.3.12)$$

From (9.3.11), successive substitution yields the formula

$$\begin{aligned} f_n(y, \xi, \lambda) &= \int_{\Gamma} d_{z_{n-1}}\Gamma \ldots \int_{\Gamma} d_{z_1}\Gamma \\ &\times \sum_{k=0}^{n} \Big(\sum_{\substack{i_1, \ldots, i_n=0 \\ i_1+\ldots+i_n=k}}^{1} P_{i_1}(y, z_{n-1}) \\ &\times P_{i_2}(z_{n-1}, z_{n-2}) \ldots P_{i_n}(z_1, \xi)\Big) \lambda^k e^{-\lambda\Phi_{n-1}(y, \xi)} \\ &(n = 2, 3, \ldots) \\ f_1(y, \xi, \lambda) &= f(y, \xi, \lambda) \\ &= (P_0(y, \xi) + \lambda P_1(y, \xi))\, e^{-\lambda|y-\xi|} \end{aligned} \quad (9.3.13)$$

where

$$\begin{aligned} &\Phi_{n-1}(y, \xi) \\ &= |y - z_{n-1}| + |z_{n-1} - z_{n-2}| + \ldots + |z_1 - \xi| \\ &(n = 2, 3, \ldots), \\ &P_0(y, \xi) = \left(\frac{d}{dn_y} + \alpha(y)\right) \frac{1}{4\pi|y-\xi|}, \\ &P_1(y, \xi) = -\frac{1}{4\pi|y-\xi|} \cdot \frac{d}{dn_y}|y-\xi| \end{aligned} \quad (9.3.14)$$

In accordance with (9.3.12) and (9.3.13), we obtain from (9.3.6) the following representation:

$$\begin{aligned} G(x, \xi, \lambda) &= \frac{e^{-\lambda|x-\xi|}}{4\pi|x-\xi|} - \int_{\Gamma} \frac{2}{4\pi|x-z|} \\ &\times (P_0(z, \xi) + \lambda P_1(z, \xi) \exp(-\lambda(|x-z| + |z-\xi|)))\, d_z\Gamma \\ &+ \int_{\Gamma} \frac{d_z\Gamma}{4\pi|x-z|} \sum_{n=2}^{\infty} (-1)^n 2^n \int_{\Gamma} d_{z_{n-1}}\Gamma \ldots \int_{\Gamma} d_{z_1}\Gamma \\ &\times \sum_{k=0}^{n} \Big(\sum_{\substack{i_1, \ldots, i_n=0 \\ i_1+\ldots+i_n=k}}^{1} P_{i_1}(z, z_{n-1}) \\ &\times P_{i_2}(z_{n-1}, z_{n-2}) \ldots P_{i_n}(z_1, \xi)\Big) \lambda^k e^{-\lambda\Phi_n(x, \xi)} \end{aligned} \quad (9.3.15)$$

where

$$\Phi_n(x, \xi) = |x-z| + |z-z_{n-1}| + \ldots + |z_2-z_1| + |z_1-\xi| \qquad (9.3.16)$$
$$\Phi_1(x, \xi) = |x-z| + |z-\xi| \quad (n = 1, 2, \ldots)$$

Under the conditions of Theorem 38, Problem (9.3.1)-(9.3.3) has a solution $v_2(x, t)$, which is given by (9.2.4). If we substitute (9.3.15) into (9.2.4), we can represent the solution $-v_2(x, t)$ of (9.3.1)-(9.3.3) in the form of an integral over the contour S of a series whose terms are products of an nth-degree polynomial in λ and an exponential function $\exp(\lambda^2 t_1 - \lambda\Phi_n(x, \xi))$.

Here, in accordance with inequality (8.3.23), this series converges sufficiently well on S that it can be integrated termwise over the contour S. Then, if we reverse the two integrals in (9.2.4), after substituting (9.3.15) we obtain

$$v_2(x, t) = \frac{1}{\pi\sqrt{-1}} \Big\{ \int_D \frac{\varphi(\xi)\, d_\xi D}{4\pi|x-\xi|} \exp(-t_2(0)) \times \int_S \lambda \exp[\lambda^2 t_1(0) - \lambda|x-\xi|]\, d\lambda$$
$$+ \int_D \frac{d_\xi D}{4\pi|x-\xi|} \int_0^t d\tau f(\xi, \tau)\, b_0^{-1}(\tau) \times \exp(-t_2(\tau)) \int_S \exp(\lambda^2 t_1(\tau)$$
$$-\lambda|x-\xi|)\lambda\, d\lambda - \int_D d_\xi D\varphi(\xi) \exp(t_2(0))$$
$$\times \int_\Gamma \frac{d_z\Gamma}{4\pi|x-z|} \sum_{k=0}^{1} P_k(z, \xi)\lambda^k \qquad (9.3.17)$$
$$\times \exp[\lambda^2 t_1(0) - \lambda(|x-z| + |z-\xi|)]$$
$$+ \int_D d_\xi D\varphi(\xi) \exp(-t_2(0))$$
$$\times \int_\Gamma \frac{d_z\Gamma}{4\pi|x-z|} \sum_{n=2}^{\infty} (-1)^n 2^n \int_\Gamma d_{z_{n-1}}\Gamma \ldots \int_\Gamma d_{z_1}\Gamma$$
$$\times \sum_{k=0}^{n} \Big(\sum_{\substack{i_1, \ldots, i_n = 0 \\ i_1 + \ldots + i_n = k}}^{1} P_{i_1}(z, z_{n-1})$$
$$\times P_{i_2}(z_{n-1}, z_{n-2}) \ldots P_{i_n}(z_1, \xi) \Big) \times$$

$$\times \int_S d\lambda \lambda^{k+1} \exp(\lambda^2 t_1(0) - \lambda \Phi_n(x, \xi))$$

$$- \int_D d_\xi D \int_0^t f(\xi, \tau)\, b_0^{-1}(\tau)$$

$$\times \exp(-t_2(\tau)) \int_\Gamma \frac{d_z \Gamma}{4\pi |x-z|} \sum_{k=0}^{1} P_k(z, \xi)\, \lambda^k$$

$$\times \exp(\lambda^2 t_1(\tau) - \lambda(|x-z| + |z-\xi|))$$

$$+ \int_D d_\xi D \int_0^t f(\xi, \tau)\, b_0^{-1}(\tau) \exp(-t_2(\tau)) \int_\Gamma \frac{d_z \Gamma}{4\pi |x-z|} \qquad \begin{matrix}(9.3.17)\\ \text{(cont.)}\end{matrix}$$

$$\times \sum_{n=2}^{\infty} (-1)^n 2^n \int_\Gamma d_{z_{n-1}} \Gamma \ldots \int_\Gamma d_{z_1} \Gamma$$

$$\times \sum_{k=0}^{n} \Bigg(\sum_{\substack{i_1, \ldots, i_n = 0 \\ i_1 + \ldots + i_n = k}}^{1} P_{i_1}(z_1, z_{n-1})$$

$$\times P_{i_2}(z_{n-1}, z_{n-2}) \ldots P_{i_{n-1}}(z_2, z_1)\, P_{i_n}(z_1, \xi) \Bigg)$$

$$\times \int_S d\lambda \lambda^{k+1} \exp(\lambda^2 t_1(\tau) - \lambda \Phi_n(x, \xi)) \Big\}$$

Thus, the solution of the mixed problem (9.3.1)-(9.3.3) will actually be constructed if we evaluate the integral

$$J = \int_S \lambda^{k+1} \exp(\lambda^2 t_1(\tau) - \lambda \Phi_n(x, \xi))\, d\lambda \qquad (9.3.18)$$

and substitute it into (9.3.17)

The integral (9.3.18) can be evaluated from (6.3.46)

$$J = \frac{\sqrt{-\pi}}{(\sqrt{t_1(\tau)})^{k+1}} \exp\left[-\frac{\Phi_n^2(x, \xi)}{4 t_1(\tau)} \right] P_{k+1}\left(\frac{\Phi_n(x, \xi)}{2\sqrt{t_1(\tau)}} \right) \qquad (9.3.19)$$

Finally, in accordance with (9.3.18) and (9.3.19), we obtain from (9.3.17) the following representation for the solution of

Problem (9.3.1)-(9.3.3):

$$v_2(x, t) = \frac{1}{4}(\sqrt{\pi})^{-3}\Bigg\{\int_D \frac{d_\xi D}{|x-\xi|}$$

$$\times\Big[(\sqrt{t_1(0)})^{-2}\varphi(\xi)P_1\Big(\frac{|x-\xi|}{2\sqrt{t_1(0)}}\Big)$$

$$\times\exp\Big(-t_2(0)-\frac{|x-\xi|^2}{4t_1(0)}\Big)$$

$$+\int_0^t d\tau f(\xi, \tau)\, b_0^{-1}(\tau)(\sqrt{t_1(\tau)})^2 P_1\Big(\frac{|x-\xi|}{2t_1(\tau)}\Big)$$

$$\times\exp\Big(-t_2(\tau)-\frac{|x-\xi|^2}{4t_1(\tau)}\Big)\Big]\Bigg\}$$

$$-\frac{1}{4}(\sqrt{\pi})^{-3}\int_D d_\xi D\int_\Gamma \frac{d_z\Gamma}{|x-z|}$$

$$\times\Big\{\sum_{k=0}^{1} P_k(z, \xi)(\sqrt{t_1(0)})^{-(k+2)}$$

$$\times P_{k+1}\Big(\frac{|x-z|+|z-\xi|}{2\sqrt{t_1(0)}}\Big)\exp\Big(-t_2(0)$$

$$-\frac{(|x-z|+|z-\xi|)^2}{4t_1(0)}\Big)-\sum_{n=2}^{\infty}(-1)^n 2^n\int_\Gamma d_{z_{n-1}}\Gamma\ldots\int_\Gamma d_{z_1}\Gamma$$

$$\times\sum_{k=0}^{n}\Big(\sum_{\substack{i_1,\ldots,t_n=0\\ i_1+\ldots+i_n=k}}^{1} P_{i_1}(z, z_{n-1})\ldots P_{i_n}(z_1, \xi)\Big)$$

$$\times(\sqrt{t_1(0)})^{-(k+2)}P_{k+1}\Big(\frac{\Phi_n(x, \xi)}{2\sqrt{t_1(0)}}\Big)\exp\Big(-t_2(0)$$

$$-\frac{\Phi_n^2(x, \xi)}{4t_1(0)}\Big)+\int_0^t d\tau f(\xi, \tau)\, b_0^{-1}(\tau)(\sqrt{t_1(\tau)})^{-(k+2)}$$

$$\times\Big[\sum_{h=0}^{1} P_h(z, \xi)P_{k+1}\Big(\frac{|x-z|+|z-\xi|}{2\sqrt{t_1(\tau)}}\Big)$$

$$\times\exp\Big(-t_2(\tau)-\frac{(|x-z|+|z-\xi|)^2}{4t_1(\tau)}\Big)$$

$$-\sum_{n=2}^{\infty}(-1)^n 2^n\int_\Gamma d_{z_{n-1}}\Gamma\ldots\int_\Gamma d_{z_1}\Gamma$$

$$\times \sum_{k=0}^{n} \Bigg(\sum_{\substack{i_1, \ldots, i_n = 0 \\ i_1 + \ldots + i_n = k}}^{1} P_{i_1}(z, z_{n-1}) \ldots P_{i_n}(z, \xi) \Bigg)$$

$$\times P_{k+1}\left(\frac{\Phi_n(x, \xi)}{2\sqrt{t_1(\tau)}}\right) \exp\left(-t_2(\tau) - \frac{\Phi_n^2(x, \xi)}{4t_1(\tau)}\right)\Bigg]\Bigg\}$$

In the same way, we can construct the actual solution of mixed problems with a Dirichlet boundary condition.

Mamedov extended the results of Chapters 8 and 9 to cases of plane problems of the corresponding forms.

CHAPTER 10

Multi-dimensional mixed problem for parabolic equations with discontinuous coefficients and time-dependent boundary conditions

10.1 A MIXED PROBLEM AND CORRESPONDING SPECTRAL PROBLEM

Let D_1 and D_2 denote bounded regions of points $x=(x_1, x_2, x_3)$ (see Fig. 9) which lie in the interior of a closed surface Γ_2. Let Γ_1 denote the boundary of the region D_1 and assume that Γ_1 is also a closed surface and that it lies in the interior of the surface Γ_2. We will find the solution of the equations

$$c^{(i)}(x)\, M\left(t, \frac{\partial}{\partial t}\right) v^{(i)} = L^{(i)}\left(x, \frac{\partial}{\partial x}\right) v^{(i)} + f^{(i)}(x, t) \qquad (10.1.1)$$

for $x \in D_i$ which satisfy the boundary conditions

$$\begin{aligned} &\lim_{\substack{x \to z \\ i=1,2}} B^{(i)}\left(x, \frac{d}{dn_z}, M\right) v(x, t) \\ &= \psi_i(z) \exp\left(-\int_0^t b_0^{-1}(\tau)\, b_1(\tau)\, d\tau\right), \quad z \in \Gamma_1, \quad i=1,2, \\ &\lim_{x \to z} B^{(3)}\left(x, \frac{d}{dn_z}, M\right) v(x, t) \\ &= \psi_3(z) \exp\left(-\int_0^t b_0^{-1}(\tau)\, (b_1(\tau))\, d\tau\right), \quad z \in \Gamma_2 \end{aligned} \qquad (10.1.2)$$

and the initial conditions

$$v^{(i)}(x, 0) = \Phi_0^{(i)}(x), \quad x \in D_i \quad (i = 1, 2) \qquad (10.1.3)$$

where

$$L^{(i)}\left(x, \frac{\partial}{\partial x}\right) = \sum_{h=1}^{3} \left(\frac{\partial^2}{\partial x_h^2} + a_h^{(i)}(x) \frac{\partial}{\partial x_h}\right) + a^{(i)}(x)$$

$$M = b_0(t) \frac{\partial}{\partial t} + b_1(t)$$

$$B^{(i)}\left(z, \frac{d}{dn_z}, M\right) v \equiv \sigma_{i0}(z) \frac{dv^{(i)}(x, t)}{dn_z} + \sigma_{i1}(z) v^{(1)}(x, t)$$

$$+ \sigma_{i2}(z) v^{(2)}(x, t) + \sigma_{i3}(z) M \left\{\frac{dv^{(i)}(x, t)}{dn_z} + \sigma_{i4}(z) v^{(1)}(x, t)\right.$$

$$\left. + \sigma_{i5}(z) v^{(2)}(x, t)\right\} = \psi_i(z) \exp\left(-\int_0^t b_0^{-1}(\tau) b_1(\tau) d\tau\right)$$

$$z \in \Gamma_1 \quad (i = 1, 2)$$

$$B^{(3)}\left(z, \frac{d}{dn_z}, M\right) v = \sigma_{30}(z) \frac{dv^{(2)}(x, t)}{dn_z} + \sigma_{31}(z) v^{(2)}(x, t)$$

$$+ \sigma_{32}(z) M \left\{\frac{dv^{(2)}(x, t)}{dn_2} + \sigma_{33}(z) v^{(2)}(x, t)\right\}$$

$$= \psi_3(z) \exp\left(-\int_0^t b_0^{-1}(\tau) b_1(\tau) d\tau\right), \quad z \in \Gamma_2$$

and n_z is the direction of the inner normal to Γ_i at the point $z \in \Gamma_i$.

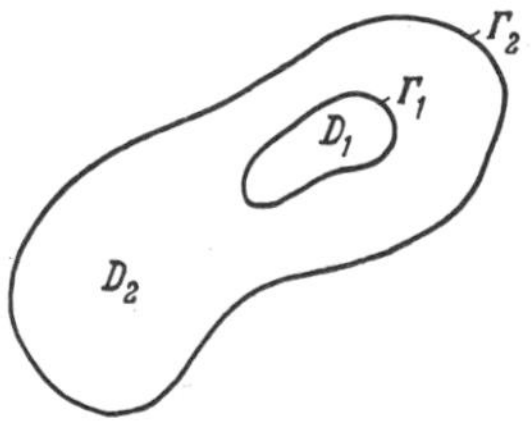

Fig. 9

Suppose that the following conditions are satisfied.

1. In the closed region D_i, the functions $a_k^{(i)}(x)$ and $a^{(i)}(x)$ are continuous; the functions $c^{(i)}(x)$ are positive and continuously differentiable; there exists a constant

$\varkappa > 0$ such that $\sqrt{c^{(i)}(x)} \geqslant \varkappa$; $b_0(t)$, $b_1(t)$ are continuous on the interval $[0, T]$ and $b_0(t) > 0$ for $t \geqslant 0$.

2. The functions $\sigma_{ij}(z)$ are continuous on Γ_i; one of the functions $\sigma_{i0}(z)$, $\sigma_{i3}(z)$ does not vanish on Γ_i.
3. Γ_i is a Lyapunov surface.

We shall refer to the problem of finding solutions of equations of the form

$$L^{(i)}\left(x, \frac{\partial}{\partial x}\right) u^{(i)} - \lambda^2 c^{(i)}(x)\, u^{(i)} = \Phi^{(i)}(x)$$
$$x \in D_i \quad (i = 1, 2) \qquad (10.1.4)$$

with boundary conditions (for $i = 1, 2$)

$$\lim_{x \to z} B^{(i)}\left(z, \frac{\partial}{\partial n_z}, \lambda^2\right) u(x, \lambda) = \psi_i(z), \quad z \in \Gamma_1 \qquad (10.1.5)$$

$$\lim_{x \to z} B^{(3)}\left(z, \frac{\partial}{\partial n_z}, \lambda^2\right) u(x, \lambda) = \psi_3(z), \quad z \in \Gamma_2 \qquad (10.1.6)$$

as the spectral problem corresponding to the mixed problem (10.1.1)-(10.1.3).

10.2 FUNDAMENTAL SOLUTION OF THE SPECTRAL PROBLEM AND A BOUND FOR ITS ABSOLUTE VALUE

In this section we shall construct fundamental solutions $P^{(i, j)}(x, \xi, \lambda)$ of equations of the form

$$L^{(i)}\left(x, \frac{\partial}{\partial x}\right) u^{(i)} - \lambda^2 c^{(i)}(x)\, u^{(i)} = 0 \qquad (10.2.1)$$

which apply in a region D_i (for $i = 1, 2$) and we shall obtain bounds for it that will be necessary for what follows.

First, we denote by R_δ the set of complex values of the parameter λ which satisfy the conditions $|\lambda| \geqslant R$ and cos arg $\lambda \geqslant \delta$, where R is a sufficiently large and δ a sufficiently small positive number.

Lemma 1 If Condition 1 of Section 10.1 is satisfied, the following assertions hold for $x \in D_i$, $\xi \in D_j$ (where $i, j = 1, 2$) and $\lambda \in R_\delta$.

1. The homogeneous equations (10.2.1) possess fundamental solutions $P^{(i, j)}(x, \xi, \lambda)$ which are analytic with

respect to λ, have a singularity at the point $x=\xi$ and possess representations of the form

$$P^{(i,j)}(x, \xi, \lambda) = P_0^{(j)}(x-\xi, \xi, \lambda) + \int_{D_i} P_0^{(i)}(x-y, y, \lambda)\, h^{(i,j)}(y, \xi, \lambda)\, d_y D_i, \tag{10.2.2}$$

where

$$P_0^{(j)}(x-\xi, \xi, \lambda) = \frac{1}{4\pi|x-\xi|} \exp\left(-\lambda \sqrt{c^{(j)}(\xi)}\, |x-\xi|\right)$$

(where in turn $|x-\xi|$ is the length of the vector $x-\xi$).

2. The following inequalities hold for the integral function $P_1^{(i,j)}(x, \xi, \lambda)$, its density $h^{(i,j)}(x, \xi, \lambda)$ and the fundamental solution $P^{(i,j)}(x, \xi, \lambda)$ itself:

$$|h^{(i,j)}(x, \xi, \lambda)| < \frac{C}{|x-\xi|^{\beta_1}} \exp(-\varepsilon|\lambda||x-\xi|) \tag{10.2.3}$$

$$|P_1^{(i,j)}(x, \xi, \lambda)| < \frac{C}{|\lambda|^{\beta_2}|x-\xi|} \exp(-\varepsilon|\lambda||x-\xi|) \tag{10.2.4}$$

$$\left|\frac{\partial^p P^{(i,j)}(x, \xi, \lambda)}{\partial x_k^p}\right| < \frac{G}{|x-\xi|^{\beta_3+p}} \exp(-\varepsilon|\lambda||x-\xi|) \tag{10.2.5}$$

where $\beta_1 = 3$ for $i \neq j$; $\beta_1 = 2$ for $i=j$; $\beta_2 = 0$ for $i=j$; $\beta_2 = 1$ for $i \neq j$; and $\beta_3 = 1$ for $i=j$, $\beta_3 = 2$ for $i \neq j$ (for $p=0, 1$).

3. For $x \in D_i$, the function

$$u^{(i)}(x, \lambda) = -\sum_{j=1}^{2} \int_{D_j} P^{(i,j)}(x, \xi, \lambda)\, \Phi_j(\xi)\, d_\xi D_j$$

is a solution of (10.1.4).

Proof If we substitute (10.2.2) into (10.2.1), we obtain an integral equation defining the unknown density $h^{(i,j)}(x, \xi, \lambda)$ of the integral function $P_i^{(i,j)}(x, \xi, \lambda)$

$$h^{(i,j)}(x, \xi, \lambda) = K^{(i,j)}(x, \xi, \lambda) + \int_{D_i} K^{(i,j)}(x, y, \lambda)\, h^{(i,j)}(y, \xi, \lambda)\, d_y D_i \tag{10.2.6}$$

$$x \in D_i, \quad \xi \in D_j$$

$$K^{(i,j)}(x, \xi, \lambda) = \\ = \left\{\sum_{k=1}^{3} a_k^{(i)}(x)\frac{\partial}{\partial x_k} + a^{(i)}(x) - \lambda^2 (c^{(i)}(x) - c^{(j)}(\xi))\right\} \\ \times \frac{1}{4\pi |x-\xi|} \exp\left(-\lambda \sqrt{c^{(j)}(\xi)}\, |x-\xi|\right) \tag{10.2.7}$$

Obviously, if the series

$$R^{(i,j)}(x, y, \lambda) = K^{(i,j)}(x, y, \lambda) + \sum_{n=2}^{\infty} K_n^{(i,j)}(x, y, \lambda) \tag{10.2.8}$$

converges uniformly with respect to $x, y \in \overline{D}_i$, its limit $R^{(i,j)}(x, y, \lambda)$ is the resolvent of the integral equation (10.2.6), and the function

$$h^{(i,j)}(x, \xi, \lambda) = K^{(i,j)}(x, \xi, \lambda) \\ + \int_{D_i} R^{(i,j)}(x, y, \lambda) K^{(i,j)}(y, \xi, \lambda)\, d_y D_i \tag{10.2.9}$$

for $x \in D_i$ and $\xi \in D_j$ is a solution of the integral equation (10.2.6).

We note that, for $\lambda \in R_\delta$, the following inequality holds for sufficiently large R:

$$|K^{(i,j)}(x, \xi, \lambda)| < \frac{C}{|x-\xi|^2} \exp(-\varepsilon |\lambda| |x-\xi|) \\ x \in D_i, \quad \xi \in D_{j1} \tag{10.2.10}$$

where D_{j1} is a region whose closure lies in the region D_j, C is a constant, $2\varepsilon = \varkappa\delta$ and

$$|K^{(i,j)}(x, \xi, \lambda)| < \frac{C}{|x-\xi|^2} \exp(-\varepsilon |\lambda| |x-\xi|) \\ x, \xi \in D_i \quad (i = 1, 2) \tag{10.2.11}$$

This last inequality (10.2.11), may be seen to be uniform for all $x, \xi \in D_i$ (for $i = 1, 2$).

With the aid of (10.2.11), we easily prove the inequality

$$|K_n^{(i,j)}(x, \xi, \lambda)| \\ < \frac{C^{n-4}(\varepsilon)}{|\lambda|^{n-4}} \exp\left(-\frac{\varepsilon}{2} |\lambda| |x-\xi|\right) \quad \text{for} \quad \lambda \in R_\delta \tag{10.2.12}$$

where $C(\varepsilon)$ is a number depending only on ε.

Keeping (10.2.11) and (10.2.12) in mind, we obtain from (10.2.8)

$$|R^{(i,j)}(x, y, \lambda)| < \frac{C}{|x-\xi|^2} \exp\left(-\frac{\varepsilon}{2}|\lambda||x-\xi|\right) \quad (10.2.13)$$

where C (here and henceforth) denotes a sufficiently large positive number.

With the aid of (10.2.10), (10.2.11) and (10.2.13), we obtain from (10.2.9)

$$|h^{(i,i)}(x, \xi, \lambda)| < \frac{C}{|x-\xi|^2} \exp\left(-\frac{\varepsilon}{2}|\lambda||x-\xi|\right), \quad x, \xi \in D_i \quad (i=1, 2) \quad (10.2.14)$$

$$|h^{(i,j)}(x, \xi, \lambda)| < \frac{C_1}{|x-\xi|} \exp\left(-\frac{\varepsilon}{2}|\lambda||x-\xi|\right), \quad x \in \overline{D}_i, \quad \xi \in \overline{D}_{j1} \quad (10.2.15)$$

where C_1 depends only on the distance between the boundaries of the regions D_i and D_{j1}, or

$$h^{(i,j)}(x, \xi, \lambda)| < \frac{C}{|x-\xi|^3} \exp\left(-\frac{\varepsilon}{2}|\lambda||x-\xi|\right), \quad x \in \overline{D}_i, \quad \xi \in \overline{D}_j \quad (10.2.16)$$

With the aid of inequalities (10.2.10), (10.2.11) and (10.2.15), Lemma 1 is proved just as in Section 9.1.

10.3 SOLUTION OF THE SPECTRAL PROBLEM AND A BOUND FOR ITS ABSOLUTE VALUE

Let us prove the following lemma.

Lemma 2 Under Conditions 1–3 of Section 10.1, the following assertions hold for all $\lambda \in R_\delta$.

1. For all $x \in D_i$ the homogeneous equations (10.2.1) corresponding to (10.1.4) contain solutions $u_1^{(i)}(x, \lambda)$ (for $i = 1, 2$) which are analytic with respect to $\lambda \in R_\delta$, satisfy the boundary conditions (10.1.5)-(10.1.6) and can

be represented in the forms of potentials of a single layer

$$u_1^{(1)}(x, \lambda) = \int_{\Gamma_1} P^{(1,1)}(x, y, \lambda)\,\mu_1(y)\,d_y\Gamma_1, \quad x \in D_1,$$

$$u_1^{(2)}(x, \lambda) = \int_{\Gamma_1} P^{(2,2)}(x, y, \lambda)\,\mu_2(y)\,d_y\Gamma_1 \tag{10.3.1}$$

$$+ \int_{\Gamma_2} P^{(2,2)}(x, y, \lambda)\,\mu_3(y)\,d_y\Gamma_2, \quad x \in D_2$$

2. Substitution of (10.3.1) into the boundary conditions (10.1.5) and (10.1.6) yields a system of three Fredholm integral equations of the second kind with respect to the densities $\mu_i(y)$ (for $i = 1, 2, 3$) which, for $\lambda \in R_\delta$, can be solved by the method of iterations, i.e. by the method of successive approximations.
3. The following inequalities hold for a solution $u_1^{(i)}(x, \lambda)$ (where $i = 1, 2$) for $x \in D_i$:

$$\left|\frac{d^k u_1^{(i)}(x, \lambda)}{dn_2^k}\right| < C, \quad z \in \Gamma_i \quad \text{for} \quad x \in \overline{D}_i \quad (i = 1, 2;\ k = 0, 1)$$

$$\left|\frac{d^s u_1^{(s)}(x, \lambda)}{dx_k^s}\right| < \frac{C}{h^{s+1}} e^{-\varepsilon|\lambda|h} \quad \text{for} \quad x \in \overline{D}_{i_1} \quad (i = 1, 2;\ s = 0, 1, 2)$$

where C is a constant, D_{i1} is an arbitrary region whose closure lies in the region D_i and h is the minimum distance between the boundaries of D_{i1} and D_i (for $i = 1, 2$).

Proof If we substitute (10.3.1) into the boundary conditions (10.1.5)-(10.1.6), bearing in mind the saltus formulae (8.2.8) and (8.2.9) for normal derivatives of the potential of a single layer, and divide by the coefficients of the normal derivatives, we obtain a system of three integral equations for determining the unknown densities $\mu_k(y)$ (for $k = 1, 2, 3$)

$$\mu_1(z) = \psi_1(z, \lambda)$$

$$+ \int_{\Gamma_1} K_{11}(z, y, \lambda)\,\mu_1(y)\,d_y\Gamma_1$$

$$+ \int_{\Gamma_1} K_{12}(z, y, \lambda)\,\mu_2(y)\,d_y\Gamma_1 + \tag{10.3.2}$$

$$+ \int_{\Gamma_2} K_{13}(z, y, \lambda)\,\mu_3(y)\,d_y\Gamma_2, \quad z \in \Gamma_1,$$

$$\mu_2(z)=\psi_2(z,\lambda)+\int_{\Gamma_1}K_{21}(z,y,\lambda)\,\mu_1(y)\,d_y\Gamma_1$$
$$+\int_{\Gamma_1}K_{22}(z,y,\lambda)\,\mu_2(y)\,d_y\Gamma_1$$
$$+\int_{\Gamma_2}K_{23}(z,y,\lambda)\,\mu_3(y)\,d_y\Gamma_2,\quad z\in\Gamma_1 \qquad (10.3.2)\ \text{(cont.)}$$
$$\mu_3(z)=\psi_3(z,\lambda)+\int_{\Gamma_1}K_{32}(z,y,\lambda)\,\mu_2(y)\,d_y\Gamma_1$$
$$+\int_{\Gamma_2}K_{33}(z,y,\lambda)\,\mu_3(y)\,d_y\Gamma_2,\quad z\in\Gamma_2,$$

where

$$K_{11}(z,y,\lambda)=-2\left\{\frac{d}{dn_z}+\frac{\sigma_{11}(z)+\lambda^2\sigma_{14}(z)\,\sigma_{13}(z)}{\sigma_{10}(z)+\lambda^2\sigma_{13}(z)}\right\}\times P^{(1,1)}(z,y,\lambda),\qquad z,\ y\in\Gamma_1$$
$$K_{12}(z,y,\lambda)=-2\,\frac{\sigma_{12}(z)+\lambda^2\sigma_{13}(z)\,\sigma_{15}(z)}{\sigma_{10}(z)+\lambda^2\sigma_{13}(z)}\times P^{(2,2)}(z,y,\lambda),\qquad z,\ y\in\Gamma_1$$
$$K_{13}(z,y,\lambda)=-2\,\frac{\sigma_{12}(z)+\lambda^2\sigma_{13}(z)\,\sigma_{15}(z)}{\sigma_{10}(z)+\lambda^2\sigma_{13}(z)}\times P^{(2,2)}(z,y,\lambda),\qquad z\in\Gamma_1,\quad y\in\Gamma_2 \qquad (10.3.3)$$
$$K_{21}(z,y,\lambda)=2\,\frac{\sigma_{21}(z)+\lambda^2\sigma_{23}(z)\,\sigma_{24}(z)}{\sigma_{20}(z)+\lambda^2\sigma_{23}(z)}\times P^{(1,1)}(z,y,\lambda),\qquad z\in\Gamma_1,\quad y\in\Gamma_1$$

$$K_{22}(z,y,\lambda)=2\left\{\frac{d}{dn_z}+\frac{\sigma_{22}(z)+\lambda^2\sigma_{23}(z)\,\sigma_{25}(z)}{\sigma_{20}(z)+\lambda^2\sigma_{23}(z)}\right\}\times P^{(2,2)}(z,y,\lambda),\qquad z\in\Gamma,\quad y\in\Gamma_1$$
$$K_{23}(z,y,\lambda)=2\left\{\frac{d}{dn_z}+\frac{\sigma_{22}(z)+\lambda^2\sigma_{23}(z)\,\sigma_{25}(z)}{\sigma_{20}(z)+\lambda^2\sigma_{22}(z)}\right\}\times P^{(2,2)}(z,y,\lambda),\qquad z\in\Gamma_1,\quad y\in\Gamma_2$$
$$K_{32}(z,y,\lambda)=-2\left\{\frac{d}{dn_z}+\frac{\sigma_{31}(z)+\lambda^2\sigma_{32}(z)\,\sigma_{33}(z)}{\sigma_{30}(z)+\lambda^2\sigma_{32}(z)}\right\}\times P^{(2,2)}(z,y,\lambda),\qquad z\in\Gamma_2,\quad y\in\Gamma_2 \qquad (10.3.4)$$
$$K_{33}(z,y,\lambda)=K_{32}(z,y,\lambda),\qquad z\in\Gamma_2,\quad y\in\Gamma_2$$

$$\psi_i(z,\lambda)=-\frac{2\psi_i(z)}{\sigma_{i_0}(z)+\lambda^2\sigma_{i_3}(z)}\qquad (i=1,\ 2,\ 3)$$

Substituting the values of $\mu_1(y)$, $\mu_2(y)$ and $\mu_3(y)$ given by Equations (10.3.2) into the integrands in (10.3.2), we obtain

$$
\begin{aligned}
\mu_1(z) = {} & \psi_1(z,\lambda) + \int_{\Gamma_1} d_y\Gamma_1 K_{11}(z,y,\lambda)\Big\{\psi_1(y,\lambda) \\
& + \int_{\Gamma_1} d_\xi\Gamma_1 K_{11}(y,\xi,\lambda)\,\mu_1(\xi) + \int_{\Gamma_1} d_\xi\Gamma_1 K_{12}(y,\xi,\lambda)\,\mu_2(\xi) \\
& + \int_{\Gamma_2} d_\xi\Gamma_2 K_{13}(y,\xi,\lambda)\,\mu_3(\xi)\Big\} + \int_{\Gamma_1} d_y\Gamma_1 K_{12}(z,y,\lambda)\Big\{\psi_2(y,\lambda) \\
& + \int_{\Gamma_1} K_{21}(y,\xi,\lambda)\,\mu_1(\xi)\,d_\xi\Gamma_1 + \int_{\Gamma_1} K_{22}(y,\xi,\lambda)\,\mu_2(\xi)\,d_\xi\Gamma_1 \\
& + \int_{\Gamma_2} K_{23}(y,\xi,\lambda)\,\mu_3(\xi)\,d_\xi\Gamma_2\Big\} + \int_{\Gamma_2} d_y\Gamma_2 K_{13}(z,y,\lambda)\Big\{\psi_3(y,\lambda) \\
& + \int_{\Gamma_1} K_{32}(y,\xi,\lambda)\,\mu_2(\xi)\,d_\xi\Gamma_1 + \int_{\Gamma_2} K_{33}(y,\xi,\lambda)\,\mu_3(\xi)\,d_\xi\Gamma_2\Big\}
\end{aligned}
\tag{10.3.5}
$$

$$
\begin{aligned}
\mu_2(z) = {} & \psi_2(z,\lambda) + \int_{\Gamma_1} d_y\Gamma_1 K_{21}(z,y,\lambda)\Big\{\psi_1(y,\lambda) \\
& + \int_{\Gamma_1} K_{11}(y,\xi,\lambda)\,\mu_1(\xi)\,d_\xi\Gamma_1 + \int_{\Gamma_1} K_{12}(y,\xi,\lambda)\,\mu_2(\xi)\,d_\xi\Gamma_1 \\
& + \int_{\Gamma_2} K_{12}(y,\xi,\lambda)\,\mu_3(\xi)\,d_\xi\Gamma_2\Big\} + \int_{\Gamma_1} d_y\Gamma_1 K_{22}(z,y,\lambda)\Big\{\psi_2(y,\lambda) \\
& + \int_{\Gamma_1} K_{21}(y,\xi,\lambda)\,\mu_1(\xi)\,d_\xi\Gamma_1 + \int_{\Gamma_1} K_{22}(y,\xi,\lambda)\,\mu_2(\xi)\,d_\xi\Gamma_1 \\
& + \int_{\Gamma_2} K_{22}(y,\xi,\lambda)\,\mu_3(\xi)\,d_\xi\Gamma_2\Big\} + \int_{\Gamma_2} d_y\Gamma_2 K_{22}(z,y,\lambda)\Big\{\psi_3(y,\lambda) \\
& + \int_{\Gamma_1} K_{32}(y,\xi,\lambda)\,\mu_2(\xi)\,d_\xi\Gamma_1 + \int_{\Gamma_2} K_{32}(y,\xi,\lambda)\,\mu_3(\xi)\,d_\xi\Gamma_2\Big\}
\end{aligned}
\tag{10.3.6}
$$

$$
\begin{aligned}
\mu_3(z) = {} & \psi_3(z,\lambda) + \int_{\Gamma_1} d_y\Gamma_1 K_{32}(z,y,\lambda)\Big\{\psi_2(y,\lambda) \\
& + \int_{\Gamma_1} K_{21}(y,\xi,\lambda)\,\mu_1(\xi)\,d_\xi\Gamma_1 + \int_{\Gamma_1} K_{22}(y,\xi,\lambda)\,\mu_2(\xi)\,d_\xi\Gamma_1 \\
& + \int_{\Gamma_2} K_{22}(y,\xi,\lambda)\,\mu_3(\xi)\,d_\xi\Gamma_2\Big\} + \int_{\Gamma_2} d_y\Gamma_2 K_{32}(z,y,\lambda)\Big\{\psi_3(y,\lambda) \\
& + \int_{\Gamma_1} K_{32}(y,\xi,\lambda)\,\mu_2(\xi)\,d_\xi\Gamma_1 + \int_{\Gamma_2} K_{33}(y,\xi,\lambda)\,\mu_3(\xi)\,d_\xi\Gamma_2\Big\}
\end{aligned}
\tag{10.3.7}
$$

We introduce the notations

$$K^{(1)}_{i_1j_1i_2j_2}(z, \xi, \lambda) = \int_{\Gamma_1} K_{i_1j_1}(z, y, \lambda) K_{i_2j_2}(y, \xi, \lambda)\, d_y\Gamma_1$$

$$K^{(2)}_{i_1j_1i_2j_2}(z, \xi, \lambda) = \int_{\Gamma_2} K_{i_1j_1}(z, y, \lambda) K_{i_2j_2}(y, \xi, \lambda)\, d_y\Gamma_2 \qquad (10.3.8)$$

$$(i_1 = 1, 2, 3;\ j_1 = 1, 2)$$

In these notations, (10.3.5)-(10.3.7) can be written in the form

$$\begin{aligned}
\mu_1(z) = \psi_1(z, \lambda) &+ \int_{\Gamma_1} K_{11}(z, y, \lambda)\psi_1(y, \lambda)\, d_y\Gamma_1 \\
&+ \int_{\Gamma_1} K_{12}(z, y, \lambda)\psi_2(y, \lambda)\, d_y\Gamma_1 \\
&+ \int_{\Gamma_2} K_{13}(z, y, \lambda)\psi_3(y, \lambda)\, d_y\Gamma_2 \\
&+ \int_{\Gamma_1} K^{(1)}_{1111}(z, \xi, \lambda)\mu_1(\xi)\, d_\xi\Gamma_1 \\
&+ \int_{\Gamma_1} K^{(1)}_{1112}(z, \xi, \lambda)\mu_2(\xi)\, d_\xi\Gamma_1 \\
&+ \int_{\Gamma_2} K^{(1)}_{1113}(z, \xi, \lambda)\mu_2(\xi)\, d_\xi\Gamma_2 \\
&+ \int_{\Gamma_2} K^{(1)}_{1113}(z, \xi, \lambda)\mu_3(\xi)\, d_\xi\Gamma_2 \\
&+ \int_{\Gamma_1} K^{(1)}_{1221}(z, \xi, \lambda)\mu_1(\xi)\, d_\xi\Gamma_1 \\
&+ \int_{\Gamma_1} K^{(1)}_{1222}(z, \xi, \lambda)\mu_2(\xi)\, d_\xi\Gamma_1 \\
&+ \int_{\Gamma_2} K^{(1)}_{1223}(z, \xi, \lambda)\mu_3(\xi)\, d_\xi\Gamma_2 \\
&+ \int_{\Gamma_1} K^{(2)}_{1332}(z, \xi, \lambda)\mu_2(\xi)\, d_\xi\Gamma_1 \\
&+ \int_{\Gamma_2} K^{(2)}_{1333}(z, \xi, \lambda)\mu_3(\xi)\, d_\xi\Gamma_2
\end{aligned} \qquad (10.3.9)$$

$$\mu_2(z) = \psi_2(z, \lambda) + \int_{\Gamma_1} K_{21}(z, y, \lambda)\,\psi_1(y, \lambda)\,d_y\Gamma_1 + \int_{\Gamma_2} K_{22}(z, y, \lambda)\,\psi_2(y, \lambda)\,d_y\Gamma_2 + \int_{\Gamma_2} K_{22}(z, y, \lambda)\,\psi_3(y, \lambda)\,d_y\Gamma_2 \tag{10.3.10}$$

$$+ \int_{\Gamma_1} K^{(1)}_{2111}(z, \xi, \lambda)\,\mu_1(\xi)\,d_\xi\Gamma_1 + \int_{\Gamma_2} K^{(1)}_{2112}(z, \xi, \lambda)\,\mu_2(\xi)\,d_\xi\Gamma_2$$

$$+ \int_{\Gamma_2} K^{(1)}_{2112}(z, \xi, \lambda)\,\mu_3(\xi)\,d_\xi\Gamma_2 + \int_{\Gamma_1} K^{(1)}_{2221}(z, \xi, \lambda)\,\mu_1(\xi)\,d_\xi\Gamma_1$$

$$+ \int_{\Gamma_1} K^{(1)}_{2222}(z, \xi, \lambda)\,\mu_2(\xi)\,d_\xi\Gamma_1 + \int_{\Gamma_2} K^{(1)}_{2222}(z, \xi, \lambda)\,\mu_3(\xi)\,d_\xi\Gamma_2$$

$$+ \int_{\Gamma_1} K^{(2)}_{2232}(z, \xi, \lambda)\,\mu_2(\xi)\,d_\xi\Gamma_1 + \int_{\Gamma_2} K^{(2)}_{2232}(z, \xi, \lambda)\,\mu_3(\xi)\,d_\xi\Gamma_2,$$

$$\mu_3(z) = \psi_3(z, \lambda) + \int_{\Gamma_1} K_{32}(z, y, \lambda)\,\psi_2(y, \lambda)\,d_y\Gamma_1 + \int_{\Gamma_2} K_{32}(z, y, \lambda)\,\psi_3(y, \lambda)\,d_y\Gamma_2 +$$

$$+ \int_{\Gamma_1} K^{(1)}_{3221}(z, \xi, \lambda)\,\mu_1(\xi)\,d_\xi\Gamma_1 + \int_{\Gamma_1} K^{(1)}_{3222}(z, \xi, \lambda)\,\mu_2(\xi)\,d_\xi\Gamma_1 \tag{10.3.11}$$

$$+ \int_{\Gamma_2} K^{(1)}_{3222}(z, \xi, \lambda)\,\mu_3(\xi)\,d_\xi\Gamma_2 + \int_{\Gamma_1} K^{(2)}_{3232}(z, \xi, \lambda)\,\mu_2(\xi)\,d_\xi\Gamma_1 + \int_{\Gamma_2} K^{(2)}_{3233}(z, \xi, \lambda)\,\mu_3(\xi)\,d_\xi\Gamma_2$$

Thus, by using the method of successive substitutions, we obtain for determining $\mu_k(z)$ a series every term of which is an integral over the surfaces Γ_1 and Γ_2. If we group these integrals in an appropriate manner and assume that we can carry out a summation term by term under the signs of the integrals over the surfaces Γ_1 and Γ_2, we find

$$\mu_1(z) = \psi_1(z, \lambda) + \int_{\Gamma_1} R_{11}(z, \xi, \lambda)\, \psi_1(\xi, \lambda)\, d_\xi\Gamma_1$$
$$+ \int_{\Gamma_1} R_{12}(z, \xi, \lambda)\, \psi_2(\xi, \lambda)\, d_\xi\Gamma_1 + \int_{\Gamma_2} R_{13}(z, \xi, \lambda)\, \psi_3(\xi, \lambda)\, d_\xi\Gamma_2$$
$$\mu_2(z) = \psi_2(z, \lambda) + \int_{\Gamma_1} R_{21}(z, \xi, \lambda)\, \psi_1(\xi, \lambda)\, d_\xi\Gamma_1 \tag{10.3.12}$$
$$+ \int_{\Gamma_1} R_{22}(z, \xi, \lambda)\, \psi_2(\xi, \lambda)\, d_\xi\Gamma_1 + \int_{\Gamma_2} R_{23}(z, \xi, \lambda)\, \psi_3(\xi, \lambda)\, d_\xi\Gamma_2$$
$$\mu_3(z) = \psi_3(z, \lambda) + \int_{\Gamma_1} R_{31}(z, \xi, \lambda)\, \psi_1(\xi, \lambda)\, d_\xi\Gamma_1$$
$$+ \int_{\Gamma_1} R_{32}(z, \xi, \lambda)\, \psi_2(\xi, \lambda)\, d_\xi\Gamma_1 + \int_{\Gamma_2} R_{33}(z, \xi, \lambda)\, \psi_3(\xi, \lambda)\, d_\xi\Gamma_2$$

where

$$R_{11}(z, \xi, \lambda) = K_{11}(z, \xi, \lambda) + K^{(1)}_{1111}(z, \xi, \lambda)$$
$$+ K^{(1)}_{1221}(z, \xi, \lambda) + \ldots + K^{(j_1, j_2, \ldots, j_{k-1})}_{i_1 i_2 \ldots i_{2k}}(z, \xi, \lambda) + \ldots$$
$$R_{12}(z, \xi, \lambda) = K_{12}(z, \xi, \lambda) + K^{(1)}_{1112}(z, \xi, \lambda)$$
$$+ K^{(1)}_{1222}(z, \xi, \lambda) + \ldots$$
$$R_{13}(z, \xi, \lambda) = K_{13}(z, \xi, \lambda) + K^{(1)}_{1113}(z, \xi, \lambda) + \ldots$$
$$R_{21}(z, \xi, \lambda) = K_{21}(z, \xi, \lambda) + K^{(1)}_{2111}(z, \xi, \lambda)$$
$$+ K^{(1)}_{2221}(z, \xi, \lambda) + \ldots$$
$$R_{22}(z, \xi, \lambda) = K_{22}(z, \xi, \lambda) + K^{(1)}_{2112}(z, \xi, \lambda)$$
$$+ K^{(1)}_{2222}(z, \xi, \lambda) + K^{(1)}_{2232}(z, \xi, \lambda) + \ldots$$
$$R_{23}(z, \xi, \lambda) = K_{22}(z, \xi, \lambda) + K^{(1)}_{2112}(z, \xi, \lambda)$$
$$+ K^{(1)}_{2222}(z, \xi, \lambda) + K^{(2)}_{2232}(z, \xi, \lambda) + \ldots$$
$$R_{31}(z, \xi, \lambda) = K^{(1)}_{3221}(z, \xi, \lambda) + \ldots$$
$$R_{32}(z, \xi, \lambda) = K_{32}(z, \xi, \lambda) + K^{(1)}_{3222}(z, \xi, \lambda)$$
$$+ K^{(2)}_{3232}(z, \xi, \lambda) + \ldots$$
$$R_{33}(z, \xi, \lambda) = K_{32}(z, \xi, \lambda) + K^{(1)}_{3222}(z, \xi, \lambda)$$
$$+ K^{(2)}_{3233}(z, \xi, \lambda) + \ldots$$

Obviously, if we can show that the series representing $R_{ij}(z, \xi, \lambda)$ converge uniformly, we can, on the basis of Lemma 1, establish inequalities of the type (8.3.10) for

$R_{ij}(z, \xi, \lambda)$. Then, Lemma 2 can be proved along the lines followed in proving Lemma 2 of Section 8.3.

Remark The existence of the Green's function

$$G^{(i,j)}(x, \xi, \lambda) = P^{(i,j)}(x, \xi, \lambda) - Q^{(i,j)}(x, \xi, \lambda)$$

for $x \in D_i$ and $\xi \in D_j$ (where $i, j = 1, 2$) (for the regular part of which Lemma 2 of this Chapter is valid for every interior point ξ of the region D_j) follows from Lemmas 1 and 2. Furthermore, the inequalities of Lemma 2 are satisfied for $Q^{(i,j)}(x, \xi, \lambda)$ uniformly with respect to $x \in D_{i_1}$ and $\xi \in \bar{D}_{j_1}$ (for $i, j = 1, 2$).

10.4 SOLUTION OF THE MIXED PROBLEM FOR EQUATIONS WITH DISCONTINUOUS COEFFICIENTS

Let R and δ denote, respectively, a sufficiently large and a sufficiently small number that all the assertions of Lemmas 1 and 2 of this chapter are satisfied for $\lambda \in R_\delta$. Let S denote a contour, chosen just as in Section 9.1, which lies inside the region R_δ.

The following theorems are proved along the same lines as Theorems 37 and 38 with the aid of Lemmas 1 and 2 of this chapter.

Theorem 40 Suppose that Conditions 1-3 of Sections 10.1 and 10.3 are satisfied. Suppose that $\Phi^{(i)}(x)$ is a continuously differentiable function in a domain D_i and that it vanishes in some boundary strip of that region. Then, the homogeneous equations corresponding to (10.1.1) have, for $x \in D_i$, solutions $v_1^{(i)}(x, t)$ which satisfy the boundary conditions (10.1.2) and the homogeneous initial conditions ($v_1^{(i)}(x, 0) = 0$). These solutions are given by

$$v_1^{(i)}(x, t) = \frac{1}{\pi \sqrt{-1}} \int_S \frac{u_1^{(i)}(x, \lambda)}{\lambda} \times \exp\left(\int_0^t b_0^{-1}(\tau)(\lambda^2 - b_1(\tau))\, d\tau \right) d\lambda \qquad (10.4.1)$$

for

$$x \in D_i \quad (i = 1, 2)$$

Theorem 41 Under the conditions of Theorem 39, if $f^{(i)}(x, t)$ is once continuously differentiable with respect to x and twice with respect to t for

$$x \in \bar{D}_i \quad (i = 1, 2), \quad t \in [0, T]$$

and if this function vanishes in some boundary strip of the region D_i for all t in a t-interval, then (10.1.1) have, for $x \in D_i$, solutions

$$v_2^{(i)}(x, t) \quad (i = 1, 2)$$

which satisfy the homogeneous boundary conditions corresponding to Conditions (10.1.2) and the initial conditions (10.1.3) and which are represented by

$$\begin{aligned} v^{(i)}(x, t) = \frac{1}{\pi \sqrt{-1}} \int_S \lambda \, d\lambda \sum_{j=1}^{2} \int_{D_j} G^{(i, j)}(x, \xi, \lambda) \\ \times \left\{ c^{(j)}(\xi) \, \Phi^{(j)}(\xi) \exp\left(\int_0^t b_0^{-1}(\tau) (\lambda^2 - b_1(\tau)) \, d\tau \right) \right. \\ + \int_0^t b_0^{-1}(\tau) f^{(j)}(\xi, \tau) \exp\left(\int_\tau^t b_0^{-1}(\tau_1) (\lambda^2 \right. \\ \left. \left. - b_1(\tau_1)) d\tau_1 \right) d\tau \right\} d_s D_j \end{aligned} \qquad (10.4.2)$$

Similarly, we can solve the similar mixed problems when a Dirichlet condition is given on the outer surface Γ_2. In this case, the second term in the second of formulae (10.3.1) is replaced with the potential of a double layer.

The contour-integral method we have been describing can be applied successfully to the solution of rather complicated mixed problems for systems which are parabolic in the sense of Petrovskiy.

References

1. AKHIYEZER, N.I. and GLAZMAN, I.M., *The theory of linear operators in a Hilbert space*, Gostekhizdat (1950).
2. BEREZANSKIY, Yu.M., (a) 'The eigenfunction expansion of general self-adjoint differential operators', *Dokl. Akad, Nauk SSSR*, 108, 3 (1956); (b) 'The eigenfunction expansion of self-adjoint operators', *Mat. Sb.*, 43, 75-125 (1957).
3. BIRKHOFF, G.D., (a) 'On the asymptotic character of the solution of certain linear differential equations containing a parameter', *Trans. Am. Math. Soc.*, 9, 219-231 (1908); (b) 'Boundary value and expansion problems of ordinary linear differential equations', *ibid.*, 9, 4 (1908).
4. BIRKHOFF, G.D. and LANGER, R.E., 'The boundary problems and developments associated with a system of ordinary linear differential equations of the first order', *Proc. Am. Acad. Arts Sci.*, 58, 51-128 (1923).
5. BROWDER, F.E., (a) 'The eigenfunction expansion theorem for the general self-adjoint singular elliptic partial differential operator; the analytical foundation; the Hilbert space argument', *Proc. Nat. Acad. Sci.*, 40, 6, 454-463 (1954); (b) 'On the eigenfunctions and eigenvalues of the general linear elliptic differential operator', *ibid.*, 39, 5, 433-439 (1953).
6. WEYL, H., (a) 'Über gewöhnliche Differentialgleichungen mit Singularitäten und die zugehörigen Entwicklungen Willkürlicher Funktionen', *Math. Ann.*, 68, 220-269 (1910); (b) 'Über gewöhnliche Differentialgleichungen mit singulären Stellen und ihre Eigenfunktionen', *Göttinger Nachrichten*, 442-467 (1910).

7. WILDER, E., (a) 'Expansion problems of ordinary linear differential equations with auxiliary conditions at more than two points', *Trans. Am. Math. Soc.*, 18, 4 (1917); (b) 'The formal development of the boundary problem, *ibid.*, 19, 2 (1918).
8. VISHIK, M.I., (a) 'Cauchy problems for equations with operator coefficients, a mixed boundary-value problem for systems of linear differential equations and an approximative method of solving them', *Mat. Sb.*, 30, 1 (1956); (b) 'Mixed boundary-value problems for systems of differential equations containing a second derivative with respect to time and an approximative method of solving them', *Dokl. Akad. Nauk SSSR*, 100, 3 (1955); (c) 'Mixed boundary-value problems for equations containing a first derivative with respect to time and an approximative method of solving them', *ibid.*, 99, 2 (1954),
9. VLASOV, V.P. and MARKIN, S.A., 'Solution of a non-steady-state heat-flow equation for a rod with masses attached to its ends', *Zh. Tekhn. Fiz.*, 30, 9 (1960).
10. GEL'FAND, I.M. and KOSTYUCHENKO, A.G., 'The eigenfunction expansion of differential and other operators', *Dokl. Akad. Nauk SSSR*, 103, 3 (1955).
11. GEPPERT, H., 'Entwicklungen Willkürlicher Funktionen nach funktionentheoretischen Methoden', *Math. Z.*, 20 (1924).
12. GOURSAT, E., *Cours d'analyse mathematique*, II, III, 5th ed., Paris, Gauthier-Villars (1956).
13. GÅRDING, L., 'Eigenfunction expansion connected with elliptic differential operators', *Compt. Rend. Douziéme Congr. Math. Scand.* (1953).
14. ZHDANOVICH, V.F., 'Solution by the Fourier method of self-adjoint mixed problems for hyperbolic systems on a plane', 1. *Mat. Sb.*, 47, 3 (1959); 2. *ibid.*, 48, 4 (1959); 3. *ibid.*, 49, 3 (1959).
15. ZAGORSKIY, T.Ya., *Mixed problems for systems of partial differential equations of the parabolic type*, Lvov University Press (1961).
16. IL'IN, V.A., (a) 'The solvability of mixed problems for a hyperbolic equation', *Usp. Mat. Nauk*, 15, No. 2 (92) (1960); (b) 'The solvability of mixed problems for a hyperbolic equation', *Usp. Mat. Nauk*. 15, No. 2 (92) (1960); (b) 'The solvability of mixed problems for hyperbolic and parabolic equations', *ibid.*, 15, No. 2 (92) (1960).
17. CARLEMAN, T., 'Über die asymptotische Verteilung der Eigenwerte partieller Differentialgleichungen', *Ber. Sachs. Acad. Wiss. Leipzig. Math. Phys. Klasse*, 88, 119-134 (1936).
18. KATO, T., (a) 'Integration of equation of evolution in a Banach space', *J. Math. Soc. Japan*, 5, 208-234 (1953); (b) 'Growth properties of solutions of the reduced wave equation with a variable coefficient', *Commun. Pure Appl. Math.*, 12, 23, 403-425 (1959).
19. CARSLAW, H.S. and JAEGER, J.C., *Conduction of heat in solids*, 2nd ed., Oxford (1959).
20. KELDYSH, M.V., 'On eigenvalues and eigenfunctions of certain classes of self-adjoint equations', *Dokl. Akad. Nauk SSSR*, 77, 1 (1951).
21. CAUCHY, A.L., (a) *Mémoire sur l'application du calcul des résidus à la solution des problèmes de physique mathématique*, VIII, Paris

(1827); (b) *Oeuvres complètes d'Augustin Cauchy*, II, Ser. VII, Paris, 393-430 (1927).

22. KREYN, M.G., 'The theory of self-adjoint extensions of semi-bounded Hermitian operators and their applications', 1. *Mat. Sb.*, 20, 3 (1947); 2. *ibid.*, 21, 3 (1947).
23. KRYLOV, A.N., (a) *On certain differential equations of mathematical physics*, Gostekhizdat (1954); (b) 'Calculation of the heating resulting from a short circuit in an oil-filled cable', *Izv. Akad. Nauk SSSR, Ser. Mat.*, 1 (1937).
24. LADYZHENSKAYA, O.A., (a) *The mixed problem for a hyperbolic equation*, Gostekhizdat (1953); (b) 'Non-steady-state operator equations and their applications to linear problems in mathematical physics', *Mat. Sb.*, 45, 2 (1958).
25. LEVI, E.E., 'On linear elliptic partial differential equations', *Usp. Mat. Nauk*, No. 8 (1941).
26. LEVITAN, B.M., (a) 'On the asymptotic behaviour of the spectral function of a self-adjoint second-order differential equation', *Izv. Akad. Nauk SSSR, Ser. Mat.*, 19, 33-58 (1955); (b) 'On the asymptotic behaviour of a spectral function and the eigenfunction expansion of a second-order self-adjoint equation', *ibid.*
27. LIDSKIY, V.B., 'Conditions under which a system of root subspaces will be complete for non-steady-state operators with discrete spectrum', *Tr. Mosk. Mat.*, 8 (1959).
28. LICHTENSTEIN, L., 'Zuer Theorie partieller Differentialgleichungen zweiten Ordnung vom hyperbolischen Typus', *J. Math.*, 158, 80-91 (1927).
29. LOPATINSKIY, Ya.B., (a) 'The fundamental solutions of a system of elliptic differential equations', *Ukr. Mat. Zh.*, 3, 3. 290-316 (1951); (b) 'A method of reducing boundary problems for a system of elliptic differential equations to regular integral equations', *ibid.*, 5, 2 (1953).
30. LYANTSE, V.E., 'On a boundary-value problem for parabolic systems of differential equations with strongly elliptic right side', *Mat. Sb.*, 35, 2 (1954).
31. MEL'NIK. D.F., *Nauk. Zap. L'vivs'k. Derzh. Univ., Ser. Mekh.-mat.*, 8 (1958).
32. NAYMARK, M.A., *Linear differential operators*, Gostekhizdat (1954).
33. NATANSON, I.P., *Theory of functions of a real variable*, New York, Ungar (1961).
34. OLEYNIK, O.A., (a) 'Solution of the basic boundary-value problems for second-order equations with discontinuous coefficients', *Dokl. Akad. Nauk SSSR*, 124, 6 (1959); (b) 'Boundary-value problems for linear equations of the elliptic and parabolic types with discontinuous coefficients', *Izv. Akad. Nauk SSSR, Ser. Mat.*, 25 (1961).
35. PETROVSKIY, I.G., (a) 'On the Cauchy problem for systems of linear partial differential equations in the class of non-analytic functions', *Byul. Mosk. Gos. Univ., Sektsiya A*, 1, 7 (1938); (b) *Lectures on partial differential equations*, trans. by A. Shenitzer, Interscience (1955).
36. PLESNER, A.I., 'The spectral theory of linear operators', *Usp. Mat. Nauk*, IX (1941).

37. PLESNEŘ, A.I. and ROKHLIN, V.A., 'The spectral theory of linear operators', *Usp. Mat. Nauk,* 1, 1(11) (1946).
38. POGOZHEL'SKIY, V., 'An investigation of the integrals of a parabolic equation and of boundary-value problems in an unbounded region', *Mat. Sb.,* 47, 4 (1959).
39. POINCARÉ, H., 'Sur les équations de la physique mathématique', *Rend. Circ. Mat. Palermo,* VIII, Part Ia (1894).
40. RASULOV, M.L., (a) 'A study of the residue method of solving certain mixed problems for differential equations', candidate's dissertation, Baku (1948); (b) 'Study of the residue method of solving certain mixed problems for differential equations', *Mat. Sb.,* 30, 3 (1952); (c) 'A formula for expanding an arbitrary function', *Dokl. Akad. Nauk SSSR,* 119, 3 (1958); (d) 'The residue method of solving mixed problems and certain related expansion formulae', *ibid.,* 120, 1 (1958); (e) 'A formula for expanding an arbitrary function in a series of fundamental functions of a class of boundary-value problems with parameter for linear partial differential equations', *ibid.,* 120, 2 (1958); (f) 'The residue method of solving mixed problems for differential equations and a formula for expanding an arbitrary vector-valued function in a series of fundamental functions of a boundary-value problem with parameter', *Mat. Sb.,* 48, 3 (1959); (g) 'The asymptotic representation of solutions of boundary-value problems with complex parameter for elliptic equations', *Dokl. Akad, Nauk SSSR,* 125, 1 (1959); (h) 'The contour-integral method of solving mixed problems', *ibid.,* 125, 2 (1960); (i) 'Actual solution of mixed problems for parabolic equations', *ibid.,* 128, 3 (1959); (j) 'Application of the contour-integral method to the solution of mixed problems for equations with discontinuous coefficients', *ibid.,* 131, 1 (1960); (k) 'Conditions for correct formulation of one-dimensional mixed problems', *ibid.,* 130, 2 (1961); (l) 'The residue method of solving boundary and mixed problems for differential equations', *Izv. Akad. Nauk Azerb. SSSR,* 12 (1957); 1 (1958); (m) 'On a problem in subterranean hydromechanics', *Nauchn. Zap. L'vovsk. Politekhn. Inst.,* No. 38, 2 (1956), (n) 'The residue method of solving mixed and boundary-value problems for linear partial differential equations', Doctor's dissertation, *Steklov Mat. Inst. Akad. Nauk SSSR,* (1958); (o) 'The contour-integral method and its application to the solution of mult-dimensional mixed problems for parabolic equations', *Mat. Sb.,* 60, 4 (1963).
41. SIDDIQI, M.R., (a) 'Zur Theorie der nichtlinearen partiellen Differentialgleichungen vom parabolischen Typus', *Math. Z.,* 35, 464-484 (1932); (b) 'Boundary problems in nonlinear partial differential equations', published by authority of the University Executive Council (1933).
42. SLOBODETSKIY, L.N., 'Potential theory for parabolic equations', *Dokl. Akad. Nauk SSSR,* 103, 1 (1955).
43. SOBOLEV, S.L., (a) *Applications of functional analysis,* Providence, Rhode Island, Am. Math. Soc. (1963); (b) *Partial differential equations of mathematical physics,* Oxford and New York, Pergamon (1964).
44. STEKLOV, V.A., *The basic problems of mathematical physics,* Part I, Petrograd (1922).

45. STEPANOV, V.V., *A course in differential equations*, Gostekhizdat (1950).
46. TAMARKIN, Ya.D., (a) *Certain general problems in the theory of ordinary differential equations and the expansion in arbitrary functions in series*, Petrograd (1917); (b) 'Some general problems of the theory of ordinary linear differential equations and expansion of an arbitrary function in series of fundamental functions', *Math. Z.*, 27 (1928).
47. TIKHONOV, A.N., 'On the heat-flow equations for certain variables', *Byul. Mosk. Gos. Univ., Sektsiya A*, 1, No. 9 (1938).
48. TIKHONOV, A.N. and SAMARSKII, A.A., (a) Equations of mathematical physics, Oxford and New York, Pergamon (1963); (b) *Partial differential equations of mathematical physics*, San Francisco, Holden-Day (1964).
49. TITCHMARSH, E.C., (a) *Eigenfunction expansions*, Oxford, Clarendon Press (1946); (b) *Introduction to the theory of Fourier integrals*, Oxford, Clarendon Press (1937).
50. KHALILOV, Z.I., (a) 'A method of solving mixed problems', *Dokl. Akad. Nauk SSSR*, 83, 5 (1952); (b) 'A method of expansion in eigenfunctions of the principal part of an equation in the solution of mixed problems', *Tr. Azerb. Gos. Univ., Ser. Fiz.-mat. Nauk*, No. IV, 5-28 (1954).
51. CHARNII, I.A., *Subterranean hydromechanics*, Gostekhizdat (1948).
52. DIKOPOLOV, G.V. and SHILOV, G.Ye., 'On correct formulation of boundary-value problems in a half-space for partial differential equations with constant coefficients', *Usp. Mat. Nauk*, 14, 5, 150-160 (1959).

Index

NORTH-HOLLAND SERIES IN APPLIED MATHEMATICS AND MECHANICS

EDITORS: H. A. LAUWERIER AND W. T. KOITER

Volume 1: I. N. VEKUA

New Methods for Solving Elliptic Equations

Volume 2: L. BERG

Introduction to the Operational Calculus

Volume 3: M. L. RASULOV

Methods of Contour Integration